Food Security and Innovations

T0326624

Franz Heidhues / Andrea Fadani (Eds.)

Food Security and Innovations
Successes and Lessons Learned

International Symposium 1996

PETER LANG

Frankfurt am Main · Berlin · Bern · NewYork · Paris · Wien

Die Deutsche Bibliothek - CIP-Einheitsaufnahme

Food security and innovations : successes and lessons learned /
Franz Heidhues / Andrea Fadani (eds.). - Frankfurt am Main ;
Berlin ; Bern ; New York ; Paris ; Wien : Lang, 1997
   ISBN 3-631-32826-5

Cover-drawing: Stefanie Heidhues

ISBN 3-631-32826-5
US ISBN 0-8204-3558-9

© Peter Lang GmbH
Europäischer Verlag der Wissenschaften
Frankfurt am Main 1997
All rights reserved.

Printed in Germany 1 2 3 4 6 7

Contents

Part One   Food Security and Innovations Perspectives and Challenges

Part Two   The Generation of Innovations

2.1   Approaches to Innovation Generation

Part Three   Policy and Institutional Framework

3.1   Policies

3.2   Institutions

Part Four   Diffusion and Adoption of Innovations

4.1   Research Issues

4.2   Extension and Adoption (Case Studies)

Acknowledgements

This volume contains selected papers presented at the International Symposium on "Food Security and Innovations: Successes and Lessons Learned", held at the University of Hohenheim from March 11 to 13, 1996.

We like to thank Dr. Hermann Eiselen and the Father and Son Eiselen-Foundation Ulm who initiated and funded the symposium. Dr. Eiselen's active support and participation in the work of the scientific and program committees was most essential for the success of the symposium.

Numerous other institutions contributed generously to the symposium's organization and implementation. The University of Hohenheim and its Center for Tropical Agriculture provided the conference facilities and university infrastructure. Several sponsoring institutions helped to finance the symposium's organization and funded the participation of scientists from numerous developing countries. Apart from the Eiselen Foundation's support , particular thanks are due to the Gesellschaft für Technische Zusammenarbeit (GTZ), the Deutsche Forschungsgemeinschaft (DFG) and the Ministry of Science and Research of the State of Baden-Württemberg.

The organization of the symposium would not have been possible without the constructive and encouraging support of the program committee; we would like to thank Joachim von Braun (University of Kiel), Hermann Eiselen (Eiselen-Foundation Ulm), Christian Gall (University of Hohenheim), Hartwig Geiger (University of Hohenheim), Astrid Gland-Zwerger (University of Hohenheim), Robert Havener (Winrock Foundation, Little Rock, USA), François Kamajou (University of Dschang, Cameroon), Dietrich Leihner (University of Hohenheim), Werner Mühlbauer (University of Hohenheim), Erwin Reisch (University of Hohenheim), Ahmed E. Sidahmed (IFAD, Rome), and Eric Tollens (Catholic University of Leuven, Belgium). Particular thanks are due to the symposium's secretariat, notably Gudrun Contag, Annerose Kammerer, Anne Schempp, and Ortrun Anne Gronski who not only carried the main organizational burden, but also prevented any issue to grow into a problem. We are also grateful to the many supporters behind the scenes, most of them members and students of the Institute of Agricultural Economics and Social Sciences in the Tropics and Subtropics who decisively contributed to a smooth progress of the symposium. We would also like to thank Robin Marsh and Annette Wiesner who undertook to edit the papers and correct the English.

Notwithstanding all this support, we alone take the responsibility for any shortcomings that may still exist in this volume.

Franz Heidhues / Andrea Fadani

Welcome Address

Hermann Eiselen

It is my great pleasure and privilege to extend a warm welcome to you on behalf of the Eiselen-Foundation in Ulm.

This Symposium was initiated and is largely funded by this foundation. Since about 15 years it supports research projects and supplies scholar- and fellowships for graduate and post-graduate students of the Hohenheim University. This support is directed towards studies of different approaches to the problem of food security in countries suffering from deficits in food supply. By the way: Far from being immodest I would like to mention that so far my foundation is the only purely private attempt in this area in Germany to address the problem of hunger in the world. Unfortunately, this seems not yet to be an attractive field for private activities. I hope that this Symposium will help to convince others, that the private sector has an important role to play in supporting research and other efforts directed against hunger in the world.

Please allow me a few more personal remarks. Back in 1960, my father met Professor Joseph Knoll who at that time returned from Rome having served at the FAO as the head of the Plant Production Division and deputy Director General. Professor Knoll told us what was not widely known in Germany in those days when we were fully engaged in the reconstruction of our country after World War II. His message was: there is much hunger in the world and it will get worse unless we start doing something about it. So my father and I started our activities to fight hunger, the most inhuman of all situations people are confronted with, by sponsoring teaching and research against hunger at this University. Why do I mention this? Because my father who passed away in 1981 would be 100 in a few weeks. It was his and Professor Knoll's idea to intensify agricultural research for food security. Therefore I thought it appropriate to honour those two men by initiating such a scientific congress in order to review what we have learned so far and to stimulate further activities to reduce hunger in our world. Today - it seems to me - there is an abundance of ideas and research results but a lag in implementation. The more - unfortunately - the funds for international agricultural research are shrinking the more we should strive to improve the transfer and the extension of know how in order to effectively help the poor to a better life.

After having made you acquainted with my motives and some of the thoughts underlying my foundation, I want to cordially thank you for your active interest:

- the members of the program committee particularly the members from abroad who have made such a big effort to assist;
- the organizers and their support team who all did a marvelous job, especially Franz Heidhues and Andrea Fadani;
- the participants, among them there are the 63 speakers from 24 countries and more than 25 scientists who agreed to chair the working groups;
- and all those who have prepared posters.

Let me conclude with my best wishes and the hope for fruitful and inspiring discussions to accompany this congress so that all participants will experience it as a benefit and encouragement for their future engagement. May this symposium be a step forward towards freedom from hunger in the world.

Food Security and Innovations: An Introduction

Franz Heidhues

In today's world, food insecurity is widespread. More than 800 million people suffer under inadequate nutrition and 180 million children live on diets that are inadequate to develop their mental and physical potential. Also in the forthcoming decades food insecurity is likely to remain the most critical issue of the development agenda. The World Food Summit has agreed on the goal to cut the number of hungry people in half by the year 2015, a goal that has been criticized as too modest. Nevertheless, with population growth in much of the developing world continuing at high rates and with increasing scarcity of land, water and other natural resources, achieving the World Food Summit's goal of halving hunger within the next two decades poses an enormous challenge.

Perspectives and Challenges

Numerous factors determine whether the challenge will be met: a proper institutional framework, conducive policy environment, human, physical and social capital formation and infrastructure development are generally recognized as important elements. The component that has been most vital in securing adequate food in the industrialization process of today's developed world has been generating and applying knowledge in food production, processing and marketing and creating the institutional and policy framework that supports acceptance of those innovations.

Similarly, in meeting the future food security challenge innovations in agriculture will play the most vital role.

During the last four decades governments, international organizations and private sponsors have spent substantial amounts of funds on developing and introducing agricultural innovations. Important productivity increases, such as the green revolution technologies, were the result. However, successes were uneven and in some regions, among them large parts of sub-Saharan Africa, the innovation process did not produce the expected results. Often it failed entirely. Also the benefits of innovations were shared unevenly.

Recognizing that eliminating hunger will only be possible if innovation driven productivity increases will provide the needed growth in food production and that the innovation process raises extremely complex issues, the sponsors and organizers decided to devote this symposium to the issue of food security and innovations and the complex interlinkages between them. The intention of the symposium was to bring together the wide-ranging experiences of different disciplines with innovation processes, to share cases of success and failure, to highlight communalities and differences and, thus, to advance our understanding of the innovation process and to identify knowledge gaps that need further research. This volume includes those papers discussed at the symposium that made a particular contribution to this objective. In this way, the editors hope to contribute to the formulation of more effective food security and innovation support policies.

The papers of **Part I** are addressing the perspectives of the world food situation and the role that innovations play in ensuring food security. Are we certain that the resources of our planet will be sufficient to guarantee food security of the expected world population of ten billion or more in the next century? Will we be able to leave to our children the resources needed to achieve this, and will we be able to develop the political, economic and ethical models ensuring a fair sharing of those resources? Dresrüsse highlights the enormous challenges that these issues pose and provides a vision for a strategy of participatory development co-operation very much needed if we are to succeed in tackling these tasks.

Globalization and liberalization of markets are mobilizing a tremendous development potential, particularly in Asia and Latin America. However, Africa is largely left behind. What has liberalization done to poor countries' terms of trade, their food security and what has been its impact on food prices and food aid availability? What needs to be done to reintegrate Africa into the mainstream of development and which role have agricultural research and innovations to play in this process? These are questions that Sir Hans Singer addresses in his global view on food security. He also sounds a warning to all those who criticize food aid. He envisions that the world will need more rather than less of it.

Understanding the innovation process and formulating a co-ordinated and synergies' maximizing innovation policy is not possible without a theory-based conceptual framework. Walter in his contribution „Foundations of Innovations" builds a theoretical frame on the basis of Schumpeter's innovator-imitator model. Integrating the subsequent contributions of economic as well as other disciplines, such as history, sociology, anthropology and political sciences, he shows the full complexity of the innovation process with its numerous feed back loops and linkages. The answers to key questions of the innovation process, what drives the innovation process, what makes individuals or enterprises to be innovators, why are some more innovative than others, why do some innovators find imitators and others don't, and what is the significance of the institutional and policy framework, are complex. The profit motive in a competitive environment that economists see as the key driving force of technical progress may go a long way in explaining the start of the process. But what keeps the process going? The evolutionary approach to economics, drawing parallels to the biological evolution theory and the theory of organization provide interesting insights. Walter sees the innovation process as an interacting process between the techno-economic and the socio-institutional systems where historical, political, social, institutional and environmental factors play a frame setting role. In this framework the innovation process is time and location dependent and, thus, remains itself a research issue, a point that von Braun strongly emphasizes in his „Conclusions for Policy and Research". Moreover, as he points out, not only can food security policy reap benefits from a better understanding of the sources and driving forces of innovation, but equally from clearer insights into the food security - innovation interface. A host of questions and ideas have been raised in various contributions to this symposium. They need to be translated into comprehensive research agenda.

Although growth in agricultural and food production can be achieved through a variety of complementary and co-ordinated actions, the rapid transfer of technology is an important ingredient to this process. The importance of technical change in developing countries' agriculture has increased because of increased costs as a result of currency devaluation, reductions in subsidies for fertilizers, water, electricity, credit, and government price support programs. Lele examines the process of technology generation and transfer along with the strength and limitations of the current models of transfer.

She discusses several reasons why research should be considered an international public good and, thus, is justified to receive public funding. An efficient system of networking is needed to increase the benefits from research carried out at various levels by the international and national research systems. Human as well as biological and physical factors explain the vast differences in the speed of technology generation and adoption among countries. She argues that efforts must be made to increase investment in research and in the development of technology. Different forms of collaboration and farmers' participation are needed.

Generation of Innovations

The papers in **Part II** deal predominantly with the generation of innovations. A number of papers demonstrate how closely linked and interwoven in practice the generation and adoption part of the innovation process are. The role of public policies and support for agricultural and food research, commodity, filière or farming system approaches for research priority setting and strategy formulation (Bosc and Freud), the use of local ecological and technical knowledge, creativity and group learning dynamics (Gupta et al.) and natural resource and environmental constraints as a source for research themes (Mohr) are addressed in Chapter 2.1. The rest of Part II presents a host of examples and case studies of innovation generation in plant and animal production (Chapter 2.2) and economics (Chapter 2.3). Natural resource, environmental, economic and institutional constraints often appear as prime movers of innovation generation, interacting with new technological possibilities, such as biotechnologies, and innovative forms of research co-operation.

Innovations in Plant and Animal Production

Several papers were presented in the symposium concerning the generation of innovations in plant and animal production. Kroschel et al. examine how control methods of the pernicious weed *striga,* one of the most harmful constraints to increased food production in Africa, can be made more effective. African farmers so far have little benefited from decades of research carried out to develop *striga* control methods. Have research and extension adequately considered local knowledge and indigenous farming practices? Has the approach in controlling *striga* been sufficiently system-oriented to take into account national and regional interdependencies? These are questions that this paper highlights.

Biotechnology has become an integral part of modern plant breeding, and different methods have been used to accelerate breeding programs. Which methods are applicable under developing countries' circumstances? Weber's paper presents different biotechnological methods and discusses how they can usefully be applied in banana, potato and cassava breeding. It is noteworthy that the transfer of biotechnological innovations does not necessarily require major investments in basic research and that small farmers can implement the technologies at low cost. Other examples are the introduction of stem borer resistance into the germ plasm of an indica rice breeding line by the transformation of indica rice breeding line IR58 with a synthetic version of a truncated *Cry*IA(b) gene from Bacillus thuringiensis and the improvement of Guinea pig breeding and husbandry (Zárate and Horst).

Integrating aquaculture and agriculture in small farm production has a long tradition in Asia. Based on empirical data Gupta et al. show that the integration of rice and fish farming can increase rice yields at low cost and risk and provide multiple benefits. An important ingredient of such a system is integrated pest management that also leads to less weed infestation.

Economics and Innovation

A precondition of broad acceptance is the innovations' profitability. A wide variety of papers discuss this topic, among them Kunze et al.'s paper analyzing the profitability of soil conservation measures in West Africa, home processing technology for soybean production in Zimbabwe (Mudimu), Gauchan's examination of fruit tree integration into the existing production system and Drescher's analysis of home gardening as an important component of the family food production system. Home gardening can be a potential and important contributor towards rural and urban household food security. Its significant contribution to the overall food supply is often overlooked and it certainly deserves more attention in agricultural research and extension.

The comparative advantage of home gardening is examined by Marsh. Two case studies, one from Bangladesh and the other from Central America, analyze under which conditions home gardening is a viable way to improve food security and what useful role community based organizations can play in introducing and diversifying home gardening.

Farm mechanization is a very controversial issue in developing countries in general and in Africa in particular. Animal traction has been one of the most important steps in the technological change and in the intensification of agriculture in many countries. On the basis of farm/household data from Benin Brüntrup investigates why the adoption of animal traction in Africa has been found to be so low and what measures can help its wider application.

Policy and Institutional Framework

Institutions and policies play a key role in the innovation process. This is generally recognized. What is less widely accepted is the fact that institutions and the policy framework are important research areas themselves.

Agricultural research is the basis of the innovation process and its contribution to food security. How to define research priorities, how to design funding mechanisms that ensure agricultural research is responding to farmers' needs and what should be the respective roles of the public and private sector in this process, these questions are discussed by Lichtblau and Chataigner (Part III, Chapter 3.1). Imagination and willingness to experiment may open up whole new avenues for research funding. Extremely interesting aspects are brought forward in research work looking at specific policy areas, such as Hitzel's and Mbabu's work on Kenya's dairy development policies, and Virchow's analysis of the resource allocation process for promoting sustainable land use systems. As Virchow points out, without poverty reduction and improved food security, sustainable land use and natural resource protection are difficult to implement. Reardon and his colleagues analyze agricultural development paths searching for the best option to meet the dual need of agricultural productivity increase and environmental sustainability. Do we have to rethink fertilizer subsidies for soil fertility and soil conservation investments? The issue is the proper role of public policy, particularly in support of investments in natural resource conservation.

Institutional innovations can have a variety of origins. Schrieder discusses innovative approaches to rural financial market development that originate in informal financial sector activities and are adopted in formal sector institutions. She analyses how financial organizations of the formal sector adapt, adopt and spread innovative practices of the informal sector, broaden access of poverty groups to financial services and thus contribute to better food security. Is lending to the rural poor increasing lending risk and the default rate? In their research Sharma and Zeller address the question what institutional structures need to be put in place so that there is no conflict between prudent financial management and lending to the poor. Addressing the financial needs of the clients and building long-term, from the clients' point of view worthwhile associations seem to be key factors.

Also von Oppen and his colleagues find an increasing need of public sector support for rural infrastructure. They show substantial efficiency and equity effects of improved market access.

Policy and institutional innovations raise issues not only at the macro and sector level. Of particular interest is their impact at the farm household level where such innovations directly influence household behaviour. Hengsdijk and his colleagues discuss a farm household modeling approach that allows analyzing the impact of innovations on household income, land use and the natural resource base. Similarly, Beerlandt, Tollens and Dercon analyze a methodology to identify the food insecure and the root causes of food insecurity at the household and local level. Too often, food security programs are planned and carried out on the basis of inadequate knowledge about where and who the food insecure are. Interventions then fail to reach the target groups and miss to address the root causes of food insecurity. A different methodological approach that is trying to encompass the complexity of the food security issue is presented by von Bach and Nuppenau in their paper on analyzing linkages between policies, socio-economic conditions and food security. Their latent variable model combines food security and health indicators with farm performance coefficients and variables describing general socio-economic conditions.

Diffusion and Adoption of Innovations

Part IV is devoted to the diffusion/adoption phase of the innovation process. Issues of a general nature, including innovations aimed at improving structure, organization, international cooperation and impact assessment of international agricultural research (Bonte-Friedheim and Ashri) as well as networking (Ausher) and farmers' participation in agricultural extension (Huddleston) are raised.

Ausher analyses the major problems in extension systems including management and professional issues. He calls for the establishment of an international *clearing house* to collect successful and unsuccessful case studies, performance data and experiences in order to improve methodologies for agricultural extension. The *clearing house* can provide extension workers all over the world with well-defined tools and methodologies and promote professionalism among them.

NGO and local institution involvement in setting priorities in research and extension (Fernandez and Beier/Boettcher) as well as a summary evaluation of the World Bank's experience with agricultural extension (Purcell) are discussed in various papers of Chapter 4.1. This assessment of the Training and Visit (T&V) system advocated by the World Bank indicates that there is no one single methodology with sufficient superior characteristics to warrant its universal use. The paper recommends that country-specific strategies and programs be developed relevant to the circumstances existing in each country. Local participation and the use of local resources in linking relief with development is being examined by Ashri and Boettcher. Programmes are found to be successful if they rely predominantly on local resources in which the local people are active participants. Good results can be achieved by combining local self-help with food for work programs of international donors and NGOs.

Specific Diffusion/Adoption Processes

Of the numerous case studies, including those presented in the poster session, Chapter 4.2 presents a cross section selection that tries to reflect the richness of experiences with specific diffusion/adoption processes discussed at the symposium. Diffusion/adoption studies in developing countries show that innovations, often developed on station, have rarely been adopted by the beneficiaries. Some studies argue that the lack of success in innovation adoption lies primarily in farmers' unawareness, while others attribute it to the inadequacy and inefficiency of the extension service. Only in rare cases is the knowledge generation process held responsible. Some of the most important papers presented along this line of argument include the following:

Lamers and Feil examine farmers' knowledge, extension capabilities as well as researchers' concept about technology. Farmers are often found to be aware of key problems they face as a result of experience, knowledge and tradition. Also resources, the environment, technology level and political, economic and market conditions may be favourable. Why then are agricultural extension services so often unable to fulfill, their assignment? Is it a lack of appropriate concepts, qualified staff or funding or have the economic and social implications of potential techniques and innovations not been adequately considered? The authors argue that farmers need clear and convincing reasons why and how new technologies will benefit them.

Proper adaptation to local socio-economic conditions (Kwon et al.), a co-operation between the private sector and government extension organizations (Smitabhindu et al.) and involvement of clients in a participatory approach requiring a change in the roles of agricultural extension workers from being teachers to facilitators (Admassie and Hagmann et al.) are issues discussed in these papers. The efficiency of an extension system can be greatly improved through dialogue with farmers, farmers' experimentation and the strengthening of the self-organizational capacities of rural communities. How to institutionalize participatory approaches into often hierarchically structured organizations is a highly complex issue. To be successful, major changes in planning, implementation, monitoring and evaluation procedures are required. Moreover, the policy environment (Zeller, Adugna et al.) and farmers' attitude towards risk (Hedden-Dunkhorst) play an important role.

In issuing this proceedings volume the editors intend to share widely the successful experiences and the lessons learned in the endeavour to promote food security through innovations. We hope that this volume will contribute to stimulating further discussion, encouraging innovative thinking, initiating new research and formulating and implementing better policies and programs.

Part One

Food Security and Innovations
- Perspectives and Challenges -

A Global View of Food Security

Hans W. Singer
The Institute of Development Studies
University of Sussex
Brighton BN1 9RE, UK

The discussion of food security is often divided into macro and micro aspects. The micro aspects relate to the way in which households cope with food insecurity and the way in which food is distributed within and between households. The macro aspects relate to general economic forces which may generate poverty and food insecurity and to measures to be taken at this general macroeconomic level. My task is to deal with the second issue, in fact to deal with it at a "macro-macro level", i.e. the global rather than the national level. As always, such a neat division between micro and macro blurs many intermediate cases and interactions between the two. Ultimately, food insecurity is an evil experienced at the individual level. Put the other way round: food security is an elementary human right. I believe it was Julian Huxley who said "Human rights begin with breakfast". Or as Berthold Brecht put it in the *Three Penny Opera* "Erst kommt das Essen dann kommt die Moral". But to deal with it at the individual level only runs the risk of obscuring the global and general forces which tend to produce and perpetuate it.

The Statistical Picture
A global view of food security must be based on global facts. World cereal production has more than kept up with world population growth, although the gap between the two growth rates has shown signs of diminishing. World per capita cereal production increased between 1970 and 1980 from 303 kg to 325 kg, but between 1980 and 1990 the improvement was marginal from 325 kg to 327 kg. The big exception to rising per capita cereal production was Sub-Saharan Africa where production fell from 135 kg per capita in 1970 to 114 kg in 1980 and 112 kg in 1990. In Latin America and the Caribbean per capita cereal production also fell between 1980 and 1990 below the level which had been reached in 1960. The marginalisation of Africa clearly emerges as one of the major problems. Related to the decline in per capita production, net cereal imports to Sub-Saharan Africa increased sharply from 3 to 9 million tons. Generally developing countries were becoming increasingly dependent on net imports for their total food supplies. Net imports rose from little more than 1 per cent of total use in 1970 to over 9 per cent in 1990; this proportion is projected by the FAO further to increase. Latin

America and the Caribbean turned from being net exporters in 1970 to become major net importers in 1990. Reliance on imports is obviously contributory to food insecurity, depending as they do on international supply, international prices, availability of foreign exchange, and willingness to provide food aid.

The increase in net imports with all the sacrifices and uncertainties involved was not sufficient to prevent a decrease in per capita food supplies in Sub-Saharan Africa. These fell from 2,100 calories per day in 1961-63 to 2,040 in 1990-92. Compared with the world as a whole, the gap in calories in Sub-Saharan Africa increased from 200 in 1961-63 to 300 in 1969-71, and 500 in 1979-81, and to 670 in 1990-92. The former centrally-planned economies also showed a drop in per capita food supplies between 1979-81 and 1990-92, although even after the drop they still remained well above average world levels. South Asia, which up to 1970 had lower per capita food supplies than Sub-Saharan Africa, pulled even by 1980 and well ahead by 1990. The most spectacular improvement has been in East Asia which had the lowest supplies of any region in the early 1960s, but is now well ahead of both Africa and South Asia.

As far as the actual number of hungry ("chronically undernourished") people is concerned, the overall improvement in per capita food supplies in developing countries has been largely offset by population increase. The number was only reduced from 893 million around 1970 to 809 million around 1991. At this rate it would take another 200 years to reduce this number to zero! Once again Sub-Saharan Africa stands out as a glaring exception where the number of chronically under-nourished people has more than doubled between 1970 and 1991. In South Asia the number of under-nourished people also increased between 1970 and 1980, but subsequently it has fallen although still above the 1970 number.

At the level of individual countries it is striking how food production per capita has sharply deteriorated in countries affected by civil war and conflict. Between 1979 and 1991 food production per capita fell at an annual rate of 3.1 per cent in Mozambique, 1.8 per cent in Rwanda, 1.2 per cent in Haiti, 5.1 per cent in Nicaragua, 2.8 per cent in Sudan, etc. Among the 40 low-income economies, more than half (26) showed a fall in per capita food production between 1979 and 1991.

This is the broad picture, setting the agenda for priority international action.

Global Failure: Six Reasons

What are the reasons for this global failure in providing food security for all? We may list six reasons:
1. First of all there is the marginalisation of Africa. This shows in all the general economic and human development indicators – from per capita GDP to child mortality and expectation of life. Where in the rest of the world there has

been progress, in Africa – excepting a few bright spots – there has been regress and deterioration. The incidence of hunger and food insecurity is higher in Africa than anywhere else, even though in terms of absolute numbers the Indian sub-continent still has more hungry people. This situation will not be changed unless as an international community we take special measures to bring Africa back into the mainstream of economic progress. This will require no less than a Marshall Plan for Africa – although of course an entirely different type of Marshall Plan from the one which benefited us so much in Western Europe. In particular it will require a Green Revolution in Africa similar in extent to the one in the Punjab of India and Pakistan. Some 30 years or so ago India and Sub-Saharan Africa each produced something like 65-70 million tons of cereals; today India in a normal year produces something like 225 million tons, while Sub-Saharan Africa produces not so much more than the original 65-70 million tons for a much larger population – in other words heavily reduced food production per capita. Naturally, like any Marshall Plan for Africa, a Green Revolution would have to be very different from the Indian precedent: Population density is less, the level of knowledge and administration is lower, soils are different, climate and water resources are different, etc. A Green Revolution for Africa would require a drastic increase in research into African poor people's food: millet, sorghum, cassava, etc. rather than wheat and rice. It would also involve a drastic increase and improvement in agricultural extension services for which the conditions are worse than they were in India.

2. Related to the problem of Africa, but not limited to it, is the spread and impact of war and conflict which we have seen in recent years. War and ethnic conflict destroys food security, but the converse is also true: food insecurity is a fertile breeding ground for war and conflict. There is a vicious circle at work. Food insecurity creates conflict over land, water and other natural resources and over food itself, while the conflict itself disrupts food production, creates refugees and displaced persons, and keeps land out of cultivation because of land mines, etc. Rwanda, Somalia and Afghanistan are the most striking cases, although Bosnia should remind us that there are other causes of war and conflict as well. The Gulf War was also a fight over natural resources although not food resources in this case. Today more than half the countries in Sub-Saharan Africa are affected by war and conflict either in their own or in neighboring countries, and resources are heavily diverted into military expenditures. The international action required would be a better system of preventive diplomacy, of timely and sufficient emergency action, and generous help with post-conflict rehabilitation and reconstruction. The necessary action has been described by the Secretary-General of the UN in

his recent reports *Agenda for Peace* and *Agenda for Development.* However, there is little sign of the necessary international action – on the contrary the UN is systematically deprived of the necessary means for such action. The weakness of the UN is certainly one of the causes of global food insecurity. Any global vision of food security would involve a fundamental change in this respect.

3. The third global reason for world hunger revolves around the tangle of deteriorating terms of trade and debt burdens of developing countries, and the nature of the structural adjustment programs currently imposed on them to deal with their resulting balance of payments difficulties. The debt burden means that a significant proportion of export earnings is needed for servicing the debt and thus is not available for financing food imports or the means needed to increase food production. The deteriorating terms of trade mean that export earnings are less than they would otherwise be, with the same consequences. There is also a vicious circle at work here: the deteriorating terms of trade create a need to finance imports by incurring debt, while the increase in debt burden forces countries to try to increase their exports, thus leading to oversupply and deteriorating terms of trade. This situation is further complicated by the nature of the stabilization and structural adjustment programs imposed by the powerful Bretton Woods institutions, with the backing of the major financial powers. The main problem with these programmes is that the "outward orientation" imposed on indebted developing countries in balance-of-payments difficulties might be good advice for each country individually, but if all developing countries are simultaneously forced to become more outward oriented, this will mean intensified competition, oversupply and deteriorating terms of trade. A global vision of food security therefore would involve dealing with the debt problem, dealing with deteriorating terms of trade and above all reform of the Bretton Woods institutions and their approach to stabilization and structural adjustment. Although there is a consensus of enlightened professional opinion on this, the necessary action seems very slow to develop.

4. The increased globalisation of markets is also a contributory factor to food insecurity. Combined with increased urbanization it has led to a shift from food crops to cash crops. The need for foreign exchange has led to priority for cash crops, especially export cash crops, for the best land, while food production has been shifted to poorer and marginal land. This tendency has been powerfully supported by the strong position of multinational corporations which produce many of the export crops of developing countries and control their trade. Six multinational corporations control 85 per cent of grain trade; eight corporations control 60 per cent of coffee trade; seven

control 90 per cent of trade in tea; three control 83 per cent of trade in cocoa; three control 80 per cent of trade in bananas, etc. These corporations have the power to secure the best land for their production and to set prices in international trade. Kenya provides a good example: coffee farming has increasingly shifted food production to marginal lands. In Ethiopia, it is reported that most of this fertile and irrigable land is primarily occupied by large commercial farms which are owned by foreign companies who have capital for irrigation and other infrastructural development. By 1976, 33 per cent of all the irrigable land in Awash valley had been developed for cotton and sugar production. More than half of this land was controlled and managed by Dutch and British companies. While the investors were largely content, it has been argued that the expansion of commercial agriculture in Awash, as well as in other commercial farming regions, was made at the expense of local small-holders and food production.[1] The international action required would be some kind of regulation of multinational corporations and their role in developing countries and trade in their products, but also greater research on increasing the productivity of food production in low-yield situations and on marginal lands.

5. Globalisation of markets combined with pressures for liberalization have made developing countries more dependent on food imports as compared with domestic production. Of the 132 countries classified as developing countries in international statistics, the great majority – no fewer than 104 – are net food importers, with total food imports of 120 million tons and projected to increase rapidly in the future. No fewer than 98 of the 104 net food-importing developing countries are classified as Low Income Food Deficit Countries (LIFDCs). Reliance on food imports is compatible with food security as long as the finance to pay for imports is secure and the international prices for food are predictable. But in the case of the LIFDCs this is far from being the case: the Sub-Saharan African countries depend for half their total food imports on food aid. Food aid is under threat and international prices for food may increase as the result of the recent GATT Uruguay Round (as will explained in more detail later). The international action required would be either to establish a financial fund to maintain food imports in times of balance-of-payments difficulties, or else to establish a food reserve for this purpose. In principle, both of these approaches have already been accepted: the financial provision exists in the form of the IMF Compensation and Contingency Fund; the latter in the form of the International Emergency Food Reserve (IEFR) administered by the FAO and

---

[1] Shujie Yao 1996. The determinants of cereal crop productivity of the peasant farm sector in Ethiopia, 1981-87, *Journal of International Development*, Vol 8, No 1, 69-82 (1996).

World Food Program. In practice however both arrangements are ineffective: the IMF fund because of the conditionality attached and the IEFR because of unwillingness of contributing countries to make the necessary amounts quickly and unconditionally available or even make necessary pledges of sufficient magnitude.

6. Behind these areas of immediate concern there are also more fundamental and long-term global forces at work which threaten future food security. Most obviously there is pressure of increasing populations – here again Africa gives the most concern. Whereas in the rest of the developing world rates of population increase are gradually declining, in Africa they remain obstinately high. Population pressure does not only directly increase the demand for food but it also indirectly reduces the supply of food through environmental degradation and by driving food production increasingly into marginal areas. So far world food production has kept up with population growth – in fact surpassing it by a factor of 1.5. This and the resulting long-term decline in international food prices has led to some complacency, but the weight of professional opinion is that the increases in yield show signs of petering out. In any case the increase in supply has been mainly in the richer countries and has certainly not extended to Africa, thus raising questions of access or entitlement to food supplies. The demand for food will be further increased as a result of rising per capita incomes in many parts of the world. While according to Engel's Law direct demand for food may not rise proportionately to incomes, there will be a shift from direct human consumption of grains towards consumption of meat and dairy products which absorb proportionately more grain in the form of feed grain, thus offsetting or more than offsetting Engel's Law.

A New Threat: Impact of the GATT-Uruguay Round

All the above global concerns regarding food security are structural problems of long standing. However, more recently a new threat to food security has emerged which is the direct result of global action and in its turn calls for remedial action by the international community. This stems from the recent GATT Agreement concluding the Uruguay Round, resulting in the recent establishment of the World Trade Organization (WTO). While there have been some optimistic estimates of the resulting rise in world incomes, there has been less discussion of the impact on food security.

Until now the agricultural policies of the richer countries – particularly the US, the EU and Japan – have provided generous subsidies to domestic farmers as well as generous export subsidies as well as food aid. The subsidies to domestic farmers have been tied to production; even where they take the form of income support for farmers they still have the effect of increasing overall production. (The case of subsidies tied to a willingness of taking land out of production is more complicated, but even here the effect on overall production is ambivalent.) This policy has resulted in agricultural surpluses in the US and EU. These overhanging surpluses have had a generally depressing effect on international food prices, in addition to a willingness to subsidise exports or give surpluses away as concessional food aid. This situation has been greatly to the disadvantage of food exporters among the developing countries, such as Argentina or Thailand, which could not afford to subsidize their own exports and had to watch their potential markets pre-empted by subsidized exports or food aid from the US and EU. As a rough estimate, the implied subsidies to food importers, adding up the general downward pressure on world prices and the export subsidies (overt or covert) as well as open food aid altogether amounted to the equivalent of something like 50-60 million tons of cereals p.a. Of this total, only about 10-15 million tons represented open or statistically acknowledged food aid. The rest was "grey" food aid or "food aid which did not dare to speak its name". Thus the statistics of food aid are very misleading, representing as they do only the tip of an iceberg.

Under the Uruguay arrangement this situation will change. The change will be only gradual and partial but the intention is to follow up in further rounds of discussion under the WTO in the direction of full liberalization. Initially domestic agricultural support measures are to be reduced by 21 per cent and export subsidies by 36 per cent over a six-year period. (There are certain exemptions and the change will be backloaded so that most of the reduction will be in the last years of the period.) This will result in a reduction of surpluses and a rise in international food prices. The present provisions are estimated to increase world prices for wheat by 5.0 per cent, for coarse grains by 3.6 per cent, for dairy products by 7.2 per cent, and for vegetable oils by 4.1 per cent – perhaps an average of 5.5 per cent for these four items which make up the bulk of food aid. Such increases spread over six years may seem modest but they are based on the very mild and partial liberalization of the Uruguay Round and would be multiplied if liberalization proceeds in subsequent rounds.

All this is good news for food exporters but bad news for food importers. Since the developing countries are now net food importers (to the extent of some 100 million tons or so in cereals alone), it is bad news overall for them and in particular for the African Sub-Saharan countries – as the statistical part has shown they are becoming increasingly net food importers. This fact that there are losers as well as gainers from the Uruguay Round Agreement is well known. The World Bank, on the basis of a new 24-region, 22-commodity model of world trade, concludes that the whole agricultural reforms will increase world incomes by $59 billion dollars, they will reduce the incomes of Sub-Saharan Africa by $200 million, Middle East and North Africa by $300 million, China by $500 million, Eastern Europe by $100 million, and Mexico by a smaller amount.[2] Compared with the $59 billion overall increase in world income, these losses amount to little more than $1 billion, so in theory the reforms represent a *Pareto optimum* in the sense that the winners could easily afford to compensate the losers. But whether in fact they will do so is a different matter.

Looking at this situation from the point of view of food aid, we may say that the need for or demand for food aid will be increased while the willingness to give food aid will be reduced. The increased need for food aid arises from the fact that the higher international prices reduce the volume of commercial imports which the LIFDCs can afford, given their limited foreign exchange resources and balance of payments pressures. The willingness to give food aid will decline because the food surpluses in the donor countries will be reduced – it was the existence of these surpluses which made food aid popular among donors as apparently free of cost. Also in the budgetary sense food aid will now involve higher costs relative to financial aid and impose increased burdens on limited aid budgets.

The Uruguay Round Agreement tries to cope with these threats by suggesting that "genuine food aid" should not be reduced. Insofar as "genuine food aid" in the sense of statistically defined highly concessional aid is targeted on poverty, food insecurity, employment-generation as well as humanitarian emergency aid, it would be an advantage if some of the "grey" or hidden food aid now being given through various kinds of export subsidies and discounts in commercial food trade were brought into the open and converted into genuine food aid. At present this "grey" or hidden food aid is untargeted on such worthy objectives – if anything the richer importers with their greater bargaining power obtain their commercial imports cheaper than the poorer importers. As pointed out before, this "grey" food aid is a high multiple of the statistically defined open food aid; hence converting this "grey" food aid could in theory result in a much larger volume of food aid than in the recent past. If effectively used and properly targeted, this increased volume of food aid could be a strong weapon in reducing or eliminating food insecurity. The present auspices for this are not good.

The US Department of Agriculture, in the latest issue of its authoritative *Food Aid Needs Assessments*, has estimated that food aid would have to be increased from 14 to 16 million tons, simply to maintain the *status quo* in the light of increased prices of commercial food imports in the most recent reporting period.

---

[2] Glenn Harrison, Thomas Rutherford, and David Tarr 1995. Quantifying the Outcome of the Uruguay Round, *Finance & Development*, December 1995, International Monetary Fund and the World Bank.

This increase is attributed to agricultural policy reforms and changes in agricultural policy in the EU and US (preceding the commitments of the Uruguay Round). The USDA also estimates that 27 million tons would be sufficient to satisfy minimum nutritional requirements, if fully and effectively targeted on this objective. The figure of 27 million tons is well within the scope of the present volume of (untargeted) "grey" food aid (estimated above at 50-60 million tons). This means that the chance to eliminate food insecurity is with our grasp. What is needed is the political will to convert some of the present untargeted "grey" food aid into genuine and effectively targeted food aid. Easier said than done!

Higher international food prices could in theory give stronger incentives to food-importing countries, including the LIFDCs, to increase their own food production. It is however not clear how much scope there is in this direction. The price elasticity of agriculture in the LIFDCs is low – an increase in production is dependent on improved transport infrastructure, irrigation, supply of fertilisers and pesticides, exclusion services, improved marketing channels, etc. Where food production is largely by subsistence farming, it will not be affected by changes in prices. In any case, if the international community relies on the incentive effect of higher food prices, it will have to supply financial aid to invest in infrastructure, buy fertilizers, etc. Clearly the auspices for such increased financial aid are not good either.

Finally, whose responsibility is it to see that the principle of the Uruguay Round of protecting the LIFDCs from higher food prices is realized? Is it the WTO, the World Food Program, the FAO, the Food Aid Convention, the Development Assistance Committee (DAC) of the OECD, the International Wheat Council? At the present time the matter seems to be lost in this tangle of institutions. This goes to show that international action to improve food security will also depend on a reform and greater effectiveness of the present system of global governance.

References

Shujie Yao 1996. The determinants of cereal crop productivity of the peasant farm sector in
    Ethiopia, 1981-87. In: *Journal of International Development*, Vol 8, No 1, 69-82 (1996).
Glenn Harrison, Thomas Rutherford, and David Tarr 1995. Quantifying the Outcome of the
    Uruguay Round. In: *Finance & Development*, December 1995, International Monetary
    Fund and the World Bank.

Perspective of World Food Supply and Demand
– Challenges and New Focuses –

Günter Dresrüsse

Head of Sub-Department **gtz**
Agriculture and Forestry
Emergency and Refugee Aid
German Technical Cooperation, Eschborn, Germany

Following the 1994 UN Conference on Population and Development, we know that by the middle of the next century, our planet will probably need to be made inhabitable for twice as many people.

In the run-up to this year's World Food Summit, are we certain that the resources of our planet will be sufficient to at least guarantee the food security of its population of ten billion? Will we be able to leave to our children the resources needed to achieve this, and will we be able to develop the political, economic and ethical models enabling us to distribute those resources so that they can benefit all human beings and not be dominated by a few?

What contribution can development cooperation – especially in agriculture – make today to help prevent this Malthusian apocalypse? Which changes in awareness, initial supports, and boosters can it develop to meet the challenges posed by the foreseeable need to triple the quantity of food we produce? What inputs can it provide to this process, and which dreams and illusions does it urgently need to abandon in order to focus the modest potentials available on achieving the "feasible"?

Here are some thoughts on the above:

The Challenge

Development Scenarios

"Full House." With this headline, followed by a "wake-up call:" "Who will feed China?", Lester Brown[1] of the Washington Worldwatch Institute outlines for us, on the eve of the new millennium, a development scenario so apocalyptic as to give the neo-Malthusians hope for a paradigmatic rebirth. The oceans overfished, pastureland overgrazed and limited agricultural potentials to feed a population of 8.9 billion people in the year 2030: these are the basic conclusions of the two publications.

They are based on analyses of the Institute, according to which the marginal productivities of global resources are falling sharply. Soil, water, air and the genetic potential of plants are largely exhausted. The final decade of this millennium marks the turning point after which it will become incomparably more difficult to continue increasing food production than in the past. Since passing this turning point, the 3% growth rates in grain production from 1950 to 1984 have fallen to just under 1%. The so-called on the shelf technology gap, i.e. the non-application of technologies due to inadequate knowledge, lack of innovation capital, or institutional constraints has been reduced significantly. Moreover – and this is emphasized especially in the case of China – large areas of agricultural land are falling prey to industrialization and urbanization. The so-called carrying capacity of the planet for the growing population is exhausted. According to Brown and Kane, only a radical change in the management of existing resources will offer any opportunity of identifying a chance for survival by the growing population. However, this will only be sufficient if at the same time radical and effective measures are taken to control population growth.

While Lester Brown was writing his book in 1993, the FAO publication "Agriculture: Towards 2010"[2] appeared, and the IFPRI Vision 2020 initiative was under preparation. The FAO and IFPRI[3] scenarios present a completely different picture of the future food supply situation. According to them, it would seem possible to maintain the needed 2% growth rate in grain production beyond the first decade of the next century. These visions operate on the assumption that production increases will make it possible to maintain the trend of falling real food prices on the global food market observed over recent decades, even in the

---

[1] Cf. Brown 1994, 1995
[2] Cf. FAO 1993
[3] Cf. IFPRI 1995

near future. From the regional perspective, however, it is assumed that there will be a serious deterioration in food security in sub-Saharan Africa, and a continuation of the delicate situation in South Asia.

According to these projections, which are, in the view of the authors and organizations, based on "realistic" assumptions vis-à-vis population growth, productivity increases, and real food prices, it will still be possible in future to feed a growing population. However, this is based on the crucial premise that major efforts are made to increase investment in agricultural research, and without delay, since the interval between investment in research and visible results at the farm level is between 10 and 20 years.

Carruthers,[4] supported by a number of US scientists, takes a different approach, proposing that, in order to produce the needed food, 20 million hectares of land withdrawn from agriculture in the United States and Europe be recultivated, and that a further 80 million hectares of savanna in Latin America be brought under commercial agricultural management. According to Carruthers, the fragile tropical and sub-tropical soils and the sensitive environment in most developing countries will be able only at considerable risk to supply the growing urban centers, which will be inhabited by an estimated four billion people by the year 2025. This food, he continues, can only be paid for by increasing exports from the developing countries to the industrialized nations of products manufactured under labor-intensive conditions. However, Carruthers gives little indication of how the logistics and infrastructure required for handling the more than 800 million tons of grain (more than quadruple today's volume of grain exports) on the world market would be developed and paid for, without food prices increasing. Such price increases would mean that the trap of "access to food" would once again snap shut, and poverty would increase.[5]

The problems which the scenarios pose for the current debate on global nutrition can be illustrated by the following example: While Brown identifies a food deficit for China in 2030 of 207 million tons of grain, equivalent to the total volume of world grain exports in 1994 (approximately 200 million tons),[6] Rosegrant estimates China's import requirement for 2020 to be only 27 million tons of grain.[7]

Where prognoses diverge in this way, and the future thus becomes "uncertain" and "unpredictable," it would seem appropriate to take a close look at the

---

[4] Carruthers 1993
[5] Cf. also McCalla 1994, who presents four different scenarios (The Conventional View; The Optimists; The Pessimists; The Developed Countries Fill the Gap)
[6] Brown 1995, p.97
[7] Rosegrant 1995, p.30

individual elements of the so-called food security equation.[8] An appropriately differentiated analysis might perhaps help identify precisely where the discrepancies arise, and at the same time promote the elaboration of a fresh perspective, along with a corresponding guiding framework for development cooperation.

The Food Security Equation

As already indicated above, access to the individual elements determining future food security is perhaps best achieved through the traditional supply-and-demand equation, on the basis of which the so-called food security balance can be obtained at the point of intersection of the two curves (supply and demand).

On the **demand side**, the following elements need to be considered:
- Population growth (i.e. the projected population at a point in time X)
- Per capita food consumption (in relation to income at a point in time X)
- Income elasticity of demand for food

On the **supply side**, the following factors are crucial:
- The newly reclaimed land available for future production (extension of farmland or reduction of erosion and reclamation of eroded land)
- Yield increases attributable to:
  - enhanced management of natural resources (soil, water, air, genetic diversity)
  - human resource development (human expertise, establishment of appropriate institutions, gender-orientation and target-group organization)
  - technological progress (e.g. biotechnology)
- Prevention of post-harvest losses and reduction of marketing costs

---

[8] This is all the more necessary in order to avoid falling prey to the regression envisaged by Serageldin (1995) as a response to an uncertain future: ... *there is a growing sense of unpredictability about the future. Under these circumstances, people tend to regress: if the future cannot be clearly defined as the goal, one lives for the present. If the present is troublesome and disconcerting, one falls back onto the past. The past here means one's ethnic, religious, cultural, or national roots. It is a drawing closer of the circle within which one can feel secure, a regression to the concept of tribe and clan".* page 4. This phenomenon can be observed in the process of political debate in many countries. The complexity of future developments tends to cause political action and reaction which is directed "within". Even Germany seems unable to escape from this phenomenon of "provincialization".

The Demand Side

Population Growth

Although population growth is perhaps the most crucial variable in the food security equation, agricultural experts tend to assign to it the status of an exogenous factor. Margaret Catley-Carlson, President of the UN Population Council, also drew attention to this phenomenon at the IFPRI Vision 2020 conference last June.[9] From a scientific angle it is also "incorrect" to attach less importance to key factors in an equation perhaps only because they are supposed to fall under another scientific discipline. Of all disciplines, agricultural science has always lived from and been a shining example of multidisciplinarity, elaborating integrated approaches and strategies. It would be difficult to understand, then, why it might adopt a reductionist perspective in this context.

The population projections of the Cairo Conference are impressive not only in quantitative terms. They also clearly show the possibilities open to the politicians and societies of this planet to influence the crucial variable within the food security equation, or rather the "survival equation" of this planet. Yet perhaps our relative indifference with regard to this opportunity is also due to our inadequate powers of imagination in the face of these abstract figures. Every year, the earth's population grows by a figure equivalent to the entire population of Germany (90 million people, 84 million of whom are born in developing countries). This means more than 10,000 people every hour – equal to the number of students attending a medium-sized German university. Even so, in view of the needs and wants of these people and their dignity as human beings, expressions such as "explosion", "avalanche" or population "bomb" are perhaps not the most appropriate terms.

Whether this world has 12, 10 or 7.8 billion human mouths to feed in the year 2050 will be determined by the people living on earth now and tomorrow, and by their behavior.

The conventional picture, as also selected above, is partially contradicted by von Blanckenburg,[10] who while agreeing with the view over the very long-term, nevertheless points out that in the course of human history, the population has always grown in spurts. He identifies these spurts as being coincident with the major changes in the mode of production, i.e. the use of the first implements for hunting and gathering, the domestication of plants and animals (approximately 10,000 years ago), and finally the scientific and industrial revolution of the modern age, which began in the 18th century and continues to this day. He establishes a close link between population growth and the mode of production, postulating at the same time the mechanism of equilibrium between supply and

---

[9] Margaret Catley-Carlson in IFPRI 1995, p. 59
[10] Blanckenburg, 1986

demand, within this framework of interaction between production technology and population growth.[11] According to this analysis, not only does technology stimulate population growth, but growth itself also stimulates technological development. This view of the dynamic process is entirely consistent with the new models and concepts to explain the growth of complex systems.

Figure 1: Growth in World Population through Time

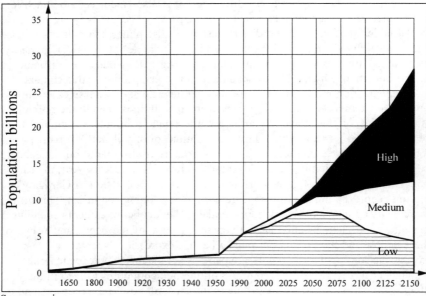

Source: various

Income Growth and Income Elasticity of Demand

Having said all that, it would be entirely inappropriate to equate the actual size of a large population with a corresponding demand for food. This all the more so in view of the fact that 700 to 800 million people are to date unable to obtain sufficient food each day. Hence the conclusions of the numerous analyses on the so-called "cereal gap" which are constantly being put forward[12] are of dubious value, or are even misleading when based on a projected market demand.[13] It is generally acknowledged that the effective demand for food on local and

---

[11] For further details see Blanckenburg 1986, pp. 19.

[12] Cf. Lele 1995, p. 13

[13] Cf. also Alexandratos 1995, p. 359

international markets is dependent on available income and the income elasticity of demand for food. Unfortunately, the prognosis regarding growing famine made by Otto Matzke at the first World Food Summit in 1974 has proved correct, i.e. that the figures would probably rise from 450 million to 750 million people by 1985.[14]

Yet even the argument which projects production (the supply side) as unchangeable due to the resource situation, needs to be called into question. Brown's[15] claim would be entirely consistent with the quotation from Ghandi at the beginning of the present paper. He asserts that, given a demand equivalent to consumption in the USA (800 kg per capita), and a projected production volume in 2030 of 2.1 billion tons of grain, only 2.5 billion people could be fed, whereas given a reduction of per capita demand to the Indian level (200 kg), i.e. a reduction of "wants" as opposed to "needs," it would be possible to feed 10 billion. But this one-sided view also inadequately reflects the acknowledged interplay between supply and demand, the balance between which ultimately has to be defined through prices.

Consequently, this ought to encourage the optimists as they establish that virtually throughout the entire century, real food prices (with the exception of minor aberrations) have shown a clearly downward trend, which has led to a marked increase in per capita calorific intake among the world's population.

The fact that increases in per capita income in Africa, as well as in many developing countries of other regions, do not exceed 2% per annum, and that only a good 50% of world grain production is consumed in developing countries, suggests, assuming an income elasticity of 0.5, an increase in effective demand for food in developing countries of not more than 30%.[16] The growth rates resulting from that scenario are considered by FAO to be "producible." Most important in the demand projections of Alexandratos and de Haen is the point that the increase in effective demand caused by income growth will occur primarily in the developing countries, and hardly at all in the industrialized nations. Furthermore, per capita consumption figures in the Central and Eastern European/CIS countries (780 kg) will be reduced as a result of changed consumption patterns and increases in storage and processing efficiency. Having said that, the difference between a doubling of grain production in the developing countries only, and an overall doubling of grain production, amounts to more or less half a billion tons of grain produced per annum.

---

[14] *"If – as is to be expected – the percentage of the world's population hit by famine remains unchanged over the next 10 years, today's figure of 400 million famine victims will have reached at least 750 million by 1985".* Matzke 1974, p. 35
[15] Brown, Kane 1995, p. 202
[16] Alexandratos 1995, p. 362/363

Hence to summarize, it can be concluded that, with regard to the demand side of the food security equation, the effective demand for food, i.e. the demand based on corresponding purchasing power, is ultimately the determining factor. Under no circumstances should this be confused with an aggregate consumption requirement, which is a hypothetical projection based on population growth and per capita caloric requirements. Even population growth can perhaps only be forecast realistically for the next 20 years, since it will be highly dependent on decisions made over the coming years by societies in the developing countries. The prognoses currently available therefore still involve a high degree of uncertainty. What would be important would be to secure agreement among scientists vis-à-vis the methodology of determining demand. It is difficult to explain to the public how such discrepant methods are still being pursued in spite of all the investment in research.

The Supply Side

Extension of Farmland

While participants at the 1974 World Food Summit still saw considerable potentials for the cultivation of appropriate land in the developing regions,[17] it will certainly not be possible to identify such potential at this year's Summit. According to a number of different studies,[18] the rising economic and ecological costs make it improbable that there will be an increase in farmland as a key resource to raise production during the next 25 years.

In addition, the results of the struggle to reduce erosion losses – no matter how urgent this may be – as well as the recovery of desertified and eroded land, would appear negligible, given the dimensions of production that need to be achieved. Nevertheless, it is striking that the state of knowledge on the current status of land losses caused by erosion and desertification is also very low, which means that there are also wide discrepancies between the pieces of information in circulation on this theme.[19]

---

[17] "In 1962, an overall average of only 45% of potential farmland in the developing countries was actually being utilized. Whilst the level of utilization in Latin America was only 23 percent, and in sub-Saharan Africa 50 percent, the Far East and Asia achieved a figure of 84 percent. The study forecasts by 1985 an increase in the level of utilization to 30 percent in Latin America, 62 percent in sub-Saharan Africa and 89 percent in Asia and the Far East." Matzke 1974, p. 52

[18] Crosson 1994, pp. 6

[19] Crosson 1994, p. 7 and 10

Increased Yields Through Enhanced Management of Natural Resources

Although Crosson also describes the impacts on production increases of erosion reduction, and the improvement of water management and climatic change (CO_2 accumulation and global warming), as negligible, the extremely different view held by Brown, i.e. that the carrying capacity of the planet is exhausted, ought at least to provide food for thought. Given the highly divergent opinions in circulation here too on the impacts of negligent natural resource management, the principle of ecological ethics should be applied, which states that in the case of uncertainty regarding the impacts of activities or management practices, natural resources should be subjected to the minimum possible burden. This is the only way to prevent future generations being robbed of a number of important options and opportunities for development through the possible overutilization of the natural resource base on which their lives will depend. This thought may become clearer if we bear in mind that two-thirds of tropical deforestation results from resource-poor farmers claiming land. They have no option for survival other than the destruction of this important resource, as they will not meet with the support needed to both make a living and conserve the forest at the same time.

It has now become clear that vital progress can still be made in this area. Improved soil tillage and fertilization, and integrated crop management offer major potential to maintain or increase production while keeping ecological burdens low. The elaboration of such strategies is of key significance for increasing production, especially in Africa, since here – like nowhere else in the world – farmers secure the resource base on which their lives depend in some cases using highly complex farming systems. Only holistic approaches, which can be jointly developed by scientists and farmers in a mutual learning process, will be capable of creating sustainable production resting on a higher income base for producers.

With regard to more emphasis on genetic diversity, it must be remembered that despite 10,000 years of farming of our planet, of the approximately 50,000 edible plants which exist, only 200 are cultivated on a regular basis. 15% of all varieties are responsible for 90% of the food, two-thirds of which are accounted for by wheat, rice and corn. Seen in this light, the risk of genetic "erosion" becomes clear, and there are numerous initiatives to counteract it. Having said that, genetic diversity does not appear at present to be under acute threat, as yet. This is thanks in large measure to key efforts of the international research institutions of the CGIAR system. Bearing in mind that 70% of African, 50% of American and 30% of Asian crops are not native to their respective regions, it then becomes clear how important it is to maintain these varieties to secure successful breeding in the future, coupled with the resulting production potentials.[20]

Human Resource Development

Experiences of the last decades of development have made it clear that human capital is ultimately the key factor behind all progress. Conversely, it seems to have been a fundamental error to elaborate technical solutions in the hope that farmers would then apply and introduce them on their farms immediately. To this very day, many scientists can still be heard to say: "There are many technologies on the shelf." In view of these scientists, the errors are made in the process of knowledge transfer, for which they are no longer responsible. In such cases, it is not people who have been placed at the center of development efforts, but technology. Yet unnoticed by many, we have since moved on from the age of the machine into the age of information, and the technology gap has now in many cases become the knowledge gap.

It is therefore now becoming increasingly clear that the challenge faced by agriculture after the turn of the millennium, i.e. to produce the quantity of food required to meet the demand, requires foremost expanding disproportionately the knowledge of producers.[21] This also applies to the design of the production process, which needs to meet not only economic standards, but also ecological ones.[22]

This knowledge has not only one dimension directly affecting the target groups (female and male farmers), but also – and above all – an institutional component, in order that the knowledge can be generated and made available. All the systems which were designed to effect knowledge transfer by means of the trickle-down effect have proved to be inefficient and extremely expensive. Development must begin at the roots, it must empower and support people, enabling them to develop their own identity and institutions on their own initiative.[23] Consequently, it is not governments who need advisory services in order to understand the significance of agriculture, and then transfer "off-the-shelf" technologies via their structures

---

[20] In this regard, cf. the interesting research experiences with genetic engineering of national and wild varieties to increase rice production. Evidently these procedures can achieve yield increases of 15 to 20% within 4 to 5 years. Lecture by Susan McCouch, IFPRI 1995, pp. 89

[21] "The entire mainstream paradigm of development has been expanded to include investment in human resources as an essential, possibly the most essential, ingredient of development strategy." Serageldin, Steer; in Serageldin 1994, p. 51

[22] "Indeed, the critical threat of resource degradation to the future sustainability of the global and LDC agricultural systems is the threat to the knowledge resource, not the threat to natural resources." Crosson 1994, p. 24

[23] Even the Vice-President of the World Bank, Ismail Serageldin, is convinced of this. Cf. Serageldin 1995, p. 117

and regional institutions on to farmers. It is the farmers themselves who need to be provided with information directly from their institutions, advised by them and provided with jointly developed technologies. *"Consulting the poor is not enough to empower them for their own development, even with the most genuine intentions."*[24] In other words, contrary to the common misapprehension, participation is not the same thing as consultation, i.e. obtaining the opinion of the farmers. *"The question, therefore, is whether those holding the dominant positions in the respective phases are ready to take the risk and show the confidence to enable those in the weaker positions to form their own opinions, and do things differently as a result. As such diversity, democracy and decentralization – the three "D"s – are closely linked."*[25] Had the appropriate strategies been developed early enough, it would now be not just a statistical fact that women in developing countries account for between 60 and 70% of agricultural labor, and that not only in Africa two-thirds of food is produced by women, and even a large proportion of farms run by women.[26] Instead, the numerous efforts to increase production in Africa would be geared primarily towards women, and would be working with the concept of "African farmer and her husband."

Given the concern within the development community regarding natural resources, the development priorities set have rather lost sight not only of the necessary production of food, but also the focus on development of the most crucial resource, human capital. Bringing these two priorities back into sharp focus would appear to be the most important step forward on the road to achieving the production targets ahead of us.

Technical Progress

Research and development must go hand in hand and define their objectives jointly, so that farmers can implement new technologies in line with their real demands. The potentials offered by modern research in this context must be fully utilized and made accessible to all farmers and especially to those in the developing countries, and adapted to their needs and ecological conditions. Even though, generally speaking, yield potentials of many varieties are being observed to fall, new approaches to variety development, fertilization, soil management and irrigation might perhaps generate production potentials creating justified hope for a new, "green," Green Revolution. In this context, it should not be forgotten that, at the beginning of the next century, each 0.1 percent increase in yield will create

---

[24] Binswanger 1994, p. 18
[25] Chambers 1995
[26] Tschiersch 1995, p.28

a saving of 25 million hectares of farmland.[27] Thus, technical progress properly designed is key to natural resource protection.

Prevention of Post-Harvest Losses and Reduction of Marketing Costs

Very little attention is paid to these two factors on the supply side, and in some cases they are even neglected entirely. Although estimated in the late 70s at 30% and more in the developing countries, post-harvest losses have often not been borne out by concrete surveys and reviews carried out since. Nevertheless, the entire post-harvest chain is subject to considerable physical as well as financial losses or missed opportunities, and this pushes up prices. Partially as a result of poor logistics and infrastructure, marketing costs in developing countries are up to 50% higher than those in the industrialized countries. Considering that in Nigeria in 1985 the network of rural all-weather roads was less than one-fifth of that of India in 1950 (despite a comparable population density),[28] it is easy to imagine to what extent inadequate post-harvest systems can be a limiting factor vis-à-vis increasing production.

To summarize, with respect to the supply side of the food security equation, it must be concluded that natural resources from both a qualitative and quantitative point of view represent a limiting rather than a promoting factor to increase production. However, the overall potential emerging in the fields of human resource development, technological progress, and the post-harvest sector does give much cause for optimism, subject to the proviso that the necessary initiatives to mobilize these potentials are actually taken.

It has to be noted at this point that the food security equation – of course – is not an abstract formula placed in a technical context with no links to its overall political, social, historical and cultural context. We all know by now, that these factors play a determinant role, representing the "entry" into the technical work which has to be designed on this background. If this is not the case, development fails, as it lacks the necessary "basics" on which it only can be founded.

The ideas and arguments regarding the food security equation presented here can only attempt to shed light on some of the ways in which the complexity of the analyses can lead to acute misconceptions and inconsistencies, even among "respected" scientists. Unfortunately, this is often to be observed at present, which makes it more difficult to elaborate "straightforward" political solutions – as are repeatedly called for. This has a negative impact on the attractiveness of "political" solutions in agriculture.

---

[27] McCalla 1994
[28] Lele 1995

The Need to Act

The Political Dimension

"We must give the highest priority to the agriculture and rural sectors since their neglect means that neither rural nor urban poverty can be reduced. And yet, despite the overwhelming needs, in all my travels as president of the Bank Group, it has been remarkably rare that any issue related to food supply, agriculture and rural poverty have been raised by partner governments or by Bank managers and staff."[29] This comment by the new World Bank President to the Bank's Agricultural Symposium in January 1996 provides a concise summary of the dilemma inherent in the political dimension of agricultural promotion: the analyses of development organizations and research institutions have repeatedly demonstrated that clearly both rapid development, such as witnessed by the Asian "tigers," as well as the solution to the complex problems of growing urbanization and increasing poverty, must emerge from the agricultural and rural sectors. Yet the political thinking of neither the governments of the developing countries, nor of the donor and industrialized nations, is centered on agriculture. Why?

Unfortunately, there have been a number of setbacks in agricultural and rural development, as a result of which it is no longer seen as the core or base of economic and social development. The reasons for these poor marks are as manifold as agricultural development itself is complex. They are to be found on the one hand in the inadequate attention paid to framework conditions in the laying of political and fiscal foundations, and on the other hand in the great complexity and short time frames in which investments have been made. They are also related to the institutional weaknesses which remain unsolved, and to what Tschiersch, Kötter and Kuhnen have termed the "urban bias"[30] of governments and key actors in society who are responsible for the above-mentioned fiscal, monetary and domestic economic decision-making. All these factors have caused an enormous transfer of resources from rural to urban areas, with all the negative consequences that this process entails.

The environmental and poverty-related problems which are growing as a result of agriculture's neglect are no longer addressed through agricultural development, but rather through specific approaches and corresponding project designs in newly-established sub-sectors. Today, these appear under the corresponding titles of natural resource management and poverty reduction programs. As a result, agriculture increasingly became linked in the minds of donors and their partners with "backward" (as opposed to the so-called "modern sector") and a sectoral or

---

[29] James D. Wolfensohn in his memorandum of December 20,1995 to "All Agriculture and Natural Resources Staff in the Bank"
[30] Tschiersch 1995

regional concentration of poverty and poor target groups. Confidence faded away, and funding for agriculture was reduced.

The Financial Dimension

"By withdrawing from rural development the Bank has left the complexity and other implementation problems in the hands of the country governments. They have not disappeared just because the Bank has withdrawn from them." writes Hans Binswanger of the World Bank,[31] thus already pointing out the dilemma of declining financing of the agricultural sector: the reorientation of donors away from agriculture, which in turn induced a reorientation of many governments in developing countries vis-à-vis their own political priorities. The falling volume of agricultural investment financed by banks and bilateral donors was followed by an economic and growth policy of the governments of many developing countries with only a very minor orientation towards agriculture. Readjustment of the so-called economic and political framework had priority.

Figure 2: Funding for Agricultural Development

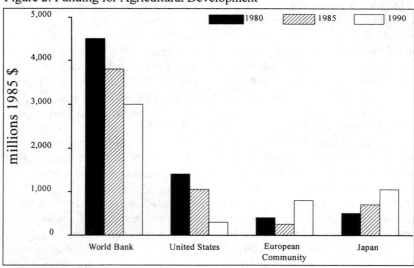

Source: Lele, 1995

These necessary new approaches and reorientations were certainly important and necessary, and to this day continue to have positive impacts on agriculture

---

[31] Binswanger 1994

(e.g. the devaluation of the CFA franc). However, this provides only insufficient compensation for the reduction in financing. The necessary investment is being focused on other sectors, and the agricultural sector is being promoted – if at all – too frequently in terms of its integration into the global market through export crops.

The Role of Agricultural Research

As investment was reduced, it was only natural that investment in agricultural research was reduced at the same time. As the light cast by its enormous successes of the green revolution faded, agricultural research did not succeed in strategically and actively addressing the criticism which was already being expressed during the early phase regarding agriculture and its negative impacts on the environment and social structures.

Instead of integrating these themes in an offensive manner, agricultural research simply noted in a fatalistic frame of mind that these issues, which had now become central to the development debate, were slowly drifting away from it. Natural resource management and poverty reduction were becoming sectors in their own right.

In German agricultural research at least, too strong an emphasis on technical plant production themes was maintained, at the expense of the economic and in some cases social activity areas. Within the field of economics, there was in turn a relative focus on microeconomics, and little attention was paid to the macroeconomic issues – especially with respect to the relevance of the agricultural sector to national economic growth and employment issues.[32]

Having said that, the considerable German inputs to tropical agricultural development should not go unmentioned at this point. The development of systemic approaches in particular, e.g. involving farm and household promotion, met with worldwide acknowledgment and international recognition. Nevertheless the criticism should be voiced that, in a situation of incomprehensible funding policy behavior, agricultural research and related activity areas did not succeed in integrating these new fields, and calling attention to the fatal consequences of reductions in funding.

One concrete example of this is the fact that, during the initial run-up to the Rio Summit, the organizers had intended to exclude agriculture as a theme of the Conference. It was only included in the agenda in response to massive pressure exerted by FAO.

---

[32] Cf. also Köster 1994

The Role of Development Cooperation

The role of development cooperation in the above-mentioned context, and in the light of the challenges also outlined above, is in fact a clear one: It must revive interest in agricultural promotion and make promotion of rural areas a central theme of its approach. It goes without saying that this can only take place on the basis of a healthy macroeconomic framework, in which both the monetary and fiscal policy framework, and the institutional environment are created for successful implementation of agricultural promotion.

Agricultural promotion must actively dedicate itself not only to the traditional and more technical – though nonetheless important and crucial – themes of variety improvement and soil amelioration, but also to the corresponding ecologically-sound production methods. Furthermore, it must become actively involved in networking in connection with the themes of poverty and employment, and the more general issues of national and global environmental protection and resource conservation. These are extremely difficult themes. However, given the long tradition of the integrated approach in agricultural research, its comparative advantage ought to be clear. Agriculture in the developing countries will have to be measured by the successful promotion of the four "E"s (equity, employment, ecology and economics).

Since the field of agricultural research is contracting as agriculture's significance dwindles in most industrialized nations, tropical agricultural research is also suffering as a result. Consequently, alongside the laudable cooperation within the CGIAR systems, it is urgent and essential that further cooperation be established among the national and bilateral agricultural promotion institutions. German development cooperation and agricultural research for developing countries in particular must surely broaden and deepen its cooperation with its partners at the European and international levels, while at the same time elaborating and addressing the themes jointly with its partners in the developing countries.

The sharp fall in the number of students of agriculture, which is linked to the general declining role of agriculture in advanced countries and the reduction in budgets and funding for development cooperation as a whole, strongly suggests that a radical structural change in the efficiency of agricultural implementation and research is called for. These developments in the right direction will need foresight, preparation, and active support.

It goes without saying that the development cooperation organizations themselves will also have to become involved in this necessary process of change. Here too, it will be necessary not only to address different themes, but also to implement structural changes in order to be successful.

Epilogue

It is absolutely essential that the thoughts outlined above on how to shape the future production of food on our planet be discussed with the necessary professional depth and exhaustiveness, within a rational and structured framework. However, this will not be sufficient per se unless the framework of discussion is more than its mere economical, political, and technical dimension.

The "survival equation" described above can only be solved successfully if there is a broad political and social consensus on the right of everyone to live – and above all survive – actively on this planet. Were that the case, then all people would need to be equally firm in making an active and determined effort to assert that right. Without the necessary passion referred to by Serageldin,[33] and without a reduction of the violence in people's heads and hearts lamented by Swaminathan,[34] this cannot be achieved, and thus the future for the inhabitants of our planet cannot be secured. Only through passionate efforts based on the moral and ethical dimension of the global food issue, will the motivation and strength to implement the developed strategies be able to grow alongside the conceptual solution, as well as the energy to take up this crucial work for the future again and again in spite of all the adversities.

It is therefore suggested to add to the 4 "E"s of agricultural development (i.e. economics, equity, employment and ecology) another set of 4 "E"s and these ought to be: empathy, emotions, ethics and empowerment.

Bibliography

Alexandratos, Nicholas; Haen, Hartwig de; 1995. World consumption of cereals: Will it double by 2025? Food Policy, Volume 20, No.4, pp.359-366,

Binswanger, Hans P.; 1994. Agricultural and Rural Development: Painful Lessons; Simon Brandt Address delivered by the author on September 21, 1994 at the 32nd annual meeting of the Agricultural Economics Association of South Africa in Pretoria, South Africa

Blanckenburg, Peter von; 1986. Welternährung, Gegenwartsprobleme und Strategien für die Zukunft, Munich.

Brown, Lester R., Kane, Hal; 1994. Full House, Reassessing the Earth's Population Carrying Capacity, The Worldwatch Environmental Alert Series, New York/London 1994

Brown, Lester R.; 1995. Who will feed China? The Worldwatch Environmental Alert Series, New York/London.

Carruthers, Ian 1993. Going. going. gone! Tropical Agriculture as We Knew It. Tropical Agriculture Association Newsletter (UK), 13(3):1-5

---

[33] "I am perturbed, however, that while the approach to the 2020 Vision is rich in acuity it sorely lacks passion. ... We do need to be aware, however, that these can be matters of life and death, of war and peace." IFPRI (1995); Ismail Serageldin, p. 130

[34] "This threat comes from the growing violence in the human heart." People & the Planet 1995, M.S. Swaminathan, p. 26

Carruthers, Ian; Kydd, Jonathan 1994. The Development and Direction of Agricultural
    Development Economics: Requiem Or Resurrection? Agricultural Economics Society
    Annual Conference April 1994, St Luke's Campus, University of Exeter
Chambers, Robert 1995. Interview in GTZ Akzente, Eschborn, 2/95
Crosson, Pierre 1994. Degradation of Resources as a Threat to Sustainable Agriculture, Paper to
    the First World Congress of Professionals in Agronomy, Santiago, Chile, September 5-8,
    1994
Deutsche Stiftung Weltbevölkerung 1995. Neue Studien zur Welternährung; DSW Newsletter,
    Nr. 8, October 1995
Diouf, Jaques 1995. Commemoration of the Fiftieth Anniversary of FAO in Quebec, Speech to
    the 50th Anniversary of FAO, Chateau Frontenac, Quebec, 16 October 1995
Economist, The 1995. The Food crisis that isn't, and the one that is; The Economist, November
    25th, 1995
FAO 1993. Agriculture: Towards 2010, Conference Paper C-93-24, Rome, 1993
IFPRI 1995. A 2020 Vision for Food, Agriculture, and the Environment; Speeches made at an
    International Conference, June 13-15, 1995
Islam, Nurul (Hrsg.) 1995. Population and Food in the Early Twenty-First Century: Meeting
    Future Food Demands of an Increasing Population; IFPRI, Washington 1995
Koester, Ulrich; Cramon-Taubadel, Stephan von; (1994) Zur Struktur und Organisation der
    Agrarforschung In der BRD, Agrarwirtschaft 43, Heft 8/9, Frankfurt 1994
Lele, Uma; Coffman, Ronnie; (1995) Global Research on the environmental And agricultural
    nexus for the 21st century (GREAN); A Proposal for Collaborative Research Among U.S.
    Universities, CGIAR Centers, and Developing Country Institutions, University of Florida,
    Cornell University
Matzke, Otto 1974. Der Hunger wartet nicht, Die Probleme der Welternährungskonferenz 1974;
    Bonn 1974
McCalla, Alex F. 1994. Agriculture and food needs to 2025: Why we should be concerned. Sir
    George Crawford Memorial Lecture, International Centers Week, Washington DC, 1994
Newsweek 1995. GRAIN DRAIN; China's peasants are reducing their crops of wheat and rice.
    The result will probably be a future grain shortage of disastrous dimensions; Newsweek,
    May 15, 1995
People & the Planet 1995. Feeding a World of 8 Billion; IPPF, IUCN, UNFPA, WWF, Vol. 4
    No. 4 1995
Rosegrant, Mark W.; Agcaoili-Sombilla, Mercedita; Perez, Nicostrato D. 1995. Global Food
    Projections to 2020: Implications for Investment; IFPRI, Discussion Paper, June 1995
Serageldin, Ismail 1995. Nurturing Development, Aid and Cooperation in today's Changing
    World, The World Bank, Washington D.C., May 1995
Serageldin, Ismail; Steer, Andrew (eds.) 1994. Making Development Sustainable,
    Environmentally Sustainable Development Occasional Paper Series No. 2, ESD,
    Washington.
Tschiersch, Joachim E.; Kötter, Herbert; Kuhnen, Frithjof; 1995. Kirchen und ländliche
    Entwicklung, Mainz 1995
Wissenschaftlicher Beirat beim BMZ 1994. Neue Akzente in der deutschen
    Entwicklungszusammenarbeit während der nächsten Legislaturperiode, Dezember 1994

Foundations of Innovations

Helmut Walter

Institute of Macroeconomics

University of Hohenheim, D-70593 Stuttgart, Germany

A Preliminary Taxonomy

Innovations have been a matter of concern from the beginning of economic science. At first glance they simply seem to serve the purpose of making new and useful things. But if we take a closer look we may soon get confused by the diversity of aspects and dimensions we have to face. From empirical studies, which usually regard innovations as single events in historical time and aim to trace their specific sources, i.e. the firm or innovator who performed it, we can learn that almost each innovation has a history of its own. How then can the huge bulk of single innovations that are undertaken almost every day all over the world be summarized and reduced to a pattern amenable to generalization? A first step may be to develop a taxonomy in order to get an overview of the different forms of innovations.

Maybe the most common way to look at the subject is to distinguish between **product-**, **process-** and **organizational** or **managerial** innovations. Other scholars differentiate **incremental** from **radical** innovations. Incremental innovations occur more or less continuously all over the economy and are as a rule conceived as marginal or simple improvements of existing methods, products or processes. Radical innovations, by contrast, are discontinuous events and are unevenly distributed over sectors and over time. They usually are followed by new investment and market opportunities, but according to Freeman and Perez (1988, pp. 45) have only localized and small impacts in the aggregate. Both authors begin by differentiating **"changes of technological systems,"** which they understand to be far-reaching changes in technology affecting several branches of the economy as **"changes in techno-economic paradigms"** or **"technical revolutions,"** that have a major influence on the behavior of the entire economy, including the institutional framework. Somewhere in this scheme the widely used term **"basic innovations"** has to be placed. But like all these denominations, their proper place in any classification scheme is open to subjective assessment.

Especially if we are interested in the economic impact of a novelty it seems to be reasonable to take all stages of the process into account. It is launched by the initial **invention**, followed by **innovation** as the very first application of a novelty in a firm, and ends with its **diffusion** in the course of successful **imitation**. And this may not be the end at all, because diffusion entails in many cases the refinement of the initial novelty by the adopters and users. Innovations develop as they diffuse, improving in reliability, quality and flexibility. This is the general concept of innovation that I would like to propose and employ in this paper; it depicts a process, rather than a single event.

Concerning the **functional sources** of innovations, E. v. Hippel (1988) has shown that the generally held belief of innovations as typically developed by product manufactures does not always fit the facts. If one asks who derives benefit from a given product, process or service innovation, it turns out that in some fields users develop most innovations and in others suppliers of innovation-related components and materials are the typical sources.

Regarding the **time** innovations come about, it has been observed, that they occur as single events, but sometimes, especially in the course of business cycles, also in clusters. But even here the picture lacks uniformity, because those clusters appear as well in upswings of the cycle as in recessions.

Foundations of Innovations: A First Approach

These short and incomplete taxonomic remarks about some notional characteristics of innovations illustrate, I think, the versatility of feasible ways to approach the subject. But the topic I want to discuss about is not one of definition, or a pure notional one, but the question how innovations are brought about. Since man is, without doubt, the moving force behind innovations, the exploration must start with the question why human beings more or less continuously feel the urge to create, develop and apply new and improved means and methods for the satisfaction of human wants. What are, in other words, the motives for innovating activities ?

Even now the answer seems to be clear and simple at first sight. It was Adam Smith, who is often designated the father of economics, who emphasized that man has an intrinsic "desire to better his condition," and this may be seen to be the decisive impetus in his search for new and better ways of production. And quite similarly, the other great economist, who may be labeled the father of socialism, namely Karl Marx, has stressed the point that, beginning with man's history as a social being, the struggle for life in a rather hostile and uncomfortable natural environment forced him to push forward the development of what Marx called the productive forces. And this, according to Marx, will be an ever-lasting desire until the days when the paradise of communist society are reached.

Later economists have suggested similar metaphors to paraphrase human features directed to improve economic conditions. Notions like "animal spirits" (Keynes, Robinson), "technical dynamism" (Kaldor), or the combined forces of necessity and human curiosity (Boulding), are ultimately meant to tell the same story. They stand for a basic disposition that man shares with all living beings and which may be conceived a general evolutionary principle, or – with respect to man – an anthropological axiom. As such it may serve as a starting point in our investigation, but it immediately provokes the question why then man has scored so differently in the game, with such varying degrees of success in his aims to realize the purpose he allegedly is fitted for.

To find answers to this question we are well advised not to refuse the help of historians, social psychologists and scientists in other branches of research. As an economist I won't dig too much into this field, but nevertheless I would like to make clear that economists should not cut off themselves from those studies, for considering the complexity of the innovation issue, those insights may presumedly be useful in analyzing economic – and these also are human – problems.

Point of Departure: The Theoretical Base

As I mentioned before, each innovation is first of all perceived as a single and unforeseeable event. So it may turn out to be not so suitable for exploration within a theory that claims to provide explanations of a very generalized character. In this strict sense there is no – and cannot be a – theory of innovation. What mainstream economics have done is to tacitly incorporate innovations in a somewhat more general context that had been termed "technical progress." Technical progress is understood to be a conglomerate of three linked forms of economic activity (see H. Walter 1977, p. 569):
1. the production of goods and services that are new or of higher quality,
2. the construction and adoption of new, superior production processes,
3. the development and utilization of new and better means and methods for the satisfaction of human wants.

These characteristics correspond with the former mentioned notions of product-, process- and organizational innovations in their time-path from first use to more or less general adoption. So it seems to be justified that we treat innovations and technical progress as very similar, if not even as synonyms. The process of technical change then is the manifestation of all kinds of innovations, including their diffusion. In the following text I will use both notions, innovations and technical progress, interchangeably.

Our question about the determinants of innovations may now be split into the following two:
1. What economic activities set in motion by what actors or organizations are appropriate to bring about and foster innovations and technical progress ?

2. How should the economic and social framework be conditioned in order to motivate and cause economic agents to be innovators ?

In the following I examine whether economic theory has shed any light on these questions and has provided us with useful answers. Economists have always treated firms or enterprises as the organizational units and entrepreneurs or managers as the personal agents assigned to serve the wants of consumers. The task of innovating then is attached first of all to the entrepreneurs, and it is widely known that the most prominent figure in the story, especially when innovations are concerned, is the Schumpeterian entrepreneur. According to Schumpeter, economic development is promoted by dynamic pioneers who push through what he called "new combinations" (J. Schumpeter 1911, pp. 100) – another synonym for innovations. If these are successful on the market, the pioneer is followed by imitators who jump on the bandwagon and so will set in motion a boom of new economic activities. At this point one cannot evade the question, what makes one a pioneer and others mere mimics. Schumpeter himself, and with him most economists, have been rather vague on this point, and we shouldn't blame them for this, because the mystery of creativity is presumedly still to be discovered.

A Social-Scientific Detour

Nevertheless social scientists have tried to lift a little the veil of ignorance, and although I am all but an expert in this field, I venture to move a little step into this difficult terrain.

Social scientists point above all to personal competence and its cognitive, motivational and acting dimensions (J. Röpke 1977). That suggests that innovative behavior may be expected first of all from agents, that

- own an intrinsic stimulus to recognize a problem and identify the structure in which it is embedded; in responding to this stimulus
- they are driven to find out and evaluate possible ways to solve the problem, and
- based on these elaborations, or according to a more or less spontaneous impetus make decisions and move on with what they think to be feasible and potentially successful.

It has always been a matter of dispute which factors ultimately determine the unequal distribution of competence, genetic inheritance or the impacts of the social environment. Since the first factor is not amenable to our influence, we have to look for outside factors that are, as everybody may imagine, innumerable (Müller and Schienstock 1978). Natural and cultural conditions like climate and religion respectively, social and institutional circumstances, like education, reference-groups, access or barriers to social and economic action, the judicial system, traditional attitudes, the way of thinking about social values, and many other things may influence the willingness and the possibility not only to be competent, but above all, the perception of what cognitive, motivational and acting competence actually means, for this may differ according to time and region. Abramovitz in his contribution to the "catching-up"-discussion (1989, p. 222) borrowed from H. Rosovsky the notion of "social capability" to encompass the vast number of forces that may influence people's, and therefore nation's, ability to be on level in the process of economic growth and development. He admits that the term is highly appealing but difficult to define.

To give just a slight impression of the range of speculations in this field I only casually point out to examples like Max Weber's (1904) thesis, that the ascetic ideal implied in the Protestant ethic had a decisive impact on the advance of capitalism. Daniel Lerner (1958) stresses psychic mobility which enables one to get accustomed with the modern and rapidly changing aspects of a dynamic society and makes a person willing to be an active participant in economic and political affairs. As a short-hand expression for these abilities he invented the term "empathy," and he thought that it would depend, among other things, on the density of elementary education. Another well-known socio-psychological approach is the one David McClelland (1961) developed by modifying the ideas of Max Weber. According to McClelland the stress must be laid on what he called "need achievement," which may be interpreted as a strong motive to strive for self-imposed performance. To close this detour into foreign area, I would like to mention the somehow more comprehensive approach by E. Hagen (1962), who was aware that economic and social change is a complex problem that cannot be reduced to a single one-factor determination, although he perceived the mental environment in which children are raised as being one of the most important factors that determine whether economic development takes place or not. The significance of the socio-institutional framework is a problem which we will return to at the end of this paper.

Back to Economics: Further Hints

It is not surprising that social science-oriented studies stress intrinsic motives when the causes for endeavors and strives for better living standards are discussed. Economists feel inclined to emphasize extrinsic incentives, especially the outstanding role of the profit-motive as a propeller and indicator of successful economic performance. One way to pursue this aim is to occupy new niches in a market segment and to gain a temporal monopolistic position. Thereby other competitors may be crowded out of the market, a process that Schumpeter called creative destruction. He held that innovations are not only based on the capability to discover and exploit favorable opportunities, but also on the ability to evade endangering of one's own position in the market. Each agent aims to create imbalances in his own favor and to eliminate those imbalances that act against him. Therefore innovations may be seen as measures of differentiation, whereas imitations are attempts to level out differences created by others. Both actions, innovations and imitations or diffusions are concurrent and mutually dependent traits of development in a competitive society. We need a framework that favors a competitive climate which allows for sufficient innovation activity, but at the same time prevents the persistence of monopolistic market positions which may, judged for themselves, be the result of former successful innovations. Schumpeter's assessment on this point has rather been in favor of big enterprise and corporation, which he perceived to be the main sources of innovations. The hints he has given has led later economists to explore so-called Neo-Schumpeter-hypotheses. These allegedly disclose some of the conditions that are conducive to the emergence of innovations and innovators.

Maybe the most prominent of these hypotheses is the assertion, that either the absolute or the relative size of firms favor innovations, because only big, highly concentrated or diversified enterprises can afford the risks and costs of exploring new fields of economic activity, finance their own research department, and are protected against rapid imitations. Undoubtedly these considerations have a touch of plausibility, and therefore much empirical research has been undertaken in this field. Unluckily, the evidence is anything but clear, and the causal connection between size and innovations is ambiguous. Size may facilitate the disposition and capability to innovate in one case, while in another, the current size may be the effect of successful innovations in the past. If size indeed has any influence on future innovative behavior, then probably not so much in regard to the willingness or disposition to do so, but more in the way in which the scale of technical operations and the corresponding characteristics of organizational know-how determine the manner in which innovations are realized (Sahal 1979, pp. 12).

Although the assertion that firm size is a prerequisite for in-house R and D must therefore be taken carefully, empirical investigations seem to show that the level and significance of organized R and D, realized in laboratories and firm departments, and measured, as a rule, through patent statistics, has risen more than other conventional economic activities. In any case they substituted the lonely inventing genius of the last century. Furthermore it has been realized that social returns to R and D exceed private returns, and these again outstrip on average long-term interest rates (Bernstein and Nadiri 1988). There is a huge number of publications on this issue, and there can be no doubt that R and D is a decisive factor in enhancing innovations, even if it is not always easy to assign an innovation to the special R and D-activity that has been accounted for it.

What has been said about R and D holds equally with respect to infrastructure. It depicts public facilities, like traffic, energy, communication, public health, recreation and others. They are complementary to the level of the economy's total production and therefore indispensable for growth and development in the long run, an issue that at once reminds us of discussions ensuing from the theories of balanced and unbalanced growth and the presumed forward and backward linkages that play an important role in these considerations. Forward linkages prevail, when particular activities of firms, e.g. the production of a new good, are followed by an increasing demand for the product at the next stage in the economy's vertical structure. Backward linkages are, respectively, positive impulses transmitted to the suppliers' stage. Although the exact relation between infrastructure and the economy as a whole is hardly quantifiable, their mutual dependence on each other in the long run is a characteristic feature of economic development.

These considerations elucidate that economic development is a process of continuous change within a complex network of producer-distributor-consumer relations. In the end only that will be produced what as an intermediate or final product finds appropriate demand. Adam Smith already recognized that the division of labor is limited by the extent of the market. So innovations are a vehicle at the disposal of manufacturers and suppliers to create new demands and thereby to overcome the impact of decreasing income elasticities of demand for existing consumer goods and the technical limits for intermediate goods respectively. J. Schmookler (1966) has elaborated and tested the hypothesis that innovation activity is demand-determined. He ascertained that increases of innovational activities are observed every time buyers at the successive production steps expand, indicated by their growing demand for investment goods. This is to say that innovations are a sequential effect of growing demand, because more demand calls for more production, this for more investments, and this often stimulates the construction of better machinery, i.e. innovations. But here again plausibility and empirical corroboration may fool us into traps of causality. It is true that demand plays a decisive role when we are asked to divide innovations into successes and failures, but it is less plausible to assume that they occur only or predominantly at times and places when and where demand goes up.

The picture I drew up to now has shown that economics revealed some reasonable hints about innovations and how they come about. Nevertheless, it is by no means unambiguous. There is no lack of hypotheses, but there are serious shortcomings in the understanding of their real significance and their interaction in the process of growth and development. The empirical evidence is highly bewildering, for there are as many corroborations as refutations to most of the hypotheses I have depicted. We gathered a schedule of important factors, like human competence, market structure, education, R and D, infrastructure, demand, and exogenous influences like tradition, religion and other things. But irrespective of the huge amount of more or less plausible details, there seems to be no systematic and coherent body of explanation, unless we feel content with the assertion that to innovate is the same as to be a successful entrepreneur in the struggle of competition. In that case the explanation of innovation would boil down to a theory of competition. This wouldn't be completely false, for they indeed have a lot in common, but both processes are not exactly the same. The neoclassical mainstream of economic theory that, as I mentioned before, incorporated innovations in the broader context of growth and technical progress, didn't have much to contribute to their explanation, because it treated technical progress as an exogenous given free good. This changed a little in the eighties, when the so-called "new" growth theory came to grips with technical progress as an endogenous variable. This approach, that was also termed "endogenous growth theory" is represented by names like Romer, Lucas (last years Nobel laureate), Grossman, Helpman and others. Again, I won't bother you with the formal content of the models, but try to concentrate on some ideas that in our context may be essential.

What's New about the "New" Growth Theory?

In one line of reasoning of the new growth theory, the increase in output and real income is attributed to privately produced knowledge that comes into being by normal firm activities, like instruction, learning on the job and all forms of extended vocational training. The benefits from these activities may be seen – at least for a while – as goods that are exclusive to the firm and, like other factors of production, subject to decreasing marginal returns. But part of it becomes instantly or after some time an addition to the pool of common knowledge to which everybody has free access. In other words: The spill-overs of privately produced education are public goods for which the exclusion principle doesn't hold. They are what economists call externalities and imply increasing returns on the aggregate level. This also means that the producer of new knowledge as a public good does not need to be paid if other agents adopt and apply it in the course of their own economic performance. By the way, this enables us to get rid of one of the crucial restrictions of traditional theory, i.e. the incompatibility of increasing returns with the adding-up theorem.

A very similar consideration has been emphasized by K. Arrow in the early sixties, when he elaborated the principle of learning by doing. But with Arrow there are no specific activities addressed to the production of new knowledge, because he linked learning with the cumulative investment activity of a society. Investments over time have two effects:

1. Repetitive handling of the same machinery enhances experience and increases productivity; this is the so-called Horndal-effect.
2. Replacement of old and addition of new capital equipment in time, i.e. gross investment, usually means the installation of new and better types of machinery that, as a rule, require different skills of the operating staff, part of which is an externality and indicates that the social benefit from new knowledge exceeds private returns.

This is only another way of saying that physical and human capital are tied together in promoting productive capacity and per-capita income. Their separation, practiced in most formal models, may lead us on a wrong path of reasoning, because decisions about the allocation of both forms of capital must be taken simultaneously. Per-capita income not only increases with a high level of physical capital, but also – one is inclined to say: predominantly – with the corresponding endowment of human capital that is complementary to it. This explains why, contrary to traditional theorizing, there are hardly differences in international comparisons of real interest rates and only in particular cases adjustments in factor proportions, real wage rates and per-capita income. In reality, unlike the aseptic world of given production functions in neoclassical models, a high level of capital intensity, i.e. capital-labor relation, does not inevitably indicate a low productivity of physical capital. For high capital intensity usually also means high capital efficiency, because its physical dimension is interrelated with – and indeed often determined by – a high level of human capital (which, as a rule, doesn't mean a high number of workers).

This also sheds light on another phenomenon of real world economics: If we disregard political influences, then up to now there have been less private capital exports from industrialized to low-income countries than neoclassical theory would predict. And this apparently is so, because marginal productivity of physical capital in these countries is not as high as traditional economic wisdom would make believe. Paul Romer (1993) has shown that the story could be different if capital exports were combined with the transmission of knowledge and a favorable attitude of the authorities in the recipient countries.

The new growth theory did not only emphasize the role of education and human capital in generating technical progress, but also promoted the integration of other factors in their endogenous growth models, factors that we have treated before. So technical progress is no longer conceived as a free good, like in earlier models, but as a result of intentional actions of private firms and/or a by-product of other activities in the economy. Furthermore innovations and new technological knowledge are shown to be embedded in the organizational structure and routine of firms, and although meant to be principally tacit, sooner or later become part of common knowledge and therefore generally accessible. The crucial point, I think, is the interrelated and cumulative character of the process. Even if it may be useful to start the analysis with single variables that may be influential on the emergence of innovations, factors like those I introduced before, it seems to be not at all sufficient to observe, enumerate and evaluate single factors by themselves and under conditions of ceteris paribus. At least some of these variables are mutually interdependent, and their decomposition by growth accounting leads us wrong. In the course of time they may once be the cause, another time the effect. Furthermore they are cumulative, or path-dependent, which means that the mentioned activities enhance knowledge about useful ways of economic performances that have emanated in one way or the other from past economic experience. To put it short: History matters ! This is an idea that conventional theorizing has completely left aside. A long time after classical economics, present-day theory has again lifted a corner of the blanket with which neoclassical reasoning has concealed the complexity of real world phenomenons. From quite another methodological angle the same has been attempted by another approach, to which I finally would like to draw attention.

The Evolutionary Approach to Economics

The complex process of economic and social development, set in motion by the human urge to better man's condition, seems to have much in common with the general principles of development of all living beings, that is, with biological evolution. Some scientists have stressed, for instance, the analogies between

- mutations or variations in biology and economic innovations respectively,
- selection on the one hand and competition and creative destruction on the other hand,
- the principle of retention of successful fits in biology and successful products, processes or methods in economics.

Now we know that mutations are random events due to mistakes in the course of replication of genetic information. Only an unimaginable small number of them turn out to be successful. Thus, an extraordinary large number of variants are required to accomplish a novelty capable of surviving. The principle of biological evolution therefore is based on gigantic waste in the sequential process of trial and error.

In economic and social evolution on the other hand, innovations are only in rare cases made by pure chance. Due to man's ability to pass accumulated knowledge to his fellows and to the following generations by employing notional and mental capabilities and capacities of storing and transmitting information, one can consciously and intentionally search for better variants of existing specimen. Even failures and misconceptions enlarge our knowledge about future possibilities. But also the discovering of new ways of performance may not ensure us to have found the best possible solution. Insofar also economic and social change is, irrespective of man's intentional aims, of course a process of trial and error. What we have to face is a complex and simultaneous process of determination and chance, of rationality and spontaneity, of order-destroying entropy and order-creating self-organization. If one is inclined to accept this picture, one is very close to the approach that has been investigated by scholars like Dosi, Freeman, Nelson, Perez, Silverberg, Soete, Winter and many others under the heading of evolutionary theory. Incidentally some of these authors are also exponents of the theory of long waves, which experienced a revival in the course of the recent Schumpeter-renaissance. Again there is no use in digging deeper into the altogether very heterogeneous contributions of this view. I will rather try to elaborate some basic ideas that seem to be useful in the context of our exploration. Thereby I will take into consideration especially publications by Nelson (1995), Nelson/Winter (1974, 1982) and Perez (1983), whose thoughts fit well, I think, into our topic.

Based on the behavioristic school of the theory of organization and of decision, Nelson/Winter start from the supposition that entrepreneurial decisions aim less to maximize well-defined target functions, but rather to attain satisfying results under the realistic assumption of bounded rationality. Rationality is bounded due to incomplete foresight with respect to all relevant information concerning the consequences of today's actions based thereupon. The pattern of those decisions is a mixture out of maintained and more or less reliable rules on the one hand, and the search for better solutions closed to the established routine on the other. The intensity of the search for improvements depends on the motivational and acting capabilities of the entrepreneur/manager, as well as on the degree of challenge emerging from the firm's environment. They determine the firm's own innovational activity, or its success in adopting outside improvements. Nelson/Winter have termed this pattern a "natural trajectory of technical progress." Among the unlimited numbers of trajectories that are potentially feasible, that one will be selected that fits the given economic, social and institutional conditions as well as possible. If thereby satisfying results are obtained, the trajectory will not be deserted without need.

What Nelson/Winter intend to show is that the world we live in is characterized by many routine progresses, i.e. incremental innovations. The occurrence of change and inertia seems to be one of the general principles that apply equally to natural and social evolution. The real big shots, or in our notion, technical revolutions, are rather the exception, but of course, they are needed to jump ahead and prepare the way for the huge number of small and middle-sized improvements which follow them. To bring about comprehensive changes in technological systems, or techno-economic paradigms in Freeman/Perez' formulation, it needs two prerequisites:

1. the bunching of (Schumpeterian) entrepreneurs, whose coming into existence is beyond our knowledge and whose activities are only amenable to our influence by avoiding to impede their way with superfluous hurdles and unnecessary regulations, and/or
2. the occurrence of exogenous events, for instance
   - basic scientific discoveries, or
   - particular challenges by political, social or environmental changes that enforce a fundamental revision of past behavior.

It seems that the last condition is affecting today's situation in several countries. We are witnessing the repercussions of some basic technical discoveries in the recent past: microelectronics, telecommunication, biotechnology and some others. At the same time we face problems in the socio-institutional substructure to match the changes in the techno-economic system. The distinction between these two systems stems from C. Perez (1983, 1985). Under the socio-institutional system she subsumes the total social milieu, in which the techno-economic determined development takes place. Its features bear resemblance to the aforementioned social and institutional factors like traditions, institutions, the forms in which private and public responsibilities are assigned, regulations in competition, political participation and others. At the height of correspondence between the two sub-systems, the socio-institutional framework is fully established, and has settled in the minds of people and tacitly claims to be universally applicable, thereby loosing the flexibility to cope with revolutionary changes in the techno-economic system. If these take place and set up a new technological paradigm, then the relatively immobile socio-institutional system may become the source of social tensions and strains (see also Freeman 1991).

Some facts seem to indicate that at present we may be in such a trap of mismatch between the two sub-systems. Basic changes in technology enhanced productivity in the originating sectors and in many fields of application. But these productivity changes had only relatively small effects on average per-capita income. Instead they led to a strong displacement of workers, or, as the OECD has put it: The new technologies seem to "...increase the potential for economic growth and productivity gains at the same time as they broaden the mismatches between labor demand and supply in terms of skills and qualifications" (OECD

1994, p. 165). The transformation of productivity increases has taken the wrong turn: not the road of wealth, but the unemployment road. On the other hand, the institutional framework, like regulations, the systems of social security and education, especially the quality-profiles of workmen and not least the behavior patterns and aspirations of people, including the political elite, that is, the core of what Perez called the socio-institutional paradigm, has not yet been adapted to the new techno-economic system. All this becomes apparent in attitudes like rent-seeking, fear or risk-aversion, like the holding of money assets instead of real investments, or in an adversative employment behavior of firms (i.e. overtime instead of new jobs).

In such a situation it is common usage to complain about a shortage of innovations. This is true, but has to be specified. Provided that the aforementioned diagnosis is right, then at least two things are indispensable:

1. the establishment of a new socio-institutional sub-system, with revised patterns of aspirations and behavior, and
2. the fostering of employment-creating innovations.

Of course, this is easier said than done. In economic theory the term of "employment-creating innovations" is understood to mean the development of new demand-creating products. But the recipe of the old-fashioned economic compensation principle, i.e. the cry for productivity-exceeding growth of output and new goods, may nowadays not be judged an unconditional panacea anymore.

So future growth and development must take the form of qualitative evolutionary change. Also on this score economists may have to learn from biological evolution. Of course, the problem is how to promote a process that enhances at the same time productivity, employment and the condition of the natural environment. It seems that we urgently need an universally improved understanding of the complexity of the world we live in and, based on this understanding, even more creativity and innovational imagination than ever before.

References

Abramovitz, M. 1989. Thinking about growth. Cambridge Univ. Press

Bernstein, J.I. and M.I. Nadiri 1988. Rates of return on physical and R and D capital and structure of production process: cross section and time series evidence. NBER-Work. pap. 2570

Freeman, C. 1991. The nature of innovations and the evolution of the productive system; in: Technology and productivity. Paris, OECD, pp. 303 - 314

Freeman, C. and C. Perez 1988. Structural crises of adjustment, business cycles and investment behaviour; in: Dosi, G, et al., Technical change and economic theory. London, New York, pp- 38 - 66

Hagen, E.E. 1962. On the theory of social change. How economic growth begins. Homewood, Ill.

Hippel, E.v. 1988. The sources of innovation. New York, Oxford

Lerner, D. 1958. The passing of traditional society. Glencoe, Ill.

McClelland, D.C. 1961. The achieving society. Princeton, N.Y.

Müller, V. and G. Schienstock. 1978. Sozialwissenschaftliche Innovationstheorien. Berlin

Nelson, R.R. 1995. Recent evolutionary theorizing about economic change. J. of Ec. Lit. 33, pp. 48 - 90

Nelson, R.R. and S. Winter 1974. Neoclassical vs. evolutionary theories of economic growth: critique and prospectus. Ec.J. 84, pp. 886 - 905

Nelson, R.R. and S. Winter 1982. An evolutionary theory of economic change. Harv. Univ. Press, Cambridge, Mass.

OECD 1994. The OECD Jobs study. Evidence and explanations. Part I: Labor market trends and underlying forces of change. Paris

Perez, C. 1983. Structural change and the assimilation of new technology in the economic and social systems. Futures, pp. 357 - 375

Perez, C. 1985. Microelectronics, long waves and world structural change: New perspectives for developing countries; in: World development 13, pp. 441 - 463

Röpke, J. 1977. Die Strategie der Innovation. Eine systemtheoretische Untersuchung der Interaktion von Individuum, Organisation und Markt im Neuerungsprozeß. Tübingen

Romer, P. 1993. Idea gaps and Object gaps in economic development. J. of Mon. Ec. 32, pp. 543 - 573

Sahal, D. 1979. Recent advances in a theory of technological change. Disc. pap series IIM/dp 79-11. Intern. Inst. of Management, Wiss.zentrum Berlin

Schmookler, J. 1966. Invention and economic growth. Cambridge, Mass.

Schumpeter, J.A. 1911. Theorie der wirtschaftlichen Entwicklung. 5. Aufl. Berlin 1952

Walter, H. 1977. Technischer Fortschritt I: in der Volkswirtschaft. HdWW, Stuttgart et al.

Weber, M. 1904. Die protestantische Ethik und der Geist des Kapitalismus; in: Archiv f. Soz.wiss. u. Soz.pol.; wiederabg. in: Gesammelte Aufsätze zur Religionssoziologie (1905), 6. Aufl. Tübingen 1972

Understanding Determinants of Agricultural Technology Adoption

Uma Lele and Shiva S. Makki
Agricultural Research and Extension Group (ESDAR)
The World Bank, Washington D.C., USA

Two Contrasting Approaches

Linear, Top-down, Market Driven and Individualistic

In a classic study of adoption of hybrid corn in the US in the 1950s, Griliches attributed differential rates of adoption to the varying profitability. He defined adoption as the percent of the total corn area planted to hybrid seeds and explained it in terms of the processes of innovation, adaptation and distribution and the rate at which it is accepted by farmers. Griliches concluded that where the profits from innovations were large and clear cut the change from the traditional to the new technology was very rapid, for example taking only 4 years to reach 90 percent in Iowa. But where profits were lower and less certain the process of adoption was slower. Griliches viewed profitability as being determined by the rates of technology development and adaptation and reflected in differences in the *origins of adoption*, and technology transfer and adoption as reflected in the *ceilings* and *the rates of approach to that ceiling* or the *slopes* (see figure 1). Griliches unique contribution was to demonstrate that adoption can be explained in economic terms. Nearly 40 years later this analysis has proved to be the foundation of research in technology adoption. The concepts have been used extensively in international analysis of technology diffusion, particularly that pertaining to the rate of technical change among small farmers in developing countries (see figure 2). The research adoption continuum is now also routinely divided into four phases, i.e.,

- those related to technology development (often referred to as basic and strategic research),
- adaptation (applied and adaptive research),
- technology transfer (often but not always confined to extension), and
- adoption.

At least implicitly, such process of technological change, which in developing countries, too, focused on improved crop varieties leading up to the Green Revolution, has been viewed as relatively *top-down and linear*. Technology development has often occurred at the level of the international research centers of the Consultative Group on International Agricultural Research (the CGIAR), or the advanced countries' research institutions (ARIs) where crop improvement methodologies are developed, the process of technology adaptation taking place at a combination of the levels of the CGIAR centers and the National Agricultural Research Systems (NARS) of developing countries, and that of adoption involving a range of national, albeit nonresearch, institutions, policies and infrastructure, e.g. the extension services, financial institutions, input and output markets, transportation networks and government policies towards pricing and subsidies. The adoption decisions with respect to crop management technologies at the farmer level have been individualistic, based on the farmers' views of short run profits. Typically the processes of technology development and adaptation have been considered (including by Griliches) as public goods, while those related to transfer and adoption being a result of public and private sector decisions often requiring effective partnerships among institutions.

Technologies have been made available as packages of practices embodied in new purchased inputs and the knowledge associated with the use of those inputs. However, evidence has shown that farmers adopt only a portion of the packages relevant to their specific needs. Hence the intensity of adoption has been measured, for example, in terms of the use of fertilizer or the water farmers apply per unit of land relative to the recommended packages, the share of the total cropped area they allocate to new varieties and yields per hectare relative to those achieved on research stations.

Lags in technology development, adaptation and adoption involve costs and benefits which can be quantified and measured in terms of the discounted net present value of benefits and economic rates of return to investments.

The experience with spread of crop technologies has led to exploration of the comparative advantages of the international and national research institutions and their implications for research priority setting of public funds. Whereas that literature has focused mainly on the interface between the CGIAR system and the NARS of developing countries, increasingly attention is being focused on the global research system, including particularly the role of the public and private research institutions of advanced countries in the process of technical change (GREAN report). Globalization of the research adoption continuum had already played an important role in the generation of the green revolution. That process has been analyzed with renewed interest in recent years due to a combination of factors, e.g., budget constraints which have increased scarcity of public funds for research and demand at both the international and national levels for more rapid and broadbased impact of research, the rapid advances in science in the areas of biotechnology, information technologies etc. which have, once again, increased the gap in research capacity between the advanced industrial and developing countries, and the liberalization of markets which has moved the role of the private sector to center stage.

Circular, iterative, socioculturally and collectively driven

Yet fundamental changes have also occurred in quite another direction in recent years in the way technical change is perceived. Those changes may be characterized as:

- being driven by concerns of equity and environmental sustainability rather than by those of productivity growth;
- focusing on knowledge intensity rather than input intensity;
- grounded in social rather than economic objectives involving appreciation of the sociocultural perspectives and practices of farmers rather than simply the perspectives of the formal public or private sector entities,
- holding a circular and iterative view of the research adoption continuum rather than either a top-down or a bottom-up view,
- often focusing on community rather than individual action; and
- of a long-run rather than a short-run nature.

Interest has focused on the *nonadopters*, i.e., those *potential* entrepreneurs whose resources are either too poor in quality or quantity, or who have little or no access to markets to participate in the process of technical change. They represent the over one billion poor who earn less than a dollar a day. Also increased is the concern about the long-term environmental sustainability of the technical change that has already occurred, e.g., in the Green Revolution areas of Asia, and the technical change that may occur in the future, on the grounds that natural resources crucial to the process of agricultural improvement are no longer freely available. The emphasis in resource erosion has focused mainly on soil degradation and the quantity and quality of water, but some have argued that the erosion of the diversity of plant genetic resources is as serious a concern for possible future increases in productivity growth or their sustainability as that of soils and water (personal communication, Iwanaga).

The rates of technical change are no longer expected to be as rapid as in the past, nor indeed are the ceiling rates of adoption already achieved expected to be maintained in the areas where input use is already high, as for instance in the Indo-Gangetic plains of South Asia, on the grounds that further intensification leads to yield plateaus and even declines. That concern has in turn led to a call for increased efficiency at several levels:

- in the way inputs are applied to plants;
- the rates of conversion of inputs into outputs;

- in the process of technology development and adaptation itself, meaning in reducing research lags through the application of new research methods (such as biotechnology and GIS at the high end of the spectrum and participatory means of managing the research adoption continuum); and
- in the organization of research as reflected, on the one hand, in increased specialization among research and technology transfer institutions and, on the other, in increased partnerships among them.

Management of natural resources has acquired center stage in the focus on research, a phenomenon which often tends to be location-specific, with few economies of scale in the generation of technology or its adaptation. Such research requires considerable local knowledge, calls for interdisciplinarity and therefore tends to be the forte of national and local research and technology transfer entities. Its costs and benefits tend to be difficult to quantify and, therefore, its assessment in a priority-setting exercise tends to be difficult if not impossible.

Adoption of resource management technologies often involves collective decisions by its users as well as entailing externalities. For example, a single farmer adapting pest management or water management in the absence of her/his neighbors doing the same concurrently may have little impact on achieving the objectives. The benefits from resource management technologies tend to accrue over a longer term, the discounted present value of which, if calculable at all, particularly as perceived by the farmers, may well be low. Besides, often the benefits of such technologies may not be accruable to the individual adopter but rather to the community as a whole and often to future generations.

Many of the actors developing these resource management technologies may well be individual farmers or groups rather than formal research organizations. Besides, adoption of some of the resource management technologies may not involve any markets. Indeed markets may oppose the introduction of some technologies if they entail less use of purchased inputs.

A Way Forward

It is clear that adoption of technologies in agriculture depends on a combination of technical, ecological, economical, social, political, and cultural factors operating at local, regional, national and international levels. Their role must be understood in order to maximize the overlap among the objectives of efficiency, equity and sustainability, i.e., to ensure the efficient development of appropriate technologies and their equitable and sustainable transfer on to the farmers' fields. This paper makes a beginning in developing a conceptual framework that might increase the efficiency of the research adoption continuum, i.e., the processes of technology development, adaptation, transfer and adoption. It evaluates the current approaches and explores their implications for the development of a new framework.

Any chain is as strong as its weakest link. In developing a new framework of the research adoption continuum, an important question is therefore the precise level at which the link tends to be the weakest, whether at the level of the generation of new technology, its adaptation, transfer, or of its adoption, and the relationship of the weakest link to other levels of the continuum. For instance, research and technology transfer are important, but of course, only partial answers to achieving the objectives of growth, poverty alleviation and sustainability. Other instruments such as human resource development, institutional and infrastructural development must come into play simultaneously. A focus on the research adoption continuum can help delineate the potential and limits of what technology can do and improve understanding of the determinants of technology adoption. As an example, a technology that depends on the production and sale of high quality seed may be quite inappropriate unless conditions and incentives exist for the emergence of the seed industry. Depending on the nature of the seed requirements those conditions and incentives may be sociocultural, demographic or economic or a combination thereof. In this context it is important to recognize that farmers adopt technology based on their own perceptions of returns, risks and costs. The commonly cited problems of nonadoption tend to be inadequate or ineffective extension, untimely input supply, and the lack of credit or infrastructure. Yet the more important immediate reasons may tend to be: lack of economic viability of technology packages; operational unfeasibility; lack of yield or income stability; and incompatibility with the farmers' needs, resources and objectives. (ICAR 1995). To better understand farmer constraints, greater investment in socioeconomic and policy research would be necessary.

Similarly, technology transfer entails the spread of *new* information as well as that of the *already available information*. A number of factors referred to earlier favor the generation of new information, e.g. recent advances in science including those in information technologies. These can enable reaching new yield ceilings (i.e. the theoretical production functions) or achieving yield stability through building resistance to a variety of environmental constraints. However, lags from the initiation of research to impact on the farmers' fields tend to be long. Huffman and Evanson (1993) assume lags of 33 years in the US public research system which entail considerable pretechnology research. Walker and Collion (1996) assume investments in certain kinds of research on potatoes to range from between 5 to 17 years depending on the nature of the research problem. Given such long gestation lags from investments to realization of benefits, the assumption of sunk costs in the past investments in technology development would tend strongly to favor efforts to achieve pay offs from earlier investments either because they are already visible or "just around the corner" (Walker and Collion 1996), and to discriminate against new projects offering benefits in later years.

On-Shelf vs New Technologies

Scientists consider some technologies as being ready to be adopted by final users with little or no adaptive research to suit specific agroclimatic conditions. Some believe that there is already much technology "on the shelf" which remains to be extended. For them extension is a greater priority than research (Hubell 1995). Others counter that "the technological shelf is bare" because much of the research conducted is not based on a feedback system between scientists and farmers. In recent years, the research focus of the international centers of the CGIAR has shifted from producing "finished products" to producing "intermediate products" which call for much more location-specific adaptation and strong national agricultural research systems. Several working hypotheses emanate from this phenomenon. The first is that in countries with strong NARS the adaptive process would be faster relative to the countries with weak NARS. Secondly, that in conditions where the strong and weak NARS share similar ecological circumstances, the scope for spillover effects of the strong NARS would be considerable. Third, the realization of actual spillover would depend on the extent to which there is either strong interaction among NARS or the extent to which regional and international research networks speed up dissemination. CIP for instance has played a role in disseminating the results of research in Argentina and India to countries as distant as China and Vietnam. Fourth, there might be a strong positive association between the strengths of NARS and of other agricultural policies and institutions. Fifth, technologies that require the presence of sound agricultural policies or the presence of input and commodity markets may spread less quickly in countries with weak NARS than technologies that do not require the presence of these factors. Many resource management technologies may fall in this latter category. Finally, because resource management technologies tend to be more location-specific than crop improvement technologies, NARS may have a stronger comparative advantage in the generation and transfer of those technologies relative to the crop management technologies.

An important policy and operational question then is whether at the margin the returns to investment, for example, in closing the technology gap between the farmers' fields and research stations, by focusing on identifying more effective technology transfer mechanisms, would be greater than on new research, and if so, under what circumstances. This question in turn leads to a number of follow-up questions:

- What constitutes the critical components of the enabling environment which will raise the technology frontiers, and those which will close the technology gaps?
- What level of investments and types of effort are needed in each case with what probability of success?
- How should we compare the returns to alternative uses of resources, given the difficulties in the assessment of costs and benefits?

A better understanding of the process of technology generation and transfer is imperative to address these questions, if not to answer them, and to design policies to speed up the technology transfer process.

The rest of this paper is organized as follows. First we discuss specific issues that influence the successful adoption of agricultural technologies. Then we explore their implications for a framework to improve the efficiency of technology development and technology transfer.

Determinants of Technology Adoption

The speed and extent of adoption are a function of the investments, infrastructure and institutions which determine the nature of technology generated and transferred. Even though past empirical studies were not comprehensive enough to analyze these issues, they certainly have helped in understanding the current and likely future constraints to the generation, generation, transfer and adoption of new innovations. Some of the specific factors/issues that influence the successful adoption of agricultural technologies raise fundamental questions as to the extent to which an exclusive reliance on market mechanisms will ensure an adequate overlap between the objectives of growth, poverty alleviation and environmental sustainability. They include:

1   Investments in Irrigation

A key source of agricultural growth has been investments in irrigation and the complimentary increase in the application of other inputs (e.g. high yielding varieties and fertilizers) which constituted the Green Revolution. The irrigated farming systems occupy only 15 percent of the arable land (270 million ha) but produce over a third of the total crops and *more than half* of the total grain production of the developing world (FAO 1995). About a third of the total agricultural population, i.e. more than 700 million people, are engaged in irrigated farming. Particularly in Asia, which has the greatest population pressure on the land, irrigated land (143 million ha) constitutes more than one third of the total cropland, contributing 80% of the food production in Pakistan, 70% in China, and over 50% in India and Indonesia (FAO 1995).

Globally irrigated area expanded by 2.3 percent from 1972 to 1975, but the rate of growth declined to less than 1 percent since 1975. External irrigation investment in Asia in the 1980s fell by 50% compared to the levels prevailing in the 1970s (Rosegrant and Svendsen 1993). Amongst the reasons were the increased costs of construction, declining real cereal prices, fiscal and environmental concerns about monoculture, susceptibility to plant diseases and pests, over exploitation of ground water, sedimentation of reservoirs, waterbased diseases such as bilharzia, malaria, diarrheas, onchocersiasis, cholera and typhus.

Due to the possibilities of multiple cropping irrigation offers substantial scope for additional employment and incomes. Thus there is clearly a disjuncture between the social and economic rates of return to investment in irrigation.

Physical and economic potential for irrigation investment remain a debated issue. FAO estimates range between 30 to 150 million additional hectarage as being suitable, three to sixteen times the present irrigated area. Irrigation development in South and East Asia has been less costly than in other regions because of reliable water sources (perennial rivers), and irrigation in flat plains. Asia's long history of irrigation has also led to substantial number of trained personnel and well developed irrigation-related institutional structures. Irrigated land in Africa is only about 12.4 million ha due to physical, economic and infrastructural constraints, e.g. only a few major rivers, seasonal water flows, and hard-to-reach groundwater in alluvial river beds. High costs of transportation and technical staff and shortage of investment capital have also contributed to the high developmental costs (World Bank/UNDP 1990).

Though public and donor investments in large-scale irrigation have been declining, small-scale irrigation (tubewells and open wells) has expanded rapidly in Asia. Tubewell irrigation has made several positive contributions. For example, in the eastern Gangetic Plains of India where water tables are high, tubewell expansion has helped address problems of sodic soils, leading to reclamation of hundreds of thousands of hectares of land previously unsuited for cultivation. Privately funded tubewells help mobilize private savings, rather than make demands on the scarce public revenues required in large-scale irrigation. They avoid problems of cost recovery and are more flexible in their management than large-scale irrigation. Tubewells also help the development of private water markets. Small-scale irrigation has accelerated intensification and rapid diversification of rainfed agriculture leading to increased production of high-value fruits, vegetables, and flowers. The arid state of Maharashtra in India, for instance, has become a major producer of fruits, vegetables and wines, contributing a third of the share of the rapidly growing Indian horticultural production. Similar successes are noted in the cases of the production of orchids and baby corn in Thailand (Paroda 1996).

Tubewells and small-scale surface irrigation technology have also spread to Africa, e.g. Nigeria and Zimbabwe, and can become more widespread in Africa. They are examples of the ways in which the Asian technological experience has contributed to African agricultural development (Barghouti and Le Moigne 1990, Le Moigne 1994).

However, over exploitation of ground water has been a serious problem in many parts of Asia. Lack of groundwater development planning and subsidies on electrification have accentuated the growing long-term water shortages while bringing short-term prosperity to pockets of areas.

The reduction in irrigation investments is bound to have an adverse impact on the future rate of technological progress, which will have to be offset by greater efficiency in water management. The heterogeneity of the rainfed conditions increases production variability, risks, and uncertainty, and makes increased investment in research and development that much more urgent.

2   Farm Size and Tenure System

The impact of farm size and tenure system on the adoption of new technologies may be more profound than observed in the existing studies because it affects several other socio-economic factors that directly or indirectly influence technology adoption. Land fragmentation and insecure land tenure constrain the adoption of technologies that need large and long-term initial investment such as tubewells, drip-irrigation, tractors, land-reclamation, etc. The relatively better endowed farmers may also have better access to market information on prices, credit, inputs, etc. This may be why several studies have indicated a positive relationship between farm size and adoption of new technologies. However, some of the constraints faced by land-short farmers and insecure tenants may well be overcome by other institutional innovations, e.g., improved social or economic organization including custom hiring, leasing, and cooperativization of marketing, processing, credit etc. The existence of such arrangements may explain why studies by Binswanger and Ruttan (1978), Jamison and Lau (1982), Barker and Herdt (1978), and Ruttan (1978) indicate that neither the farm size nor the tenure system was a serious constraint in the adoption of specific improved varieties.

The greater spread of new technologies in East and Southeast Asia vis-a-vis South Asia is clearly explained in part by land policies. Much of the East and Southeast Asian success in land distribution (Japan, China, Taiwan, South Korea and Malaysia) relative to South Asia was a result of either external occupation or coercive means, not an outcome of a democratic process or market mechanisms.

The states of Kerala and West Bengal in India, which have had successful land redistribution also have either had benevolent feudal rule when land redistribution occurred (e.g. Kerala) or a relatively stable communist rule. Through radical redistribution, of assets, the autocratic state has enabled East and Southeast Asian countries to increase agricultural incomes with far more rapid reduction in chronic poverty than has been possible in South Asia.

Whether the insecurity of tenure is a similar disincentive in Africa is a debated issue, although population pressure tends to lead to increased appropriation of communal land by private, including political, entrepreneurs, a phenomenon likely to accentuate without individual land rights and a growing population pressure on the land (Migot-Adholla and Bruce J.W. 1994). The issues of land access and security of tenure have received less attention in the analysis of technological development and transfer than they deserve.

3   Human Capital

Education is probably the single most important factor that has consistently contributed to the successful adoption of new innovations. An overwhelming number of studies suggest that farmers with better education are early adopters of modern technologies. Education improves the ability of farmers to appreciate the potentials of a new technology and use of modern inputs leading to a more efficient transfer process. Education also improves farmers access to information and credit, and improves the allocative ability and hence resource use efficiency (Shultz 1964; Kebede et al. 1990; Strauss et al. 1991; Huffman 1977).

Importance of education has increased with the knowledge-intensive and community-based nature of many new resource management technologies needed in the future, particularly the need for women's equal access to education and greater role in decision making. Countries in East and South East Asia are at a greater advantage in the development and adoption of new technologies relative to their counterparts in South Asia, again with vast differences among and within countries. Studies in India show, for instance, a different attitude of men and women to the use of pesticides (Ramadevi 1995a, 1995b), although women do not seem to be in a position to influence the decisions of their husbands. Besides, with the introduction of new technologies involving purchased inputs, such as pesticides, concurrent with women's lesser education and social taboos on their movements, women's access to modern farming practices seems to be limited (Eboh 1993).

4   Risk and Uncertainty

New innovations come with some risks and uncertainties. Farmers' attitude towards risk is known to significantly affect the extent and rate of adoption of new technologies. Griliches's observation that farmers tend not to adopt the technology if it is more risky than the existing technologies but has only a marginal advantage in mean returns has been observed in developing countries as well (Perrin and Winkleman 1976). Depending on risk aversion farmers choose different technologies: those technologies that minimizes their exposure to possible loss, even if it means foregoing probable but uncertain higher income; while those who are risk seeking (on the other extreme) take chances to get possible high payoffs (Kerr 1994). Unfamiliarity with the new technology may hold exaggerated perceptions about the riskiness of its returns (Anderson and Hazell 1994). Risk averse farmers need to be convinced about the potential and success rates of the innovation. Farmers' decisions to adopt or not to adopt depend on their subjective probabilities of success of the new technology. These subjective probabilities are a function of the farmers' exposure to information regarding new technology. Adesina and Baidu-Forson (1995) have shown that farmers' participation in on-farm tests have significantly contributed to higher adoption rates. Saha et al. (1994) show that adoption of new technology is conditional on farmers' knowledge about the technology's potential. Kabebe, et al. (1990) show that the degree of risk aversion significantly influences farmer decision to adopt a new technology. They also show that the possibilities of technology adoption increase dramatically with the level of education and access to outside information. Purvis et al. (1995) demonstrate that uncertainty about costs and irreversibility of investment decision have significantly influenced farmers' decisions to adopt new innovations.

5   Access to Financial Markets

Access to credit by small farmers has been a key determinant in the rate and success of technology adoption in Asia, particularly as adoption has been closely associated with the use of modern inputs. Lack of credit has limited the purchase of improved seeds, application of appropriate levels of fertilizers, and timely control of pests and diseases (see Bhalla 1979; Frankel 1971; Wills 1972). In most developing countries the poor do not participate much in the formal financial sector, instead receiving financial services through the informal sectors or through traditional mechanisms such as non cash savings.

Rural credit markets are generally the scene of pervasive market failure due to high transaction costs stemming from inadequate information and "institutional capture" by powerful social groups. Commercial banks are unwilling to lend to the poor because they are perceived as a high risk and low return investment, requiring expensive servicing. On the part of the rural poor it is costly to access formal financial institutions, they are often far away and require much paperwork.

The main source of credit to the rural poor has been the informal financial sector, with moneylenders as an important source of funds within the sector. Informal sector interest rates are generally higher than in the formal sector, partly because credit is subsidized in the formal sector and partly because moneylenders operate in interlinked credit and labor markets which are also geographically segmented. Hence informal sector lenders may have a monopoly or near monopoly in providing credit services which allows them to charge higher than competitive rates.

Microfinance to small farmers needs to be increased substantially in order to facilitate technology adoption. There are two main approaches to achieving this: ex-ante credit disbursements to the poor, in order to allow households to ease their intertemporal investment constraints or savings mobilization first where households savings are a prerequisite for credit disbursement. The "savings first" approach is based on the following premises: (i) credit allocation in the past has benefited the larger farmers; (ii) credit disbursement has been associated with repayment problems and high rates of default, particularly by the wealthier farmers; (iii) credit programs have distorted financial markets in ways that have interfered with the efficient evolution of finance for broad sectors of the economy; and (iv) savings generation in rural areas has been quite high, though savings may be held as non monetary assets (e.g. livestock).

There is a need to develop more innovative financial systems for improving the access to credit by the poor. Two considerations will have to be followed: (i) credit allocation will have to be far more effectively targeted to the poorer households which many studies have, in fact, shown to have higher repayment rates than the wealthier households, and (ii) credit will have to be subsidized if it is to reach the poor due to the presence of high costs of administering small loans. Success stories such as the Grameen Bank are based upon the provision of highly targeted subsidized credit to the poor.

6   Farmers Perceptions

Farmers adopt technology based on their own perceptions of returns, risks and costs. Studies have indicated that farmers' perceptions of technology characteristics significantly affect their adoption decisions (Adesina and Baidu-Forson 1995; Bzugu and Igodau 1989). The practical implications of this result is two-fold. First, the new technology must be need-based so that farmers will readily learn and accept the technology. Second, farmers need information so that they understand and appreciate all the aspects of the technology. The second issue has considerable implications for extension, which is still one of the weakest links in the research adoption chain. In one example, Adesina and Baidu-Forson have shown that improved knowledge regarding porridge quality, adaptability to poorer soils, straw quality, etc., have contributed to higher adoption of modern sorghum varieties in West Africa.

Combining new institutions with traditional socioculturally based ones will be important in the promotion of resource management technologies in which farmer perceptions are critical. Most forms of resource degradation are slow and difficult to detect, they involve externalities and spillovers, often requiring community level consensus, action, and even financing.

7   Information

It is evident from the preceding discussion that information critically determines the degree of success. Alkire, et al. (1992) have shown a significant positive relationship between the access to information and the adoption of new technologies. Examining the various sources of information available to farmers they found that contact with input suppliers was the most important source of new information. Private input dealers are not only reliable sources of information to farmers but also effective agents of technology transfer. In an another study, Eboh (1993) indicated that women have limited access to farm information and technology in Nigeria. Bzugu and Igodau (1989) have also indicated that lack of adequate market information on prices and demand contribute to slow adoption of new technologies. These studies call for more attention to access to information as a means to speed up technology transfer. Women play an important role in farming and for sociocultural reasons reaching them is more difficult than their male counterparts. Making information on technology available to women for a faster and wider adoption of new technologies should therefore receive priority.

The rapid growth of electricity, rural roads and infrastructure has extended the reach of television in villages to a remarkable extent, providing a new potentially powerful source of information. Many countries use radio and television as a means of agricultural extension. Their use could be far more extensive, but we know little about its power or impact. Research carried out at various levels by international and national research systems of developing and developed countries can increase benefits to agroecologically similar areas provided the synergies of research and technology transfer experiences *among* various levels are exploited through smart networking including among NARS (ESDAR Report 1995; GREAN Report 1995).

8   Private Sector Input Supply

Growth of private distributors has become an important source of information for farmers. Alkire, et al. (1992) examined various sources of information available to farmers and found that contact with input suppliers was the single most important source of new information.

Private input dealers are also effective agents of technology transfer. Development of the seed industry is a case in point. It has been an important phenomenon with increasing role for the private seed producers in a sector which was previously dominated by public sector organizations. Liberalization of the seed industry may be one of the important sources of recent growth in agricultural productivity in Asia. There is increasing collaboration between the seed producers, international and national agricultural research institutions, and agricultural universities.

Impact evaluation of ICRISAT technologies shows, for instance, that the spread of ICRISAT's rainfed hybrid pearl millet, sorghum, and groundnut varieties is directly related to the strength of the seed and fertilizer companies. Again following Griliches, within India the spread is much greater in the state of Maharashtra than in Andhra Pradesh (based on discussions with Bantilan, Kelley, and Ryan at ICRISAT, India). Similarly in Nigeria the spread of mosaic resistant cassava is greater than in the rest of the humid zones in West Africa and similar findings are reported by Walker et al in the studies of the adoption of improved potato germplasm. Whereas the spread has been made possible by better rural infrastructure, active agriculture universities, and a more active private sector, there are a number of sociocultural aspects of the seed industry about which we know little, e.g. the reasons why the True Potato Seed (TPS) technology is moving more rapidly in Vietnam and Uganda than in Kenya.

Farmers in Punjab, India, similarly indicated how they acquire information on modern variety seeds, fertilizers, pesticides, etc., from private input distributors. But the information seems obviously to be of variable quality. Organization of the seed industry and training of distributors in technologies which entail the use of purchased inputs could play a far more important role in the future in much the same way that retail distributors in the US play a role in disseminating knowledge and information about new technologies. However, even in cases where purchased inputs are not an important source of information, understanding community efforts in seed production and distribution could play an important role in spreading the use of new technologies faster.

9   Price Policies

Pricing policies are by far the most controversial issue in technology adoption. A price policy that increases the profitability of a new technology and ensures stable predictable prices accelerates the adoption process. Many observers of Asia (e.g. Timmer 1993, Byerlee 1993, Lele and Goldsmith 1989, Lele and Bumb 1995) have stressed the strong role that guaranteed minimum output prices for the major cereals (particularly rice and wheat) and fertilizer subsidies played in generating the Green Revolution. Not only were the grain response coefficients to nutrient application higher (about 10/1) in the case of these two crops, thanks to good research and irrigation, but the fertilizer price/output price ratios have also been far more favorable than those typically observed in Africa, particularly since markets have been liberalized, leading to the plummeting of fertilizer use (Lele 1995).

Miller and Trolley (1989) have examined the effect of favorable price policies (price supports and input subsidies) on speeding up adoption of new technologies. They conclude that market interventions favor technology adoption but distort resource allocation and cause waste, reducing the real benefits to farmers. Policy reforms can, for instance, improve the sustainability of scarce resources such as water by pricing them appropriately to reflect their market value.

Removal of price supports and fertilizer subsidies in Africa has, however, not resulted in the expected increase in the fertilizer application, nor to the emergence of private markets in fertilizers to any significant extent in situations of low and risky farmer demand for fertilizers, high transportation costs and low profits. For instance, application of phosphorus fertilizers is necessary, not simply to increase the adoption of new varietal technologies of maize, but often to maintain soil fertility in situations of reduced fallows and continuous cultivation of maize without crop rotations. Public action is clearly necessary to ensure maintenance of soil fertility in Africa since the private sector is unlikely to play a role in situations of slow and long term benefits of a small magnitude.

10 Infrastructure

The importance of and the differences in the levels of irrigation investments between Asia and Africa are well recognized. Less well recognized is the investment in rural roads in the development of markets. But these differences have been quite important both within Asia and between Asia and Africa. For instance, with similar population densities in India in the 1950s as those in Nigeria in the mid 1980s, the coverage of surfaced all-weather roads in India in the 1950s was already 6 times that of Nigeria in the mid 1980s. Even more important, the rural road maintenance calls for well-developed decentralized maintenance capacity of local governments and private sector contractors. The presence of such capacity has resulted in the maintenance and even improvement in the rural physical infrastructure in most parts of Asia. Whereas the rural feeder network expanded in Nigeria (following the oil boom), maintenance capacity, however, has been weak. Indeed even in the countries with a strong history of development and maintenance of the rural infrastructure, such as Kenya, maintenance capacity has deteriorated. This means that per unit of distance traveled marketing costs in Asia are far lower relative to that of Africa (Ahmed and Rustogi 1987). Besides, the Asian shares have perhaps become even more favorable than before and relative to Africa due to the increasing disparity among them in terms of their transportation network, particularly following a decade of retrenchment in rural roads in Africa.

There are however vast differences in rural infrastructure within Asia. For instance, rural infrastructure and its connection with trunk highways and rails have been better developed in India than in China, explaining the much higher and more decentralized nature of the public sector stocks of grain or grain equivalent needed in China relative to India (Johnson 1994).

11   Investments in Agricultural Research

Continued investments in agricultural research and extension is critical for sustaining the growth of agriculture sector. Industrial countries typically invest 2% or more of their agricultural GDP in research compared to developing countries that typically invest less than 1%, with only a few exceptions such as Malaysia that invests nearly 4% on research. Developing countries that have invested relatively more in agriculture research have had greater success in meeting food demand (e.g. many Asian countries) than their counterparts with much less investment. That success is largely due to adaptive research and effective transfer of technology to a wide area.[1] In Africa, on the other hand, investments in agricultural research are not only low but declining in recent years, resulting in greater dependence on donor resources (Pardey et al. 1995; Lele 1996).

Large countries in Asia enjoy scale economies in research, they are well endowed with trained personnel. Their investments in agricultural research as a share of agricultural GNP have been higher and more stable than in Africa (Pardey et al. 1995). Lately, however, shortages of operating resources, inbreeding in training and inadequate incentives for performance have become major problems even among Asian NARS (Pardey 1995, Lele 1995).

The scale economies and strong collaborations among the international and national research centers in Asia referred to earlier are demonstrated by the semidwarf varieties from CIMMYT. Since their availability in the mid 1966, they covered more than 85 percent of the wheat area in India in 1990. Indian wheat breeders released 175 varieties of wheat in 15 years between 1965 and 1990. All wheat varieties in India, including the rainfed areas, are now semidwarf.

In Pakistan annual yield gain from varietal improvement has been 1% annually from 1978-90. Despite 80 percent of the wheat in Pakistan being under irrigation, the average yield levels are lower than in India (1.8 tons compared to 2.5 tons)

---

[1] Adaptive research involves bringing in and modifying technologies and institutions produced elsewhere (Alston et al. 1995).

(Byerlee 1994). The problems of poor seed supply, inadequate extension, and unremunerative wheat prices explain the poorer yields in Pakistan as they do in the much of rainfed Africa. The same problems operate in the Eastern part of the Indo-Gangetic Plain in India where yields per ha per crop are less than 1/2 of those in the Indian Punjab region. It is noteworthy that according to the estimates made by the Rice Wheat Consortium only a third of the 12 million tons under the rice wheat system has reached yield ceilings. Two thirds show vast scope for closing the yield gap (personal communication with Abrol 1995).

As economic policy and regulatory environment, including intellectual property rights, have improved in developing countries, private sector research has increased. So too has the partnership between the private and the public sectors, particularly in applied and adaptive research. The private sector will undoubtedly become a more important source of technology in the future, including for the subsistence of small-scale farmers.

12   Agricultural Extension

Agricultural extension has been one of the weakest links in technology transfer and yet extension systems have been allowed to collapse under the weight of the budget constraints, particularly in Latin America and Africa. Extension agents often fail to interact with researchers both in understanding the potentials of new technologies and in bringing back farmers' concerns to researchers. As agriculture becomes more knowledge-intensive, the role of extension becomes even more critical. In the past, agricultural technology transfer was always associated with public extension system, but increasingly technology transfer is being realized through an array of other mechanisms, including diverse types of NGOs and the private sector. In the future, the private sector including input dealers, agribusiness enterprises, and private consultants will have an increased role in technology transfer (Alex and Byerlee 1996).

13   Post-Harvest Marketing Facilities

Lack of post-harvest marketing facilities reduce the profitability of new technology. Producers in developing countries have only limited access to markets, poor knowledge of value-added, and most often much of their valuable produce is lost to spoilage and rodents, highlighting the significant missed opportunities to realize their economic potential (IDRC 1996). Farm commodities are often sold in local markets where they are produced, missing broader domestic and international market opportunities. None of the adoption studies have examined this critical issue. Commodity processing, storage, hauling/transportation facilities, rural connecting roads, etc. would greatly enhance the marketability of the product, thereby increasing the profitability of the technology. When an economy moves from subsistence farming systems to more commercial agricultural system, post-harvest marketing facilities become critical (e.g. Asia). One of the major concerns is the unavailability of credit during post-harvest seasons so that farmers can hold on to the product until the prices are favorable.

14   Political Support

Strong political will to modernize agriculture as the foundation of overall economic progress has been an important driving force in most agriculturally successful Asian countries (Timmer 1993). Providing food and other agricultural goods to the rapidly industrializing and urbanizing populations at low and stable prices and without undue reliance on basic staple food imports has been a geopolitical imperative for many large Asian countries. Stable food supplies and prices have been critical to political stability and they in turn have been stimuli for sound agricultural and rural policy frameworks to help the millions of small farmers increase their productivity. The precise elements of that framework have, however, differed considerably among countries, with different degrees of success. The issues of interaction among social change, political culture, investments, and technological progress have received only limited attention in policy analysis or formulation notwithstanding the overwhelming evidence of the importance of education in the adoption studies (Wade 1994). Sectoral blinders among ministries are so strong that those in agriculture will have little to do with those in irrigation or education.

15   Social and Cultural Factors

Collective action is difficult in socioculturally differentiated and politically fragmented communities. For instance, in India the poor have been able to participate actively in the democratic process. They have greater access to services than they had in the immediate post-independence period. Yet the electioneering process has also been divisive socially in terms of an accentuated stress in the campaigns on the already well entrenched caste-based differences. The social polarization in the South Asian villages may be adversely affecting the access of individual households to information, credit, and markets, an area about which we know less since the advent of the first Green Revolution. On the other hand, a thriving non governmental (the so-called NGO) sector in India, Bangladesh or Sri Lanka, compared to the East and Southeast Asian countries, may reflect a social response to a combination of the region's persistent poverty, social inequities, and the relatively more freewheeling democratic systems. Notwithstanding the rhetoric of participation, devolution and local consultation, rigorous, comparative and quantitative analysis of how these factors influence community action and production responses, e.g., in water or forest management, is limited and is long overdue.

16   The Presence of Regional, National, and International Research Centers

The presence of International research centers provide the national research and extension systems of the countries with greater access to the technologies developed in the centers through a more routine and face to face interaction than might be the case for other countries. For example, ICRISAT's location in India, IITA's location in Nigeria, and IRRI's location in Philippines may explain the more rapid spread of crop technologies developed by the centers in those countries. Gertler (1995) has shown that proximity or close contact between scientists and farmers greatly improves the successful implementation of advanced technologies. This has implications for CGIAR-NARS collaborations. NGOS and the farmers' service centers (Krishi Vignana Kendras) are becoming an important means of reaching farmers and increasing their participation. They will be explored in a study of *Accelerating Adoption of CGIAR Technologies* currently being launched by the World Bank's Agricultural Research and Extension Department, in collaboration with selected CGIAR centers and NARS.

17   Understanding Stakeholders

It is clear that an iterative process of understanding the constraints on adoption and implications for research requires much greater understanding of all the actors and stakeholders. The direct actors involve donors and policy makers in developing countries who finance research and related activities crucial for technology generation and transfer, administrators of technology and policy, national and international scientists, the private and the NGO sectors, research institutions, universities and extension services.

Not all the actors are "stakeholders." Unlike in the case of the farming women and men for whom decisions with regard to technology adoption are often matters of survival, or relative prosperity vs. bankruptcy, for other actors few such *personal* stakes may be involved. Yet their decisions tend to have profound implications for technology generation and transfer. The equally important but often "hidden" actors include the managers of irrigation, electrical and telephone systems who determine if the supply of water and communications will be predictable, thereby affecting the farmers' perception of risks and uncertainty, the bankers or women's savings groups providing working capital, contractors or community level organizations maintaining feeder roads, retailers, wholesalers, multinationals, millers, processors and exporters. Clearly, we need to identify the multitude of actors in multiple sectors at several levels and interactions among them to determine current and more desirable future *alternative* sources of the supply of, and the demand for technologies.

18   Research Priority Setting

With the number of constraints identified in the preceding discussion it is clear that research priority setting is critical. It is also obvious that research priorities must be very different at the level of the CGIAR centers with their role at the strategic end of the research compared to that of most NARS, although large NARS that enjoy scale economies in research may also play a major role in technology transfer to others with similar agro-ecologies through the spillover effects of their research. Small NARS on the other hand have to focus more on the applied and particularly the adaptive end of research including particularly on resource management research which tends to be highly location specific. Beyond these general guidelines, however, priority setting is made difficult by the difficulty of quantifying and measuring all costs and benefits of research, for example, the values one should place on the conservation of biodiversity, the risks, uncertainty and the long gestation lags associated with certain kinds of research and the presence of sunk costs which may make harvesting the benefits of resources already invested in research much more attractive than conducting new research, an area which has yet to be explored. Policy makers attach high weights to sociopolitical and environmental objectives, yet without the knowledge of the scientific possibilities of success. Scientists may tend to be more concerned about their research projects, while economists may focus on priorities simply based on quantifiable benefits and costs.

Past research priorities for instance were often based on the estimation of demand for food grains in developing countries (Gryseels et al. 1992). The result was an all-out effort to increase production of certain commodities, mainly cereals. Since the mid-1960s, global food production has increased by 80%, with more than half of that increase in developing countries. Yield levels of rice, wheat and maize nearly doubled over the 1960 to 1994 period as a result of improved varieties, irrigation, fertilizer, and a range of improved crop and resource management technologies (Plucknett 1993).

While successful in increasing production and still an important consideration, the supply-driven approach has several limitations. Even while considering aggregate demand, such a top-down approach ignores producer preferences for yield stability, byproducts, resource allocation, and the need for crop's incorporation into the larger farming system, and consumer preferences for quality, tastes, cooking, milling or storage, and so on. These considerations have significantly slowed down the adoption of several technologies, particularly resource management technologies.

The farmer participatory approach (some times referred as bottom-up approach) gained popularity in the 1980s when it was realized that adoption of HYVs alone would not realize the potential yield gain. This was particularly true in rainfed areas where efficient resource management is more crucial for the survival of poor farmers. Participatory research is embodied in the farming system research (FSR) movement of the 1980s (Byerlee 1994). As identified by Byerlee, the salient features of FSR include: (i) an explicit focus on the needs and circumstances of small-scale farmers in the design of new technologies; (ii) a recognition of the complexity of small farm systems and system interactions engendered by inter-cropping, multiple cropping, crop rotations, subsistence food supply, risk management and resource constraints; (iii) research methods that emphasize ex-ante diagnosis of farmers' constraints and testing of technologies in farmers' fields with farmer participation; (iv) recognition of diversity of farmers and the need for low-cost innovations, and (v) use of interdisciplinary teams involving technical and social scientists. Donors and international research centers enthusiastically embraced the concept and many national programs established on-farm research systems.

After more than a decade of experience with FSR, it is not clear whether FSR succeeded in meeting its objectives, particularly in rainfed areas, where it was concentrated. Tripp (1991) and Anderson (1991), for example, indicate that FSR fell short of its objective of promoting rapid adoption of improved technologies.

Limited success of FSR lead to efforts towards understanding the entire process of technology generation and transfer. The probability of research resulting in adaptable technology, likely adoption levels and sizes of production gains were initially assumed to be equal across commodities in setting research priorities when in fact there are considerable differences in the rates of adoption in practice by commodities, regions and types of research (McCalla and Ryan 1992). Kelley et al. (1995) and Walker and Collion (1996) emphasize the need to understand the probability of success in achieving research results in alternative research programs by extensive discussions with scientists, an approach also favored by Evenson and followed in Rosegrant and Evenson (1995). Bantilan and Johansen (1995) showed the importance of understanding the research-adoption-impact continuum in setting research agenda. They break down the various stages of the research process, its output and likely consequences on adoption (see figure 2).

The ideal approach for future priority-setting is to integrate the two approaches into an iterative process of learning and improvising. Micro-management of research can affect scientific entrepreneurship and, therefore, can be counter productive towards increasing food production. There is a wealth of informal evidence that a successful research program rests heavily on the spirit, imagination, judgment, and integrity of agricultural scientists who are allowed freedom of inquiry (Alston, Norton, and Pardey 1995). However, scientific merit alone is not sufficient to justify public support for agricultural research, particularly when resources are limited. Farmers' needs and requirements are important for the successful adoption of new technologies. Future priority setting should follow a circular scientist-farmer-scientist framework in which all actors contribute in setting the research agenda based on the *need* and the *availability* of resources.

Conclusion

In the preceding pages several interrelated arguments were presented. First, the issues of technology development and adoption have been discussed by using two quite different sets of philosophical underpinnings, one focusing on efficiency, profits, markets and individuals with relatively short-run implications, the other focusing on equity, environmental sustainability, collective action, and a long-term horizon. Second, where profits are high, visible and immediate, adoption of new technologies tends to be rapid. Third, investments in social capital such as irrigation, education, transportation, communication, information, research and technology development increase profitability of technologies and increase the rates of adoption. It goes without saying, although the paper does not address this issue, that without rapid agricultural growth countries would not be able to fund the necessary investments in the much-needed social capital.

Finally, to generate and transfer relevant technologies research is needed at the level of advanced countries' institutions as well as the CGIAR centers, national research institutions and at the level of the farmers with strong interactions among those levels as well as with policies and institutions that enable the adoption of the new technologies. Whereas we know that a large number of factors influence adoption of technologies by farmers, our ability to assess the costs and benefits of the various options is much too limited to establish a good set of priorities. More research is needed to understand those interactions, to assess, quantify and measure costs and benefits to establish research priorities. It is clear that the iterative process of understanding the constraints to adoption and implications for research requires much greater and broader analytical work than currently exists.

Acknowledgment

A paper prepared for an International Symposium on Food Security and Innovations: Successes and Lessons Learned, An International Symposium at University of Hohenheim, sponsored by Eiselen-Stiftung Ulm, March 11th through 13th, 1996, Stuttgart, Germany. The contributions of Hemani Saigal are gratefully acknowledged. The comments by Russel Freed and Gary Alex are well appreciated. Discussions with the NARS in Asia and Africa in the context of the APAARI and SPAAR meetings, and the Rice-Wheat Initiative and discussions with ICRISAT, IRRI, and CIMMYT scientists also made a valuable contribution.

References

Adesina, A.A and J. Baidu-Forson 1995. "Farmers' perception and adoption of new agricultural technology: evidence from analysis in Burkina Faso and Guinea, West Africa", _Agricultural Economics_, Vol. 13, No. 1, pp. 1-9.

Ahmed, R., and Rustagi, N. 1987. _Marketing and Price Incentives in African and Asian Countries: A Comparison_, Reprinted from _Agricultural Marketing Strategy and Pricing Policy_, (Ed. Dieter Elz), International Bank for Reconstruction and Development 1987, in Reprint No. 107, International Food Policy Research Institute, Washington D.C.

Alex and Byerlee 1996. "Strategic Issues for Agricultural Research Policy to 2000 and Beyond." Working Draft, The World Bank, Washington D.C.

Alkire, S, A. Sofranko and A. Khan 1992. "Farmer's access to information and its impact on technology adoption in North West Frontier Province, Pakistan", _Journal of Rural Development and Administration_, Vol. 24, No. 4, pp. 9-24.

Alston, J.M., G. W. Norton, and P.G. Pardey 1995. Science Under Scarcity: Principles and Practice for Agricultural Research Evaluation and Priority Setting. Cornell University Press: Ithaca, New York.

Anderson, Jock. 1992. "Agricultural research institutions and the priorities in an era of resource scarcity: discussion", _American Journal of Agricultural Economics_, Vol. 74, pp. 1111-1113.

Anderson, Jock. and Peter Hazell 1994. "Risk Considerations in the Design and Transfer of Agricultural Technology" in Agricultural Technology: Policy Issues for the International Community edited by Jock Anderson, CAB International, Wallingford, U.K.

Bantilan, M. C. S. and C. Johansen 1995. "Research Evaluation and Impact Analysis of Biological Nitrogen fixation", _Plant and Soil_ 174:279-286.

Barghouti, S., and Le Moigne, G. 1990., _Irrigation in Sub-Saharan Africa: the Development of Public and Private Systems,_ World Bank Technical Paper N0. 123, The World Bank, Washington D.C.

Bhalla, S. S. 1979. "Farm and Technical Change in Indian Agriculture." In Agrarian Structure and Productivity in Developing Countries, edited by R. Berry and W. Cline, Baltimore: Johns Hopkins University Press.

Binswanger, Hans P., and Ruttan 1978. V.W "Induced innovation: technology, institutions, and development", Baltimore: Johns Hopkins University Press.

Byerlee. D. 1993. _Modern Varieties, Productivity and Sustainability: Recent experience and Emerging Challenges,_ Paper presented at the 1993 AAEA/IFPRI Pre-Conference Workshop: "Post-Green Revolution Agricultural Development strategies in the Third World: What Next?", July 30 1993, Orlando, Florida.

Byerlee, D. and G. Traxler 1995. "National and international wheat improvement research in the post-Green revolution period: evolution and impacts", _American Journal of Agricultural Economics_, Vol. 77, No. 2, pp. 268-278.

Byerlee, Derek and Greg Traxler 1995. "National and international wheat improvement research in post-green revolution period: evolution and impacts", *American Journal of Agricultural Economics*, Vol. 77, pp. 268-278.

Bzugu, P. M. and C. O. Igodan 1989. "Determinants of Adoption of Improved Practices Among Sorghum Farmers in Michika Local Government Area, Gongola State, Nigeria." *Journal of Rural Development and Administration*, 21:1-8.

Eboh, E. C. 1993. "A Household survey of farm women's access to agro-information and technology: implications for extension training and rural development in Nigeria", *Journal of Rural Development and Administration*, Vol. 25, No. 4, pp. 1-11.

Food and Agriculture Organization 1995, *Water Development for Food Security,* World Food Summit Technical Paper (unedited version).

Frankel, F. R. 1971. India's Green Revolution- Economic Gains and Political Costs. Princeton, N.J.: Princeton University Press.

Gertler, M. S. 1995, "Being there: Proximity, Organization, and the Culture in the Development and Adoption of Advanced Manufacturing Technologies." Economic Geography, 71(1):1-26.

GREAN Report 1995. *Global Research on the Environmental and Agricultural Nexus for the 21st Century: a Proposal for Collaborative Research among US Universities, CGIAR Centers, and Developing Country Institutions, eds.* Lele, U., and Coffman, R. Report of the Taskforce on Research Innovations for Productivity and Sustainability, University of Florida, Gainesville, Florida.

Griliches, Zvi 1957. "Hybrid Corn: An exploration in the Economics of Technological Change." Econometrica 25(4): 501-522.

Gryseels, G., C. T. de Wit, A. McCalla, J. Monyo, A. Kassam, E. Craswell, and M. Collinson 1992. "Setting Agricultural Research Priorities for the CGIAR", Agricultural Systems, 40:59-103.

Hayami,Y and Ruttan, V.W 1985. *Agricultural Development: an International Perspective,* Johns Hopkins, Baltimore.

Hubbell, D.H 1995. *Extension of Symbiotic Biological Nitrogen Fixation Technology in Developing Countries,* in Fertilizer Research.

Huffman, W. E. 1977. "Allocative Efficiency: The Role of Human Capital." *Quarterly Journal of Economics*, 91:59-80.

Huffman, W. E. and R. Evenson 1993. Science for Agriculture: A Long Term Perspective. Iowa State University Press, Ames, Iowa.

Indian Council of Agricultural Research 1995. *Technology Assessment and Refinement through Institution-Village Linkage Programme,* An Approach Paper, New Delhi.

Jamison, D. T. and L. J. Lau 1982. Farmer Education and Farm Efficiency. Baltimore: Johns Hopkins University Press.

Johnson, D.G. 1994. *Does China have a Grain Problem,* in China Economic Review, Vol 4, No. 1 1994, pp. 1-14

Kebede, Y., K. Gunjal, and G. Coffin 1990. "Adoption of New Technologies in Ethiopian Agriculture: The Case of Tegulet-Bulga District, Shoa Province." *Agriculture Economics*, 4:27-43.

Kelley, T. G., J. G. Ryan, and B. K. Patel 1995. "Applied Participatory Priority Setting in International Agricultural Research: Making Trade-offs Transparent and Explicit", *Agricultural Systems* 49:177-216.

Kerr, J. M. 1994. Risk and Stability, in Evaluating ICRISAT Research Impact edited by M. C. Bantilan and P. K. Joshi, ICRISAT, Patencheru, Andhra Pradesh.

Le Moigne, G. 1994. *Water Policy and Water Markets: Selected Papers and Proceedings from the World Bank's Ninth Annual Irrigation and Drainage Seminar,* World Bank Technical Paper N0. 249, The World Bank, Washington D.C.

Lele, U. 1995. *Building on the NARS-CGIAR Partnership for a Doubly Green Revolution: A Framework for the IFAD-Led Initiative,* Paper prepared for the Meeting on Strengthening NARS-CGIAR Partnerships: NARS Outline Action Plan, October 28 1995, Washington D.C.

Lele, U., and Stone, S. 1989. *Population pressure, the Environment and Agricultural intensification: Variations of the Boserup Hypothesis,* MADIA Discussion Paper No. 4, The World Bank, Washington D.C.

Lele, U., and Goldsmith, A. 1989. *The Development of National Agricultural Research Capacity: India's Experience with the Rockfeller Foundation and its Significance for Africa,* MADIA Discussion Paper, The World Bank, Washington D.C.

Lele, U., and Bumb, B. 1995. *The Food Crisis in South Asia: the Case of India,* in Lateef, K. S., (ed), *The Evolving Role of the World Bank: Helping Meet the Challenge of Development,* The World Bank, Washington D.C.

McCalla, Alex F. and James Ryan 1992. "Setting agricultural research priorities: lessons from the CGIAR study", *American Journal of Agricultural Economics,* Vol. 74, pp. 1095-1100.

Migot-Adholla and Bruce J.W.(eds) 1994, *Searching for Land Tenure Security in Africa,* Kendall/Hunt, Iowa, USA

Miller, Tracy and George Trolley 1989. "Technology adoption and agricultural price policy", *American Journal of Agricultural Economics,* Vol. 71, pp. 847-857.

Pardey, P.G., Roseboom, J., and Bientema, N. M. 1995. *Investments in African Agricultural Research,* EPTD Discussion Paper No. 14, International Food Policy Research Institute, Washington D.C.

Pardey, P. G., Anderson, J. R., and Roseboom, J. 1991. *Agricultural Research Policy: International Quantitative Perspectives,* Cambridge University Press, Cambridge.

Paroda, R. S. 1996. "The APAARI Vision Towards NARS-CGIAR Partnership", Paper presented at the APAARI Meetings held in New Delhi, India, February 1-2 1996.

Plucknett, D. L. 1993. Science and Agriculture Transformation. IFPRI Lecture.

Purvis, Amy et al. 1995. "Technology adoption decisions under irreversibility and uncertainty: an Ex ante approach", *American Journal of Agricultural Economics,* Vol. 77, pp. 541-551.

Ramadevi, K. 1995. *Gender Analysis of Intrahousehold Allocation of Resources and Benefits - an ex-post Study of Groundnut Crop Production Technology in the Semi-Arid Tropics of India,* Draft Paper, ICRISAT, India.

Ramadevi, K. 1995. *Gender Impact of Groundnut Crop Production Technologies: A Case Study of Semi-Arid Tropics in India,* Draft Paper, ICRISAT, India.

Rosegrant, Mark W. and Robert E. Evenson 1995. "Total factor productivity and sources of long term growth in Indian agriculture", Washington, D.C.,: IFPRI, EPDT Discussion paper No. 7.

Rosegrant, M., and Svendsen, M. 1993. *Asian Food Production in the 1990s: Irrigation Investment and Management Policy,* Food Policy, Vol 18, No. 1.

Schultz, T. W. 1964. Transforming Traditional Agriculture. New Heven, Conn.: Yale University Press.

Shah, Atanu, Alan Love and Robert Schwart 1994. "Adoption of emerging technologies under output uncertainty", *American Journal of Agricultural Economics*, Vol. 76, pp. 836-846.

Strauss, John et al. 1991. "Role of education and extension in the adoption of technology: a study of upland rice and soybean farmers in Central-West Brazil", *Agricultural Economics*, Vol. 5, pp. 341-359.

Timmer, P. 1993. *Food Price Stabilization: the Relevance of the Asian Experience to Africa* in Russell, N.C., and Dowsell, C.R., (eds), *Policy Options for Agricultural Development in Sub-Saharan Africa*, CASIN/SAA/GLOBAL 2000.

Trigo, E.J. 1995. *Agriculture, Technological Change, and the Environment in Latin America: a 2020 Perspective,* Food, Agriculture and the Environment Discussion Paper Number 9, International Food Policy Research Institute, Washington D.C.

Wade, R. 1994. *Village Republics: Economic Conditions for Collective Action in South India*, ICS Press, San Francisco, California.

Walker, T. and M. Collion 1996. Priority Setting at CIP for the 1998-2000 Medium Term Plan, CIP, Lima, Peru.

Wills, I. R 1972. "Projections of Effects of Modern Inputs on Agricultural Income and Employment in a C.D. Block, U.P., India." American Journal of Agriculture Economics, 54:452-60.

World Bank/UNDP 1990. *Irrigation and Drainage Research: A Proposal,* Agriculture and Rural Development Department, Washington, D.C.

Figure 1: Percentage of Total Corn Acreage Planted with Hybrid Seed

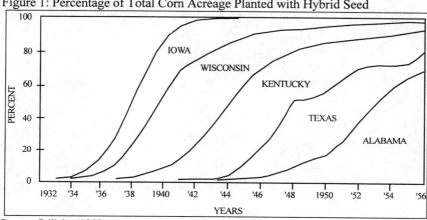

Source: Griliches 1957.

Figure 2: Research Impact Continuum

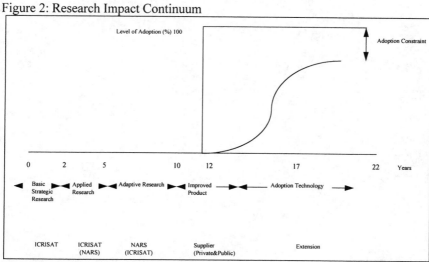

Source: Bantilan and Johansen 1995.

Food Security and Innovations: Conclusions for Policy and Research

Joachim von Braun

Institute of Food Economics and Consumption Studies
Chair for Food Economics and Food Policy
Christian-Albrechts University of Kiel, Germany

The following concluding remarks are an attempt to mainly highlight some conceptual issues of the food security – innovation interface which emerged from the symposium and some research findings which point at lessons learned. At the outset, it is noteworthy to underline the fact that this symposium successfully stimulated natural scientists and social scientists to talk to, and work with each other. While this has good tradition in agricultural science, it nevertheless should be highlighted as a fulfilled pre-condition for a symposium which is geared towards practical problem solving in the food security and innovation domains.

Change in the Fundamental Forces of Economic Conditions

Innovations for food security must consider the emerging changes in fundamental forces of economic conditions globally and in developing countries in particular. We may like to think in terms of a stylised production function, where a set of complex 'inputs' drive the growth and development outcomes. In brief, these forces are

- labor and its quality,
- capital, broadly defined, including human capital,
- the natural resource base, and
- the technical and institutional knowledge base.
- Above all, efficient arrangements of the state and civil society shape the productivity of the factors of economic change, and the synergy of these factors.

In all these five areas fundamental changes are underway in an increasingly globalized economy.

We see that growth of the **labor** force remains a key driving power of economic growth and development in many parts of the world (von Braun 1995). Even if world population may stabilize in the second half of the next century at about 10 to 14 billion people, the labor force, that is population in the age bracket between 15 and 65, will expand for a longer period of time. Improvements in population quality through better health along side of economic growth would lead to further expansion of the labor force available for productive work. In many developing country regions today, low income people's work ability is reduced by health problems equivalent to 15 to 25 percent of work time. In addition to expanding overall work force, migration is rapidly increasing in many parts of the world. This relates to migration within large countries, such as China and India, and across borders between poorer and richer regions, such as South and North America, and Eastern Europe and Western Europe, and in East Asia, as well as traditionally in the Middle East. These movements have large implications for labor intensity of agriculture and food processing. Movements of people also give rise to complex new mixes in dietary patterns and the inherent human demand for diverse diets is further stimulated by increasing income and urbanization.

Turning from labor to **capital**, one needs to stress the tremendous demand for, and the heterogeneity of that crucial factor in economic growth. Domestic savings in developing countries will remain most important to the accumulation of the investment resources. In rural economies, however, migration and ageing, possibly accompanied with unsatisfactory progress in achieving better health for the population, may result in hardly promising aggregate outcomes of structural transformations in labor and capital.

Sustainable utilization and management of **natural resources** under conditions of accelerated economic growth and pressing food needs will be a core problem of the next century. Agricultural research systems have a central role to play in achieving sustainability in natural resource utilization. A tremendous array of sustainability issues related to water, soil, biodiversity, and climate, and the linkages of all of these is confronting us. The follow-up actions of the global environmental agenda after the Earth Summit of Rio in 1992 points at the many tasks. In the context of natural resources we also have to take account of what is probably to be the most important agricultural production factor of the 21st century, namely genetic resources.

Economies as a whole are increasingly shifting to **"knowledge based economies"**, that is economies which are increasingly based on production, distribution and use of knowledge and information. In many parts of the so-called developing countries this process is rapidly underway, and in many other parts, notably Sub-Saharan Africa, this transformation is yet to come in the next century. Innovations in economic theory during the past two decades teach us that the positive external effects of knowledge spreading widely beyond the original innovator is the key non exhaustible factor of production (P. Romer 1986). Through its linkages to labor and capital, it is actually new knowledge which makes these two traditional factors ever more productive. Technical progress in agriculture has vividly driven home this lesson.

Last not least **political and institutional conditions** shape the domestic and international economic context. The critical role of the state and its institutions, as well as the functioning of civil society has been underlined clearly by the troublesome transformation of the former planned economies in Central and Eastern Europe. At the same time the tremendous acceleration of the economic growth in China and India after opening up market possibilities points to the role of policy and institutions. At the global level, the establishment of new rules of the game, especially in the context of the WTO, are setting the new framework conditions for international agriculture likely for a long time to come. In the long run it may be the establishment of (intellectual) property rights creating new and efficient systems of exchange, stimulating innovation which are even more relevant to agriculture and the food systems in the next century. In crude economic terms, the hunger and malnutrition problem is probably one of the largest, world-wide waste of potential 'economic resources' – the lives of billions of potentially productive people now and over the coming decades – and is probably the biggest failure of institutional (market) functioning yet to be resolved. The size of the problem has been well publicized by the recent World Food Summit (FAO 1996).

Appropriate technological innovations in agriculture reduce unit costs of production and marketing and induce economic gains by stimulating agricultural growth, improving employment opportunities, and expanding food supplies, all of which involve and benefit poor producers and consumers and help to reduce food insecurity. *National and international agricultural organizations and research systems* in particular are the forces driving the technological innovation required to achieve the sustainable agricultural growth that will make the needed food available to the world's growing population. Renewed actions are needed to accelerate technological innovation in many smallholder-dominated regions of the world in order to meet the nutritional goals directly and indirectly.

Long-term effects of alternative development strategies for growth and poverty reduction have shown the striking relevance of the choice of economic strategy. The discussion of policy for improving nutrition must not be limited to direct food- and agriculture-related policies. *Non-agricultural and economy-wide policies* such as industrial protection and fiscal policies are highly relevant for food and agricultural prices, income, and the employment of the poor, and thus also for food security over the short term and long term (Krueger, Schiff, and Valdés 1988).

Implications of Conceptual Considerations

Policy and program action for improved food security through stimulated innovation need a theoretical base and conceptual framework. These can be seen as subsets of the larger theoretical foundations of development, and the institutional and technical base of innovation. In addition, historical perspectives may help. Without conceptual frameworks and theoretical foundations policy actions for improved food security and technological change may end up designed in a piecemeal fashion and potential synergies between actions in the socio-economic and the technical area of food-related development may be overlooked.

The reviews of state of the art at the symposium facilitated it to come quickly to consensus on definition and concepts of food security on the one hand, and innovations on the other hand. The taxonomy by Walter (Part One) was certainly most helpful for structuring debate. However, conceptual gaps remain on the relationships *between* food security and innovations. The forward and backward linkages between the two and the scope for and limitations of fostering these linkages through policy, investment in technology as well as people's mobilization remain on the research agenda.

One may, of course, start with the well-known framework of sequential processes of the two different types: Type one portrays the process:

invention —> innovation —> diffusion —> imitation

The process of a second type, with a clearer focus on the role of research in innovation, portrays the sequence of:

basic research —> strategic research —> applied research —> adaptive research —> testing —> demonstration —> wide-spread use

While these traditional concepts of sequential innovation processes have some validity, many of the interesting case studies presented at the symposium have highlighted the importance of feedback in these processes, and the role of indigenous innovation in a system's context of the farm and household setting. Moreover, clearly a new focus on implementation issues of innovation is needed, and in particular related to the testing and demonstration activities. New challenges and opportunities arise from the growing private sector role in agriculture innovation as biotechnologies offer new opportunities and as public systems of innovations remain weak in many low income country settings. This needs further consideration when designing priority setting systems for innovation, which must go beyond traditional analysis of constraints to growth in the food economy. Institutional strengthening and access to knowledge facilitation are key elements to be considered in priority setting, such as underlined by Bonte-Friedheim (Part Four). The descriptive approach towards processes and sequences of innovation may be useful to focus on how to put research findings to work, but they are not a substitute for theory of innovation.

There clearly is a need for broader framework on technology generation and adoption, as pointed out and conceptualized by Lele (Part One).

Theoretical reflections on causality linkages between food security and innovations may center around three positions.

1. Position One postulates *"to achieve food security we need innovations"*. This position focuses on the key role for technological change to stimulate agricultural growth and employment. It is assumed that poverty reducing effects result, if innovations facilitate growth in total factor productivity, including productivity of low income people.

2. Position Two postulates *"to get innovations, we need food security (broadly defined, that is nutritional and health improvement)"*. This position underlines the key role of improved human resources, as a pre-condition for the stimulation of innovation capacities.

3. A third position may attempt a *synthesis between the first and the second including a dynamic perspective on the interactions between food security and innovation*: at low levels of income a certain degree of change in food security improvement requires a certain rate of change in innovations. However, rates of change of the two is mutually constraint by their levels. Progress in the two, therefore, may proceed by mechanism of movement of the earth worm (Regenwurm), which moves forward only once its tail has pushed forward, and whose tail only moves forward once its head segment has stretched out. Food security and innovations may very well be in such a push-pull or interdependent relationship (Figure 1), each taking key developmental roles.

Figure 1: Food Security-Innovation Linkages

Recent theoretical clarifications and advances certainly underline that good nutrition is the pre-condition for economic development (Fogel 1993). The power of high externalities of knowledge and its non-declining returns underlines the fundamental role of invention and innovation. The spreading of information technology facilitates not only spreading of information, but also learning by doing and strengthening of learning systems. At the macro level the power of trade for facilitating knowledge transmission is known since long but has been underestimated or even negated in north-south relationships of food industry and agriculture. Lessons from evolutionary economics pointed at by Walter (Part One) include that waste in investment for invention and innovation is part of a trial – and – error process. Elements of failure are part of typical innovation processes and carry important lessons. Narrow-minded interpretation of technological change, such as the "green revolution", would, for instance, either emphasize aberrations or successes only, rather than the whole process.

Historical perspectives on the interlinkages between food security and innovation point at the key role of institutional change. Whether this is

- Japan's experience in the last decades of the 19th century with the removal of feudal barriers and the development of communication and transport along with agricultural research and technology, as well as commercialization development, or whether it is
- Germany's experience with the key role of training and research institutions in agriculture, which came into existence in the first half of the 19th century, as initiated by concerned people to address the hunger issue (such as von Thünen, Voigt and others), and later through the development of co-operative systems which were directly stimulated by famine situations in the 1860s, upon which Raiffeisen and others acted.
- Similarly, the studies by Robert Fogel suggest that in France and Britain in the past century improved food security and nutrition resulted in the much more productive work force which was the pre-condition for economic growth and industrialization.

In some of these contexts political reform preceded the build-up of capacity for institutional and technical innovation. Crises played a role in some of these examples, too, to get action and political change. The creation of sufficient political base and empowerment of the food insecure is a research issue, and not just an advocacy area, as Hans Singer has underlined (Part One).

Regarding concepts for priority setting, the driving question, as posed by Michel Griffon at this symposium, is, **how** policy and institutional innovations can facilitate technical innovations for food security (Figure 2).

Figure 2: The Driving Question

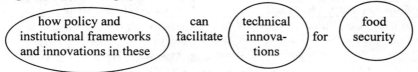

As for instance Reardon et al. (Part Three) indicate, the macro economic policy reforms are not enough to create the conditions for capital-led intensification which is so necessary in the West Africa Sahel. Public investment and complementary infrastructure remains critical to make farm capital investments attractive and affordable. The strong impact of physical market access on agricultural productivity which can be influenced by policy and institutions was underlined by von Oppen et al. (Part Three). The further roles of institutional innovations, for instance in the area of financial systems and their interaction with technological innovations was highlighted in a set of stimulating studies by Schrieder, Sharma and Zeller (Part Three).

Food Security: the Goal ... Innovations: the Means

Food security is a goal, and innovations is the means. This, however, does not mean that narrow targeting of innovations towards food security is to be advocated. The limitations of technology targeting in low income countries rural settings are to be kept in mind. The potentials for such targeting should not be overlooked, but specific narrow targeting of technologies towards certain areas, or farm types, or population groups (say by gender), do not suggest too much scope for it. This may be different with institutional innovations, where the poor food-insecure are prime actors in participatory approaches. It may very well be that institutional innovations leading towards empowerment of the poor will facilitate increased scope for technology targeting, but less so vice-versa.

An enormously rich set of highlights from this symposium can be pointed at and is structured in Box 1 along the food chain.

Box 1: Selected Highlights on Food Security related Innovations

Food Security: The Goal	Innovations: The Means
1) Policies / Institutions	• New Extension Approaches (Participatory) • Funding Alternatives (Public / Private) • Resource Allocation (Sustainable Land Use) • Credit Systems • NGO Networks (Honey-Bee)
2) Resources / Factors	• Erosion Control / Water Harvesting (e.g. Burkina Faso)
3) Production / Processing Issues	• Biological Control (Cassava) • Integrated Striga Control • Biotechnology for Pest Resistance (Rice) • Rice - Fish Systems (Bangladesh) • Home Gardens • Crop Intensification / Capital-Led • Diversification (Fruit Trees, Soybeans) • Small Scale Processing Women (e.g. Cheese) • Post-Harvest Technology
4) Trade / Market Issues	• Key Role of Market Access • Market Formations (Breeding-Goat Auctions)
5) Food Security of People	• Methods for Food Security Project Effects (Indicators, Cost Effectiveness) • Food Aided Employment Program (e.g. Nepal)
6) Nutrition Well-being	• ?

A broad range of research approaches has been applied in often multi-disciplinary studies presented in the symposium, such as social learning, the 'filière approach', emphasizing farmers as partners in participatory approaches, and traditional impact assessment. The fundamental issue of the driving forces of invention and innovation remains a mystery to be addressed by basic research.

- What are the sources of creativity in research and similarly in indigenous farm level innovation?
- What makes one an innovator, a pioneer, and what role do individuals versus communities or teams play in innovation ?

We seem to understand the process which relates to recognition of problems, and the related decisions and actions for problem solving, but this does not mean we comprehensively understand the sources of innovation. Agricultural research on innovation might reap some benefits from moving closer to these basic research issues in innovation. Understanding the mystery of innovation, especially related to what makes groups innovative, and what creates and initiates Boserup-effects may pay off. The sharing of (expected) returns to innovation within and across groups, again be they farmers or researches, are critical aspects of the incentives for innovation to be considered. The imitating innovator may actually be more important than the Schumpeterian entrepreneur, as Walter points out (Part One). Policy and research must not be obsessed with innovation as such, but also cherish and support the creative users of new technology. Creativity in use of technology made available can go long ways towards success, as not only James Bond (agent 007) has amply demonstrated.

Innovation generation especially for complex issues, such as the food security - innovation interface may best be addressed through "bunching" of groups of entrepreneurs and innovators as attempted in this symposium. A host of synergistic ideas can be pointed at which are yet to be translated into comprehensive research agendas. Some are growing out of this symposium. The new waves towards participatory interaction between researchers and farmers certainly must not stop there, but lead into formal research and technology utilisation at farm level. The blending of formal and informal systems of innovation as highlighted by Anil Gupta (Part Two) remains a large institutional challenge and a research issue in itself. Competitive environments in research are certainly needed, but must not undermine co-operation in teams and networks and across disciplines. The fundamental role of historical and international cross sectional experiences to be linked with systematic teaching in sustainable university environments cannot be over-emphasized (see Admassie, Part Four).

The food security - innovation interface clearly has an important ethical dimension. The altruistic support of this symposium by Dr. Eiselen testifies to this. Hans Singer (Part One) has pointed at the well-known Brecht statement "Erst kommt das Fressen, dann kommt die Moral". Empowerment of the poor, more power to ethics, participation and democracy are fundamental forces to help turn around the phrase and to overcome the immoral state of affairs expressed in the lack of access to food by the poor.

References

von Braun, Joachim (Ed.) 1995. *Employment for poverty reduction and food security.* Washington, D.C.: International Food Policy Research Institute.

Fogel, Robert W. 1994. Economic growth, population theory, and physiology: The bearing of long-term processes on the making of economic policy. *The American Economic Review* 84 (3): 369-395.

Food and Agriculture Organization of the United Nations (FAO) 1996. *Technical background documents 1-5,* World Food Summit, Rome.

IFPRI (International Food Policy Research Institute) 1995. A 2020 Vision for food, agriculture, and the environment. Washington, D.C. International Food Policy Research Institute.

Krueger, Anne O., Maurice W. Schiff, and Alberto Valdés 1988. Agricultural incentives in developing countries: Measuring the effect of sectoral and economy-wide policies. *The World Bank Economic Review* 2 (September): 255-271.

Romer, Paul 1986. Increasing Returns and Long Run Growth. Journal of Political Economy. Vol. 94, pp. 1002-1037.

The World Bank 1996. *Global Economic Prospects and the Developing Countries,* The World Bank Book, Washington, D.C.

Part Two

The Generation of Innovations

Part 2.1

The Generation of Innovations
Approaches to Innovation Generation

Agricultural Research and Innovation in West and Central Africa: Insights from a Filière Approach

Pierre-Marie Bosc and Ellen Hanak Freud
Centre de Coopération Internationale en Recherche
Agronomique pour le Développement (CIRAD)
42 rue Scheffer, 75116 Paris, France

Abstract

A review of research results and innovation diffusion in the humid forest and moist lowland savanna zones of West and Central Africa challenges the conventional wisdom that this region has been bypassed by science-based productivity growth. The significant "success stories" in smallholder agriculture suggest the need to rethink the current policy reform agenda, aimed at a withdrawal of the state from agricultural services and fertilizer subsidies. The lessons from both large and small-scale commercial agriculture are that research should explicitly integrate economic analysis of the commodity systems – or filières – for products where the economic base is less well organized, to simulate the conditions which would obtain if smallholders were funding and directing their own research operations.

Key words

Innovation, research strategies, filière analysis, West & Central Africa

1 Introduction

Although few would dispute the need for science-based progress in African agriculture, the current wave of thinking on the performance record is less than positive: rising food imports, falling market shares for agricultural exports, low average rates of fertilizer use, and an apparent failure by agricultural growth rates to keep pace with the growth of the population are all seen as evidence that Africa has been bypassed by the Green Revolution (Cleaver & Schreiber; Spencer & Badiane). In part, observers ascribe the blame to the agricultural research system, considered to have generated little pay-off despite large sums spent (Pardey et al.). Inappropriate priority-setting is at the heart of the "research failure" critique: research has not always focused on the right commodities (Lipton) and it has pursued strategies for input-based yield increases which have not taken into account constraints faced by small farmers (Collinson; Carr). In response to such critiques alternative research approaches have been promoted, beginning with "farming systems" research since the late 1970s, and, more recently, "farmer participatory" research. But such approaches have proven more difficult to channel into concrete results than traditional commodity research (McCalla).

In part, the low productivity trap is also attributed to "policy failure" (Krueger et al.; World Bank, 1993, 1994). If, at the macro-economic level, this critique has become synonymous with a call to lower tariff barriers and introduce flexible exchange rate regimes, it has become the herald of a call for "less government" within agriculture. Government intervention has come under scrutiny not only in the area of output marketing, but also for services traditionally considered at least partly public in nature: credit, input supply, seed production, extension, and even research (World Bank, 1993; Umali; Jaffee & Srivastava; IICA).

This paper challenges some of the current thinking, based on an extensive review of the record of research and technology transfer in the humid forest and moist lowland savanna zones of Western and Central Africa (Bosc & Hanak Freud, 1995a and b). This review yields the following insights:

(1) The record itself is less bleak than global studies suggest. Science-based innovations have been introduced on a wide scale, not only in large commercial agricultural operations (oil and coconut palm, rubber, dessert bananas, and pineapple), but also in certain smallholder operations: cotton, and to a more limited extent maize, in a number of the francophone countries, maize and cassava in Nigeria, and pineapples, rubber and oil palm in Côte d'Ivoire. Selective adoption of new technologies (particularly improved planting material) has occurred over a much wider range of crops and countries.

(2) Successful technology transfer has been characterized by a specific set of favorable conditions both upstream (input supply) and downstream (processing and marketing) related to the commodity in question. Often, the "enabling environment" for innovation has contained publicly-supported components, particularly for the upstream activities.

(3) In both large-scale and smallholder agriculture, the most successful research programs, as judged by widespread adoption, have been those maintaining close linkages with the economic base--the producers, processors, and end-users within the commodity systems (often known in English as "sub-sectors" and in French as *filières*). In most successful cases, research priorities were defined, at least implicitly, on the basis of an appreciation of the economic parameters of the commodity system.

These findings suggest that both policymaking organs and research institutions can be well served by taking a commodity systems perspective in making decisions on technology policy. For policymakers, a *filière* perspective can facilitate the identification of bottlenecks in input and output marketing which impede innovation, and which may warrant public attention. For research institutions, this perspective can be a vital tool for priority-setting, able to incorporate elements of the farming systems and farmer participatory research approaches, but to situate them in the context of market conditions (Bernsten & Staatz).

In the following discussion, we outline the main components of a *filière* approach, present the role this has played in successful research strategies, and highlight the conditions both upstream and downstream within the commodity systems which have favored widespread innovation. We conclude with implications for agricultural research and technology policy.

2   Elements of a *Filière* Approach

Commodity systems, or *filières*, refer to the successive chain of activities from production to the final sale of the output on local or export markets. The chain begins with the activities upstream to production itself: supply of chemical inputs, agricultural machinery, planting material, etc. The production stage encompasses both recurrent activities of crop management, and initial investments in land clearing, water and soil management. Downstream are the processing and marketing activities.

An economic analysis of commodity systems has both quantitative dimensions (understanding the structure of costs along the chain and the nature of demand for the product both locally and internationally) and qualitative ones (understanding the organizational strengths and weaknesses of the system and the relationships among various actors along the chain). Such an approach permits one to gauge, in overall terms, how well the system functions in relation to its market objectives.

The approach has been formalized for use by development practitioners in ex ante and ex post project evaluation (Chervel & Le Gall; Freud). Although some applications require a fair degree of methodological sophistication, the basic building blocks form part of the information set of most large-scale agro-industries and well-organized producers' organizations: the structure of costs, the market situation, and the institutional set-up at the various stages along the chain. This is a primary reason why agricultural research systems maintaining close links with agro-industries have been particularly successful in developing useful technology. When the economic actors within the *filière* are not well organized, a greater burden of information gathering and analysis falls on the research system.

3   The Role of a *Filière* Perspective in the Region's Research Strategies

Table 1 schematizes the relationships between the degree of innovation by product and several facets of the institutional environment which appear key: the organization of production, the conditions within the *filière* both upstream and downstream, and the strength of linkages between research and the economic actors of the *filière*.

Table 1: Institutional Conditions for Innovation Diffusion

Product	Types of innovation adopted widely	Organization of production	Research-*filière* linkages	Upstream conditions: input supply & credit	Downstream conditions: market access & reliability
Oil palm	Whole package	Agro-industry & smallholders (outgrowers)	+++	Vertical integration	
Rubber	Whole package	Agro-industry & smallholders (outgrowers)	+++	Vertical integration	
Dessert banana	Whole package	Agro-industry	+++	Vertical integration	
Pineapple	Whole package	Agro-industry & smallholders (special schemes)	+++	Vertical integration	
Cotton	Whole package	Smallholders (special schemes)	+++	Vertical integration	
Robusta coffee	Planting material (limited)	Smallholders (unorganized)	+	Planting material	Guaranteed purchases
Cocoa	Seeds & spraying (limited)	Smallholders (unorganized)	+	Seeds & input subsidies	Guaranteed purchases
Maize	Seeds, fertilizers & animal traction	Smallholders (some project links)	+(+)	Seeds, fertilizer subsidy (nigeria) & credit (cotton schemes)	Strong urban demand (Nigeria) & guaranteed revenue (cotton)
Rice	Seeds (mangrove & upland systems)	Smallholders (unorganized)	+	Seeds	Limited urban demand (cheap import policy)
Cassava	Planting material (massive), fertilizer (ltd)	Smallholders (some project links)	++	Planting material	Strong urban demand, availability of processing
Yam	Planting material	Smallholders (unorganized)	+	Planting material, mini-sett technique	Strong urban demand
Sorghum	None	Smallholders (unorganized)	+	Seeds	No demand for new varieties
Plantain	None	Smallholders (unorganized)	+	None	Strong urban demand

"+": little contact (some links via extension), "++": moderate contact (links via extension & on-farm testing, farming systems research), "+++": close contact with entire filière (production, processing, marketing)

The research programs for many of the commercial crops have maintained the strongest connections with the economic base. For crops grown on large-scale plantations, the growers' and processors' associations were behind the creation of research institutes in the colonial period, and the linkages have remained strong.

Cotton research in the francophone countries, again established by economic interests in the colonial period, has also maintained strong links with the *filière*, although the production base has always been smallholders. Here the linkage has been assured within the context of a vertically integrated system: input supply, credit, processing and marketing are all managed under the auspices of national cotton production companies associated with a private French company, CFDT (Compagnie Française pour le Développement des Fibres Textiles).

In general, agricultural research systems concerned with these products have not explicitly conducted economic analyses of the *filières* in question. However, the close links with the economic base have ensured that these research programs all implicitly used a *filière* perspective in defining research objectives. This has translated into a search for cost-cutting productivity increases on-farm, and to solutions for technical problems at the stages of processing where relevant. The principal research results, widely adopted, bear witness to this approach.

For oil palm, objectives of improved yield capacity, reduced investment and labor costs, disease resistance, and better quality oil have been combined in breeding strategies. Successive improvements in the hybrid population have resulted in much improved yield capacity, with a higher quality oil. Extraction rates have been raised. The new varieties reach maturity earlier, thus cutting down on investment costs, and have a longer economic life, thanks to slower trunk growth.

For rubber, major achievements have been made in yield potential (an increase of 8 to 10-fold since the 1920s). Labor inputs for tapping have been radically diminished through a combination of improved tapping techniques and methods of artificially stimulating latex production, which reduce the number of times any individual tree needs tapping.

For dessert bananas, research has produced a package of recommendations combining high-yielding varieties with water management and cost-minimizing methods of chemical pest control, such as early warning systems for control of the black sigatoka fungus which require only half the number of applications of fungicide as in Latin American plantations. Quality under overseas maritime transport has been improved via refrigeration of immature bunches, which are artificially stimulated to ripeness upon arrival.

Pineapple research has made similar progress in raising yield potential and in achieving quality improvements for the export market (control of timing of maturity, color, size, look, and taste). A number of these issues are particularly important for the fresh fruit market, and research has participated in the finding technical solutions to the transition of smaller producers toward fresh fruit production when the market for canned pineapple disappeared in the late 1970s.

Cotton research has made advances along the entire commodity chain, combining objectives of yield increases, fiber quality improvement, and higher fiber extraction rates, sought to compense for comparatively high labor costs in the region's ginneries. Although chemical control of pests remains an integral part of the "package," improved varieties are also less susceptible to a number of insects and diseases (jassides, bacteriosis). Other productivity-enhancing techniques specifically geared to the smallholder clients include improved cultivation techniques via animal traction (for plowing, sowing, and weeding), and chemical phytosanitary treatments via ultra low volume sprayers, which are light to carry and substantially reduce the water requirements for mixtures. Adoption rates for the various elements of the package are extremely high: improved seed use is wholly adopted; in most countries, over 90% of cotton area receives fertilizer and pesticide treatments, and over 60% of cotton area is cultivated with animal traction. Average yields of seed cotton are over 1 ton/ha, the average for rainfed cotton worldwide.

The research approaches for cotton have not, until quite recently, been "participatory" in nature, but they have been characterized by close linkages with the development programs, and research has made it a point to understand the weak points in the production cost structure under smallholder management. It is not coincidental that cotton research was among the first to employ agricultural economists, and to do systematic cost and profitability calculations. Since the mid-1980s, more formal, multi-disciplinary analyses of the *filière* have assisted both research and the cotton companies to cut costs (Ministère de la Coopération).

In contrast, when research has not had close links with the economic base, and has not geared its research strategies accordingly, intensification has failed to take hold, despite the presence of a support infrastructure upstream and favorable marketing conditions. Two examples are coffee and cocoa. While the improved varieties have generated some producer interest, given their higher yield potential and earlier maturing characteristics, the rest of the "package" consisting of pesticides and fertilizer applications, has been adopted very selectively. For coffee, where labor costs at the harvesting stage present a heavy burden on overall production costs, the problem has barely been addressed.

For food crops, there has not been the same type of integrated, sub-sector-wide linkages between research and the economic base. This absence is understandable, given the much more scattered and unorganized nature of both production and market demand. However, some commodity research programs have benefitted from close links to producers via farming systems research feedback and interaction with extension and development projects. This has helped to guide varietal development along lines which made adoption by smallholders more likely, such as low input requirements and disease resistance. The two clearest examples are maize and cassava research.

Cassava research has explicitly taken into account the likelihood that users would be operating under "sub-optimal" conditions, on poor soils, with little or no chemical input use. Several varieties of the "bitter" cassava most commonly consumed in Nigeria and Central Africa generate roughly 75% higher yields of fresh cassava than unimproved varieties, matures earlier, and exhibit increased tolerance to cassava mosaic disease and cassava bacterial blight. Information collected by the Collaborative Study on Cassava in Africa (COSCA) shows that in Nigeria, by the early 1990s, 90% of villages surveyed had some farmers growing the improved varieties; adoption occurred on a large scale (more than half of farmers) in 60% of the villages (Nweke). Although one of the breeding objectives was to produce a high yield response with limited chemical inputs, farmers closely linked to the market also use fertilizers.

Maize research has released a number of "hardy" open pollinated varieties, which respond well with low doses of fertilizer. Some exhibit tolerance to diseases, including maize streak virus and helminthosporiosis. Introduction into the northern Guinea savanna of Nigeria has been widespread (Smith et al.). Whereas no farmers in the survey were using improved varieties in 1970, by 1989, all farmers reported adoption (mainly the early-maturing open pollinated varieties, which are tolerant to drought conditions). In the savanna areas, the spread of maize has been accompanied by the spread of animal traction and fertilizer use. In the cotton-growing zones of the francophone countries, there is also evidence of the spread of improved varieties, often with fertilizer application (Fusillier).

For the other food crops, adoption of research results by smallholders has been limited to improved varieties, cultivated with extensive techniques. Where research has been successful in locating suitable varieties, destined for either home consumption or local markets, this has typically been linked not only to on-farm productivity enhancement, but also to the ability of those varieties to meet post-harvest, organoleptic, and market demand requirements (for rice, see Adesina and Zinnah; for sorghum, Bosc and Hanak Freud 1995a; for yam, Onweme and Chaléard).

4 Conditions for the Successful Adoption of Innovations by Smallholders

There is little mystery in the successful adoption of research results in the case of plantation agriculture; not only have these systems been able to work closely with research, they have not faced the same degree of capital constraints for machinery, inputs and labor as do smallholders, who typically face conditions (shortages of manpower and capital, aversion to risk, combined in many cases with a lack of land pressure) which make the adoption of complete technical packages less attractive, if not impossible. Yet the experience in cotton, maize and cassava shows that these obstacles are not insurmountable.

Successful smallholder intensification requires attractive and secure market access. This precondition appears even stronger than for growth of output without intensification, since intensification requires greater risk-taking in cash outlays.

The marketing channels need not be official (in the CFDT cotton network they are; in food crop marketing in Nigeria, they are not); but they need to be reliable. For food crops, urban demand may be too limited to constitute a reliable market. This problem was encountered with intensive maize production in Ghana under the Global 2000 scheme. Once prices plummeted with the rise in output, it became impossible for farmers to repay their seasonal credit. Intensive maize production in the cotton schemes in Mali dropped off significantly once guaranteed official purchasing was stopped. Since then, the proceeds from cotton appear crucial for the financing of the inputs for maize.

Secure market access may require access to processing facilities. This is clear for cotton, for which ginneries were constructed in tandem with the expansion of output. Availability in a village of small-scale mechanized facilities for processing *gari* – which has a long shelf-life and is in high demand by urban consumers – has been a key factor in the expansion of intensive cassava production with the improved varieties in Nigeria.

Upstream, the cases of successful intensification have in common: chemical input availability at affordable terms (input credit and/or subsidies in the cotton schemes, in Nigerian maize and cassava), and official drives to distribute improved planting material.

5   Lessons for Research and the Policy Environment

At the policy level, these findings raise strong doubts about the compatibility of the current reform agenda and the objective of creating an enabling environment for intensification in smallholder African agriculture. Concerns for budgetary orthodoxy and "government failure" notwithstanding, there is a need for pragmatism when public action may be warranted to compensate for missing markets.

One obvious area is the supply of improved genetic material. The special conditions of production (hybridization, cloning, slow multiplication processes for some crops) and the risks involved in commercial distribution (fragility of seedlings, uncertain demand) make it extremely unlikely that private operators will step in on the scale warranted.

Another is the chemical input supply system. The evidence from the region, as well as the Asian Green Revolution, suggests grounds to reexamine the current position against fertilizer subsidies, which can lower the risks associated with adoption. It also suggests that the current trend toward dismantling the vertical integration of the cotton *filières* in the context of privatization is misguided. Vertical integration appears to be the only way to ensure well-functioning input credit systems in the context of fragile financial sectors, and it provides a measure of output market reliability.

To enhance the downstream conditions for food crops (including oilseeds), two types of instruments can play a role: at the macro-economic level, policies which give local sources of supply a competitive edge over imports (this has been a key element of the Nigerian policy since the mid 1980s), and, at the local level, programs to support the diffusion of artisanal processing technologies, which can enhance product stability at production locations far from demand centers (the case of gari), and which are often both of lower cost and more in tune with local demand requirements than industrial-scale counterparts.

Concerning research, the lessons revolve around the ways to achieve greater integration with the economic agents of the agricultural sector. There has been a tendency to regard the research successes relating to large-scale agriculture in Africa as exceptions, and as largely irrelevant for smallholders (Collinson; Lipton). We would argue that the experience is relevant, even when the technologies themselves are not as well suited to use by smallholders. The question is rather how to successfully imitate the research-producer interaction that occurs when farmers are well organized and understand their market conditions. In addition to economic analysis, this will require support to emerging producers' organizations.

Applying an economic analysis of the *filière* to priority-setting in research implies putting the accent on commodity-based research. What of the relationship to natural resources management-related research? Here too, systems research can provide useful orientations to commodity research (McCalla). Moreover, it is likely that resource management technologies will need to have a commodity orientation, given the importance of linkages to the market in the adoption process. In this context, it should be remembered that commercial considerations were a primary motivating force for the Californian farmers who spearheaded the integrated pest management movement (Kiss & Meerman).

References

Adesina AA, Zinnah MM. 1991. Adoption and economic impact of improved mangrove swamp rice varieties in West Africa. WARDA annual report. Bouaké, Côte d'Ivoire.

Bernsten RH, Staatz JM. 1993. The role of subsector analysis in setting research priorities. East Lansing, Michigan State University, Dept. of Agric. Econ., staff working paper no. 92-104.

Bosc PM, Hanak Freud E. 1995a. Agricultural innovation in the cotton zone of francophone West and Central Africa: progress achieved and challenges ahead. In B.T. Kang et al (eds.) Moist savannas of Africa: potentials and constraints for crop production. Ibadan, Nigeria: IITA.

Bosc PM, Hanak Freud E. 1995b. Agricultural research and innovation in tropical Africa. Collection Repères, Montpellier, France: CIRAD.

Carr S. 1989. Technology for small-scale farmers in Sub-Saharan Africa: experience with food crop production in five major ecological zones. World Bank technical paper number 109.

Chaléard JL. 1988. Croissance urbaine et dynamisme rural: l'igname des Lobi. In Dynamiques des systèmes agraires, la dimension économique. Paris: ORSTOM.

Chervel M, Le Gall M. 1970. Manuel d'évaluation économique des projets: la méthode des effets. Paris: Ministère de la Coopération, 2nd edition.

Cleaver KM, Schreiber G. 1992. The population, agriculture and environment nexus in Sub-Saharan Africa. Agriculture and rural development series No. 1, Technical Department, Africa Region, World Bank.

Collinson M. 1982. Farming systems research in Eastern Africa: the experience of CIMMYT and some national agricultural research services, 1976-81. East Lansing, Michigan State University: International Development Paper No. 3.

Freud C. 1988. Quelle coopération? Un bilan de l'aide au développement. Paris: Karthala.

Fusillier JL. 1994. La diffusion de la culture du maïs en Afrique de l'Ouest. Montpellier, France: CIRAD, working paper no. 16, unité de recherche économie des filières.

IICA (Inter-American Institute for Cooperation in Agriculture). 1993. Public and private sector roles in the provision of agricultural support services. Proceedings of the international symposium, San José, Costa Rica, May 17-19.

Jaffee S, Srivastava J. 1992. Seed System Development. World Bank discussion paper No. 167.

Kiss A, Meerman F. 1991. Integrated pest management and African agriculture. World Bank technical paper no. 142, Africa Region Technical Department.

Krueger AO, Schiff M, Valdés A. 1991. The political economy of agricultural pricing policy. Baltimore: Johns Hopkins Press for the World Bank.

Lipton M. 1988. The place of agricultural research in the development of Sub-Saharan Africa. World Development, 16:10.

McCalla A. 1991. Eco-regional basis for international research investment. Paper presented at World Bank symposium on Agricultural Technology, Airlie House, Virginia, Oct. 21-23.

Ministère de la Coopération. 1991. Le coton en Afrique de l'Ouest et du Centre. Paris: Documentation française, série études et documents.

Nweke FI. 1994. Cassava distribution in Africa. COSCA working paper no 12. Ibadan, Nigeria: IITA.

Onweme IC. 1990. Une analyse critique de la techique de mini-bouturage de l'igname et de son adoption par les agriculteurs au Nigéria. In Racines, tubercules et legumineuses. German Foundation for International Development, Feldafing, Germany.

Pardey P, Roseboom J, Anderson J (eds.). 1991. Agricultural research policy: international quantitative perspectives. Cambridge University Press.

Spencer D, Badiane O. 1995. Agriculture and economic recovery in African countries. In Peters GH and Hedley DD, Agricultural competitiveness: market forces and policy choice. Aldershot, UK: Dartmouth.

Smith JW, Barau AD, Goldman A, Mareck JH. 1994. The role of technology in agricultural intensification: the evolution of maize production in the northern guinea savanna of Nigeria. Economic Development and Cultural Change, pp. 537-54.

Umali D. 1993. Public and private sector roles in agricultural research: theory and experience. World Bank discussion papers no. 176.

World Bank. 1993. A strategy to develop agriculture in Sub-Saharan Africa and a focus for the World Bank. Agriculture and rural development series No. 2, Technical Department, Africa Region.

World Bank. 1994. Adjustment in Africa. Baltimore: Johns Hopkins Press for the World Bank.

Farmers' Innovations for Sustainable Resource Management and Conservation of Biological Diversity

Anil K. Gupta, with Jitendra Suthar, Muralikrishnan, Riya Sinha, Ch. Srinivas, Kirit Patel, Vijay Chauhan, Dileep Koradia, Alka Rawal, Astad Pastakia, Shailesh Shukla and Vijaya Sherry Chand
Society for Research and Initiatives for Sustainable Technologies and Institutions - Indian Institute of Management, Ahmedabad, India

Abstract

Growth rates in use of chemical inputs, irrigation water (ground as well as surface), electricity etc., have increased at a pace far higher than the growth rate of food production. The reasons are not far to seek and were not difficult to predict. Yet, planners in developing countries as well as developed countries still seem to be convinced about more of the same[1].

But a silent revolution has been going on, unnoticed and uncelebrated. This has never been seen as a source of healing the sick soils, souls and spirits. But can the technological and institutional innovations by small farmers in disadvantaged regions provide spur for such a revolution? We believe that these can, and our faith stems from thousands of innovations that we have already documented in the Honey Bee Network. But will these innovations be able to rescue the spirit of non-sustainably used resources on their own? Perhaps not, and hence our argument for blending the two knowledge systems, the formal and organized one with the informal and unorganized one.

We narrate in part one of the paper the diagnoses of the problem. What can formal science do and can not do in the context of meeting the challenge of sustainable natural resource use. In part two we discuss the context in which farmer's innovations emerge and evolve at the individual as well as the collective

---

[1] It is a different matter that economic restructuring brought upon due to deficit financing in most developing countries does not leave much scope for continued subsidies to input industries. But the political compulsions of serving dominant interest groups have their own implications for transition. Thus in place of direct subsidies, some of the governments have increased the indirect subsidies by decreasing import duties on pesticides and not recovering overdue electricity dues.

level. In part three the problem of knowledge erosion is discussed and the case of Honey Bee network is presented which aims at stemming this erosion. In part four, we present some suggestions for rewarding creativity and some lessons for rethinking about the mainstream technology generation and diffusion systems.

Keywords_____

Biodiversity, indigenous knowledge, patents, intellectual property rights, farmers' rights, plant genetic resources

Part One: Where have we gone wrong?

The crisis of food production and geopolitical considerations created conditions in many developing countries, particularly in India, to strive for food self-reliance. The possibility of using high yielding varieties (more appropriately, highly responsive varieties) brought about what is popularly known as the Green Revolution. Simultaneous changes in the banking institutions, price supports, procurement and distribution of infrastructure and extension machinery along with subsidized inputs made the transition to high growth agriculture possible. It is well known that this growth took place primarily in well irrigated, good soil and level land areas. A large part of arid and semi arid regions and mountain areas were left nearly untouched by the Green Revolution technologies. The non-sustainability of different inputs can be understood by looking at the conditions that became limiting with the passage of time.

In case of fertilizer, several factors have contributed to declining productivity such as: a) imbalance in the use of chemical fertilizers, b) excessive mining of native soil's fertility leading to micro nutrient imbalances, c) changes in the soil physical and chemical properties because of absence of or low quantities of farm yard manure (FYM) applications, and d) the modification of soil microbial diversity due to excessive nitrogen application and also other chemical inputs, etc.

The case of water is even more serious. In the case of ground water, excessive mining of water led to a) increase in the cost of energy for extracting water, b) ingress of the sea salinity in coastal regions, c) toxicity by fluoride and some other elements due to the creation of cavity and oxidation processes, etc. In the case of surface irrigation, there are problems with excessive irrigation, irregular supply, lack of complimentarity between surface and ground water, lack of on-farm development, high seepage from canals leading to water logging and rise of salinity, influx of weeds, etc.

The declining water table also meant increasing cost of energy which further affects the viability of the returns to the investment. Both increase and decrease in the water table in different areas have made the respective farming systems non-sustainable. In some areas water is being mined from as deep as 1000 mts. or more. In a few cases, the water being extracted could be called fossil water which is not going to get recharged, and was stored when the earth was being formed.

The case of pesticides is the most obvious and at the same time the most pathetic. Not only large numbers of pesticides which are banned in the European countries are exported to developing countries, but among the ones which are not banned, the information provided to the farmers is totally inadequate, leading to considerable ecological and human health damage. Excessive use of pesticides has led to a) elimination of useful predators and other beneficial insects including pollinators, b) toxic residues in the soil, water, and other products affecting human and ecosystem health, c) deleterious effects on soil microbial diversity, and d) resistance among pests and diseases leading to tread mill effect, etc.

There are several other areas where we have made costly mistakes. Declining crop biodiversity is an important one. Studies by Hargrove (1981) and others have shown that as many as one third of modern varieties of rice had a common parent for important traits leading to very high risk of diseases or pests spreading on a large scale. The uniformity of crops and varieties has also meant a tremendous increase in weed infestations and consequent applications of chemical herbicides. What are the lessons from all these mistakes and how can one see their social and political implications:

a. Modern agriculture as conceived and operationalized under the Green Revolution strategy is not sustainable. There has to be a change in the strategy, structures and the processes of understanding interrelationships between different parts of the ecosystems.

b. The dominance of large corporations and big scientific establishments generated a false hope that 'Lab to Land ' model will not only sustain the Green Revolution model but also provide spur for continuous innovations.

c. The institutions emerging as a consequence of chemical intensive subsidized agriculture could not generate a worldview which will easily help in restoring eco-compatible resource use systems. The barriers in making a transition to an alternative system should be recognized and faced squarely.

d. The increasing imbalances among regions, commodities, and social classes would endanger the social amity and intensify struggles for greater control over natural and other resources among deprived sections of society. Some times these struggles will dissipate lots of creative energy of a society and generate false identities including the rise of fundamentalism of various kinds.

e. The public sector science and technological systems which delivered the goods for so long may be squeezed of resources and thus market forces may further accentuate the technological imbalances unless small scale, alternative technological innovations can find space for their expression.

Part Two: Survival in Bypassed Regions-Towards Alternative Indigenous Ecological and Technological Knowledge Systems

But with all these constraints, some system or pattern has to be developed to reduce complexity in nature. These patterns constitute the basis of indigenous ecological knowledge systems. Within these patterns, some occur with greater regularity than others. Language and folk culture generate symbolic or other means of memorizing these patterns. It is not surprising that communities which depend upon a particular natural resource often are reported to have many more words to capture the variability in that resource as compared to communities which are independent of this resource. For instance, a coastal community dependent upon marine fishery resources may have far more words to classify waves in the sea than a fishing community dependent upon inland sources. Eskimos similarly have been reported to have large number of words for snow.

The taxonomic basis of soil, clouds, waves, winds, plants etc., thus constitutes the bedrock on which indigenous creativity and innovation is built. An artisan who would like to economize on the use of wood in replacing a worn out shoe of a plough, has to find a suitable material to replace or repair the shoe. In a workshop of innovative artisans in south India, a blacksmith reported the outcome of a material science research that he pursued for some years. He found that the iron of scrap leaf springs or suspension of automobiles was most suitable for making shoe caps for the shear of the wooden plough. The precious wood used for this purpose was thus saved through a creative blending of traditional technology with a modern material.

It is this process of blending that we intend to discuss next to illustrate how coping strategies imply combinations of materials, methods, and products to generate or improve options for survival in high risk environments.

Combinational Heuristics

The search for innovative solution can be through several routes. Various combinations of old and new methods, materials, and products generate a whole range of choices for which sustainability can be determined on the basis of renewability of the resources involved.

a) Old methods, old materials and old products signify the traditional wisdom which may have relevance even in contemporary contexts. For instance, Virda is an age old technology for conserving rain water in a saline arid region with saline ground water. In an otherwise flat land region, the rain water temporarily gets stored in some minor depressions or tanks. Within these tanks, the pastoralists dig shallow wells lined with frames of wood of *Prosopis juliflora* having grass layers between different square wooden frames as well as between the earth column and the frames. Just ten inches of rainfall provide sufficient storage of fresh water in these wells above the saline ground water. These Virdas are covered with silt and sealed. Depending upon the need one Virda is opened at a time and the water remains sweet for two to three months after which it turns saline through upward movement of saline water.

This technology has enabled the pastoralists in Banni pastures to survive for several centuries. Ten inches of rainfall in this area may fall within a few days and hence the need for a robust, efficient and adaptive strategy. In such a case, modern science does not merely help explain the functional viability of the technology but also provides the basis for abstraction and generalization.

b) Old methods, old materials and new products

The wool on the mane of the camels is known to be very hardy and resistant to corrosion. Traditionally the pastoralists make different kinds of ropes, carpets, bags etc., out of wool from different parts of the camel's body. Once somebody figured out the use of these carpets as oil filters in oil refineries, a new product got developed out of an old method and material. Similarly, sisal rope has been used in various activities both for commercial and domestic purposes. It was found these ropes could withstand corrosion from the sea better than any other material. Thus a new use for an old material made by an old method generated a new opportunity for value added and income generation in some of the most economically depressed regions. Sisal grows in poor soils in semi-arid regions.

c) New method, old material and old product

Processing of sisal is very painful because of various tannins released in the water tank in which sisal plants are immersed for some time. While taking the fibre out, the tannins cause blisters on the hand. Simple technologies have been developed to take the fibre out without having to go through this painful process. An old material can be used applying a new method for old products or uses. Modern science can blend with the method leaving other choices intact.

In many of the cumin growing regions, farmers had observed that the plots on the roadside had better productivity than the interior ones. They figured out that the dust which settled on the plants saved them from certain pests and fungal diseases. Some other farmers observed a similar pattern near the brick kilns. Dusting with ash or fine soil became a new method for controlling pest and fungal diseases in this crop. In many other crops, the use of ash has been well known as a dusting material for a long time.

Similarly, in the case of termite control in the light soil areas, farmers had known that moisture keeps the termites under check. However, they had also known another seemingly unrelated phenomena that sorghum plants when young were not eaten by the cattle because of some toxic compounds (Hydrocyanides). One farmer in a dry region thought of cutting, chopping and putting the sorghum plants in the irrigation channel. The assumption was that the toxic compound in the plant would mix with the water and help in overcoming the termite problem in this field. This is what actually happened. In this case a whole new field of research has been identified. So far the sorghum breeders were looking for land races with low hydro-cyanide content. This innovation opens the opportunity for selecting high HCN content sorghum lines. If this technology works in different parts of the world, dry farmers could grow a small patch of high HCN varieties to be used for pest control purposes.

d) Old methods, new materials and new products or use

Some innovative farmers have used a drip of castor oil channeled through a tinbox with a wick hanging over an irrigation canal. The castor oil drops into the water and spreads into the soil. In a crop of banana, this oil adds to the lusture of banana by making its skin shiny. Apparently, consumers like such bananas more and pay a better price. This drip is also used in other crops for soil based pest control.

Similarly examples can be found for other cells. What these examples show is that farmers can be extremely creative in solving local problems. But the issue is whether these knowledge systems will survive the onslaught of free markets and big science?

Part Three: The Threats to Localized Knowledge: The Case of the Honey Bee Network

Erosion of knowledge is as much, if not, much more serious a problem than the erosion of natural resources. We can probably reverse the declining productivity of natural resources like soil through watershed projects or other resource conservation strategies. However, erosion of knowledge can not be easily reversed once lost. The regeneration of resources and knowledge associated with these resources have to be seen in a single as well as multiple generation framework (Gupta 1990, 1992, 1996; Gupta et al. 1994).

Consider first the single generation situation. The ideal sustainable situation occurs when both resources and knowledge have been conserved, but what happens when one or the other is eroded.

When the resources are conserved and the knowledge becomes eroded (as in the case of state-controlled conservation of resources through parks or sanctuaries keeping people out of the resource), the sustainability of the system becomes endangered. If knowledge is eroded, the erosion of resources can't be far behind.

When the knowledge is conserved but the resources are eroded, the sustainability of the system is more likely if local knowledge is incorporated in strategies of regeneration. The knowledge will also be eroded, however, if it is not used.

The least sustainable single generation situation occurs when both the resources and knowledge become eroded. This is so because the knowledge may only be available in old book shops or waste paper markets, or street stores. The folk knowledge once eroded may be almost impossible to reconstruct or rejuvenate. Erosion of knowledge was never so rapid as in our generation because of declining inter-generational communication.

As bleak as the single generational picture is, consider now, the multi-generational situation. Again, the ideal situation occurs when both knowledge and resources have been conserved.

The situation where knowledge has eroded and resources have been conserved is not a likely scenario. This is so because a resource cannot be sustained over generations without drawing upon local knowledge at all. Under conditions of no human intervention or access, certain resources like forests may be conserved over generations without incorporating local knowledge. But with the increasing influence of human-made factors on the survivability of forests through acid rain, global warming, and erosion of upper catchments etc., as well as increasing population pressures, we doubt such a situation could occur.

The case of erosion of resources and the conservation of knowledge over several generations leads to a possibility of sustainability if knowledge has been documented through efforts like the Honey Bee Network and is available to people. In this case, regeneration of resources is possible within a long time frame.

The worst case of all occurs when both knowledge and resources have become eroded over several generations. Only rare repositories of knowledge may exist among some bypassed communities. Whether the analysis is performed in a single or multiple generational setting, the key issue is the same. That is, the conservation of knowledge is as important as the conservation of resources, if not more so. Thus, any system of conservation should be directed not only at rewarding communities for the conservation of resources, but also at rewarding them for the valuable knowledge they hold, create and recreate.

In the context of the biologically rich, low-mean/high-variability income areas discussed earlier, emphasis has been placed on providing short-term relief, employment, and other means of subsistence in high-risk environments in order to alleviate poverty. The economic stress on the community erodes their self-respect and dignity. The will of the people to struggle and innovate gets subdued. Both the resource and the knowledge around this resource get eroded.

The Case of Honey Bee

In order to stem knowledge and resource erosion, the Honey Bee Network, a global voluntary initiative, was launched six years ago. Its purpose is to network the people and the activists engaged in eco-restoration and reconstruction of knowledge about precious ecological, technological, and institutional systems used by people.

This network aims at identifying the innovators (individuals or groups) who have tried to break out of existing technological and institutional constraints through their own imagination and effort. What is remarkable about these innovations is the fact that most require very low external inputs, are extremely eco-friendly and improve productivity at very low cost.

It is necessary to note here that organizations of creative people, which take the form of networks or informal cooperatives or just loose associations, would generate a very different kind of pressure on society for sustainable development. The spirit of excellence, critical peer group appraisal, competitiveness and entrepreneurship so vital for self-reliant development, is likely to emerge from networks of local "experts", innovators and experimenters. It is true that every farmer or artisan does experiment. But not every one is equally creative and not in the same resource-related fields. The transition of the developmental paradigm from "people as victim's perspective" to that of "the people as potential victor's" is the answer. The former may generate patronizing and externally driven initiatives whereas the latter may spur endogenous initiatives by people themselves.

The Honey Bee Network newsletter is brought out in six languages in India (English, Hindi, Gujarati, Kannada, Tamil, and Telugu) and Zonkha in Bhutan so that dialogue with the people takes place in their own language. The creative people of one place should be able to communicate with similar people elsewhere to trigger mutual imagination and fertilize respective recipes for sustainable natural resource management. The Honey Bee Network is head-quartered at SRISTI (Society for Research and Initiatives for Sustainable Technologies and Institutions c/o Prof Anil K Gupta, Indian Institute of Management, Ahmedabad), an autonomous NGO.

It is realized that the technological innovations cannot survive without institutional innovations and support structures. Hence, we have been documenting the ecological institutions which have evolved from the people to manage knowledge and resources as common property.

Honey Bee insists that two principles are followed without fail: 1) whatever we learn from people must be shared with them in their language, and 2) every innovation must be sourced to individuals/communities with name and address to protect the intellectual property rights of the people.

It is possible to take the current global debate on biodiversity and peasant knowledge beyond rhetoric. Our network extends into 75 countries at present. Some of our colleagues have started similar documentation in their respective regions. Offers have been received from Nepal, Sri Lanka, Uganda, Paraguay and Mali for local language versions.

Honey Bee also appeals to fellow researchers, activists and planners in other developing countries to identify native wisdom both to inspire and to provoke the young minds to explore. In every country a very strong oral tradition of knowledge generation, validation, scrutiny and diffusion exists. Honeybee strongly believes that boundaries between formal and informal knowledge systems may often be false. The informal system may have formal rules waiting to be discovered. The formal system may have informal beliefs, accidents, or conjectures providing impetus for further enquiry.

Honey Bee has already collected more than five thousand innovative practices, predominantly from dry regions, to prove that disadvantaged people may lack financial and economic resources, but are very rich in knowledge. That is the reason we consider the term "resource poor farmer" as one of the most inappropriate and demeaning contributions from the West. If knowledge is a resource and if many poor people are rich in this knowledge, why should they be called resource poor? At the same time, we realize that the market may not be pricing peoples' knowledge properly today. It should be remembered that out of 114 plant derived drugs, more than 70 per cent are used for the same purpose for which the native people discovered their use (Farnsworth 1988). This proves that basic research linking cause and effect had been done successfully by the people in the majority of the cases. Modern science and technology could supplement the efforts of the people, improve the efficiency of the extraction of the active ingredient or synthesize analog of the same, there-by improving effectiveness (Gupta 1991).

The scope for linking scientific research by the scientists and the farmers is enormous. We are beginning to realize that peoples' knowledge systems need not always be considered informal just because the rules of the formal system fail to explain innovations in another system. The soil classification system developed by the people is far more complex and comprehensive than the USDA soil classification system. Likewise, the hazards of pesticide residues and associated adverse effects on the human as well as entire ecological system are well known. In the second issue of Honey Bee out of ninety four practices, thirty four dealt with indigenous low external input ways of plant protection. Some of these practices could extend the frontiers of science. For instance, some farmers cut thirty to forty day old sorghum plants or Calotropis plants and put these in the irrigation channel so as to control or minimize termite attack in light dry soils. Perhaps hydrocyanide present in sorghum and similar other toxic elements in Calotropis contributed towards this effect.

Honey Bee in that sense is an effort to promote markets of ideas and innovations but in favor of sustainable development in high risk environments. The key objectives of SRISTI are to strengthen the capacity of grassroots level innovators and inventors engaged in conserving biodiversity to a) protect their intellectual property rights, b) experiment to add value to their knowledge, c) evolve entrepreneurial ability to generate returns from this knowledge, and d) enrich their cultural and institutional basis of dealing with nature.

Of course, no long term change in the field of sustainable natural resource management can be achieved if the local children do not develop values and a worldview which is in line with a sustainable life style. Thus, education programs and activities are essential for perpetuating reform. That is the reason why we have organised biodiversity contests among school children to identify little eco-geniuses.

Part Four: Rewarding Creativity of the Farmers, Tribals and Pastoralists

The issue thus is: how do we go about compensating or rewarding indigenous or local communities for their valuable knowledge and conservation contributions. For the first time, communities and individuals who conserved biodiversity despite remaining poor have a chance of overcoming their poverty by being compensated/rewarded for their traditional as well as contemporary creativity. Even more promising is the possibility that this can happen without any need for patronizing protection from the state (which kept them poor and illiterate for so long). That is not the only promise. We could even hope that the polity of this country for once could get out of the hands of self-seeking, rent-extracting, class of non-competitive, non-creative and non-inventive industrial, trading, professional and farming elites. The game is very clear. Those who have faith in the inventive capabilities of the economically poor but intellectually rich communities and individuals would like to exploit the opportunity offered by GATT and the Rio agreement. Nonetheless, there are those who still live under the illusion that a patronizing and protective regime is what poor are looking forward to.

Those who are opposing the protection of intellectual property rights are doing so perhaps because they have no confidence left whatsoever in native genius. Their argument seems to be very simple, "since we have won in the past in any global struggle, what is the guarantee that we will in the future when odds are against us". A mentality of failure, cynicism and defeatism is unlikely to generate any hope even under the best of circumstances and all odds favoring us.

Congressional Research Service of US Congress went into the question of people's knowledge and its protection recently (Axt, Corn, Lee and Ackerman

1993, henceforth, The Report[2]). The report noted an increasing awareness that plant and animal species in the tropical rain forests and elsewhere were disappearing at an accelerating rate due to human activities destroying or affecting their habitat. The Report further noted the resurgence of interest among pharmaceutical companies and government research agencies in screening plant and animal species for medicinal properties useful in treating various diseases (biodiversity screening). The Report stressed that the destruction of habitat had "proven fatal not only to the numerous plant and animal species but also to many indigenous peoples dependent upon that habitat, and continues to threaten many that still exist."

The search for local germplasm or new plant sources for deriving herbal pesticides, veterinary drugs, or other products is done globally by multinational corporations as well as national and inter-organizational associations. Among the issues that must be addressed in bio-prospecting are:

a) Whether those who want to access this kind of biodiversity have the capability of doing so on their own (INBio felt otherwise and thus entered into a deal with Merck)?

b) Whether the external organization can access the same material or knowledge about it from other sources? In many cases the knowledge may be available from other sources though not the entire material. In such a case, the bargaining position of the provider is weakened compared to the one holding a monopoly.

c) Even in the case of monopoly, can the external organization access the material through alternative legal or illegal routes? Any material obtained without due process of law, transparency, and prior informed consent of the communities and the national institutions designated for the purpose, should not be granted patents. Where a local community supplies local knowledge or natural resources from their region, they should be entitled to a share in the value added. The reason for this is that the people dependent on this resource could suffer losses in several ways, for example, their access to plants, sites, or habitats could be reduced when outsiders find new uses for the same. It seems ironic that because the people shared their knowledge, they could lose access to the habitats which helped them generate the knowledge in the first place. They could also suffer losses because the plants which they conserved have been selectively harvested (through so called "scientific forestry"), thus, disturbing the ecological balance and endangering their life support system.

---

[2] Axt, Josephine R., M. Lynne Corn, Margaret Lee and David M Ackerman, 1993, Biotechnology, Indigenous Peoples, and Intellectual Property Rights, CRS Report For Congress, Washington: Congressional Research Service, Library Of Congress

d) Even if the scientific knowledge exists in some developing countries, it may not be possible for that nation to commercialize the products based on biodiversity prospecting. The skill and capital trade-offs have to be made recognizing the respective strengths of the different partners.

e) Should patents be granted on plant products traditionally used by third-world people if specific improvements have been brought about? The Rio treaty suggests that free access to germplasm should continue despite whatever mechanisms are created for compensating communities responsible for the protection of such plasm[3]. In fact, some have argued that the national sovereignty granted under the Rio treaty does not grant property rights to nations over the germplasm that they have. It is difficult, however, to see how this resource can be considered different from a coal or a petrol reserve in so far as sovereignty is considered. Unlawfully acquired germplasm for developing varieties or drugs would not confer property rights superior to those of the original providers[4]. This implies the need for regulations in developed countries requiring full disclosure by any corporation seeking patent protection on a plant based drug or any other natural product. The disclosure should verify that the source material has been rightfully and lawfully acquired. "Rightful" acquisition would involve moral as well as ethical issues in access to biodiversity. For instance, even if a local community has not asked for any compensation for sharing the material or the knowledge about it, is the corporation bound by an ethical conduct to set up trust funds and other forms of reciprocity for local communities? Is it incumbent to ensure that the superior ethics of local communities, remaining poor despite conserving biological diversity and the knowledge around it, does not become a reason for perpetuating their poverty, and thus endangering the survival of diversity itself? "Lawful" acquisition implies that prior informed consent and approval and involvement of local communities and creative individuals have been ensured, provided that the donor country has laws requiring such a consent and approval. If a country does not have such laws, as for instance, India, then acquiring any material will be lawful or legal but may not be rightful.

The Rio treaty thus provides for compensation in the form of providing countries (i.e. which provide genetic resources) an access to and transfer of technology which makes use of those resources, including technology protected by patents and other intellectual property rights at mutually agreed terms[5]. This

---

[3] Rio, Art 15.2
[4] Rio, Art 15.3
[5] Rio, Art.16.3. This is one of the most controversial clauses of the treaty. It created considerable anxiety among the corporate leaders in the west, who, of course, did not want to share their technological advantage with the third world. The latter claimed that much of the

should happen through involvement and approval of these communities, ensuring an equitable sharing of the benefits. Article 15.5 requires Prior Informed Consent (PIC) to be obtained from the contracting parties for obtaining access to genetic material or associated knowledge in countries which have enacted legislation requiring PIC.

The practices documented by Honey Bee and the SRISTI Network should be considered eligible for registration in the joint name[6] of SRISTI and the concerned farmers or communities when we can convince ourselves about the genuineness of the innovation. The registration system should not discriminate on the basis of obviousness to a small group of farmers in a village or a taluka. The point to be noted is that the practice could not have been discovered or invented by a lay person with average knowledge in the field.

Lessons for Rewarding Creativity

To summarize, we present a scheme in which four kinds of incentives for rewarding creativity and conservation of biodiversity can be generated.

1.1 Material-specific: In cases in which specific individuals have contributed to conservation of land races or wild plants with specific economic and inventive uses, their rights to receive a licensing fee or royalty must be recognized.

1.2 In the case of material-non specific i.e. community or a larger group, the compensation would flow to a group through trust funds, risk fund or insurance funds to encourage inventive communities to do more experimentation and perhaps progress on the path of entrepreneurship. Insurance funds should also ensure that communities or farmers growing land races obtain a price advantage compared to the high yielding varieties.

There are several ways in which revenue can be generated for providing various incentives to individuals or collectives:

i) a cess or tax on the sale of seeds or crop varieties using the given germplasm conserved or contributed by the specific individual or community;

ii) share in the returns from commercializable plant-derived product such as herbal pesticides, veterinary medicines, vegetative dyes, anti-oxidant compounds, nutritional supplements etc.;

iii) a tax on the market arrivals in grain markets in Green Revolution regions or high yielding varieties of different crops (including various other cash crops), to

---

biotechnological advances depended upon raw material, i.e., biodiversity which southern countries provided.

[6] The joint name is suggested only because when legal disputes arise, SRISTI may be able to fight for the rights of the third world farmers more competently. The economic returns from any tripartite agreement should primarily accrue to the inventing community and/or individuals.

be used for conserving diversity and providing incentives to communities and individuals conserving diversity;

iv) a license fee to be collected from public as well as private sector companies for using germplasm still conserved by communities in backward regions even if available in national or international gene banks;

v) the license fee could be supplemented by larger investments in infrastructural development in these regions particularly in education and other basic needs.

There are several other ways by which the revenue can be generated. The important point to be understood is that people will not conserve biodiversity while remaining poor indefinitely.

One can innovate in many ways to identify the precise areas and communities that are conserving rare germplasm. The primary school children and teachers can be involved in country wide documentation of the bio-diverse regions, races, wild plants of economic importance etc., in the form of a campaign led by committed NGOs and professionals, apart from community leaders. State departments of agriculture and revenue staff can also be involved in urgent inventorisation of knowledge, materials and claimant communities and individuals.

Farmers growing local varieties under particular threat will need to be compensated for not shifting to high yielding varieties in selected areas. Mechanisms can be worked out for in situ conservation through the involvement of state agricultural universities and other conservation bodies.

1.3 The non material-specific rewards deal with honor and recognition of individuals and specific groups of people who have contributed most in conserving biodiversity.

1.4 The non material and non specific instruments deal with changes in policies, educational curriculum at different levels, institutional norms for providing credit and other support systems. Banks would not consider financing a herd of local well bred Gir cows, or bio-diverse farms at the same scale at which they would finance input intensive farms. Students are not taught anything inspiring about the contribution of communities which conserve biodiversity. On the other hand they are shown as backward.

2. A scheme needs to be developed for supporting all those *panchayats* which will undertake systematic cultivation of local land races in every season in large enough areas for enabling some seed exchange. Villages which have conserved local varieties like Jackrana variety of pearl millet or Khirchia variety of salt tolerant wheat need to be provided some funds for local development, linked to the contribution these land races are making in plant breeding on an ongoing basis. This will give a signal to other communities as well. Funds under this scheme may be allocated by an autonomous body rather than bureaucracy.

3. The patent act must provide for recognition of indigenous innovations. A data base like that of SRISTI can provide a valuable beginning point. There is a scope for "defensive patents" where certain innovations valid for larger social use can be patented, not to prevent their diffusion but to prevent their being patented by some third party.

Creativity at the grassroots can indeed spur a new paradigm for development which builds upon what people know, excel in and have pride in.

References

Farnsworth, N. R. 1985. Medicinal Plants in Therapy. Bulletin of World Health Organisation, 63 (6).pp 965-981

Gupta, Anil K. 1991. Sustainability Through Biodiversity: Designing Crucible of Culture, Creativity and Conscience. Presented at International Conference on Biodiversity. King Paper No.1005

Gupta, Anil K., Kirit K. Patel, Astad R. Pastakia, Vijaya Sherry Chand 1995. Building Upon Local Creativity and Entrepreneurship in Vulnerable Environments. In: Vangile Titi and Naresh Singh (Eds.). Empowerment For Sustainable Development: Towards Operational Strategies. Canada: Fernwood Publishing Co.

--------- 1991. Biodiversity, Poverty and Intellectual Property Rights of Third World Peasants: A case for renegotiating global understanding, in: M.S Swaminathan and S. Jana (Eds.) Biodiversity: Implications for Global Food Security. Madras: M. S. Swaminathan Research Foundation

--------- 1995. Compensating Local Communuties For Conserving Biodiversity: How much, who will, how and when. In: L. Guruswamy and Jeff McNeely (Eds). Seeds They Preserve, Arizona: University of Tulsa (forthcoming)

--------- 1996. Knowledge Centre: Building Upon What People Know, presented at the IFAD International Conference on Hunger and Poverty, Brussels.

Hargrove, T.R., W.R. Coffman and L. C. Victoria 1980. Ancestry of Improved Cultivars of Asian Rice. Crop Science Vol.20. pp.721-727

Limited Natural Resources and a Growing Population: Challenges for the Role of Agricultural Research

Hans Mohr
Center for Technology Assessment in
Baden-Württemberg, Stuttgart, Germany

Abstract

Requirements of the growing global population for foodstuffs, wood, and other plant raw materials, including combustible biomass, must be satisfied essentially by an increase in yield. However, the imperative increase in agricultural productivity [useful biomass • ha^{-1} • $year^{-1}$] must be accompanied by an increase in farmer's income [financial net yield]. This can only be achieved if the need for expensive production factors such as energy, pesticides and fertilizers is alleviated by practice-orientated research. Breeding, including gene technology, is particularly important, as an improvement in genetic properties is energetically cheap if compared with improvements in soil fertility. Moreover, theoretical and empirical research to increase yields by the optimization of multiple production factors is encouraged.

Keywords

Population, natural resources, yields, production factors, energy conversion, sustainable agriculture.

Introduction

Currently some 14 million km^2 of the earth's surface (approximately 10%) is used for agriculture (data from Mohr and Schopfer 1995). This proportion can no longer be substantially increased without taking massive ecological risks and without enormous investment of capital, technical innovation and energy. The large areas taken up by tundras, deserts, savannahs, bushlands and tropical rainforests are hardly suitable for productive agriculture. Furthermore, everywhere in the world considerable areas of potential agriculture are sacrificed for human settlements and to develop infrastructure (e.g. roads and tracks for railways). Even larger areas are irreversibly lost for agriculture and forestry because of incorrect treatment, such as deforestation, overgrazing, salinization, contamination or erosion. As the human population is still increasing exponentially (1830: $1 • 10^9$; 1930: $2 • 10^9$; 1960: $3 • 10^9$; 1990: $5.4 • 10^9$; 2000: $6.5 • 10^9$; 2020: an estimated $8.5 • 10^9$) the agriculturally usable area per capita is continuously reduced (1980: 0.30 ha • head^{-1}; 2000: 0.22 ha • head^{-1}). Requirements of the continuously growing population for foodstuffs, wood, and other plant raw materials including combustible biomass must therefore be satisfied essentially by an increase in yield. However, there are natural limits to the *increase in yield*. For this reason there is no *technical* solution to the difficulties arising from an ever-increasing global population.

It is well known that agricultural productivity is as a rule far below the productivity (net primary production) of the natural vegetation at the same site (=1), in particular in the Third World (relative agricultural productivity RAP<<1). RAP=1 is only reached in a few European countries, including Germany, at the cost of excessive fertilization (Esser 1991).

An increase in RAP from the presently 0.1 - 0.2 in the Third World to 0.3 - 0.5 is urgently needed since it is the only means to cope with the demands of a growing population. However, this increase of RAP can only be achieved with an additional input of inorganic fertilizer, in particular nitrogen, which requires fossil energy (see table 3). Moreover, the question of an appropriate financial reward (profitability, see table 1) comes heavily into play: Agriculture, even under subsistence conditions, is an economic enterprise, not a matter of charity.

Yield

Biological yield (table 1) means the total dry mass of plants, including roots (biomass), produced per unit area and per growth period. *Economic yield* is related only to those plant organs or components for which the *crop* is grown, e.g. grain, tubers or drugs. Generally, a high biological yield is the basis for a large economic yield.

Table 1: Different Forms of Yield (after Mohr and Schopfer 1995)

Biological yield	Biomass• ha^{-1} • year^{-1}
Economic yield	Crop• ha^{-1} • year^{-1}
Financial yield	Money• ha^{-1} • year^{-1}
Financial net yield	Money• ha^{-1} • year^{-1}
= yield minus costs (profitability)	or
	Money • person^{-1} • year^{-1}

The economic, and financial, yield depends, of course, on the particular requirements of people. An example: Recently, the interest in combustible biomass as a substitute for oil has suddenly risen. It is possible that in the foreseeable future particularly efficient C_4 plants may provide biomass for energy production as cheaply as oil, natural gas or coal, as these products become more expensive, mainly due to increasing negative external effects, such as pollution and global warming, and eventually objective shortage.

However, for rational production and transportation aiming at a high conversion factor (see table 2) biomass would have to be produced on large areas which would be lost for conventional crops, e.g. for foodstuffs.

Yield and Energy

Modern highly productive agriculture requires much fossil fuel and other non-solar energy in order to convert solar energy into yield (table 2). The energy conversion factor (r) differs according to the conditions and the crop produced.

Table 2: Schematic to Define the Energy Conversion Factor r

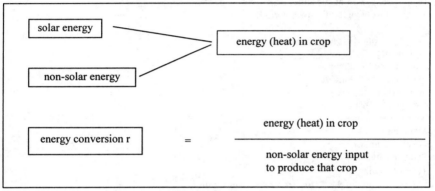

Some recent examples of energy conversion factors:

rape oil methyl ester (superior diesel fuel)	$r = 2$
maize kernels	$r = 5$
wheat grain	$r = 6$
Triticale, total plant mass above ground	$r > 15$
$(160 \text{ dt dry mass} \cdot ha^{-1} \cdot year^{-1})$	

These values were obtained with high-yielding varieties (strains, cultivars) of oil rape (Brassica napus L., ssp. oleifera DC.), maize (Zea mays L.), wheat (Tritium aestivum L.) and Triticale (=Triticosecale W.), a high-yielding hybrid of wheat and rye (Secale cereale L.) (Flaig and Mohr 1993).

Non-solar energy consumption includes diesel fuel, energy invested in building machines and instruments, electricity, production of fertilizers and herbicides, the human workforce, animals, etc. With regard to nutrition the energy conversion factor is always <1; for example, it is 0.2 for white bread. Rule of thumb: In order to produce 1 kg white bread the non-solar energy equivalent of 1 l fuel oil is presently required.

The increase of yield per unit area (see table 3) reduces the energy conversion factor, particularly on marginal soils and when irrigation is required. The change of utilization in favor of agriculture (woodland, wasteland, prairie, etc. → agricultural land) is therefore dependent on cheap fossil energy.

Table 3: Factors Limiting Yield. Non-Fixed Factors are given in the Order of Energy Costs Required under Field Conditions for more Favorable Production. (Results of a Seminar on the Topic "Agriculture and Energy")

Fixed factors:

CO_2 concentration (350 $\mu l \cdot l^{-1}$)
Light (total period of sunshine)
Temperature (length of growth period)
Type of soil
Factor variation expensive:
Soil moisture (irrigation)
Soil fertility (fertilization)
Plant diseases (pesticides)
Weeds (hoeing, herbicides)
Storage after harvest
Nutritional value
Marketing
Factor variation cheap:
Plant density
Time of sowing
External quality of yield (free of diseases, uniformity)
Genotype

Human Appropriation of Renewable Fresh Water

Humanity now uses 26 % of total terrestrial evapotranspiration and 54 % of runoff that is geographically and temporally accessible. Increased use of evapotranspiration will confer only minimal benefits globally because most land suitable for rain-fed agriculture is already in production. New dam construction could increase accessible runoff by about 10 % over the next 30 years, whereas population is projected to increase by more than 45 % during that period (Postel, Daily and Ehrlich 1996).

Aims of Crop Physiology

This field of agricultural research is concerned with the increased production of biomass (yield), whilst maintaining stable anthropogenic ecosystems (fields, grasslands, gardens, plantations, etc.). A precondition is an understanding of the processes on which production of usable biomass is based. Crop physiology aims particularly at reducing the high energy requirements of agricultural production.

Breeding is very important, as an improvement in genetic material is energetically cheap with modern technology if compared with improvements in soil fertility (see table 3).

In case of combustible biomass, where a high energy yield is a prerequisite, rigorous breeding goals had to be defined:

Beside high biological yields (> 15 t dry mass • ha^{-1} • $year^{-1}$) an increase in C/N and C/S ratios as well as an increase in water-use efficiency

$$\left[\frac{g \text{ dry matter formed}}{kg \text{ water lost}} \right]$$

turned out to be crucial. Moreover, strong improvements of the ability of the plant to absorb minerals, in particular macroelements such as N, P, K and Ca, are needed. The inherent conflict of goals requires the utmost skill of the breeder.

Clearly, these are challenges which can only be met, if traditional breeding is supported by methods derived from gene technology. Experts agree that the production of combustible biomass which can compete on a free market with traditional fossil fuels depends on gene technology for rapid breeding (von Schell and Mohr 1995).

Productivity

Agriculture must survive essentially as an integral part of a free economy. A measure of the economic success of a branch is its productivity which for agriculture can be expressed - besides profitability (see table 1) and RAP - in terms of additional people fed by one farmer. In Germany, the increase of productivity in agriculture compares favorably with the corresponding numbers in industry and trade. Whilst in about 1850 most of the population of Germany was employed in agriculture of minimal profitability (see table 1), in 1950 only 23 % of all those gainfully employed worked in agriculture. Today, this number has fallen to less than 4 %. However, one German farmer today feeds almost 90 people, compared with 10 in 1950; this is by use of means of production which require much financial investment and are energetically expensive. Nevertheless, foodstuffs are now comparatively cheap: A citizen of the Federal Republic of Germany today consumes approximately 15 % of income for the biggest food basket ever offered, compared with 35 % in the middle of the 1950s. In early phases of human history, and even in the nineteenth century, many people (often most) were not able to cover their food requirements adequately for financial reasons.

Prospects

Research efforts in yield physiology can contribute to agriculture, in particular crop production, mainly in the following areas (Mohr and Schopfer 1995):
- definition of breeding goals,
- development of **theoretical** modeling systems for multiple factor analysis in yield physiology,
- **empirical** research to increase yields by the optimization of multiple production factors,
- new efforts in plant breeding, including gene technology,
- improvement of herbicides via a thorough understanding of their mode of action,
- physiology of storage organ formation. This aspect is closely related to the physiology of metabolite transport and allocation.

In doing any particular research we must keep in mind that everywhere in the world the superior goal is to contribute to **sustainable** agriculture. This implies not only to maintain the soils and the ecological cycles of materials and energy, but also to preserve the landscape. Moreover, the imperative increase in agricultural productivity must be accompanied by a fair financial reward. Otherwise sustainable agriculture cannot be implemented. Even though further structural adaptations are mandatory, we are convinced that the requirements for sustainable agriculture can be met in our region and elsewhere, provided the traditional agricultural practise is combined with the progress made in agricultural research and development.

References

Esser, G. 1991. Eingriffe der Landwirtschaft in den Kohlenstoffkreislauf. In: Enquête-Kommission "Schutz der Erdatmosphäre" des Deutschen Bundestags (Ed.), Studienprogramm Landwirtschaft, Band 1; Teilband 1, pp. 1-136 (Studie A). Economica Verlag, Bonn

Flaig, H., Mohr, H. 1993. Energie aus Biomasse - eine Chance für die Landwirtschaft. Springer, Heidelberg

Mohr, H., Schopfer, P. 1995. Plant Physiology/Physiology of Crop Production. Springer, Heidelberg

Postel, S.L., Daily, G.C., Ehrlich, P.R. 1996. Human appropriation of renewable fresh water. Science 271. pp.785-788

von Schell, Th., Mohr, H. 1995. Biotechnologie/Gentechnik - eine Chance für neue Industrien. Springer, Heidelberg

Part 2.2

The Generation of Innovations
Innovations in Plant and Animal Production

Possibilities and Constraints in Implementing *Striga* Control Methods in African Agriculture

J. Kroschel[1], J. Sauerborn[2], S. Kachelriess[1], V. Hoffmann[3] and H. Mercer-Quarshie[4]

[1]Deutsche Gesellschaft für Technische Zusammenarbeit (GTZ) GmbH, University of Hohenheim (380), Germany;
[2]University of Giessen, Tropical Crop Science, Schottstr. 2, 35390 Giessen, Germany;
[3]University of Hohenheim (430), 70593 Stuttgart, Germany;
[4]Savanna Agricultural Research Institute (SARI), P.O. Box 483, Tamale, Ghana

Abstract

The semi-parasitic weeds of the genus Striga are widely distributed in the savannah regions of Africa, and infestation by Striga in cereals is considered to be one of the major biological constraints on African agriculture. Decades of research have been carried out to develop Striga control methods. However, the African farmer has hardly benefited from these efforts. The participation of farmers in the development of control strategies has not been adequately considered and they have not been well advised in the practice of control methods. At present, research can offer only limited control options due to the complexity of the host-parasite interaction. It has become clear that methods are individually not efficient and economic enough for the control of Striga. An integrated control approach is urgently needed, i.e. that different control methods should be applied simultaneously over a period of years. In addition, farmers should be trained to understand the parasite's biology in order to comprehend and apply appropriate control methods. Therefore, a group extension program which works with pictures and a felt-board similar to the GRAAP- and CFSME-extension approaches has been developed in collaboration with extension workers from northern Ghana, which will enable extension workers to support farmers adequately in finding the best combination of control methods for their individual farms.

Keywords

Striga, farming systems, control, implementation, extension, Africa

Introduction

Semi-parasitic weeds of the genus *Striga* (Scrophulariaceae) are an increasing problem in crop production in the savannah regions of Africa. *S. hermonthica* (Del.) Benth. and *S. asiatica* L. Kuntze parasitize cereals such as maize, sorghum and millet, whereas *S. gesnerioides* (Willd.) Vatke attacks dicotyledons, mainly cowpea and tobacco. *Striga* is considered at this time to represent the largest single biological constraint on food production in African agriculture. The area of Africa actually infested with *Striga* has been estimated at 21 million ha. The loss of yield caused by the infestation amounts to about 4.1 million tons of grain. Altogether grain production in Africa is potentially at risk on 44 million ha of land located in the *Striga* zone (Sauerborn 1991). A drastic change in the farming system is responsible for the increase of the *Striga* infestation. The rapid demographic growth in the past 20 years forced farmers to shorten their fallow periods and to increase land-use intensity. Host plants are consequently cropped more frequently supporting an increase in the *Striga* seed population and correspondingly leading to greater infestation of the crops. In the traditional farming systems *Striga* was not a problem. The seed population in the soil decreased due to decomposition during long fallow periods. Nowadays, farmers are often confronted with a formerly unknown weed problem.

Decades of research have been carried out to develop *Striga* control methods. However, the African farmer has hardly benefited from these efforts. Within the supra-regional project "Ecology and Management of Parasitic Weeds," which has been supported by The Deutsche Gesellschaft für Technische Zusammenarbeit (GTZ) and the University of Hohenheim, experiences have been gained with regard to research and implementation of *Striga* control methods since 1988. The objective of this paper is to summarize the *status quo* of *Striga* control in Africa and to discuss promising innovations in *Striga* research. In addition, constraints involved in implementing available control methods will be presented considering the situation of small-scale farmers with their limited means to adopt methods using examples from different farming systems in northern Ghana. Finally, we will conclude with some lessons learned and our approach to managing *Striga* in African agriculture.

Striga Biology versus Control and Innovative Research

Striga biology differs from normal weeds and exhibits specific characteristics which have important implications for its control:

- The main damage to the host already occurs underground before *Striga* emerges.
- *Striga* seeds remain viable for more than a decade. Control measures have therefore to be applied continuously over a period of up to ten years to reduce significantly the number of seeds in the soil.
- *Striga* plants produce an extremely high number of seeds. Sprich (1994) counted about 23.000 viable seeds per *Striga* plant. Consequently, it must be

ensured that *Striga* is not allowed to produce new seeds so as to prevent an increase in soil seed population.

- For the prevention of *Striga* seed production, weeding needs to be done at a certain stage of *Striga* development, which does not coincide with the "normal" weed control practices of farmers. In addition, weeded *Striga* plants need to be collected at the field border and burnt since they are able to mature and set seed even though they have been uprooted.

Research efforts have focused on individual applied methods, e.g. breeding for resistance, crop rotation with trap and catch crops, transplanting, chemical control with herbicides and nitrogen fertilizer, the use of organic manure, of synthetic stimulants and ethylene, and recently biological control. Benefits of most of the control strategies, e. g. crop rotation, hand-pulling or the use of herbicides (e. g. 2,4-D) will be visible only after a couple of years. Thus, with these strategies the losses encountered due to *Striga* will not be prevented within a short period of time under severe infestation levels. Highly sophisticated technologies like the use of ethylene to trigger ineffective *Striga* seed germination, as used in North Carolina to eradicate *S. asiatica,* are presently impractical for Africa. In addition, the use of synthetic germination stimulants also offers little practical option. The application of high dosage of nitrogen fertilizer (more than 80 kg N per hectare, mainly as ammonium sulfate or urea) which also would have a negative effect on the initial *Striga* stages is not readily applicable in African farming systems.

Innovative research with respect to *Striga* control should focus on methodologies which have an immediate effect on the initial stages of the *Striga* life cycle in order to prevent or reduce reinfestation already in the first year of application. This means, methods must have a direct impact on the *Striga* seed bank, seed germination, attachment or early shoot development (see figure 1). This effect may be expected mainly from the use of resistant varieties, and as recent research work has indicated, by the use of fungi specific to *Striga* spp. applied as a bioherbicide.

Resistant varieties, which means less attack by *Striga,* usually defined in terms of numbers of parasite attached to the host compared to susceptible ones, exist mainly for sorghum with some progress in recent years in maize and in cowpea. Experiences with resistant sorghum varieties have shown that they are very often not accepted by farmers because of their seed quality, that they are mostly not adapted to a wide range of agro-ecological zones and, in addition, are sensitive to other pest problems. "Framida," a *Striga* resistant sorghum variety and distributed on a large scale in northern Ghana by the Sasakawa Global 2000 program supported by the World Bank, was not accepted by farmers. Its taste did not meet with farmers' preferences and, according to farmers, it performed well only on fertile soils or when additional fertilizer was applied (Runge-Metzger 1993). The resistant sorghum variety SRN 39 is characterized by a very close head which makes it very sensitive to pests in areas with higher precipitation. In addition, the resistance mechanism, which is mainly due to a low stimulant production offers only a reduced control option in highly infested fields where SRN 39 is also highly infected.

Figure 1: The Life Cycle of *Striga* Exhibits Specific Characteristics which have Important Implications for the Development of Control Methods

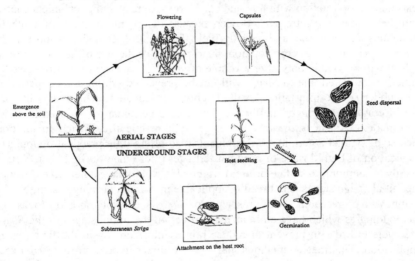

The development of cultivars with durable resistance are complicated by variation in the parasite gene pool (Riches 1994). A number of strains of *S. gesnerioides* occur in West Africa of differing ability to parasitize cowpea genotypes. Lane et al. (1994) discovered a new *S. gesnerioides* strain in southern Benin with virulence on the formerly resistant cowpea variety B301. A further question is whether sources of resistance with durability can be found in the future, i.e. when a resistant cultivar is grown repeatedly at the same site. Riches (1994) has recently discussed the issue of the selection pressure exerted by the host on the parasite population and concludes that the risk of selection and build-up of a virulent sub-population needs to be considered when cultivars with incomplete resistance are used, as is commonly the case with sorghum. If few individuals which successfully parasitize the resistant crop develop from seeds which are able to respond to a lower threshold of stimulant, this selection could lead to the breakdown of the resistance. Breeding for *Striga* resistance could profit from gene technology. Genes for *Striga* resistance could be identified and then combined and transferred into high-yielding varieties which are adapted to specific agro-ecological zones.

Different fungus species of the genus *Fusarium*, mainly *F. nygamai* and isolates of *F. oxysporum* were found to be highly pathogenic to *S. hermonthica* and reduced the incidence by more than 90% in *in vitro* trials (Abbasher & Sauerborn 1992; Ciotola et al. 1995; Kroschel et al. 1996). The microbial antagonists are able to penetrate and parasitize *Striga* seeds (Sauerborn et al. 1996a), and reduced seed germination, attacked germ tubes and *Striga* shoots. A control effect was also observed in field trials in Côte d'Ivoire by inoculating *F. nygamai* as solid media into the soil pre-planting. The incidence of *S. hermonthica* was reduced significantly compared to the control, and maize yield was improved (Sauerborn et al. 1996b). However, innovative research on bioherbicide development have their own constraints and difficulties to overcome and many questions are still open until a suitable product can be produced. Since individually applied methods currently available to control *Striga* are not efficient enough, an integrated control approach is urgently needed, i.e. different control methods should be adopted by farmers and applied simultaneously over a number of years.

Indigenous Farm Household Systems and *Striga*

For several reasons (e. g. ethnic groups, population densities, eco-zones) a high variation of farming systems exist in Africa, for which the adoption of different control methods can be expected. To evaluate the constraints involved in implementing *Striga* control methods studies were carried out in northern Ghana, 1) to evaluate the indigenous farming practices and their possible impacts on *Striga* population, 2) to identify farmers' control strategies, 3) to determine the adoption capacity of proposed control methods, and 4) to assess the economic feasibility of selected strategies. Since the human population density is the most important determinant for the recent evolution of farming systems in the area under consideration, the study was carried out in different regions where the population density varied between 8 and more than 120 persons per km². Three different farming systems which have evolved under low (Tumu, Upper West Region), medium (around Tamale, Northern Region) and high (Bolgatanga, Upper East Region) population densities were selected for this study (compare table 1). Whereas the length of the fallow period is negligible in the high density system, it is still more than 10 years in the low density system.

Table 1: Characteristics of Indigenous Farming Systems in Northern Ghana

Region	Tumu, Upper West Region	Tamale, Northern Region	Bolgatanga, Upper East Region
Population density	LOW	MEDIUM	HIGH
Person/km^2	10	52	159
Area cultivated (%)	4	19	23
Land cultivated per person (ha)	0.42	0.38	0.16
Length of fallow period (years)	10 - 15	2 - 3	negligible
Length of cultivation period (years)	4 - 6	4 - 6	permanent
Compound fields (% of cult. land)	1	5 - 10	40 - 60
Main crops	maize, millet, yam	maize, groundnut, rice	sorghum, millet, groundnut
Major factors limiting production	labor peaks, capital	labor peaks, capital	capital, land

Source: Runge-Metzger 1993.

The Impact of Farming Practices on *Striga* Control

In the low populated area around Tumu only about 33% of the agricultural land is cultivated. There, fallowing is the most prominent strategy to control *Striga*. In the medium populated area around 80% of the cultivated land is cropped. Length of fallow is too short to fight *Striga* effectively. Around Bolgatanga, where population density is highest, a regeneration of soil fertility through fallowing has become impossible. The *Striga* incidence is closely related to soil fertility and farmers have used *Striga* as bioindicator showing the depletion of their soils. Increasing the soil fertility status using crop residues and organic manure is therefore an important tool in *Striga* management. In some areas, stalks of cereals are collected and stored as a source of fuel while in others crop residues are usually burnt before soil preparation (see table 2). Organic manure is collected and used in the medium and high population areas, but these efforts are mainly restricted to compound fields. Hand-pulling for normal weeds is performed 2-3 times by farmers with the last weeding in late August or early September. At this time of the season only few *Striga* plants have already emerged. Therefore, *Striga* growth, flowering, and seed production is not completely prevented. Additional *Striga* weeding is only performed by 18% of the farmers interviewed, and only 5% collected the plants at the edge of the fields (Sprich 1994). Similar *Striga* weeding practices are reported from Tanzania (Reichmann et al. 1995).

Crop rotation is only practiced to a limited extent in the low and medium populated areas. Usually pseudo-rotations, i.e. rotation of intercrops, prevail. Intercropping is highest in the Tamale area. The diversity of crops cultivated in the low and medium populated area is higher compared to the Bolgatanga area, where only legumes, particularly groundnut and cowpea, and cereals are grown. In general, the proportion of land allocated to cereals is very high, covering between 67% to 83% of the cropped land. This is largely due to the fact that they are grown as the main staple food and mostly intercropped. Therefore, the introduction of an effective and diversified crop rotation to reduce the *Striga* infestation will be very difficult under the conditions of the Bolgatanga area.

Table 2: Farming Practices in Farming Systems in Northern Ghana

Region	Tumu, Upper West Region	Tamale, Northern Region	Bolgatanga, Upper East Region
Population density	LOW	MEDIUM	HIGH
Fallowing	+++	+	-
Crop residues	burnt	fuel	fuel, fodder
Use of organic manure	-	++	+++
Weeding	2-3 times	2-3 times	2-3 times
Intercropping (%)	60	79	48
Proportion of cereals (%)	83.2	67.6	77.5
Area allocated to crops and crop mixtures (%)	cereals (43.2), cereal-legumes (40), root & tubers (10.8), fibres (5.8), legumes (0.2)	cereals (17.1), cereal-legumes (60.5), root & tubers (17.6), fibres (4.8)	cereals (77.5) legumes (22.5)

Source: Runge-Metzger 1993.

Adoption of *Striga* Control Methods

Several individual *Striga* control strategies were proposed and explained to farmers in the selected regions of northern Ghana in order to evaluate their acceptability under different farming systems. To make farmers aware of the necessity of these measures *Striga* biology, i.e. its life cycle, was also imparted to them. Of the proposed measures hand-pulling was thought to be feasible by 50% to 90% of the farmers, depending on the farming system (see figure 2). Late weeding after harvest prevents flowering and reseeding of *Striga* on sorghum as a ratoon crop.

The use of herbicides and nitrogen fertilizer is not regarded as a feasible control strategy by farmers since they cannot afford them. Agro-chemicals are mainly entering the farming systems through cotton cultivation. Nitrogen is used mainly in maize and rice production at a very low dosage (15 to 20 kg N/ha) in the Tumu and Tamale area. This may even exacerbate the problem as low rates of nitrogen even stimulate *Striga* growth and seed production. If spot application is practice, at least 40-80 kg/N should be applied to effectively suppress *Striga* (Vogt 1993). In Bolgatanga, farmers neither use fertilizer nor any pesticides. Farmers in this area are mainly very poor subsistence farmers, a major constraint for purchased-input dependent control measures. Particularly in the medium and high populated areas the use of sufficient quantities of organic manure is unrealistic since the amounts necessary are not available.

Figure 2: Interest of 70 Farmers, Interviewed in Low (Tumu), Medium (Tamale) and High (Bolgatanga) Populated Areas of Northern Ghana, in Adopting *Striga* Control Methods in the Future

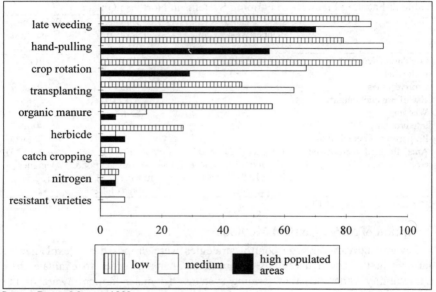

Source: Runge-Metzger 1993.

IITA (1993) and Dawoud et al. (1996) reported that transplanting sorghum from seedbed to the field leads to a decrease of *Striga* infection. In many parts of Africa transplanting of sorghum is used in traditional farming to compensate for the stand loss of sorghum. For farmers this method could be an acceptable strategy on a limited scale, e.g. in highly infested field spots. Farmers in low and medium populated areas considered crop rotation especially with trap crops an acceptable way for *Striga* control. According to Sprich (1994), trap crops such as cotton and soybean can reduce the *Striga* seed bank by about 30% annually through inducing ineffective germination. Even more effective was catch cropping with sorghum and maize. Conventional cropping of a maize-sorghum mixture increased the *Striga* seed bank by 300% (see table 3).

Table 3:   The *Striga* Seed Bank in Soil[1] in Northern Ghana as affected by two
Year Cropping with Selected Crops or Fallow

Treatment	Change of *Striga* seed bank (%)			
	1990	1991	Mean	Significance[2]
Conventional cropping				
- maize-sorghum	+513.2	+116.6	+314.9	A
- maize-groundnut	+180.0	+59.2	+119.6	B
- fallow	-17.3	-6.4	-11.9	C
Trap cropping				
- cotton	-33.6	-29.7	-31.7	C
- cowpea	-25.3	-19.7	-22.5	C
- groundnut	-18.7	-23.4	-21.1	C
- soybean	-35.2	-34.1	-34.7	C
- sunflower	-37.5	-32.8	-35.2	C
Catch cropping				
- maize-sorghum	-44.8	-40.2	-42.5	C

[1] calculated on the basis of the seed content per 100g air-dried soil taken up 0 to 15 cm soil
depth; [2] significant differences are indicated by case letters at the 0.05 level
Source: Sprich 1994.

The idea of catch cropping is to stimulate germination of *Striga* seeds by host
plants but to avoid flowering and seed shed of the parasite. Therefore, 6 to 8
weeks after sowing, the *Striga* host plants are harvested as fodder or ploughed
into the soil. When applied in dense stands, this method is further improved and
would be especially useful in areas where the growing season allows a preceeding
crop for 6-8 weeks or to restore fields which are abandoned due to *Striga*
infestation. In general, farmers refused to apply this method because of the loss of
one year's harvest.

Economics of *Striga* Control at Household Level

In removing normal weeds, crop losses can be prevented in the same cropping
season. In the case of a parasitic weed infestation, farmers cannot prevent yield
losses even though they employ available control methods. Therefore, farmers
have to employ a long-term approach which includes investments in technologies
with uncertain short-term return.

Assessments of the economics of *Striga* control measures have been carried out
under the conditions of northern Ghana by Runge-Metzger (1993). Depending on
the actual magnitude of the *Striga* infestation, benefits of the different strategies
will differ from one situation to the other. Therefore, the threshold levels were
calculated in terms of incremental yields required to recover the costs of the
different control strategies, taking farmers time preference into account.

Since the data is limited with regard to long-term effects, on-farm research calculations had to include various assumptions. However, some economic principles could be deduced which might be important for farmers' decision alternatives.

One *Striga* plant was taken as the control threshold, as the high reproduction rate makes for a very quick build-up of severe contamination on subsequent host crops. Regular monitoring of *Striga* infestation is therefore an essential component of a control strategy. Farmers in all regions surveyed in northern Ghana showed a high interest in experimenting with hand-pulling as well as with late weeding (see figure 2). To suppress *Striga* in the long run the whole package of weeding, including regular monitoring, hand-pulling and late weeding, needs to be employed annually (e.g. a 110 to 130 days sorghum variety would require three to four periods of hand-pulling). Net benefits of this package can be expected only after three to four years. The break-even incremental yield of this control package has to be 43 to 55 kg per hectare per annum, considering a discount rate of 10% and 20%. Under the conditions prevailing in the lowly populated area of Tumu in northern Ghana, farm households are more likely to prefer external inputs like herbicide and mineral fertilizer. Both measures demand cash expense, but with no immediate effect expected. For example, contact herbicides (e.g. Paraquat) applied as a spot treatment will give returns, as hand-pulling, only after three to four years. In order to pay off an incremental yield of at least 27 to 37 kg of maize has to be produced per hectare per year. Since these initial cash investments cannot be afforded by most of the farmers, this technology has a low adoption capacity at the moment. According to a study of the adoption potential of 2,4-D herbicide for *Striga* control in Mali, Debrah & Sanogo (1993) concluded that the maximum farmers are willing to pay represents between 3% and 18% (equalling to about 5.6 to 12.9 US $) of their total annual household incomes. This indicates that expensive technologies with initial investments equivalent to more than 20% of the household's annual income are not likely to be adopted without access to external sources of financing.

Current Knowledge about *Striga* Biology among Farmers

Knowledge about *Striga* biology by farmers is quite limited. In Ghana, only 37% of the farmers knew that *Striga* multiplies by seeds but never had seen them. They tended to believe that *Striga* reproduces by stolon. Most of the farmers had no knowledge of *Striga* seed distribution. Less than 10% of the interviewed farmers knew that *Striga* parasitizes and damages its host plants directly by withdrawing nutrients and water. They mainly believed that *Striga* releases toxic substances which they thought are also responsible for losses in other crops. In neglecting the biology of the parasite, farmers were often not successful with available control methods, e.g. farmers pulled *Striga* regularly in Malawi but left the weeded plants between the crop rows (Shaxson et al. 1993). Consequently, the soil was reseeded and the farmers disillusioned about continuing with this strategy.

Indigenous *Striga* Control Strategies

Research has rarely considered indigenous farming practices to control *Striga*. According to Sprich (1994), investigations into the indigenous *Striga* control strategies in northern Ghana provided beside control methods used like hand-pulling, rotation or cowdung application no further information which could be used in an integrated approach. From Sudan, Ethiopia, as well as Eritrea it is reported (Elhassan, Sudan; Beyen-Eesh, Ethiopia, pers. com.) that catch cropping called "serwala" is employed. Sorghum is sown very densely and about six weeks after sowing the crop is disc-harrowed or hand-hoed to normal crop stand. Without losing a cropping season, the *Striga* seed bank is effectively reduced. Since this method has been developed in the presumed center of origin of *Striga* it would be worthwhile to further evaluate this technology.

Potential and Shortcomings of Agricultural Extension for the Implementation of *Striga* Control Measures

In many African countries the Training and Visit (T&V) system has been introduced and modified. The "Unified Extension System" in Ghana is also based on this approach. Within the existing framework front line staff (FLS) have been unable to effectively support farmers to combat *Striga*. Appropriate extension materials are lacking. The need for practical training of FLS was revealed during surveys (Sprich 1994) and through evaluations at training courses, which indicated that the knowledge about the biology and control of *Striga* is poor. Relevant scientific knowledge should benefit farmers. In the Northern Region of Ghana, materials were developed to enable extension staff to transfer available knowledge to the farmers and create awareness amongst them about the biology of *Striga* and possible control methods. Extension agents were trained and visual materials were developed as a series of 41 hand-colored pictures, based on the experiences with and related to the GRAAP-methodology and the CFSME-approach (Hoffmann 1995), which could be used by extension staff with farmers groups. The extension series is divided into three sections:
1. Awareness-creation,
2. Biology, and
3. Control methods.
The material was developed by Hummler (1996) and refined by Osterburg (1995) in cooperation with FLS of the MoFA (Ministry of Food and Agriculture) and

two non governmental organizations (Action Aid and Association of Church Development Projects). Pictures were drawn by a local artist well experienced in drawing rural life. The materials of the "*Striga* Control Program" consist of: a cloth board with 2 wooden ledges and a string (costs about US $ 8), 41 pictures (copied on both sides = 82 copies) colored with color pencils (possible in six hours work), two card papers with *Striga* seeds and the handbook/guideline (ten pages).

Figure 3: Picture from the "*Striga* Control Programme" showing "Handpulling" of *Striga* Plants in the Field

The pictures are shown to the farmers and the FLS acts as moderator and stimulates a discussion within the group. Necessary information and hints for his moderation are written at the back of the pictures.

After the presentation of each picture, series of pictures are fixed accordingly on the felt board, e.g. indicating the life cycle of the parasite. The use of pictures was generally accepted by both FLS and farmers and the demonstration of "live material" (*Striga* seeds) enhanced the attractiveness of the program. The program does not include a packaged message, as often expected. One of the major achievements of the program is that it clarifies the biology of *Striga* through discussion among extension agent and farmers, who then deduce possible control methods. The program stresses increasing understanding among farmers to differentiate between "normal" and parasitic weeds and between host plants, neutral crops and trap crops. It tries to explain the different control measures and offers options to farmers. It also contributes to a change in farmers' perception towards a long-term approach for successful *Striga* control. The program has to be followed by a more detailed discussion with individual farmers to tailor a suitable approach for each farm. The development and use of simple, visual "farm planning tools" is now required. The use of some tools from Participatory Rural Appraisal (Werner 1993), e.g. cropping calendars, historical profiles, flow-charts are being considered. This requires additional skills the extension agent may currently be lacking.

Despite the positive response by extension workers and farmers to the program some constraints have been observed, e.g. the length of the program (approx. two hours). Depending on the liveliness of the discussions, half way through the program farmers often became tired. Some of them even left when control methods were dealt with. FLS suggested focusing recommendations on only two "optimal" methods, as other methods, they believed, like catch cropping would never be adopted by farmers. Although it was explained that "optimal" methods could differ from farmer to farmer there remained a disagreement. The extension staff obviously expects one universally applicable, scientifically proven control package. This indicates very clearly that it is first of all of prime importance that the extension staff are also convinced by the recommended control measures. Their effectiveness should be proved in demonstrations and adaptive trials at on-farm level. Such trials could also help to develop adequate, individual control strategies, which would take into consideration the limited adoption capacity of farmers due to social, economic and agronomic factors prevailing in the farming system of a given zone. Regional trials and additional training of extension agents should contribute to the better understanding of the complexity of the problem and the possible solutions. It is necessary, that the curriculum of pre-service training institutions for extension staff incorporate *Striga* biology and control, as well as the necessary methodological orientation.

Extension approaches and visual aids cannot simply be copied, but have to be adapted through a creative process, by participatory material development with researchers, extension agents and farmers. The 'Striga Control Program' developed for northern Ghana gives only an example of such extension material. Such programs are rarely "ideal," but, necessarily, emerge through pragmatic compromise between conflicting objectives and negotiation among different actors of differing interests and needs. The constraints of a real working situation then make the participatory material development process more worthy of replication than the material itself.

Furthermore *Striga* control demands a regional approach to ensure that individual efforts and achievements are not lost through re-infestation of fields. This would be facilitated if *Striga* control becomes a regional or, rather, a national issue with the necessary budgetary allocation and priority attention. Currently it cannot be predicted if and how *Striga* control measures will be introduced via the extension system, but with continuous evaluation of experiences lessons will be learned which will help to adapt and refine existing control methods, develop new methods and further improve extension messages, materials and methods in such a way that they will fit into the system and suit farmers' needs.

Acknowledgements

We are grateful to the Deutsche Gesellschaft für Technische Zusammenarbeit (GTZ) GmbH which has financed different studies presented within this paper. Special thanks are expressed to co-workers of the Savanna Agricultural Research Institute (SARI), Tamale, for their help in conducting the studies in northern Ghana. We also thank the Ministry of Food and Agriculture, Tamale, and the extension workers of the Northern Region for their overall support in developing the '*Striga* Control Program.'

References

Abbasher, A.A., J. Sauerborn 1992. *Fusarium nygamai* a potential bioherbicide for *Striga hermonthica* control in sorghum. Biological Control 2, 291- 296.

Ciotola, M., A.K. Watson, S.G. Hallett 1995. Discovery of an isolate of *Fusarium oxysporum* with potential to control *Striga hermonthica* in Africa. Weed Research 35, 303-309.

Debrah, S.K., D. Sanogo 1993. Ex-ante evaluation of the profitability and adoption potential of 2,4-D for *Striga* control: A contingent valuation analysis. Internal Report, ICRISAT-WASIP, Bamako, Mali, 35pp.

Dawoud, D., J. Sauerborn, J. Kroschel 1996. Transplanting of sorghum: A method to reduce yield losses caused by *Striga*. In: M.T. Moreno, J.I. Cubero, D. Berner, D. Joel, L.J. Musselmann & C. Parker (eds.): Advances in Parasitic Plant Research. Proc. VI Parasitic Weed Symposium, Cordoba, Spain, 777-785.

Hoffmann, V. 1991. Bildgestützte Kommunikation in Schwarz-Afrika. Grundlagen, Beispiele und Empfehlungen zu angepaßten Kommunikationsverfahren in ländlichen Entwicklungsprogrammen. Margraf Verlag, Weikersheim, FRG. 331 pp.

Hummler, K. 1996. *Striga*-Beratung, Entwicklung eines visuell unterstützten Beratungsprogrammes zur Kontrolle von *Striga hermonthica* in der Nordregion Ghanas. In: Kommunikation und Beratung 5, Sozialwissenschaftliche Schriften zur Landnutzung und ländlichen Entwicklung. Margraf Verlag, Weikersheim, FRG, pp 206.

IITA, 1993. Annual Report. International Institute of Tropical Agriculture, Oyo Road, PMB 5320, Ibadan, Nigeria.

Kroschel, J., A. Hundt, A.A. Abbasher, J. Sauerborn 1996. Pathogenicity of fungi collected in northern Ghana to *Striga hermonthica*. Z. PflKrankh. PflSchutz, Sonderh. XV, 389-395.

Lane, J.A., T.H.M. Moore, D.V. Child, K.F. Cardwell, B.B. Singh, J.A. Bailey 1994. Virulence characteristics of a new race of the parasitic angiosperm, *Striga gesnerioides*, from southern Benin on cowpea (*Vigna unguiculata*). Euphytica 72, 183-188.

Osterburg, B. 1995. Development and Implementation of an extension programme for the control of the parasitic weed *Striga* in northern Ghana. Internal report, supra-regional GTZ-project "Ecology and Management of Parasitic Weeds", University of Hohenheim, FRG, 56pp.

Reichmann, S., J. Kroschel, J. Sauerborn 1995. Distribution and infestation of *Striga* species in Shinyanga region of Tanzania and evaluation of control methods. In: Brighton Crop Protection Conference Weeds, Brighton, UK, Vol. I, 151-156.

Riches, C.R. 1994. Variability of parasitic weeds and their hosts: implications for witchweed management in Africa. Aspects of Applied Biology 39, 145-154.

Runge-Metzger, A. 1993. The economics of *Striga* control in different farming systems in northern Ghana. Internal report, supra-regional GTZ-project "Ecology and Management of Parasitic Weeds", University of Hohenheim, FRG, 51pp.

Sauerborn, J., I. Dörr, A. Abbasher, H. Thomas, J. Kroschel 1996a. Electron microscopic analysis of the penetration process of *Fusarium nygamai*, a hyperparasite of *Striga hermonthica*. Biological Control 7, 53-59.

Sauerborn, J., A.A. Abbasher, J. Kroschel, D.W. Cornes, A. Zoschke, K.T. Hine 1996b. *Striga hermonthica* control with *Fusarium nygamai* in maize. In: V.C. Moran & J.H. Hoffmann (eds.): Proc. of the IX International Symposium on Biological Control of Weeds, 19-26 January 1996, Stellenbosch, South Africa, 115-120.

Sauerborn, J. 1991. The economic importance of the phytoparasites *Orobanche* and *Striga*. In: Ransom, J.K., L.J. Mussselman, A.D. Wosham, C. Parker (eds.) Proc. 5th Int. Symp. on Parasitic Weeds, Nairobi, Kenya, 137-143.

Shaxson, L.J., C.R. Riches, J.H. Seyani 1993. Incorporating farmer knowledge in the design of weed control strategies for smallholders. Brighton Crop Protection Conference Weeds, Brighton, UK, 1149-1154.

Sprich, H. 1994. Bedeutung der Fruchtfolge zur Ertragssicherung in getreide-betonten Produktionssystemen der Guinea-Savanne unter besonderer Berücksichtigung des parasitschen Unkrautes *Striga hermonthica* (Del.) Benth. PLITS 12 (3). Margraf Verlag, Weikersheim, FRG, 149pp.

Vogt, W. 1993. Entwicklung der Wirt/Parasit-Beziehung *Sorghum bicolor/Striga hermonthica* unter dem Einfluß verschiedener Stickstofformen und Standortsfaktoren. PLITS 11 (3). Margraf Verlag, Weikersheim, FRG, 166pp.

Werner, J. 1993. Participatory Development of Agricultural Innovation. Procedures and Methods of On-Farm Research. GTZ & SDC, TZ-Verlag, 251pp.

The Role of Biotechnology in Plant Production

Gerd Weber
Special Plant Breeding and Biotechnology
Institute for Plant Breeding, Seed Science and Populationgenetics
University Hohenheim, Germany

Abstract

An introduction is given on biotechnological methods available for plant breeding and production. They include techniques like meristem culture, anther culture, embryo rescue, somatic hybridization, and transformation. The application of biotechnology to plant breeding and production in developing countries is demonstrated with examples. Micropropagation of banana is used for generating large numbers of "suckers" for planting. Potato meristem culture is employed for producing virus – free planting material. In a planned project cassava with resistance against CMD shall be developed. A concept of cooperation in basic and adaptive research for implementing biotechnology in plant breeding and production is discussed.

Keywords

CMD resistance, black sigatoka disease, transformation, cassava, plantain, potato

In recent years biotechnology has become an integral part of modern plant breeding. Different methods originating from cell culture as well as molecular biology have been used to accelerate breeding programs.

1 Biotechnological Methods Available for Plant Production

Individual cells from many species may be manipulated *in vitro* and successively regenerated into plants. Afterwards plants originating from tissue culture will typically be used in conventional breeding programs. Among the different approaches taken in biotechnology some key-techniques have evolved and are currently available:

1.1 Micropropagation of Sterile Plants or Cells in Tissue Culture for Rapid Multiplication

Small explants originating from different organs of many plant species may be transferred into tissue culture and grown under aseptic conditions. Depending on the composition of the growth media they will either continue to grow as differentiated parts of the original plant or they may change their appearance to grow in an undifferentiated meristematic fashion as callus tissue. Calli as well as tissue at more advanced stages of differentiation may easily be maintained *in vitro* and multiplied. After cycles of multiplication the derivatives of the original explants may be placed onto mediums stimulating organ differentiation to give rise to new plantlets. They can be adapted to greenhouse or nursery conditions and may, for instance, be used directly as starting material for crop production or subjected to further breeding.

1.2 *In Vitro* Culture of Meristems for Providing Pathogen – Free Planting Material

Starting from very small parts of the shoot tip, including a single meristematic dome, plants can be propagated. After sterilizing proper buds, meristems are dissected under a microscope and placed in an appropriate medium. Under those conditions they will continue with morphogenesis and eventually regenerate into plants ready to be transplanted into soil. This technique is frequently used to produce "virus-free" planting material. Normally, viruses are not found in tissue without a vascular system.

1.3 Anther- or Microspore Culture for Generating Doubled Haploid Plants in Breeding Programs

Immature pollen grains, either as anthers or isolated microspores of a number of species are capable of developing into embryos. Under proper tissue culture conditions they may be regenerated into plants. Anther- or microspore culture techniques are employed for producing haploid regenerates. Subsequent doubling of chromosomes will result in doubled haploid plants, i.e. a homozygous line. In plant species amenable to this technique anther culture is used to shorten breeding programs considerably.

1.4 Embryo Culture for Rescuing Embryos

In wide crosses, fertilization and the beginning stages of embryo formation still occur. However, maturation of embryos often is aborted before seeds are fully developed. In such cases, excision of embryos from individual ovules and their subsequent germination in vitro may rescue the embryo and allow its maturation in tissue culture.

1.5 Somatic Hybridization Facilitating Combination of Genotypes in Species not Amenable to Conventional Crossing

Hybridizations by conventional techniques are often hampered by incompatibility barriers due to phylogenetic distances of the species involved.

Furthermore, it may be desirable to combine chloroplasts and mitochondria from different origins in one cell. In both cases, cell fusion will be the only way to achieve these goals. Plant cells may be converted into protoplasts by removing their cell wall enzymatically. Protoplasts may be fused by polyethylene glycol (PEG), electric pulses, or laser pulses to form fusion products which eventually may be regenerated into somatic hybrid plants.

1.6 Gene Transfer for Introducing Single, Agronomically Important Genes into Crop Plants

Unlike conventional or somatic hybridization the technology of gene transfer attempts to transfer only one or few genes into a recipient. Genes with known functions may be transferred into plant tissue or single plant cells by vectors like *Agrobacterium tumefaciens*, physical techniques like introduction of DNA into protoplasts by PEG, or by ballistically introducing gold particles covered with DNA into plant cells. The targeted tissue may regenerate into transgenic plants which will transmit the newly acquired gene faithfully through meiosis into the next generation.

2 Application of Biotechnological Methods in Plant Breeding and Production in Developing Countries

In the following paragraph applications of biotechnological methods for plant production in developing countries will be presented on three examples.

2.1 Micropropagation of Banana and Plantain

Banana and plantain, i.e. clones with edible fruits of the genus *Musa*, are important cultivated crops. These clones of major importance are triploid and seed sterile. Consequently, they must be propagated vegetatively. Normally buds developing into small shoots may be used as new planting material. However, formation of suitable buds is not very reliable. Furthermore, the capacity to form shoots depends on the genotype and is influenced by environmental factors. Therefore it is often difficult to obtain reliable quantities of planting material (Cronauer and Krikorian 1986).

Establishment of rapidly growing aseptic shoot cultures offers a solution to this predicament. A large number of shoots of uniform age and size may be produced continuously.

Reproduction of pathogen-resistant clones is another application of sterile micro-propagation of banana or plantain. Over many years the devastating "Sigatoka" disease has caused tremendous losses in banana and plantain crops.

Sigatoka disease was first described on the Fiji islands in 1913 and is now referred to as "Yellow Sigatoka". It is a fungal disease caused by *Mycosphaerella fijiensis* L. In 1964 another variant of this disease, named "Black Sigatoka", was found on Fiji. This more virulent form of the leaf spot pathogen was named *Mycosphaerella fijiensis* var. *difformis* (Stover 1980). This disease may be controlled by repeated application of fungicides. However, this practice has generated large environmental problems (Castillo 1995).

Further virulent forms of the pathogen have appeared and spread during the last decades in the Caribbean, Africa, parts of Asia, Australia, and the Pacific Islands. New sources of resistance have been identified (Pearson et al. 1983) and their inheritance analyzed (Ortiz and Vuylsteke 1994). Recently, Black-Sigatoka-resistant hybrids were developed (Vuylsteke et al. 1993, 1995). Due to nearly complete seed sterility of the hybrids, resistant clones have to be propagated in vitro (Vuylsteke 1989).

Explants for tissue culture may be isolated from the flowering shoot. After removing some leaves the entire explant will be surface sterilized. Then the leaves covering the apical meristem will be removed exposing the meristematic dome. Cultured on an appropriate medium the explants will multiply as well as proliferate into new clusters of shoots (Krikorian and Cronauer 1984). These can be subdivided for mass propagation. After removing the plantlets from tissue culture they may be adapted to growth conditions in the greenhouse. Eventually they are ready to be transplanted into the field.

2.2 Production of Pathogen-Free Potatoes

Potatoes constitute an important nutrient source in many tropical and subtropical countries. However, the potato plant is also subject to a number of diseases caused by viruses. Micropropagation *in vitro* from certified virus-free clones can establish a reliable source of planting material. As the clones can be maintained in vitro for long periods of time, new planting material can continuously be derived from these stocks.

Starting from surface-sterilized stem cuttings, tissue cultures can be initiated and the tissue multiplied. During this phase, tissue may be removed from established in vitro clones and regenerated into plants. After adaptation to growth under normal conditions in regular soil, these regenerates may be grown under controlled conditions and analyzed for the presence of viruses. Regenerated plants are inspected for symptoms of virus infection. In addition, sap can be taken and used for inoculation of indicator plants which are particularly susceptible to specific viruses. Finally, immunological assays (ELISA) may be performed to detect specific viruses.

In vitro clones of plants verified to be virus-free can then be micropropagated in tissue culture as a certified stock. Portions of these cultures can be removed continuously, regenerated into plants, and distributed as planting material. The methods required for this procedure have been successfully adapted to local farming conditions (van Uyen and van der Zaag 1983).

2.3 Cassava Resistant to Cassava Mosaic Disease (CMD)

Cassava is the third largest source of calories across the tropics. Cassava is a vegetatively propagated crop. Cassava mosaic disease (CMD) is considered to be the most destructive disease throughout cassava growing regions of the world. It is caused by different strains of geminiviruses: African Cassava Mosaic Virus, East African Cassava Mosaic Virus, and Indian Cassava Mosaic Virus (ICMV) (Hong et al. 1993). Losses of 45% due to ICMV were reported from India (Mathew and Muniyappa 1992).

Generation of virus-free planting material using in vitro meristem culture has been tried previously (Kartha et al. 1974, Robertson and Sakina 1989, Komen 1991). However, rapid spreading of the disease has thwarted these efforts in most cases.

Breeding for resistance against CMD would be a sensible way to approach this problem. Crosses with identified resistant varieties have been performed, however, breeding of cassava is difficult. Furthermore, cassava plants must not be distributed to different growing regions to prevent spreading of the virus. In combining techniques from biotechnology and molecular biology, tools have become available to address this problem.

For this purpose, a project is planned involving research institutions in South America (CIAT), Germany (Universities of Hohenheim and Stuttgart), and India (CTCRI). Prospective virus-resistant varieties will be crossed with agronomically important cultivars in South America. Virus populations will be analyzed in India. Pathogen-free *in vitro* clones generated from these crosses will be shipped to Germany for identifying resistance towards CMD by *in vitro* testing with ICMV. Molecular markers will be correlated with the resistant phenotype. Based on these markers loci for resistance shall be mapped in South America using the recently developed molecular marker map of cassava (Fregene et al. 1996). Using molecular markers for breeding will avoid constraints imposed for phytosanitary reasons.

Identification of cultivars resistant to ICMV and their distribution among farmers should be greatly improved.

Additionally, it is planned to develop resistance towards different strains of geminiviruses in cassava using a biotechnological approach. Eventually, DNA molecules known to effectively suppress virus replication will be introduced by transformation into cassava (Stanley et al. 1990). Cassava cultivars should have stable resistance against CMD when naturally occurring resistance will be combined with transgenically induced virus suppression.

3   Future Prospects of Biotechnology for Plant Production

One major factor for the success of biotechnological methods in plant production in developing countries is their efficient implementation to achieve practical results. Success in plant production has to be achievable without continuous investments into basic research.

It is interesting to compare the availability of biotechnological methods for plant production and the actual use of these techniques in developing countries. Micro-propagation of plants and generation of pathogen-free planting material by meristem culture are currently being employed in a number of projects (potato, banana, avocado, cassava). These particular techniques were developed early on and their application in plant production has been well established in universities and research institutions. Therefore, the transfer to practical breeding did not require major investments in basic research. Small cooperatives of farmers were able to successfully implement biotechnological methods cost-efficiently (Schilde-Rentschler 1993).

Most other techniques (somatic hybridization, transformation) have not enjoyed comparable success because application in plant production could not be achieved without prior commitment to basic research.

Transformation of a crop plant with an important gene, like resistance to a pathogen, could dramatically improve crop yield. Currently, more often the lack of an isolated gene rather than the technology to transfer it is hampering progress. Although in developing countries very competent scientists and research facilities are often available, projects requiring basic research often lack sufficient funding.

One major advantage of genetic engineering is that candidate genes, e.g. for resistance or stress tolerance, may be identified and isolated in laboratories of developed countries. The primary transfer of these gene constructs into widely adapted genotypes of target crops could either be performed there or in national research centers in developing countries. Successive transfers within a crop species could well occur in developing countries conventional or marker-assisted backcrossing. This second step will require only limited capital investment. On the other hand, improvement of polygenic traits, such as grain yield in cereals, will probably continue to be the domain of classical selection schemes for the forseeable future.

4   Lessons Learned

Many advanced techniques have been developed in the area of biotechnology of higher plants. However, few have been implemented in plant production in developing countries. Based upon previous experiences, the following points are important for introducing biotechnology as a tool for plant production in developing countries.

1. Besides substantial commitment for financing of basic research, collaboration on a large scale will be necessary to address these problems. Basic research involving, for instance, the development of new techniques or isolation of genes would be conducted in industrial countries. However, it is essential to address problems that are truely relevant to developing countries. Otherwise transfer of knowledge will be difficult.

2. To be able to achieve this goal, scientists from universities and research facilities in developed countries have to gain on-site experience with existing agricultural problems in developing countries. At the same time on–the-job training for scientists from developing countries is of great importance. Sufficient funds have to be granted by governments or private funding agencies of the industrialized countries to support such endeavors.

3. Furthermore, exchange of knowledge and coordination of research efforts are required. There are organizations which have been established with the mandate to coordinate cooperation, like the Cassava-Biotechnology Network and the African-Plant-Biotechnology Network.

Acknowledgments

The help of Dr. L. Schilde-Rentschler, Tübingen, is a gratefully acknowledged for providing detailed information on potato micropropagation as well as generously supplying slides.

References

Castillo, L. E. 1995. Ecological consequences from pesticide use. Final Report, GTZ, Tropenökologisches Begleitprogramm PN 90.2136.1. San José, Costa Rica.

Cronauer, S. S., Krikorian, A. D. 1986. Regeneration in bananas and plantains. pp. 179 - 185, Cell Culture and Somatic Cell Genetics of plants, Vol. 3, (I. K. Vasil ed), Acad. Press, London.

Fregene, M., Rodriguez, F., Angel, F., Gomez, R., Bonierbale, M., Iglesias, C., Tohme, J., Roca, W. 1996. A molecular marker based genetic linkage map of cassava (Manihot esculenta Crantz). Submitted.

Hong, Y. G., Robinson, D. J. and Harrison, B. D. 1993. Nucleotide sequence evidence for the occurrence of three distinct whitefly-transmitted geminiviruses in cassava. J. Gen. Virol. 74, 2437 - 2443.

Kartha, K. K., Gamborg, O. L., Constabel, F., Shyluk, J. P. 1974. Regeneration of cassava plants from apical meristems. Plant Sci. Lett. 2, 107 - 113.

Komen, J. 1991. Biotechnology Research Unit of CIAT successfully established research networks on cassava and beans. Biotechnology and Development Monitor 684 - 690.

Krikorian, A. D., Cronauer, S. S. 1984. Aseptic culture techniques for banana and plantain improvement. Economic Botany 38, 322 - 331.

Mathew, A. V. and Muniyappa, V. 1992. Purification and characterization of Indian cassava mosaic virus. Journal of Phytopathology 135, 299 - 308.

Ortiz, R., Vuylsteke, D. 1994. Inheritance of black sigatoka disease in plantain-banana (Musa spp.) hybrids. Theor. Appl. Genet. 89, 146 - 152.

Pearson, M. N., Bull, P. B., Shepherd, K. 1983. Possible sources of resistance to black Sigatoka in the Papua New Guinea Biological Foundation banana collection. Tropical Pest Management 29, 303 - 308.

Robertson, A. I., Sakina, K. E. 1989. A slice of reality from Africa. Tibtech 7: 814 - 815.

Schilde-Rentschler, L.1993. Biotechnologische Verfahren in der Pflanzenzüchtung - Chancen und Risiken für die Entwicklungsländer. Pflanzengenetische Ressourcen, Erhaltung und multiple, nachhaltige Nutzung, Beiträge zur 21. Witzenhäuser Hochschulwoche, (Jutzi, S. C., Becker, B., eds.).

Stanley, J., Frischmuth, T., and Ellwood, S. 1990. Defective viral DNA ameliorates symptoms of geminivirus infection in transgenic plants. Proc. Natl. Acad. Sci. USA 87, 6291 - 6295.

Stover, R. M. 1980. Sigatoka leaf spots of bananas and plantains. Plant Dis. 64, 750 - 755.

Van Uyen, N., Van der Zaag, P. 1980. Vietnamese farmers use tissue culture for commercial potato production. Amer. Potato J. 60, 873 - 879.

Vulysteke, D., Ortiz, R., Ferris, S., Swennen, R. 1995. "PITA-9": Black-sigatoka-resistant hybrid from the "False Horn" plantain gene pool. Hort. Sci. 30, 395 -397.

Vulysteke, D., Swennen, R., Ortiz, R. 1993. Registration of 14 improved tropical Musa plantain hybrids with Black Sigatoka resistance. Hort. Sci. 28, 957 - 959.

Vulysteke, D. 1989. Shoot - tip culture for the propagation, conservation, and exchange of Musa germplasm. Practical Manuals for Handling Crop Germplasm in vitro 2. IBPGR, Rome.

Insect Resistant Indica Rice Variety IR58 after Transformation with a Synthetic *CryIA(b)* Gene from *Bacillus Thuringiensis*

J. Wünn, S. Barella, H. Behn, S. Bieri,
P.K. Burkhardt, A. Klöti and I. Potrykus
Swiss Federal Institute of Technology (ETH)
Institute for Plant Sciences, 8092 Zürich, Switzerland

Abstract

We transformed Indica rice breeding line IR58 with a synthetic version of a truncated cryIA(b) gene from Bacillus thuringiensis *via particle bombardment to immature zygotic embryos. The gene is expressed under control of the CaMV 35S promoter, which allows efficient production of the lepidopteran specific δ-endotoxin in transgenic plants. Stable integration of the transgene could be shown by southern analysis of R_0, R_1 and R_2 generation plants. DNA dot-blot analysis revealed a segregation ratio close to 3:1, indicating the insertion of the cryIA(b) gene in a single locus on one chromosome. Protein analysis showed the activity of the transgene in all three generations analyzed so far.*

*The insecticidal effect of the transgenic IR58 plants could be shown by insect bioassays. Feeding studies revealed mortality rates of up to 100% for two of the most destructive insect pests of rice in Asia, the yellow stem borer (*Scirpophaga incertulas*) and the striped stem borer (*Chilo suppressalis*), and feeding inhibition of the two leaffolder species* Cnaphalocrocis medinalis *and* Marasmia patnalis. *Introduction of stem borer resistance into the germplasm of an Indica rice breeding line makes this agronomically important trait available now for conventional rice breeding programs.*

Keywords

Rice, stem borer, Bacillus thuringiensis, transgenic plants, resistance

Introduction

Rice is one of the world's most important crop plants and is the staple food for more than 2 billion people. Its worldwide production reached 530 million tons in 1994 and more than 80% of it is based on Indica rice cultivars (IRRI 1989). Around 50% of the yield are lost every year due to insect pests, diseases and weeds (Grayson et al. 1990). Among the 100 insect species attacking rice plants in Asia, 20 are known to cause significant economic damage. The lepidopterous stem borers are generally considered to be the most destructive ones. They infest rice plants during their whole life cycle, from seedling stage to maturity. The yellow stem borer is the most important rice pest in tropical Asia, whereas the striped stem borer is predominantly found in temperate climates. These two insect species are responsible for an annual yield loss of 5-10% in Asia, with occasional outbreaks of up to 60% (Pathak and Khan 1994). Complete yield loss is rare, but an infestation of one stem borer species in Indonesia totally destroyed more than 13,000 ha of rice in 1990 (Khan et al. 1991).

Soon after hatching, the stem borer larvae enter the leaf sheath, feeding for around one week on leaf sheath tissue. After that, they bore into the stem, where they continue feeding on the inner stem tissue. There they develop through several larval stages to the pupa. Adults leave the stem and live as nocturnal moths. If plant infestation occurs during the vegetative growing stage of a rice plant, the damage is known as deadheart: leaves turn brown and the affected tillers dry out. With their high tillering capacity, modern rice varieties can easily compensate such damage. If the infestation occurs during booting stage, panicles do not emerge at all, or, if they emerge, they remain unfilled, resulting in the so-called whiteheads.

Chemical control of stem borers is difficult and often ineffective as the larvae hide inside the stem, protected from sprayed insecticides. Therefore, rice breeders have been looking for years for stem-borer-resistant rice varieties. But despite screening far more then 30,000 rice varieties for this trait (Khan et al. 1991), genes for sufficient levels of resistance have not been found and none of the rice varieties developed so far has more than a moderate level of resistance.

An attractive alternative of protection is the production of proteins with insecticidal activity by the rice plant itself. The entomocidal spore-forming soil bacterium *Bacillus thuringiensis* (Bt) offers a promising variety of so-called *cry* genes that encode insect-specific δ-endotoxins. Since the late 1980s, these *cry* genes have been transferred to higher plants including tobacco (Vaeck et al. 1987), tomato (Fischhoff et al. 1987) and cotton (Perlak et al. 1990), resulting in insect-resistant plants. More recently, monocotyledonous plants such as maize (Koziel et al. 1993; Armstrong et al. 1995) and Japonica rice (Fujimoto et al. 1993) have also been successfully transformed with these genes. To achieve high expression of these prokaryotic genes in higher plants, modifications of the coding sequence, such as removal of potential RNA processing and polyadenylation signals and optimization of the codon usage, have been made (Murray et al. 1991; Perlak et al. 1991). Truncation of the coding sequence of such synthetic Bt-genes has further increased expression levels.

In the case of rice leaffolders, yield loss is not as dramatic as for stem borers. Recent studies (Way and Heong 1994) showed that rice plants can quickly recover from damaged foliage, even when large leaf areas were damaged.

However, many farmers consider such damage as the main source of yield loss, stimulating the application of insecticides. As 20% of insecticide sprays are directed against leaffolders (Heong et al. 1994), reduction of leaffolder damage could lead to an enormous decrease of insecticide use, which would be beneficial for health and income of farmers, predators and parasites as well as for the environment itself.

Aim of the Work

The goal of this work is the reduction of the enormous yield losses in rice farming which are caused every year by lepidopteran insect pests and to contribute therefore to future food security.

The development of a stem-borer-resistant Indica rice variety servers as a first step towards a goal. With the transfer of the *cryIA(b)* gene from *Bacillus thringiensis* to one of the elite Indica rice breeding lines, the trait for stem borer resistance could be established in the rice gene pool. This allows the production of other stem-borer-resistant rice varieties by conventional breeding methods. Protected against stem borer attack, such plants would reduce the stem-borer-specific yield losses and the use of conventional insecticides considerably.

Research Work

We used a synthetic version of a truncated *cryIA(b)* gene from *Bacillus thuringiensis,* which has been shown to be effective against lepidopterous insect pests (Koziel et al. 1993), for transformation of Indica rice variety IR58, one of the elite Indica rice breeding lines released by the International Rice Research Institute (IRRI) in the Philippines. For transformation we used a Particle Inflow Gun, constructed according to Finer et al. (1992). The scutellum side of 700 zygotic immature embryos was bombarded. From one transformation event 11 highly fertile plants were regenerated. Southern analysis of R_0, R_1 and R_2 generation plants showed the stable integration of the transgene in the genome of variety IR58. Besides the expected signal corresponding to the *cryIA(b)* expression cassette, five additional signals were detected, indicating the presence of rearranged copies of the transgene in the rice genome.

Out of 48 selfed R_1 plants, analyzed by DNA dot-blot analysis, 35 showed the presence of the transgene, whereas 13 plants did not give any signal. This segregation ratio close to 3:1 indicates the integration of the transgene in a single locus on one chromosome. The expression of the *cryIA(b)* gene was analyzed by ELISA. A maximum of 84 ng Bt protein per mg total soluble protein was found in leaves of 12- to 14-week old plants of the R_1 generation. The presence of the Bt protein in transgenic plants was further demonstrated by western blot analysis, where a protein with the expected size of 60 kDa was found in all plants tested.

Figure 1: Mortality of Stem Borer and Leaffolder Larvae respectively after
Feeding for 2- 4 days on Leaves from Transgenic R_1 and R_2 Plants

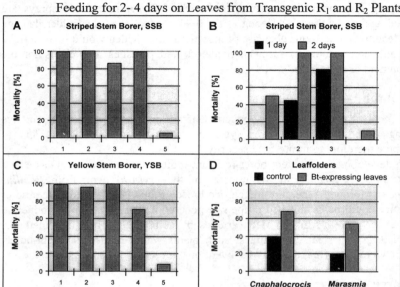

A: SSB larvae feeding on R_1 plants. Mortality was scored after 3 days. 1-4: transgenic R_1 plants;
5: untransformed IR58 plant. B: SSB larvae feeding on leaf pieces of R_2 plants. Mortality was
scored after 1 and 2 days respectively. 1-3: transgenic R_2 plants; 4: untransformed IR58 plant. C:
YSB larvae feeding on leaf-pieces of R_2 plants. Mortality was scored after 3 days. 1-4:
transgenic R_2 plants; 5: untransformed IR58 plant. D: L2 Leaffolder larvae feeding on leaf-
pieces of R_2 plants for 4 days.

With 67% for *Cnaphalocrocis medinalis* and 55% for *Marasmia patnalis,* mortality levels were
not as high as in case of the evaluated stemborers, but a clear difference between non-
transformed control material and the Bt-expressing plants could be detected. Despite this lower
mortality rate a dramatic effect of feeding inhibition could be detected. Leaves from *cryIA(b)*
expressing plants were efficiently protected against feeding damage of these two leaffolder
species, whereas leaves from non-transformed control plants were heavily damaged (figure 1).

The insecticidal activity of the *cryIA(b)* protein produced in the transgenic
IR58 plants was demonstrated by insect bioassays. Both laboratory petri dish
assays and tests of whole plants at booting stage under greenhouse conditions
have been performed. In petri dish assays, neonate larvae of different lepidopteran
rice pests were fed with leaves of the transgenic plants. For the yellow stem borer
and the striped stem borer, up to 100% mortality was found after feeding for 2-4
days on Bt containing leaf tissue. The feeding damage in these samples was
limited and larvae did not reach further larval stages, indicating an early cessation

of feeding by the larvae. Larvae feeding on non-transformed control leaves of variety IR58 reached second and third instar stages and heavily damaged the leaf material. Mortality in control dishes was 5% (see figure 1).

Whole Plant Assay

To assess the effectiveness of the *cryIA(b)* protein in whole transgenic plants, booting stage plants were infested with YSB larvae under greenhouse conditions. Four to five weeks after infestation, surviving larvae were exclusively found on non-transgenic control plants, whereas no living larvae could be detected on Bt-expressing plants (Tab.1). In non-transformed control plants larvae in advanced stages, pupae and adults were found. Stemborer-typical whitehead damage was only observed in non-transgenic control plants. The relatively low survival rate of 33% reflects the typically high mortality of YSB larvae under natural conditions (see table 1).

Table 1: Insecticidal Effect of Whole Transgenic Plants

Plant material	Total # of tillers	Surviving larvae	Larval stage	# of whiteheads
Control	47	33%	advanced, pupae, adult	17
R$_2$-1	50	no survivors	-	0
R$_2$-2	51	no survivors	-	0
R$_2$-3	52	no survivors	-	0

Plants were manually infested with 20 neonate YSB larvae each. Four respectively five weeks after infestation, plants were dissected and analyzed for surviving larvae, larval stage and feeding damage.

Discussion

With the transfer of a synthetic *cryIA(b)* gene into the germplasm of an elite Indica rice cultivar, the stem borer resistance trait is available now for improvement of other modern rice varieties by conventional breeding. The Bt protein produced in our transgenic IR58 plants led to an efficient protection against stem borer attack. Under laboratory as well as under greenhouse conditions, feeding activity and larval development were stopped before the larvae could inflict any significant damage to the plants. Typical stem borer whitehead damage was found in non-transgenic control plants only. According to the biosafety guidelines of the Philippines, these assays were done in the containment greenhouse at IRRI, where only small plant populations could be tested. We hope to conduct further experiments on a larger scale and under tropical field conditions. However, field tests of Bt rice have not yet been approved in any tropical rice-growing country.

Now that the *cryIA(b)* gene is in an improved Indica rice variety, it can be readily transferred to other Indica varieties by IRRI or the national breeding programs of developing rice-growing countries. There is currently free exchange of conventional rice breeding materials among these countries, and similar exchange of transgenic rice should be possible once biosafety regulations have been established by all the countries involved. In this way the stem borer resistance trait can be crossed into local varieties, so that rice farmers in developing countries become the end beneficiaries of this high-tech approach.

Such non-commercial distribution of biotechnologically developed germplasm has the potential to contribute significantly to the solution of one of the most important problems in developing countries − food security − without creating new dependencies.

Pest Resistance

The widespread evolution of pest resistance to chemical insecticides demonstrated the potential of insects to overcome different insecticidal approaches. As insect resistance to *Bacillus thuringiensis* has already been reported (Whalon et al. 1993; Tabashnik et al. 1994), we are looking for strategies to retard the evolution of pest resistance to Bt toxins. One possibility in this direction is the combination of several independently acting insecticidal genes in the same plant. Candidates for such a strategy are Bt genes which are known to bind to different receptor sites in the brush border membrane of the midgut of lepidopterous insect pests, or other insecticidal genes, for example genes encoding for proteinase inhibitors or lectins (Ryan et al. 1989; Boulter et al. 1990). A second possibility of resistance management is the reduction of selection pressure of the target insects by maintenance of non-Bt refugia. This could be achieved by the use of tissue-specific promoters within plants, or by mixtures of Bt and non-Bt plants within a field.

To investigate the potential of such approaches, we are currently using several combinations of different promoters (CaMV 35S, maize-ubiquitin, maize-PEPC, pollenspecific, see figure 2) and additional Bt genes for transformation of Japonica rice variety Taipei 309, for which an efficient transformation system is established in our lab.

Figure 2: Bt Constructs used for Rice Transformation

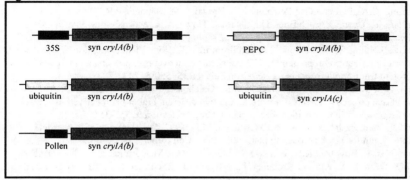

CaMV 35S and maize-ubiquitin are constitutive promoters, whereas the PEPC promoter directs expression to photosynthetic active tissue and the pollenspecific promoter from *Brassica* to pollen.
Insect bioassays will allow the identification of the most promising combinations. These combinations will then be used for transformation of Indica rice breeding lines which is still a very inefficient and time-consuming procedure.

Lessons Learned

The use of conventional insecticides showed that pests have been able to adapt more quickly to insecticides than new ones were developed (National Research Council 1986). To avoid such a fate for Bt transgenic plants, the different strategies for resistance management have to be studied carefully. Before releasing Bt rice to the farmers, several years of intensive research are needed, including large-scale field test experiments. Knowledge gained from such experiments combined with the experience from other Bt transgenic crops should help in establishing Bt rice as a long-lasting, sustainable tool for insect control.

Acknowledgments

We gratefully acknowledge M. Koziel and N. Carozzi, Ciba Geigy, NC, USA, for supplying the *cryIA(b)* gene, the PEPC promoter and for their help in protein analysis. We thank M.B. Cohen, A.T. Angeles and R.M. Aguda, IRRI, Los Banos, The Philippines, for their help in insect bioassays. Thanks also go to I. Altosaar, University of Ottawa, Canada, for supply of several Bt-constructs and to M. Schrott, ETH Zurich, Switzerland, for critically reading the manuscript.

References

Armstrong, C.A., Parker, G.B., Pershing, J.C., Brown, S.M., Sanders, P.R., Duncan, D.R., Stone, T., Dean, D.A., DeBoer, D.L., Hart, J., Howe, A.R., Morrish, F.M., Pajeau, M.E., Petersen, W.L., Reich, B.J., Rodriguez, R., Santino, C.G., Sato, S.J., Schuler, W., Sims, S.R., Stehling, S., Tarochione, L.J. and Fromm, M.E. 1995. Field evaluation of European Corn Borer control in progeny of 173 transgenic corn events expressing an insecticidal protein from *Bacillus thuringiensis*. Crop Science **35**: 550-557.

Boulter, D., Edwards, G.A., Gatehouse, A.M.R., Gatehouse, J.A. and Hilder, V.A. 1990. Additive protective effects of incorporating two different higher plant derived insect resistant genes in transgenic tobacco plants. Crop Protection **9**: 351-354.

Finer, J.J., Vain, P., Jones, M.W. and McMullen, M.D. 1992. Development of the particle inflow gun for DNA delivery to plant cells. Plant Cell Reports **11**: 323-328

Fischhoff, D.A., Bowdish, K.S., Perlak, F.J., Marrone, P.G., McCormick, S.M., Niedermeyer, J.G., Dean, D.A., Kusano-Kretzmer, K., Mayer, E.J., Rochester, D.E., Rogers, S.G. and Fraley, R.T. 1987. Insect tolerant transgenic tomato plants. Bio/Technology **5**: 807-813.

Fujimoto, H., Itoh, K., Yamamoto, M., Kyozuka, J. and Shimamoto, K. 1993. Insect resistant rice generated by introduction of a modified δ-endotoxin gene of *Bacillus thuringiensis*. Bio/Technology **11**: 1151-1155.

Grayson, B.T., Green, M.B. and Copping, L.G. 1990. Pest management in rice. Elsevier, Barking, UK.

Heong, K.L., Escalada, M.M. and Mai, V. 1994. An analysis of insecticide use in rice: case studies in the Philippines and Vietnam. Int. J. Pest Management **40**: 173-178.

International Rice Research Institute. 1989. IRRI toward 2000 and beyond. International Rice Research Institute, Los Banos, The Philippines.

Khan, Z.R., Litsinger, J.A., Barrion, A.T., Villanueva, F.F.D., Fernandez, N.J. and Taylo, L.D. 1991. World bibliography of rice stem borers 1794-1990. International Rice Research Institute, The Philippines.

Koziel, M.G., Beland, G.L., Bowman, C., Carozzi, N.B. Crenshaw, R., Crossland, L., Dawson, J., Desai, N., Hill, M., Kadwell, S., Launis, K., Lewis, K., Maddox, D., McPherson, K., Meghji, M.R., Merlin, E., Rhodes, R., Warren, G.W., Wright, M. and Evola, S. 1993. Field performance of elite transgenic maize plants expressing an insecticidal protein derived from *Bacillus thuringiensis*. Bio/Technology **11**: 194-200.

Murray, E.E., Rocheleau, T., Eberle, M., Stock, C., Sekar, V. and Adang, M.J. 1991. Analysis of unstable RNA transcripts of insecticidal crystal protein genes of *Bacillus thuringiensis* in transgenic plants and electroporated protoplasts. Plant. Molec. Biol. **16**: 1035-1050.

National Research Council. 1986. Pesticide Resistance: Strategies and Tactics for Management. National Academy Press, Washington D.C., USA, 448pp.

Pathak, M.D. and Khan, Z.R. 1994. Insect pests of rice. International Rice Research Institute, The Philippines.

Perlak, F.J., Deaton, R.W., Armstrong, T.A., Fuchs, R.L., Sims, S.R., Greenplate, J.T. and Fischhoff, D.A. 1990. Insect resistant cotton plants. Bio/Technology **8**: 939-943.

Perlak, F.J., Fuchs, R.L., Dean, D.A., McPherson, S.L. and Fischhoff, D.A. 1991. Modification of the coding sequence enhances plant expression of insect control protein genes. Proc. Natl. Acad. Sci. USA **88**: 3324-3328.

Ryan, C.A. 1989. Proteinase inhibitor gene families: Strategies for transformation to improve plant defense against herbivores. BioEssays **10**: 20-24.

Vaeck, M., Reynaerts, A., Höfte, H., Jansens, S., De Beuckeleer, M., Dean, C., Zabeau, M., Van Montagu, M. and Leemans, J. 1987. Transgenic plants protected from insect attack. Nature **327**: 239-247.

Way, M.J. and Heong, K.L. 1994. The role of biodiversity in the dynamics and management of insect pests of tropical rice - a review. B. Entomol. Res. **84**: 567-587.

Whalon, M.E. and McGaughey, W.H. 1993. Insect resistance to Bacillus thuringiensis. p. 215-232. *In*: Advanced engineered pesticides. Kim, L. (ed.). Marcel Dekker, Inc., New York.

Tabashnik, B.E. 1994. Evolution of resistance to *Bacillus thuringiensis*. Annu. Rev. Entomol. **39**: 47-79.

Improvement of Guinea Pig Breeding and Husbandry in Bolivia

Anne Valle Zárate and Peter Horst
Humboldt University of Berlin
Institute of Basic Animal Sciences,
Lentzeallee 75, D-14195 Berlin, Germany

Abstract

A Bolivian-German project for the improvement of guinea pig breeding and husbandry is presented as a model case for animal research projects in collaboration with universities of developing countries to promote education and scientific research directed to agricultural development.

The background of the project is described to explain the role of guinea pigs in small farmer production systems of the Andean region. The experimental concept starts from the evaluation of the local genetic resources, analyzing different possibilities for their incorporation in breeding plans. Special emphasis is put on designing appropriate breeding stock for different socioeconomic and ecological farming conditions. Research is systematically linked to development activities. Both approaches are utilized to give university education a practical orientation by incorporating students of both participating universities in all project activities.

Some project results are presented. The project's contribution to university education is judged to be very positive. The autochthonous small animal species guinea pig has been extremely advantageous for meeting the objectives of the project in relatively short time. In the future, integration of socio-economic and ethnologic approaches should be sought and farmer's participation enhanced. Limits of communication and of publication of project results must be overcome by implementing a methodology of linguistic engineering.

Keywords

University-research partnership, guinea pig improvement, breeding

1   Concept of the Project

The first priority of a long-term international co-operation in research and development is to build personal confidence and general agreement about basic concepts. A further prerequisite consists of the mutual interest of participating persons and institutions in gaining scientific knowledge by means of a joint, multidisciplinary research program through contributions from different subject areas and cultural backgrounds. Secondly, the success of a project depends on the appropriateness of the research concept and the elaboration of effective strategies (Horst 1989). This holds true especially for a project's sustainability. Schematic stages for project planning and implementation are shown in figure 1. Indeed, the steps indicated do not only succeed one another, but the whole process has to be developed in a circuit with several back-stoppings.

The project for improvement of guinea pig breeding and husbandry in Bolivia "Mejocuy" was founded in 1987 in co-operation between the Universidad Mayor de San Simon in Cochabamba, Bolivia, and the Technical University of Berlin, and is still running.

The objectives of the project are threefold:

1. To promote **education** in the partner universities, primarily in the discipline of animal breeding, by connecting theoretical lectures to scientific research, training of technical skills and application to practical field conditions in the rural area of Bolivia;
2. To conduct a **research** project to gain knowledge about the local genetic resources of guinea pigs (an important meat supplier for subsistence in the Andes); emphasis is being put on phenotypic and genetic characterization, determination of basic biological and zootechnical parameters as well as the development of breeding and husbandry strategies allowing intensification of production in the rural area;
3. To supply improved breeding stock for diffusion into smallholder farms through **extension** programs and to offer a training center for guinea pig husbandry to students from the university and to farmers and technicians from development projects.

2   Background of the Project

Traditionally, guinea pigs have been the main source of animal protein for the rural population of the Andes (Bolton 1979; Gade 1967). On the smallholder level, raising is characterized by low external inputs and low extraction rates, in contrast to the biological potential of the species.

Women are mostly responsible for animal husbandry and generally have full responsibility for small animals from raising to marketing in smallholder production systems of the Andes (Chauca 1991; Valle Zarate 1995). In traditional communities of the High Andes, guinea pig production is generally for home consumption. In the Andean Valleys, the rate of commercialization is generally higher, but intensive commercial production is very rare (see table 1).

Figure 1:   Stages of Cooperative R & D Projects
in Tropical Animal Production

◆ Defining of research concept and research objectives
  * Exploration of most suitable animal species

◆ Creation of international research partnership
  * Tropical country
  * Scientific institution
            - personal qualification
            - technical standard
            - institutional infrastructure

◆ Evaluation of research background
  * Macro-economic significance of the subsector
  * Socio-economic profile of production systems
  * Bio-technological limitations in reproduction and production

◆ Formulation of a development oriented research program with the aims of:
  * Solving biological constraints
            - genetic potential
            - disease status
  * Improving technical deficiencies
            - housing and construction
            - feeding and supplementation
            - reproduction management
            - hygienic conditions
  * Elaborating appropriate extension technologies and experimental testing in the field
  * Transferring of positive results to national improvement programs

◆ Realization of a joint working program
  * Building up of research facilities
  * Scientific and technical training and exchange
  * Establishment of experimental material
  * Application of experimental treatments
  * Data collection and data management
  * Data analysis and interpretation of results
  * Analysis of the project with respect to achievements and pitfalls and derivation
    of conclusions for future strategies

◆ Development of a research and training unit for:
  * Interdisciplinary research
  * Academic teaching
  * Technical training
  * Extension in development and research

◆ Revision and continuation

Following Quijandria (1988), 90 % of all guinea pig keeping farms in the Andean region pertain to the extensive level. Chauca (1991) shows for Bolivian conditions that flock sizes are generally lower in the highland (often < 10) than in the valleys (up to 50), and estimates that 60 - 70 % of production from extensive systems is utilized for home consumption. However, market demand is high since 40 - 50 % of the urban and 35 - 80 % of the rural population consume guinea pig meat. Market supply and prices fluctuate considerably over the year with traditional production adapted to seasonal fluctuations of the Andean production system (Bolton 1979; Chauca 1991; Valle Zarate 1995). Thus, guinea pig flock sizes may be 5 - 8 fold increased and diminished over the year. Flock size is mainly determined by feed availability, for extensive systems by natural vegetation, for semi-extensive systems by forage.

The advantages of guinea pigs as an easily manageable and consumable small animal with little demand for care, capital and labor, good utilization of roughage, adaptation to extreme climates and low susceptibility to diseases explain their high significance for small farmers in the regions of origin of this species. The moderately high reproduction rate along with the high variability in population make it especially suitable for the High Andean ecosystems with marked seasonality of production. The latter factor and its small size make guinea pigs a promising vehicle for research innovations and make it possible to conduct breeding experiments at low cost and in a relatively short time, thus demonstrating a methodology which can be extended to other domestic animals.

3   Experimental Concept

The core of the project consists of the breeding program, linking together research in other disciplines and development activities. The research concept in breeding is illustrated in figure 2.

It comprises the following steps: collection of genetic material from different regions all over the country, screening of regional subpopulations, performance testing of local population in a long-term on-station test, establishment of a national gene pool, comparison of the local population with an exotic improved line in pure breeding and through a crossbreeding test, implementation of breeding programs (selection and crossbreeding) and continuous production and delivery of improved breeders. Breeding products are simultaneously tested under specific ecological and socio-economic conditions to determine genotype x environment interactions and assure the appropriateness for diverge field conditions. Associate research was conducted mainly in the areas of nutrition and reproduction also covering topics of zoonoses and disease prevention.

Table 1: Classification of Guinea Pig Management Systems in Bolivia

Intensity of management	extensive	semi-extensive	semi-intensive	intensive
Number of animals (a)	< 10 10 - 20 20 - 50	< 50 50 - 80	50 - 100 - 500 - 1000	500 - 1000 > 1000
Animals are kept				
- within the house	free (highland)	separated in corner (highland)	no	no
- in small stables or cages near the house	free (valleys)	separated in pens (valleys, highland)	separate huts (valleys, highland)	permanent solid stables (valleys)
- in separate stables	no	no	yes	yes
- by	women and children	women and children	women (men)	men
Feeding	kitchen wastes, (highlands); byproducts (valleys)	+ forage	+ forage (+concentrate)	forage or/and concentrate
Breeding	uncontrolled	occasionally controlled	new sires, occasionally bought	selected breeders
Investment	no	low	medium	high
Risk of production	low	medium	high	low
Commercialization (% animals)	0 - 30	0 - 50	50 - 70	~100

(a) smaller numbers generally refer to highland, bigger ones to valleys

Source: modified from Valle Zárate, 1995

Figure 2: Evaluation of the Local Genetic Resource of Guinea Pigs in Bolivia as a Basis for the Choice of an Appropriate Breeding Program

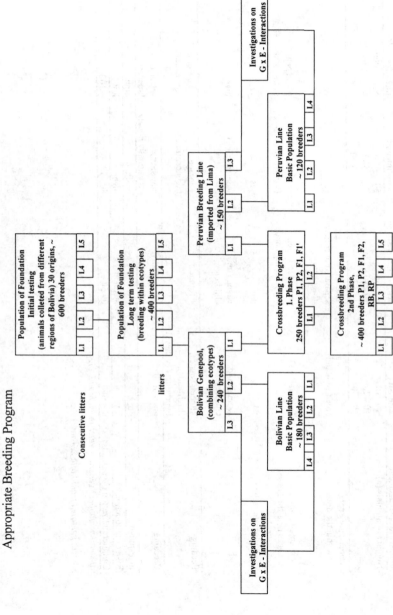

Source: *Valle Zárate, 1995*

Relevancy for development has been considered already by the choice of the research topic and by systematic incorporation of field trials. All investigations are directed primarily towards Andean small farmer production systems with emphasis on the subsistence level. Special attention is paid to rural women as the main actors of small animal raising and the main victims of impoverishment. Within the institutional limitations of universities, the project has established its own extension service in direct co-operation with rural communities, specifically women groups, working with permanent involvement of postgraduate students. To broaden the impact, extension services are also channeled through non-governmental organizations (NGOs) engaged in rural development and training of farmers chosen by then communities and of technicians from government organizations and other NGOs.

4 Lessons Learned

The breeding experiments have been conducted successfully and led to the implementation of breeding programs for continuous production of improved breeding stock. On the basis of test results, specialized genotypes are provided for specific socio-economic conditions utilizing national and imported breeding stock and considering genotype x environment interactions. The national genetic resource of guinea pigs in Bolivia has been broadly characterized (Valle Zarate 1995), and now plays an important role in the production of optimized breeding stock. Scientific knowledge and experiences for husbandry improvements have been gained through conducting numerous investigations in the fields of housing, nutrition, reproduction, and disease prevention.

Research results have been published mainly as thesis papers (26 graduate thesis papers concluded in Bolivia, 2 doctorates in preparation in Germany, 1 habilitation concluded in Germany). International diffusion, however, is not satis-factory. The need to handle different languages simultaneously (Quechua, Aymara, Spanish, English, German) bears a considerable logistics problem. Methods for linguistic engineering should be explored. The autochthonous small animal species guinea pig has been extremely advantageous for meeting the research objectives of the project in a relatively short time. Techniques applied and results achieved will be partially adopted from this model case for breeding work with other domestic animals in the region.

The direct project impact on rural development has not been systematically analyzed so far. The university's logistic limitations will not allow for continuous extension work. Nonetheless, the relevancy of the research topic for the small farmer sector is without doubt. Future research approaches should be consequently directed to active participation of farmers in the most deprived rural areas of the High Andes in an effort to link traditional knowledge to technical innovations. Therefore, interdisciplinary systems research should be given priority, integrating socio-economic and ethnologic approaches. Impact monitoring must likewise be maintained with an appropriate methodology. On the institutional level, the project has been integrated into guinea pig research in the Andean region and a national network is being promoted in this field in collaboration with other Bolivian universities.

The project contribution to university education is judged to be very positive. The traditional educational system is generally limited to theoretical lectures and repetition of knowledge. Incorporating research into this system tends to induce a discriminating scientific approach. Additionally, the direct involvement of students in research and development activities in rural areas provides a beneficial introduction to approaches with practical orientation. Important advantages have been derived for the German university through incorporation of graduate and postgraduate students in the project activities.

Based on these successful experiences, this project may claim to have achieved an overall model for development activities in animal production together with the preceding project on crossbreeding goats in Malaysia (Horst 1989). As already outlined in figure 1 such a project has to systematically follow clearly identified and jointly agreed upon stages:

- defining feasible concepts and objectives
- creating substantial partnerships
- monitoring local research backgrounds
- fixing and revision of short- and long-term aims
- formulation of systematic working programs and time horizons
- integration of research, training and extension activities on the basis of an interdisciplinary approach.

From the beginning, the guinea pig project in Bolivia as well as the goat project in Malaysia (Horst 1989), have implemented this model in all these stages, although the model could only perform all aspects and the financial basis for such complex and long lasting programs was not always sufficient. The most important aspect for the fulfillment of this model was manifested by the institutional advancement and, especially, by the personal dedication to the jointly agreed way of scientific cooperation and by mutual confidence in the common activities. In this connection a national university involvement in such a research program must be seen as a special element of this model.

As universities are devoted to education and research, development cooperation via partnerships between universities should be focused on development research problems. As research concepts and research operations can have worldwide usefulness this component can ideally be used for international development and co-operation. Besides, as conceived by Humboldt, research should be a vehicle for advanced academic learning and could, therefore, also contribute to the promotion of the scientific standard of local universities. National universities should have a special participation in implementing long-term international development programs. This position, however, has not been fully realized up to now, neither in national nor in international development projects.

The scope of the co-operative project presented here is reflected in two spheres:

- *in a narrow sense* – of concentrating on the development of a subsector in animal production which is strongly underdeveloped in science and in practice and which is, in addition, particularly connected to the poor, and
- *in a wider sense* – of stimulating academic activities in research, education and international exchange of knowledge in order to mobilize joint potentials for continuous development-oriented interdisciplinary research.

Acknowledgments

Research work has been made possible by the high participation and spirit of members of the Mejocuy project, Cochabamba, and the interested participation of rural families.

References

Bolton, R. 1979. Guinea pigs, protein and ritual. Ethnology 18 (3): 229-252.

Chauca F., L. 1991. Programa de investigación y promoción de cuyes. IBTA, CIID; La Paz, Bolivia.

Gade, D.W. 1967. The guinea pig in andean folk culture. The Geographical Review 57 (2): 213-224.

Horst, P. 1989. The creation of a dual purpose goat in Malaysia as a model case for collaborative research and development. Proc. of a Conference "African small ruminant research and development" held at Bamenda, Cameroon, 18th-25th Jan.

Koeslag, J.H. 1989. The guinea pig as meat producer. ILEIA, Deventer, Netherland, Vol. 5 (1): 22-23.

Quijandria, B. 1988. Producción de cuyes. Organización de las Naciones Unidas para la Agricultura y la Alimentación, Roma.

Valle Zárate, A. 1993. Das Meerschweinchen als landwirtschaftliches Nutztier unter besonderer Berücksichtigung von Hauterkrankungen. Proc. 8. Arbeitstagung über Haltung und Krankheit der Kaninchen, Pelztiere und Heimtiere, Celle, DGV: 284-291.

Valle Zárate, A. 1995. Evaluierung der lokalen genetischen Ressourcen von Meerschweinchen zur landwirtschaftlichen Nutzung in der Andenregion Boliviens. Habilitationsschrift. Humboldt-Universität zu Berlin.

Valle Zárate, A. 1995. Promotion of rural women by guinea pig raising in Bolivia. 8th Intern. Conf. of Institutions of Tropical Veterinary Medicine (AITVM), 25th-29th Sept., Berlin.

Van Niekerk, N. 1992. La cooperación internaciónal y la persistencia de la pobreza en los Andes bolivianos. unitas/MCTH, La Paz, Bolivia.

Integrated Agriculture-Aquaculture:
A Way for Food Security for Small Farmers and
Better Resource Management and Environment

**M.V. Gupta[1], M. A. Rahman[2], M.A. Mazid[2] and
J.D. Sollows[1]**
[1]International Center for Living Aquatic Resources Management,
MCPO Box 2631, Makati City 0718, Metro Manila, Philippines
[2] Fisheries Research Institute, Mymensingh, Bangladesh

Abstract

*Traditionally fish have been a natural component of rice-ecosystems. Intensive
agriculture has led to degradation of fish habitats, resulting in disappearance of
fish from rice fields. The economic viability and impact on the environment of
integrating aquaculture with agriculture during rainfed and irrigated rice
growing seasons were studied in 256 farms in Bangladesh. Farmers on an
average obtained fish production of 230 and 214 kg.ha^{-1} during irrigated and
rainfed seasons, respectively. The cost of production was higher in integrated
farms by US$ 22.33 and US$ 44.68.ha^{-1} (13.6% and 17.6%) as compared to
monoculture rice farms during irrigated and rainfed seasons, respectively.*
*The increase in net benefit from integration amounted to $217.55 and
$239.45.ha^{-1}, during irrigated and rainfed seasons, indicating a net increase in
benefits to farmers by 61.3% and 80.1% respectively, during the two seasons.*
*Integration resulted in increased rice yields on an average by 10.25-11.58%, in
82% and 56% of integrated farms during irrigated and rainfed seasons
respectively, and a decrease in pest population by 40.5-166.7%. Weed infestation
in integrated farms was less by 42.9-68.6%.*

Keywords

*Integrated farming; sustainability; resource management; food security;
environment impact; fish culture* ·

Introduction

For 116 million people of Bangladesh, a country with a high population
density of 783 people per sq.km, rice and fish are the staple food. Small farmers
constitute the bulk of the population and the land holdings are small, being less
than 0.4 ha on an average (BBS 1994). Given the scarcity of land and the need to
meet the demand of increasing population, alleviate poverty and malnutrition,
there was no alternative but to continue intensification of agriculture. The country
has made substantial progress in attaining self-sufficiency in food grain

production: high yielding rice varieties (HYV) account for half of the rice area and the cropping intensity has increased to 179%. Rice production has increased from 12.5 million t in 1980 to 18.34 million t in 1993. Along with intensification, fertilizer use has increased from 334,690 t in 1978 to 921,650 t in 1990 and pesticides from 5,051 t in 1978 to 7,700 t in 1993. There is increasing concern that intensive agriculture may not be sustainable, due to its high demand for soil nutrients and damage to the environment. Rice yields in recent years are stagnating or declining despite increased use of inputs, suggesting degradation of land and questioning the sustainability of intensive agriculture (Pagiola 1995) and the crop sector is showing negative growth.

Fish is the main source of animal protein, providing 8 g.day^{-1}, or 12% of the average per capita total intake of protein (63.5 g) and 71% of the total animal protein intake in Bangladesh (BBS 1988). In spite of the importance of fish in nutrition, per capita intake is very low, estimated at 8.3 kg.annum^{-1}. These average consumption figures in reality camouflage the very low intake among rural households. It has been estimated that while per capita fish intake among the high income segment of the urban population is 22 kg.annum^{-1}, it is only 4.4 kg.annum^{-1} among the low-income rural population (World Bank 1993). Average per capita daily fish intake in the rural sector has declined from 97% of urban sector intake levels in 1973 to 75% in 1986 (BBS 1988), which is leading to protein deficient malnutrition. Even this low intake in rural areas is mostly obtained by catching fish from open-access capture fisheries.

Fish has been a natural component of rice fields. In the past, farmers used to catch wild fish from flooded rice lands. Some of these fish, such as *Amblypharyngodon mola* are reported to contain very high amounts of vitamin A (Thilsted and Hassan 1993), which is deficient among rural population causing blindness, especially among children. The increasing demand for food is leading to increased pressure on natural resources through intensive agriculture, with concomitant increase in the use of fertilizers and pesticides, which are detrimental to fish populations. This, combined with implementation of flood protection programs, resulted in depletion and degradation of fish habitats and fish populations from rice fields have almost disappeared (Gupta and Mazid 1993).

While intensification of agriculture to meet the needs of the growing population is an inescapable imperative, at the same time it is a pre-requisite to assess the ecological sustainability and look at systems that could provide food security to small farmers through environmentally compatible integrated farming systems and resource management. In view of the above, research was undertaken to assess the feasibility of integrating aquaculture with agriculture by small-holder farmers and the impact of integration, if any, on rice production and environment.

Materials and Methods

There are three rice farming seasons in Bangladesh: (i) irrigated, dry season rice farming, locally known as *boro,* during January-February to May-June, (ii) rainfed rice farming, locally known as *aman* during July-August to November-December, and (iii) a third crop season, locally known as *aus,* in areas where there is sufficient soil moisture, during April-May to July-August. Of these, rainfed rice and irrigated rice are the main crops.

The study was undertaken in 256 farms in Mymensingh district during five rice growing seasons: three rainfed and two irrigated. The area of farms where integrated farming was undertaken was 0.04-1.20 ha. Some of these farms had a sump or a shallow ditch from which the farmers used to catch wild fish. Those who did not have a sump or ditch excavated a ditch in the lower side of the plot as refuge for fish during adverse conditions. The area of the ditch ranged from 8 to 680 m^2, with a depth of 0.5-0.8 m. Twelve varieties of high yielding varieties of rice were transplanted during the irrigated season and 18 varieties during the rainfed season, of which 15 were HYV. Fish fingerlings were stocked 15-20 days after transplantation of rice. Water depth in rice fields was 0-30 cm during the irrigated season and 5-47 cm during the rainfed season. The rearing period of fish varied from plot to plot and from season to season and ranged 34-113 and 42-138 days during the irrigated and rainfed seasons, respectively.

Insect/pest populations were monitored in four integrated and monoculture rice farms each during the irrigated season. Integrated and monoculture rice farms were selected in pairs in the same area, with the same variety of rice and management and of the same farmer. Twenty hills at random (distance between monitored hills was 2 m) from each plot were sampled for insects and the observed insects were collected and identified. In all, five samplings were done, the first 15 days after transplantation of rice and thereafter at weekly intervals, till harvesting of rice. The insects were identified and grouped into pests and useful insects which prey on insects.

For qualitative and quantitative assessments of weeds in integrated and monoculture rice farms, seven farms each were monitored at fortnightly intervals. In all, four samples were taken during the rice growing season, the first about 30 days after transplantation of rice and before weeding by farmers and subsequent samplings at fortnightly intervals. All weeds present in 1 m^{-2} area at three randomly selected places in each farm were collected. The weeds were then identified and their number and weight were noted.

Results

Fish Production

There was wide variation in the fish species cultured and stocking densities practiced by farmers (see table 1). Species selection by farmers mostly depended on availability of fingerlings: common carp (*Cyprinus carpio*) during the irrigated season and silver barb (*Puntius gonionotus*) during the rainfed season. Few farmers stocked Nile tilapia (*Oreochromis niloticus*). Some farmers in addition stocked carps: catla (*Catla catla*), rohu (*Labeo rohita*), mrigal (*Cirrhinus mrigala*), silver carp (*Hypophthalmichthys molitrix*) and grass carp (*Ctenopharyngodon idella*). Stocking densities varied widely with an average of $3,864.ha^{-1}$ (s.d. 2,815) during the irrigated season and $4,534.ha^{-1}$ (s.d 4,304) during the rainfed season. Fish production averaged 230 (s.d. 198) and 214 (s.d. 247) $kg.ha^{-1}$ during irrigated and rainfed seasons, respectively. Farmers who stocked at higher densities, which was the case mostly with multi-species combination, obtained higher fish production of 577 (s.d. 382) and 485 (s.d. 367) $kg.ha^{-1}$ during the irrigated and rainfed seasons, respectively.

Multiple regression analysis indicated a statistically significant positive correlation between stocking density and fish production, production increasing with increasing density during both seasons. Densities less than $3\ 000.ha^{-1}$ resulted in fish productions of 164 and 118 $kg.ha^{-1}$ during dry and wet seasons, respectively, while densities of $3\ 000$-$6\ 000.ha^{-1}$ gave fish production of 276 and 175 $kg.ha^{-1}$, respectively. Fish production were highest, 616 and 571 $kg.ha^{-1}$ during the irrigated and rainfed seasons, respectively, when stocking densities were over $6\ 000.ha^{-1}$ (see table 1).

Size of fingerlings at stocking varied from species to species and in general was in the range of 3.8-11 cm. Size of fish at harvest varied widely among farms and among species, depending on the length of culture period, water depth in rice fields, stocking density and survival. During the irrigated season, *C. carpio* attained the highest mean weight of 108 g at harvest, with lowest mean recovery of 55.6%, followed by *P. gonionotus* with average mean weight of 85.3 g and 62.5% recovery. Only 8 plots were stocked with *O. niloticus* and they reached an average weight of 76.9g, with 66.3% survival. During the rainfed season, *C. carpio* reached a mean average weight of 74.5 g, with a recovery of 55.8%, while it was 56.1 g and 66.2% in case of *P. gonionotus*.

Though the size of fish at harvest was small due to short rearing period, farmers still consume and are able to get a good market for the small fish.

Multiple regression analysis indicated significant positive correlation between fish culture period and depth of water in rice fields with fish production during the irrigated season, but no such correlation was observed during the rainfed season.

Table 1: Fish Production at Different Stocking Densities in Integrated Farms during Rainfed and Irrigated Seasons

Stocking density (no./ha)	Irrigated season		Rainfed season	
	No. of farms	Fish production (kg.ha^{-1})	No. of farms	Fish production (kg.ha^{-1})
0 - 3,000	103	164 (92)	57	118 (71)
3,000 - 6,000	30	276 (150)	28	175 (134)
>6,000	14	616 (351)	15	571 (396)

Note: Standard deviations are in parentheses.

Rice Production in Integrated Farms

The principal commodity in this farming system is rice and any adverse effect on rice yields would call into question the viability of the integrated system. Hence, the effect of integration on rice production, if any, was studied. Rice yields from integrated farms and monoculture rice farms (control) were monitored. Since production depends on soil fertility, rice variety and management practices, for the purpose of comparison, integrated and monoculture rice plots adjacent to each other, with the same rice variety and management practices and in many cases plots of the same farmer, were selected for monitoring. Integrated farms had higher rice yields in 82.4% cases during the irrigated season and in 56.2% cases during the rainfed season, as compared to monoculture rice farms (see table 2). Increase in rice yields on an average was 10.25% during the irrigated season and 11.58% during the rainfed season.

Table 2: Rice Production in Monoculture Rice Farms and Integrated Farms

Season	No. of farms	Rice yield: monoculture rice farms (kg.ha^{-1})	Rice yield: integrated farms (kg.ha^{-1})	Integrated farms with higher yields (%)	Mean difference from control (%)
Irrigated	34	4,702 (3,046-6,000)	4,980 (3,264-6,571)	82.4	+10.25 (-13.3 - +57.6)
Rainfed	25	3,498 (1,976-6,250)	3,811 (2,058-4,940)	56.2	+11.58 (-21.3 - +66.7)

Note: Ranges are in parentheses.

Economics

Capital costs involved in integrating aquaculture with rice farming are the labor costs towards excavation of a ditch or sump and strengthening of dikes, where necessary, using family labor and/or hired labor. The operational costs include cost of fingerlings, supplementary feeds and fertilizers and irrigation. While fingerlings are cash costs, fertilizers and supplementary feeds are partly non-cash costs, as farmers used partly on-farm wastes. Cost (cash and non-cash) of integrating aquaculture with agriculture amounted to \$72.15 and \$66.52.ha^{-1} during irrigated and rainfed seasons, respectively (see table 3). Cost of fingerlings accounted for 58.7% and 67.2% of total costs during irrigated and rainfed seasons, respectively. Cost of feeds and fertilizers accounted for 10.3% and 21.6% of total costs. Gross and net benefits from fish culture component in integrated farming are given in table 4. Mean net benefit was more or less same during irrigated and rainfed seasons, being \$123.70 and \$119.98.ha^{-1}, respectively. Of the total 144 and 101 integrated farms studied during irrigated and rainfed seasons, 15 (10.4%) and 12 (11.9%) farms, respectively, lost money on fish culture, mostly due to flooding and loss of fish due to escape and theft.

Table 3:   Cost (US\$.ha^{-1}) of Fish Production in Integrated Rice-Fish Farming

Season	No. of farms	Feed and fertilizers	Fingerlings	Plot preparation	Irrigation	Total
Irrigated	144	7.40	42.32	18.63	3.80	72.15
		(7.78)	(39.38)	(24.40)	(6.38)	(53.00)
Rainfed	101	14.35	44.72	7.20	0.25	66.52
		(15.07)	(32.68)			(56.70)

Note: Standard deviations are in parentheses.

A comparison of cost of production of rice in monoculture rice farms and in integrated farms (see table 5) indicated that rice production costs in integrated farms as compared to monoculture rice farms, were lower by 8.8% and 10.7% during irrigated and rainfed seasons, respectively, due to less use of fertilizers and pesticides and less labor for weeding. Cost of fertilizers in integrated farms averaged 14.3% less as compared to monoculture rice farms during the irrigated season and 43.3% during the rainfed season. Average weeding costs in integrated farms were lower by 29.3% during the irrigated season and 23.2% during the rainfed season. Pesticide costs were lower by 86.3% during the irrigated season in integrated farms.

Lower production cost for rice combined with higher yields in integrated farms resulted in increasing net benefit from rice alone to 22.6% and 11.9% in integrated farms during irrigated and rainfed seasons, respectively (see table 6). The net benefit from integration increased to 61.3% and 80.1%, as compared to monoculture rice farms, during irrigated and rainfed seasons, respectively. Though 10.4% and 11.9% of farms incurred loss on fish culture during the irrigated and rainfed seasons, respectively, in none of the cases, was net benefit lower in integrated farms as compared to monoculture rice farms, due to increased benefit from rice.

Table 4: Costs (US\$.ha^{-1}) and Benefits of Fish Component in Integrated Rice-Fish Farming

Season	No. of farms	Costs	Gross benefit	Net benefit
Irrigated	144	72.15	195.85	123.70
		(53.00)	(151.93)	(127.35)
Rainfed	101	66.52	186.50	119.98
		(56.75)	(183.20)	(153.68)

Note: Standard deviations are in parentheses.

Table 5: Production Costs (US\$.ha^{-1}) of Plots Stocked with Fish and Comparable Unstocked Plots

Season	No. of farms	Cost of production				
		Monoculture: rice (control)	Integrated: rice	% difference from control	Integrated: rice and fish	% difference from control
Irrigated	22	328.45	299.58	-8.8	373.13	+13.6
		(63.45)	(72.73)	(12.6)	(95.85)	(23.1)
Rainfed	10	127.20	113.58	-10.7	149.53	+17.6
		(23.35)	(20.23)	(9.6)	(23.83)	(15.5)

Note: Standard deviations are in parentheses.
Total cost of production for fish and rice in integrated farms on an average was higher by 13.6% and 17.6% as compared to monoculture rice farms, during irrigated and rainfed seasons.

Table 6: Net Benefit (US\$.ha^{-1}) from Integrated Farms and Comparable Monoculture Rice Farms

	No. of farms					Net benefit
		Monoculture: rice (control)	Integrated: rice	% difference from control	Integrated: rice and fish	% difference from control
Irrigated	22	355.00	435.13	+22.57	572.55	+61.28
		(114.98)	(139.40)	(24.4)	(187.70)	(38.0)
Rainfed	10	299.05	334.48	+11.85	538.50	+80.07
		(90.13)	(89.85)	(54.7)	(122.23)	(86.0)

Note: Standard deviations are in parentheses.

Pest Infestation and Pesticide Use

During the irrigated season, 35.3% and 10.1% of monoculture and integrated farms, respectively, used pesticides. Use of pesticides was very low during the rainfed season, having been used by only 16.7% of the monoculture rice farmers. Low or non-use of pesticides in integrated farms was attributed by farmers to low infestation of pests.

The study revealed that pest population (larval and adult stages of stemborer, rice bug, green leaf hopper, white leaf hopper, short horned grasshopper, golden cricket, gall midge, rice ear head bug, mole cricket, rice skipper and black bug) was higher in monoculture rice farms as compared to integrated farms by 40.5-166.7% during different times of crop growth (compare figure 1). Of these, major pests were stemborers, grasshoppers and rice bugs. In spite of low or no use of pesticides in integrated farms, pest infestation was low, indirectly indicating a role for the fish in controlling pests, through predation, and integration could lead to integrated pest management (IPM).

Weed Infestation

Labor costs for weeding were low in integrated farms, the reason for which was given by farmers as low weed infestation, due to grazing and dislodging of weeds by fish. Farmers' perceptions were verified and weed populations were quantified in integrated and monoculture rice farms through a study of the occurrence of weeds in integrated and monoculture rice farms at fortnightly intervals. The quantity of weeds by number and weight was highest before first weeding by farmers, declining during subsequent samplings. Weed infestation in integrated farms was less by 42.9-68.6% by number and 40.6-66.9% by weight as compared to monoculture rice farms, during different samplings (compare figure 2), resulting in lower labor requirement for weeding.

Impact of Research and Adoption by Farmers

One year after the conclusion of the research, surveys were undertaken in one of the study areas, to assess the adoption of integrated rice-fish farming practices among rice farmers. These surveys revealed that a large number of farmers, having been convinced of the benefits of integration, have and are taking to integration and intensified operations with higher benefits. Intensification included increased stocking densities and higher use of inputs for fish culture, with fish production reaching as high as over 1 t.ha^{-1}. It is interesting to note that the farmers who were not involved in research but adopted integration after seeing operations of their neighbors went in for intensification. Besides culturing fish, farmers were able to use the water from refuge ditches for irrigation of rice in case of drought, thus saving the rice crop.

Figure 1: Number of Pests collected from Integrated and Monoculture Farms

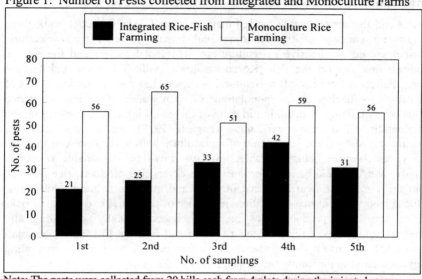

Note: The pests were collected from 20 hills each from 4 plots during the irrigated season.

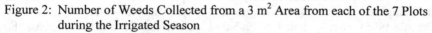

Figure 2: Number of Weeds Collected from a 3 m^2 Area from each of the 7 Plots during the Irrigated Season

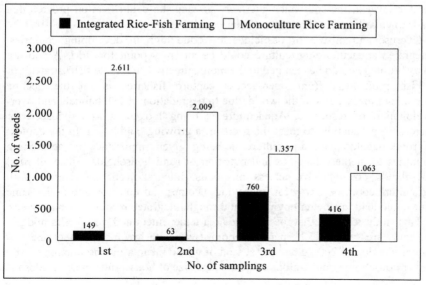

Conclusions

Rice and fish are the staple food of many people of Asia. In recent years, there is growing concern of the environmental impact of intensive agriculture. Pesticides used in intensive agriculture are detrimental to fish and the aquatic foodweb that support the fish (Koesoemadinata 1980; Takamura and Yasuno 1986). Pollution from run-off agricultural pesticides has been identified as one of the causes for decline in fish populations of open waters. At a time when rice yields are stabilizing or declining in spite of increased input use, questioning the sustainability of intensive agriculture (Pagiola 1995), the present study has conclusively shown that integration of aquaculture with agriculture can increase rice yields, besides being a viable, low-cost, low-risk, sustainable economic activity, with multiple benefits: production of diversified products, rice and fish from the same land area; increased incomes and nutrition to farm households; reduced labor costs in rice cultivation; lesser use of pesticides and spread of risks due to diversity of produce. Thus integration is economically and ecologically beneficial and is a way for food security for small farmers. In spite of the small size of fish at harvest due to the short rearing period, farmers are continuing integrated farming indicating the sustainability of the system.

Yield declines observed in long-term HYV cropping trials are thought to result from anaerobic conditions in irrigated rice production systems, resulting in declining supply of nutrients to growing crop (Cassman et al., as quoted by Pagiola 1995). Fish by their feeding habits, disturb the soil and thus increase the aerobic layer at the soil-water interface, slowing the denitrification process that leads to volatilization of nitrogen (Fillery et al. 1984).

Overuse and misuse of pesticides are quite high in developing countries. Integrated aquaculture-agriculture could be an entry point for IPM. A "do not spray" strategy could be changed to the more attractive "integrate fish" strategy.

Fish production from open-access capture fisheries is on the decline throughout many parts of the world, due to degradation of fish habitats and over-exploitation of resources. Aquaculture is being looked at as a panacea for increasing production, to meet the needs of a growing population. In the context of rural development, aquaculture is being given importance in developing countries to increase incomes and nutrition of rural households. Since all rural households do not have access to ponds, integration of aquaculture with agriculture could be a way for improving incomes and nutrition and at the same time could lead to a better environment through integrated resource management.

This study revealed that the average area under integrated rice-fish farming in the study area was 0.25 ha per household. Even with low management and low fish production of 200 kg.ha^{-1} per season, it would mean a fish production of 100 kg per household (from 2 crops). The average size of households in Bangladesh is

5.6 persons (BBS 1994). Thus, by integrating aquaculture with agriculture, rural households can have per capita fish consumption of 17.85 kg.annum^{-1}, which is double the national average consumption of 8.3 kg.annum^{-1}.

There are some 8 million ha of rice farms in Bangladesh. However, all may not be suitable for integration, due to land topography and soil structure. Even if 5% of these rice farms are brought under integration and with low fish productions of 200 kg.ha^{-1}.season, it would mean an annual fish production from rice farms of some 160,000 t, valued at US$160 million per year. To realize this potential, what is needed is the commitment on the part of the planners, administrators and extension workers, to provide information/training to the farmers and ensure easy availability of fingerlings at affordable prices of required size and species at the appropriate time.

References

BBS. 1988. Report on the Bangladesh household expenditure survey, 1985-86. Bangladesh bureau of Statistics. Ministry of Planning, Dhaka.

BBS. 1994. 1988. Statistical Year Book of Bangladesh, Bangladesh Bureau of Statistics, Ministry of Planning, Dhaka.

Fillery, I.R.P., J.R. Simpson and S.K. De Datta. 1984. Influence of field environment and fertilizer management on ammonia loss from flooded rice. Soil Sci. Soc. Am. J. 48: 914-920.

Gupta, M.V and M.A. Mazid, 1993. Feasibility and potentials for integrated rice-fish systems in Bangladesh. Twelfth Session of the FAP Regional Farm Management Commission for Asia and the Far East. FMCAFE/TR/93/05. 18p.

Koesoemadinata 1980. Pesticides as major constraints to integrated agriculture-aquaculture farming systems, p.45-51. In R.S.V. Pullin and Z. Shehadeh (eds.) Integrated agriculture-aquaculture farming systems. ICLARM Conf. Proc.4, 258 p.

Pagiola S. 1995. Environmental and natural resource degradation in intensive agriculture in Bangladesh. Environment Department Paper no. 15, World Bank, 32 p.

Takamura, K. and M. Yasuno 1986. Effects of pesticide application on chironomid larvae and ostracods in rice fields. Appl. Entomol. Zool. 2:370-376.

Thilsted, S. and N.H. Hassan 1993. A comparison of the nutritional value of indigenous fish in Bangladesh - the contribution to the dietary intake of essential nutrients. XV International Congress of Nutrition, Adelaide, Australia.

World Bank 1993. Bangladesh Fisheries Sector Review. Report No. 8830-BD. 195 p.

Part 2.3

The Generation of Innovations
Economics and Innovations

The Economics of Erosion Control Innovations in Northern Burkina Faso

Dagmar Kunze[1], Artur Runge-Metzger[2], and Hermann Waibel[1]
[1] Institut für Gartenbauökonomie; Universität Hannover; Herrenhäuser Str. 2; 30419 Hanover, Germany
[2] European Union, Delegation of the European Commission, Harare, Zimbabwe

Abstract

Decreasing annual rainfall and high erosion rates have made erosion control and water harvesting measures an important task in all of the sub-Sahelian region of western Africa. The construction of stone lines, dikes and dams has been proven a sustainable measure which is widely accepted by the rural population of northern Burkina Faso. As farmers are obviously willing to invest large amounts of labor in construction and maintenance they seem to consider the yield gains and risk reduction as profitable.

The objective of a field study which was conducted in Bam Province of Burkina Faso from 1992 to 1994 was to investigate economic profitability of erosion control measures under farmers' conditions. Main aspects concerned yield changes in small farmers' staple food grain production of sorghum and millet as well as the competition of rock bund construction with other dry season activities such as commerce, crafting and gold-mining. Based on farm surveys, assessment of impact on farmers' fields and investment calculations considered different types of costs: construction and maintenance costs, opportunity costs of dry season activities as well as subsidies offered by development organizations mostly concerning transport facilities, farmers' training and extension.

Keywords

Western Africa, Burkina Faso, erosion, water harvesting, rock bunds, investment calculations

Introduction

Self-sufficiency in cereal production is one of the most important objectives of farm households in sub-Sahelian western Africa. The regions' rainfall regime is characterized by a gradual reduction of annual rainfall over the last decades (Mortimer 1989; Speirs and Olsen 1992), a southward shift of agroclimatic zones

(Matlon 1986), and a high inter- and intra-annual variation of rainfall. These climatic changes have made water management of rainfed agriculture an increasingly difficult task.

Anthropocentric factors such as over-grazing, decline of natural vegetation and extension of cultivated land on marginal areas exacerbated by a rapidly increasing population have led to high rates of soil erosion which are estimated to amount to 35 t/ha soil loss per year (Raymond and Lindskog 1994).

Governments and farmers have tried to counter soil degradation through the introduction of soil conservation measures since the beginning of the 1960s. These measures are largely based on indigenous knowledge about the collection and distribution of water used for agriculture, a technique commonly called water-harvesting. Depending on the availability of construction material, bunds of laterite, dirt, grass, living bushrows, wooden barriers, terraces and tied ridges are found across all sub-Sahelian countries.

The decision on investment in resource conservation measures has to be taken at the government as well as at the farmers' level. In particular, after the droughts in the 1970s and early 1980s the Government of Burkina Faso with the assistance of various donor organizations has decided to support farmers in the implementation of soil conservation measures notably in the northern provinces. For the future, however, it remains questionable whether the same extent of government subsidies can be afforded on national level. Furthermore, it has to be investigated if such government interventions are economically justified and whether the results of ex-ante economic analysis (de Haen and Runge-Metzger 1989) can be confirmed.

In this paper investment analysis is used to estimate the profitability of soil conservation measures taking into account farm survey data on yield increase, empirical data on opportunity costs of inputs provided by the rural households as well as government subsidies. The study regions' most widespread type of construction are permeable rock bunds which vary from small stone lines to larger dikes and dams. Contrary to existing analysis this study investigates the economics of erosion control measures under farmers' conditions. So far, investment calculations were mostly based on yield increases of on-station or farmer managed trials, without consideration of opportunity costs or estimates with reference to minimum wage labor or rainy season farm wages and varying subsidies.

In the following the expected benefits and costs will be reviewed briefly. Thereafter, the methodology and the results of a field study undertaken in 1992-94 will be presented.

Economics of Soil Conservation Measures – Theoretical Considerations and Review of Past Results

In principle, investment in soil conservation techniques competes with other on- and off-farm investments. Farmers have to decide to which activities and enterprises to allocate their scarce resources. Therefore, a careful assessment of the economics of the various investments needs to be conducted. Appropriate economic analysis will depend on the goals of the farm households. Profitability, stability, and food self-sufficiency are regarded as important objectives of farm households.

Expected benefits of soil conservation measures include higher yields, reduced variation of yields and therefore a lower production risk, and lower soil erosion rates. Costs include the labor and transport costs for actual construction and maintenance. Furthermore, on-farm benefits and costs are influenced by government interventions such as subsidized services and distorted prices.

Expected incremental yields: Expected incremental yields depend on the development of yields without meliorative measures, the potential direct yield increases due to reduced soil and water erosion as a result of rock bunds, and indirect yield increases through an increase in the productivity of fertilizer and manure.

With respect to the development of yields without meliorative measures, Ruthenberg (1980) pointed out that permanent crop cultivation and soil management without proper nutrient supply in semi-arid zones of western Africa will lead to a decrease in crop yields. However, yields will eventually stabilize at a low level equilibrium. For Saria, a central region of Burkina Faso with an annual rainfall average of 700 to 800 mm, long-term fertilizer trials arrived at a steady state yield level of 162 kg/ha for sorghum during the period of 1963 to 1983 for the non fertilized control (Pieri 1989). It is likely that this level will be even lower in the Sudano-Sahelian zone, where rainfall averages 500 mm or less. In their assessment of soil conservation measures some authors assume an annual yield decline of 2% (Kotschi et al. 1986) for non-ameliorated plots in this region.

The direct yield increase very much depends on the actual type of conservation measure. On the basis of numerous field trials the construction of earthen ridges and tied ridges along contourlines have proven to increase cereal yields effectively. However, these may cause yield depression in case of high rainfall seasons because of water-logging. Furthermore earth ridges cause high maintenance costs which farmers in northern Burkina Faso were not willing to accept (Marchal 1986; IFAD 1992).

Instead, permeable rockbunds allow for slow water filtration, decreased soil loss caused by erosion and increased soil fertility and biomass production as an effect of higher water and mineral supply. Being a more permanent type of construction they need less maintenance. Yield increase in years of low rainfall is higher and may even prevent total harvest loss (van Driel and Vlaar 1991; Tapsoba and Hebie 1992; Lamachère and Serpantie 1988).

In figure 1 various plausible, but hypothetical yield curves are displayed. With rock bunds and other forms of permeable constructions higher water supply will shift the main constraint of plant growth from water shortage to limited supply of plant nutrients.

Figure 1: Hypothetical Yield Across Years with and without Resource Control

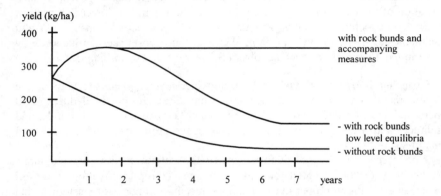

Thus, the minimum yield level will probably be slightly higher than without water control measures. Only accompanying measures such as mineral and organic fertilizer application will improve soil fertility and prevent yield declines. In the long run yield declines are likely when the nutrient stock is not replenished regularly. Under such circumstances the innovation would lead to a more rapid depletion of soil nutrients as compared to a situation without soil conservation measures.

In this study we assumed a constant yield increase over time in the absence of any empirically based estimates of the yield decline curve.

Variability of yields is usually high in the study region and according to Pieri (1989) augmenting over time. It mainly depends on inter- and intra-annual rainfall variability and expected to decrease with better water availability through soil conservation measures (Vlaar 1992).

Opportunity costs of labor and capital: Resource conservation takes place during dry season. Usually, the rural population is organized in village groups to facilitate the implementation of resource conservation measures. The process of construction includes the collection of stones, transportation to the construction site, layout of contour lines and actual construction. Villagers are supported by government or development organizations in transporting stones. Tools, such as levelling tubes, wheelbarrows, shovels and spades are placed at their disposal. In order to speed up the process mainly government trucks are being used as means of transportation. Maintenance usually includes the replacement of stones displaced by animals. In case of high sedimentation, when bunds are silted-up, they have to be made permeable again to avoid water-logging.

According to Reardon (1995) the assessment of conservation investments as well as other productive investments has to consider opportunity costs of labor and cash at the household level. The development of farm and non-farm sectors are generally affected by rural households capital and liquidity constraints. High short-run payoffs, stable long-term payoffs and the potential to serve as a deposit or as an insurance (such as livestock) are important investment criteria for farm households. "The investments need to be attractive, not just that 'net profitability is greater than zero,' but also more profitable than competing opportunities off-farm" (Reardon 1995).

At farm level, profitability is directly related to the labor input by the rural population. Wright (1982) estimated 100 person days per hectare for stone lines, whereas 490 days per hectare were found for dams (AFWP 1986). Generally, labor input increases with the distance between the construction site and the source of material.

Estimation of opportunity costs is one of the most important factors from the farmers' point of view. In many cases, opportunity costs of labor for farmers in western Africa are assumed to be very low or zero especially during dry season (Sanders et al. 1990; Jones 1986).

In this paper, particular attention will be paid to the estimation of gender-specific opportunity costs of labor using empirical data. In addition, opportunity costs might be underestimated for Burkina Faso where other off-farm activities are growing, such as small-scale gold mining which is increasingly observed in the central plateau region.

Cost of Transport and Materials

Subsidization: In general, economic analysis of resource conservation has to take into account the effect of government interventions to predict technology diffusion without government support.

However, in this paper analysis has been carried out on household level exclusively. Actual costs for transport, equipment, training and extension were included in some of the calculations, because this alternative is likely to be the situation for households when support is not provided by the government.

Profitability of the investment: Profitability of the investment can be assessed at two levels. Firstly, a financial analysis at farm level will have to be undertaken in order to understand decision-making at farm household level. Secondly, since the government subsidizes the transportation process, the economic viability of the investment has to be investigated.

So far, most authors only looked at the economic analysis in order to determine ex-ante overall profitability. For instance, Kotschi, Klimm and Hippel (1986) estimated an internal rate of return of 25% to 31% for dikes and dams respectively. Other authors found 22% to 36% (de Haen and Runge-Metzger 1989) or 9% to 117% for rock bunds according to varying transport costs (Kaboré et al. 1993).

Data Collection

Data used in this study include farm survey and project data. A sample of 349 households in 27 villages was stratified into three zones, north, centre and south, based on the hypothesis of varying farming systems. The survey focused on labor input of various dry season activities including resource conservation. Differentiation between the various types of construction is based on technical data of PATECORE, a German sponsored resource conservation project, from 1993. Rock bunds consist of simple rows up to 30 cm (40 m³ material per hectare), larger stone dikes between 30 and 50 cm height (75 m³) and dams which can attain 2 meters (125 m³).

Agronomic data, collected by the national extension service for PATECORE, included grain and straw yields of sorghum and millet on comparable sites of conventional farmers' fields with and without dikes and dams. Transport costs were calculated by the area ameliorated under the different types of permeable rock bunds as an average of three years from 1991 to 1994 on the basis of project data. Subsidies such as equipment, training and extension were taken from PATECORE for the same period.

Grain and straw prices are based on Kongoussi market prices during dry season. Sorghum grain prices amount to 66 CFA, millet grain to 79 CFA and straw to 5 CFA per kilo. Based on the results of the farm household survey surplus production is generally stored and sold during dry season when prices are higher. Opportunity costs of land which has to be sacrificed under rock bund construction was estimated based on the average net return of the crop area without rock bunds (PATECORE 1993).

All monetary units in CFA refer to the equivalent of 1 $ = 294 FCFA before devaluation in January 1994.

Results of the Study

Benefits of rock bund construction: Yields of sorghum and millet grain and straw under stone dikes and dams in a 1993 farm survey are shown in table 1. For stone lines, a widespread type of rock bunds, the available yield data was insufficient and therefore excluded from economic analysis.

Ameliorated plots in all cases produced higher yields than non-ameliorated plots. Differences between plots with dikes and dams existed in all cases in favor of dams, but proved to be only in the case of sorghum grain significant at an alpha level of 1% (groups B and C in table 1). Millet yield is generally lower than sorghum in grain but not in straw, and the data suggests that the increase in millet production with conservation measures is higher than in sorghum production. This effect might be due to a higher potential of yield increase in millet which is usually grown on less nutritious, sandy soils.

Table 1: Grain and Straw Yields of Sorghum and Millet on Ameliorated and Non-Ameliorated Plots in 1993

Type of construction	Sorghum yield (kg/ha)			Millet yield (kg/ha)			
	grain	straw	n	grain	straw	n	groups
Non-ameliorated	330	2758	31	185	2387	36	A
Stone dikes	411	3028	23	310	3683	26	B
Stone dams	682	3391	9	410	3930	4	C
Average difference to non-ameliorated plots in %	+ 48	+ 14		+ 75	+ 56		
DUNCAN test significance **p = 1% AC,BC** *p = 5%				AB,AC**	AB,AC*		

Source: unpublished data of the Research Division, PATECORE, 1994

Across location yield variability proved to decrease with soil conservation measures as is demonstrated in table 2. According to the results, highly variable yields in grain vary 10% to 25% less with dikes and dams. The coefficients of variation for straw suggest an important reduction in variability only in the case of millet.

Table 2:   Coefficient of Variation for Sorghum and Millet Yield with and
           without Ameliorative Measures in %

	Without measures	Stone dikes	Stone dams
Sorghum grain	58	47	40
Millet grain	57	39	26
Sorghum straw	55	59	59
Millet straw	78	40	44

Source: unpublished data of the Research Division, PATECORE, 1994

Costs of rock bund construction: Farm survey data show that labor input
differs by the type of measure. As shown in table 3 simple rock bunds have the
lowest labor requirements while that of dams comes up to 300 person-days per
hectare. Actually measured labor inputs compare well to those estimated by other
authors mentioned before.

Table 3:   Labor Input for Construction and Maintenance of Rock Bunds in 1993

Activity	Type of construction	Labor input (person-days/ha)[1]
Construction	rock bunds	97
	stone dikes	183
	stone dams	279
Maintenance	all types	1.7

[1] Data was drawn from 55 of 349 households,
which ameliorated in total 85 ha with this type of measure in 1993.
Source: farm survey data, 1993

Furthermore, data from 30 construction sites suggests significant differences in
men's and women's labor participation according to the type of construction.
Children under the age of 15 were not included in the estimate. Men's and
women's participation was equally distributed at the construction of rock bunds
whereas at larger types of construction men contributed a higher percentage of
labor days. Average participation was 56% to 44% for men and women
respectively.

These results compare to the farm survey data in 1993. In a sample of 746
participants of construction activities 59% were men and 41% women. Average
number of working hours per working day was 5.7.

Maintenance is to a larger extent part of men's responsibilities. Labor input is
the same for all types and is fairly low. In a sample of 91 farmers, participation in
working days was 71% for men and 29% for women. On average, a day of
maintenance labor took five hours for men and four hours for women.

Due to these differences in participation, it is important to estimate gender-
specific opportunity costs of labor for the various activities of men and women.

Table 4: Participation of Men and Women in Construction of Rock Bunds (1993)

Type of construction	Participation (% of labor days)		
	men	women	n
Rock bunds	50.0	50.0	1774
Stone dikes	60.5	39.5	736
Stone dams	64.5	35.5	1269
All types	56.2	43.8	3779

X^2-test; significance at ***$p=0.1\%$

Source: calculation based on unpublished data from the Technical Division (CAST)
PATECORE in 30 villages, 1993

The estimation of opportunity costs of labor in dry season: Construction of rock bunds competes for family labor with other dry season cash income earning activities such as growing of green beans, gold mining, crafts and petty trade. The net income of these activities determines the opportunity cost of labor.

Results of the 1993 survey show the difference in opportunity costs of labor according to gender and the type of activity. Women's opportunity costs are generally lower than men's. On average women earn 180 CFA/day, which is about half of men's rate (420 CFA/day) as shown in table 5. Trading activities lead to high labor returns for men, whereas women usually employ in small commerce with lower outcomes. Gold mining is an important and increasing activity.

As during the dry season men and women are occupied for 5 to 6 hours per day, wage rates average 30 and 70 CFA per hour for women and men, respectively.

Considering the actual working capacity of 140 days during dry season and taking into account subsistence activities and slack period lower limits of opportunity costs were calculated at 160 CFA for men and 110 CFA for women respectively (28 CFA per men's and 20 CFA per women's hour). Assuming scarcity of labor determines the upper limit of the opportunity costs of labor referring to the averages as calculated in table 5.

Government intervention: Government intervention includes subsidies funded with the support of development organizations. In the study area, transport facilities, equipment, farmers' training and extension are provided free of charge.

The actual costs of these activities were calculated from data provided by PATECORE referring to the situation of the project area.

Table 5:   Opportunity Costs of Labor during Dry Season According to Income
           Generating Activity and Gender in 1992/93

Activity	Daily income (in CFA)			
	women	n	men	n
Commerce	160	35	900	49
Wage labor	-		530	7
Gold mining	260	28	450	43
Vegetable production	-		400	25 [1]
Modern crafts	480	3	330	31
Selling millet beer	150	17	-	
Blacksmith	-		230	7
Traditional crafts	130	20	150	75
House construction	-		260	8
Farm-related activities	100	3	240	9
Average	**180**	**106**	**418**	**251**

[1] n represents in this case households, because younger family members
help in cultivation and income distribution among members is unknown.
Source: Farm survey data, 1993

Investment Analysis

Investment analysis has been performed for different assumptions as regards
transportation costs, cost of equipment, training and extension related to rock
bund construction and opportunity costs of labor (see table 6). Results therefore
allow conclusions to be drawn as regards the profitability of rock bund
investments under different locational and political factors.

Table 6:   Types of Investment Analysis According to Subsidies and Opportunity
           Costs

Alternatives	Transportation costs[1]	Costs of equipment, training and extension[2]	Opportunity costs of labor
A1	yes	yes	high
A2	yes	yes	low
B1	yes	no	high
B2	yes	no	low
C1	no	no	high
C2	no	no	low

[1] transportation costs: 28700 CFA for dikes, 47800 CFA for dams per ha;
[2] equipment: 8200 CFA; training: 4000 CFA; extension: 5900 CFA per ha

Results of the calculations show (see table 7) that investments in stone dikes under conditions where sorghum is grown is not profitable for farm households unless all inputs are taken over by the government and low opportunity costs of labor prevail. This can be explained with the low and questionable yield impact of stone dikes in sorghum grain and straw production, as demonstrated in table 1.

Stone dams on the other hand are more effective in retaining soil fertility and in preventing water run-off and therefore allow the realization of the yield potential of sorghum (see table 1). Such investments appear to be attractive even if transportation costs and the costs of the extension service are included. This refers to locations where government services are less intense or non-existent. Even if farmers have to cover all costs the IRR still reaches 13.7%.

The situation in millet growing areas, usually comparatively marginal lands under sub-Sahelian conditions, is different from sorghum. Here, stone dikes are often an attractive option for the use of the farm household's labor capacity in dry season even if high opportunity costs are assumed. Stone dams which are technically more sophisticated do not lead to significantly higher IRRs as in the case of sorghum. Hence, in view of the much higher transportation costs, stone dikes seem to be the appropriate type of soil conservation measures for areas where millet is dominantly grown.

Table 7:   Internal Rate of Return of Investment Alternatives in %

Alternative	Sorghum		Millet	
	Stone dikes	Stone dams	Stone dikes	Stone dams
A1	-3.2	13.7	12.1	13.3
A2	1.7	22.6	20.0	22.0
B1	-1.0	16.3	16.0	15.8
B2	5.7	27.9	27.7	27.2
C1	4.5	27.3	26.2	26.6
C2	20.0	62.9	60.0	61.4

Experiences Gained and Lessons Learned

Results of our analysis based on farm-level data generally confirms the findings of respective analysis of other research. Additionally, it can be shown that investments in rock bunds are attractive for farm households even if opportunity costs of labor are relatively high. Results also show that the currently provided government subsidies as regards the transportation of construction material could be eliminated provided appropriate financing schemes are offered to farmers.

IRRs react strongly to a change in the opportunity costs of labor which shows that this assumption is crucial. As pointed out by the survey, opportunity costs may be higher than assumed in previous studies but rock bunds appear to be an attractive alternative for dry season labor activities.

It is therefore necessary to pay more attention especially to off-farm income alternatives of farm household members. In addition to that, the intra-household equity issue has to be included in the analysis as rock bunds clearly have gender-specific effects.

References

AFVP 1986: Les digues filtrantes. miméographie, (Association Francaise des Volontaires du Progrès), Ouagadougou.

de Haen, H., A. Runge-Metzger 1989: Improvements in Efficiency and Sustainability of Traditional Land Use Systems through 'Learning from Farmers' Practice' – Concept and Initial Results from Semi-Arid West Africa. Quarterly Journal of International Agriculture, 326-350.

IFAD 1992: Soil and Water Conservation in Sub-Saharan Africa, Int. Fund f. Agricultural Development, Rome.

Jones, CH.W. 1986: Intra-Household Bargaining in Response to the Introduction of New Crops: A Case Study from North Cameroon; in Lewinger Moock, J. (Ed.) 1986: Understanding Africa's Rural Households and Farming Systems, WestviewPress, Boulder, Colorado.

Kaboré D., M. Bertelsen, J. Lowenberg-DeBoer 1993: The Economics of Rock Bund Construction on Sorghum and Millet Fields in Burkina Faso.

Kotschi, J., E. Klimm, G. Hippel 1986: Aménagement des Terroirs et Conservation des Ressources dans le Plateau Central, Rapport D'étude de projet, GTZ, Nr. 83.2059.0

Lamachere, J.M., G. Serpantie 1988: Valorisation agricole des eaux de ruissellement en zone soudano-sahélienne Burkina Faso – région de Bidi. ORSTOM, Ouagadougou.

Marchal, J.-Y. 1985: Vingt ans de lutte antiérosive au nord du Burlina Faso, Cah. ORSTOM. Sér. Pédol., vol XXII, no.2, 173-180

Matlon, P.J. 1986: A critical review of objectives, methods and progress to date in sorghum and millet imporvement: a case study of ICRISAT/Burkina Faso; in: Ohm, H.W. and Nagy, J.G.: Appropriate technologies for farmers in semi-arid west Africa

Mortimer, M. 1989: The Causes, Nature and Rate of Soil Degradation in the Northernmost States of Nigeria and An Assessment of the Role of Fertilizer in Counteracting the Processes of Degradation; Env. Dep. Working Paper No. 17, World Bank, Washington.

PATECORE (Projet Amenagement des Terroirs et Conservation des Ressources Naturelles) 1993: Fiches Techniques en Conservation des Eaux et des Sols, Kongoussi, Burkina Faso

Pieri, Ch. 1989: Fertilité des terres de savanes, Ministère de la Coopération et CIRAD-IRAT, Paris.

Raymond, M., P. Lindskog 1994: Impact des réalisation des mesures anti-érosives sur la gestion des terroirs dans la Province du Bam au Burkina Faso; Rapport annuel 1993, Tome 1: Rapport Principal, CIEH, PATECORE, Burkina Faso.

Reardon, T. 1995: Sustainability Issues for Agricultural Research Strategies in the Semi-arid Tropics. Focus on the Sahel; Agricultural Systems 48, p. 345-359.

Ruthenberg, H. 1980: Farming Systems in the Tropics, Clarendon Press, Oxford.

Sanders, J.H., J.G. Nagy, S. Ramaswamy 1990: Developing New Agricultural Technologies for the Sahelian Countries: The Burkina Faso Case. Economic Development and Cultural Change 39.

Speirs, M., O. Olsen 1992: Indigenous Integrated Farming Systems in the Sahel, World Bank Technical Paper No. 179, Africa Technical Dep. Ser., Washington D.C.

Tapsoba, F. A., S. Hebie 1992: Etude d'Inventaire et de Diagnostic Technique et Socio-Economique des Aménagements Anti-Erosifs et de la Petite Irrigation dans les Provinces du Bulkiemde, Bazega et Mouhoun; Ministère de l'Eau/FEER (Fonds de l'Eau et de l'Equipement Rural)/Fao; Projet BKF/87/052, Burkina Faso.

van Driel, W.F., J.C.J. Vlaar 1991: Impact des digues filtrantes sur le bilan hydrique et sur les rendements agricoles dans la région de Rissiam, Burkina Faso: Soil Water Balance in the Sudano-Sahelian Zone (Proceedings of the Niamey workshop, Feb. 1991): IAHS Publ. No. 199.

Vlaar J.C.J. 1992: Les techniques de conservation des eaux et des sols dans les pays du Sahel, CIEH/University of Wageningen.

Wright, P. 1982: Projet Agro-Forestier (OXFAM). Rapport de fin de campagne 1981 sur les techniques de récolte et conservation des eaux d'écoulement au Yatenga, Haute Volta, OXFAM, Ouagadougou.

Economics and Ecology of Biological Control of the Cassava Mealybug *Phenacoccus manihoti* (Mat.-Ferr.) (Hom., Pseudococcidae) in Africa[1]

Ralf P. Schaab and Jürgen Zeddies
University of Hohenheim, Institute of Agricultural
Economics (410 B)
D-70593, Stuttgart, Germany

Abstract

Pest populations of the cassava mealybug (CM) Phenacoccus manihoti Mat.-Ferr. (Homoptera: Pseudococcidae) were reduced successfully with the biological control agent Epidinocarsis lopezi (De Santis) (Hymenoptera: Encyrtidae) almost throughout sub-Saharan Africa. Quantitatively the fauna related to CM dropped significantly after the introduction of E. lopezi.

The methodology for economically evaluating the project consisted of a combination of field trials and socio-economic surveys. Main information for analysis was provided by the International Institute of Tropical Agriculture (IITA) in Cotonou, Benin. Costs and benefits for the biological control of P. manihoti were calculated over 40 years (1974-2013) in 27 African countries.

A reasonable (and discounted) calculation resulted in US$ 46.9 million (nominal: US$ 34.2 million) costs and US$ 9.4 billion benefit. This is equivalent to a cost-benefit ratio of 1:200. Cost benefit ratios may vary between 170 to 431 depending on different scenarios.

Keywords

P. manihoti, E. lopezi, biological pest control, cost-benefit analysis, Africa

1   Introduction

The cassava mealybug (CM) was first registered in Zaire in 1970 (Leuschner 1978). A biological control project against *Phenacoccus manihoti* Mat.-Ferr. (Homoptera: Pseudococcidae) has existed since 1977 (Herren 1988). Over the

---

[1] Based on the paper: 'Economics of Biological Control of the Cassava Mealybug *Phenacoccus manihoti* (Mat.-Ferr.) (Hom., Pseudococcidae) in Africa' (by R.P. Schaab, P. Neuenschwander, J. Zeddies, H.R. Herren), presented at the 'Sixth Symposium of the International Society of Tropical Root Crops – Africa Branch (ISTRC-AB), October 22.-28. 1995, Lilongwe, Malawi, Africa.

years, the CM spread through the cassava belt in Africa. Parallel to the extension of the pest, its biological control was carried out in many countries (Herren & Neuenschwander, 1991). The biological control agent is *Epidinocarsis lopezi* DeSantis (Hymenoptera: Encyrtidae).

The biological control of *P. manihoti* in Africa was one of the largest projects undertaken in classical biological pest control. Research, quest for enemies, quarantine, breeding, pre-release studies, monitoring of the ecology, coordination of activities, training, post-release studies, evaluation etc. were carried out by the IITA in collaboration with many other institutions during the last two decades. A detailed overview is given by Neuenschwander, 1993.

This paper investigates the hypothesis that the project described was economically positive. Additional objective of the investigation is the description of the ecological development caused by the pest and the natural enemy.

2   Materials and Methods

Cassava tips and insects were collected within farmer fields in W-Kenia for ecological comparison (375 paperbag-units – average 2.5 tips per bag – from 75 fields).

The economic analysis was mainly based on the scientific experiences within the IITA since 1977. Observations were carried out in most of the countries in which *P. manihoti* was registered (literature will be listed in a detailed publication later on). Under the auspices of P. Neuenschwander, spreadsheets were compiled with information about the dynamics of the pests and beneficiaries through the years, the countries and the agroecological zones.

The appropiate method for the economic evaluation of a biological control is a cost-benefit analysis resulting in a cost-benefit ratio (CBR). The revenue was deduced from annual costs and benefits of biological control as parameters for the economic profit (NORGAARD 1988). Because of uncertainties in some biological and economic parameters, a range of possible results was computed by sensitivity analyses.

For the analyses, four different scenarios for the evaluation of the benefit were used. Calculation with cassava assumes that anything will be like it was before the mealybug. Alternative calculation assumes that additional fields are available after the beneficiary increased cassava yield. In this case, the enrichment of the alternative calculation consists of the speculative use of maize.

Scenario 1: Additional cassava production under *E. lopezi*

If *E. lopezi* resulted in a country-specific additional quantity of cassava which could be harvested, the "saved loss" in tons was multiplied with a "world market price." However, a 'world market price' for cassava is distorted because of the high grain prices in the European Union (EU) (Lynam 1987) and their grain subsidies (Schumacher 1990). From 1995 to 2013 the 'world market price' for cassava is assumed to be US$ 90 per ton as a rough approximation.

Scenario 2: Additional cassava evaluated under import conditions

In an import scenario, i.e. countries dependent on grain supply from the outside, costs for transport to the interior of the country must be added to the farm-gate price (i.e. 'world market price,' valued in scenario 1).

Actually, the costs for transportation are about US$ 140 per ton per 1000 km (US$ 5000 the 36t trailer for 1000km). For the calculation the distance from the nearest harbor to the middle of each different country was chosen. Constant costs were calculated through the years.

Scenario 3: Additional production of an alternative crop, i.e. maize

If *E. lopezi* results in a higher cassava yield, it can be assumed that on the fields not used any more for cassava production an alternative crop like maize will be produced. The assumed maize production per hectare in each country was multiplied with the amount of this newly gained area and valued with the world market price for (yellow) maize (FAO Production Yearbooks 1979-93) adding a quality bonus of 20% for white maize.

Scenario 4: Additional maize evaluated under import conditions

The price of scenario 3 with additional costs for transport to the interior of the country, see scenario 2.

All possibilities of benefit valuation (scenario 1.-4.) were compounded or discounted with 6% at an investment base of 1994. A period of 40 years, i.e. 1974-2013, was chosen as an adequate duration for calculation of a continental biological control mechanism. An additional revenue of a prolonged period of economic calculations beyond 2013 becomes disregardable due to the effect of discounting.

The spread of the CM through most of the countries was known from numerous surveys and was calculated separately for savanna, rainforest, and highland zones. The releases and, where known, the spread of *E. lopezi* from about 150 release sites have also been documented and were used in this compilation.

The following information is needed for a cost-benefit analysis of different scenarios; the available findings in research and most probable assumptions were incorporated:

- Costs for biological control activities;
- Cassava yield per hectare and production per year and country;
- Distribution of cassava production by ecological zones;
- Spread of the pest *P. manihoti* through the years within the different ecological zones;

- Spread of the parasitic wasp E. lopezi through the years within the different ecological zones;
- Dynamics of damage coefficients through the years from the
  - pest alone (before release of the beneficiary),
  - pest and beneficiary combined;
- Assumptions about a world market price for cassava;
- Cost of transport to the interior of Africa;
- Discount rate of interest for costs and benefits (i.e. 6%);
- Average yield of alternative crop, per hectare in each country (i.e. maize);
- World market prices for alternative crop.

For each area newly infested by CM, losses were attributed as 80% (Nwanze 1982). Within five years it was assumed this value dropped in steps of about 10% each year to 40% in the highlands and savanna and 20% in the rainforest. This occurred presumably because farmers adapted as well as they could to the new challenge and planted more tolerant varieties. Indigenous predators, particularly coccinellids, became used to the new food source and reduced the pest population (Neuenschwander et al. 1987). It is considered during the period without E. lopezi that coccinellids are important. Under full biological control by E. lopezi, local predators proved to be rather insignificant (Gutierrez et al. 1988).

According to several impact studies (Neuenschwander et al. 1989), the reduction of yield loss due to E. lopezi was computed for each area as follows. For the savanna: first year 0%, second year 25%, third year 37%. For the forest zone, the correspondent reductions were 0%, 10%, and 15%. This leaves a residual damage concentrated in "hot spots" of infestation on sandy soils as described from several surveys (Neuenschwander et al. 1990). For the highlands, reductions (0%, 10%, 20%, 30%, 35%) were computed by support of field experiments in Kenya (Schaab unpubl.).

Economic data were available from official sources by African governments, IITA, the Food and Agricultural Organisation of the United Nations (FAO, Pro- duction Yearbooks 1975-1995), the Centro Internacional de Agricultura Tropical (Carter et al. 1992; CIAT 1993), and the German Ministry of Agriculture. Further information was provided by the Collaborative Study on Cassava in Africa COSCA (Nweke et al. 1989) and the publications by Dorosh 1988 and Lynam 1987.

As a summary of the different variables and cases, used in the spreadsheets, the following formula was developed for evaluating the benefit of E. lopezi:

$$Ben_{El} = \sum_{z=1}^{27} \sum_{i=1}^{40} \{(\sum_{j=1}^{3} TPr_j * ElPr_j * Gco_j) * 0.3dm * Y\$/t_a * DF_i\}$$

$$|_{a=A1,A2,A3,A4}$$

Where:

z1, z2, ... z27	27 African cassava countries (Angola, Benin, ... Zambia)
$i_1, i_2, ... i_{40}$	Specific year i_1 =1974 - i_{40} = 2013
j1, j2, j3	Agro ecological zones: savanna(1), rain forest(2), highland(3)
TPr	Total production of cassava per country and year (fresh weight)
ElPr	Cassava production area with influence of *E. lopezi*
Gco	Gain (=saved loss) coefficient of *E. lopezi*
dm	Dry material with a conversion factor (fresh to dry) 1: 0.3
$Y\$/t_a$	Price of cassava for substituted production for different scenarios:

$$|_{a=A1,A2,A3,A4}$$

Scenarios:

A1 = additional cassava yield, valued at an world market price.

A2 = substituted cassava, valued at world market price plus transport costs to the interior

A3 = maize grown on saved area, valued at world market price.

A4 = substituted maize, valued at world market price plus transport to the interior

DF_i	Discount factor for the specific year i.

Costs of controlling *Phenacoccus manihoti*

The total costs were divided in four parts:

- the costs of the IITA,
- overhead costs of the donor countries evolving there (approx. 15% additionally to the IITA expenditures for administration, planning, evaluation etc.),
- costs of African governments, and
- costs of African farmers.

The following formula was developed:

$$Costs_{El} = \sum_{i=1}^{40} (IITA_i + O_i + AG_i + F_i) * DF_i$$

Where:

$Costs_{El}$	Total costs (in US$)
i=1-40	Specific year: i1 = 1974 ... i40 = 2013
IITA	Costs for the International Institute of Tropical Agriculture
O	Overhead of donor agencies
AG	Costs of African governments
F	Costs for the African farmer
DF	Discount factor in the specific year i (6%)

Net profit of biological control

From costs and benefits the net profit (Pro_{Net}) derived as:

$$Pro_{Net} = Ben_{El} - Costs_{El}$$

3   Results

Quantitatively the collection of cassava tips had the following result (compare figure 1): 15 insects from Oyugis (---,---), 658 insects were separated out of the paperbags from Siaya (CM,---) and 197 insects from Migori (CM, E.l.). Additional collections of insects were carried out but are not included in the results above because it was not standardized for a quantitative comparison.

Figure 1:   Quantitative insect situation in cassava caused by different pest situations: *Oyugis*: no CM; *Siaya*: only CM; *Migori*: CM and *E. l.*

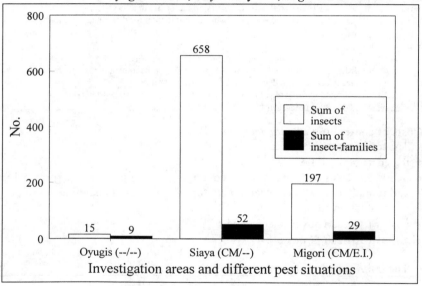

Mealybugs, *Bemisia tabaci* and mites are not included in this comparison. They were scored and investigated on farmers fields and the experimental fields.

The economic analyses of biological control of *P. manihoti* includes 27 countries in Africa (see table 1). The cassava area in these countries represents the actual (1995) infected regions with *P.manihoti*. The 27 countries produce about 94% of the total African cassava output.

Benefit of *Epidinocarsis lopezi* in Africa. The total benefit of biological control of *P.manihoti* per country (by means shown above) is visualized in figure 2. The benefit of *E. lopezi* is directly related to the total cassava production per country. The biggest benefits are attributed therefore to the cassava producing countries Zaire, Nigeria, Ghana, Tanzania, Mozambique and Uganda. They produce more than 78% of all cassava of the 27 countries involved in the analysis.

Table 1: Basic Data of Economic Analysis

Country	% Sa-vanna	% Rain-forest	% High lands	Cassava. Prod. 1991 in 1000 tons		% in Africa	CM infested since	E.l. infested since
1 Angola	18	2	80	1,850		2.83	1975	1983
2 Benin	95	5	0	889		1.36	1979	1983
3 Burundi	0	0	100	580		0.89	1987	1988
4 Cameroon	29	40	31	1,378	**	2.11	1985	1985
5 C. Afric. Rep.	75	25	0	520		0.80	1984	1988
6 Congo	60	40	0	780		1.19	1973	1982
7 Cote d'Ivoire	40	60	0	1,250	**	1.91	1985	1986
8 Equ. Guinea	0	100	0	55	*	0.08	1989	1989
9 Gabon	20	80	0	250		0.38	1975	1986
10 Gambia	100	0	0	6		0.01	1976	1984
11 Ghana	67	33	0	3,040	**	4.65	1982	1984
12 Guinea Bissau	100	0	0	6	est.	0.01	1982	1984
13 Guinea (Con.)	90	0	10	450		0.69	1986	1989
14 Kenya	29	1	70	650		0.99	1990	1990
15 Liberia	10	90	0	300		0.46	1990	1990
16 Malawi	89	1	10	168		0.26	1985	1985
17 Mozambique	95	>0.5	5	3,690		5.65	1986	1988
18 Niger	100	0	0	216		0.33	1986	1986
19 Nigeria	15	85	>0.5	20,000		30.6	1979	1981
20 Rwanda	0	0	100	560		0.86	1984	1985
21 Senegal	100	0	0	14	*	0.02	1976	1984
22 Sierra Leone	60	40	0	90		0.14	1982	1985
23 Tanzania	40	10	50	6,266		9.59	1987	1988
24 Togo	95	5	0	500		0.77	1980	1984
25 Uganda	5	0	95	3,350		5.13	1992	1992
26 Zaire	45	35	20	18,227		27.9	1972	1982
27 Zambia	5	0	95	270		0.41	1984	1984
all 27 countries				65,355		100		
average:	36.6	41.9	21.5					

Sources: Neuenschwander 1994, unpubl., *Carter et al. 1992, CIAT 1993, (CIAT data are mainly based on FAO production yearbooks), **Nweke et al., 1989

The benefits of all 27 countries accumulated in the 40 years of analysis resulted to US$ 9.4 billion. The average yearly gain of biological control for CM in Africa amounted to US$ 235 million. Calculated for the actual cassava area of about 9 million hectares, there is a reduced loss of US$ 26 per hectare and year. Assumed that small-scale African farmers are planting cassava on about 1/3 hectare on average, there is a net gain per African cassava-cultivating family of US$ 8.7 per year.

Depending on the four different scenarios for valuation the benefit, the results cover a range of economic possibilities demonstrated by figure 3.

Under import conditions, the transport of food to the interior of the countries would strongly increase the costs of substitution. Including transport to the interior of all 27 African countries, the benefit by saved investment would come to US$ 20.23 billion.

Figure 2: Benefits (Scenario 1) due to *E. lopezi* per Country (1974-2013)

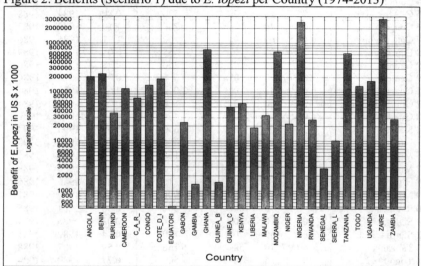

Costs of biological control by *Epidinocarsis lopezi* in Africa. The costs of the complete biological control activities are listed in table 2. Nominal, the costs accumulated to US$ 34.2 million from 1979 (commencement of the program) to 2013. Related to the basic year 1994 and discounted at a rate of 6%, they cumulated at US$ 46.9 million.

1. *Costs at IITA level.* The total costs for the IITA related to cassava mealybug amount to US$ 37.7 million (nominal US$ 27.4 million).

2. *Overhead costs of donor agencies.* On top of the IITA expenditures, 15% have to be calculated as overhead within the donor countries. The total sum is US$ 5.7 million discounted (US$ 4.1 million nominal).

3. *Costs of African governments.* An estimated amount of US$ 100,000 was calculated per country and the whole period of analysis. This a hypothetical

Table 2: Costs (US$) of Biological Control by *Epidinocarsis lopezi* in Africa

Year	Comments	Year	Disc. factor 6%	Costs of IITA	Dis-counted	Over-head donors	Dis-counted	Costs African Governm	Dis-counted	Costs Total nominal	Costs Total discounted	Cassava at farmgate	Cassava at farmgate plus transport	Maize (as substitute) at farmgate	Maize at farmgate plus transport
1972	first CM														
1973	infections														
1974		-20	3.21	0.00	0.00	0.00	0.00	0.00	0.00	0.00	0.00	0	0	0	0
1975		-19	3.03	0.00	0.00	0.00	0.00	0.00	0.00	0.00	0.00	0	0	0	0
1976		-18	2.85	0.00	0.00	0.00	0.00	0.00	0.00	0.00	0.00	0	0	0	0
1977		-17	2.69	0.00	0.00	0.00	0.00	0.00	0.00	0.00	0.00	0	0	0	0
1978	first costs	-16	2.54	0.00	0.00	0.05	0.11	0.00	0.00	0.00	0.00	0	0	0	0
1979	of bio contr.	-15	2.40	0.30	0.72	0.05	0.11	0.00	0.00	0.35	0.83	0	0	0	0
1980		-14	2.26	0.70	1.58	0.11	0.24	0.00	0.00	0.81	1.82	0	0	0	0
1981		-13	2.13	1.00	2.13	0.15	0.32	0.00	0.00	1.15	2.45	0	0	0	24
1982		-12	2.01	1.00	2.01	0.15	0.30	0.00	0.00	1.15	2.31	0	0	16	117
1983		-11	1.90	1.80	3.42	0.27	0.51	0.00	0.00	2.07	3.93	0	35	80	205
1984		-10	1.79	2.00	3.58	0.30	0.54	0.20	0.36	2.50	4.48	0	164	135	250
1985		-9	1.69	2.50	4.23	0.38	0.63	0.20	0.34	3.08	5.20	21	241	151	343
1986		-8	1.59	2.00	3.18	0.30	0.48	0.20	0.32	2.50	3.98	98	314	184	405
1987		-7	1.50	1.50	2.26	0.23	0.34	0.20	0.30	1.93	2.90	114	624	196	546
1988		-6	1.42	1.50	2.13	0.23	0.32	0.30	0.43	2.03	2.87	135	789	306	600
1989		-5	1.34	1.31	1.76	0.20	0.26	0.30	0.40	1.81	2.43	329	890	342	666
1990		-4	1.26	1.27	1.60	0.19	0.24	0.30	0.38	1.76	2.22	400	886	383	666
1991		-3	1.19	1.22	1.45	0.18	0.22	0.30	0.36	1.70	2.03	408	1063	407	699
1992		-2	1.12	1.17	1.31	0.17	0.20	0.20	0.22	1.54	1.73	542	1144	406	699
1993		-1	1.06	1.10	1.17	0.17	0.18	0.20	0.21	1.47	1.56	612	1038	396	685
1994	Base year	0	1.00	1.10	1.10	0.16	0.16	0.20	0.20	1.46	1.46	506	968	383	666
1995		1	0.94	0.80	0.76	0.12	0.11	0.10	0.09	1.02	0.96	452	897	371	648
1996		2	0.89	0.70	0.62	0.11	0.10	0.00	0.00	0.81	0.72	395	854	354	617
1997		3	0.84	0.60	0.50	0.09	0.08	0.00	0.00	0.69	0.58	376	818	339	593
1998		4	0.79	0.50	0.40	0.08	0.06	0.00	0.00	0.58	0.46	360	782	324	568
1999		5	0.75	0.40	0.30	0.06	0.04	0.00	0.00	0.46	0.34	325	742	307	539
2000		6	0.71	0.30	0.21	0.05	0.03	0.00	0.00	0.35	0.24	308	703	291	512
2001		7	0.67	0.20	0.13	0.04	0.02	0.00	0.00	0.24	0.15	292	667	276	486
2002		8	0.63	0.20	0.13	0.03	0.01	0.00	0.00	0.23	0.14	276	633	261	461
2003		9	0.59	0.20	0.12	0.03	0.02	0.00	0.00	0.23	0.14	261	597	247	435
2004		10	0.56	0.20	0.11	0.03	0.02	0.00	0.00	0.23	0.13	246	563	233	411
2005		11	0.53	0.20	0.11	0.03	0.01	0.00	0.00	0.23	0.12	232	531	220	388
2006		12	0.50	0.20	0.10	0.03	0.01	0.00	0.00	0.23	0.11	219	501	207	366
2007		13	0.47	0.20	0.09	0.03	0.02	0.00	0.00	0.23	0.11	207	473	195	345
2008		14	0.44	0.20	0.09	0.03	0.01	0.00	0.00	0.23	0.10	195	446	184	325
2009		15	0.42	0.20	0.08	0.03	0.02	0.00	0.00	0.23	0.10	184	421	174	307
2010		16	0.39	0.20	0.08	0.03	0.01	0.00	0.00	0.23	0.09	173	397	164	290
2011	projection:	17	0.37	0.20	0.07	0.03	0.02	0.00	0.00	0.23	0.09	164	375	155	273
2012	last CM	18	0.35	0.20	0.07	0.03	0.01	0.00	0.00	0.23	0.08	154	354	146	258
2013	infections	19	0.33	0.20	0.07	0.03	0.01	0.00	0.00	0.23	0.08	146	334	138	243
Sums (in million US$)				27.37	37.66	4.11	5.65	2.70	3.61	34.17	46.92	9321	20226	7969	13971
cost : benefit ratios (with discounted costs) 1:												200	431	170	298
cost : benefit ratios (with nominal costs) 1:												274	592	233	409

average sum for each of the 27 countries involved in the analyses; numbers add up to US$ 3.61 million discounted (US$ 2.7 million nominal).

4. *Costs on farm level.* The African farmers had no expenses for the biological control of *P. manihoti*, because the donor agencies and the African governments financed the local and the overall campaigns.

Figure 3: Total Benefits (40 years) due to *E. lopezi* in Africa

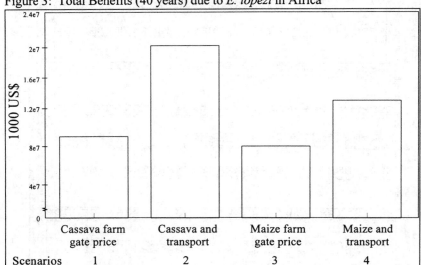

Net profit. Net profit for the biological control of CM amounted to US$ 9324 million for scenario 1.

Cost-benefit ratios (CBR). Costs and benefits of the biological control of *P. manihoti* result in different ratios depending on the different scenario. The ratios are listed in table 3. Assumption 1 results in a cost-benefit ratio of 1:200 through 40 years of analysis and discounted figures. Alternatives range from a CBR of 1:170 to 1:431. Calculated costs for transport increased the CBR enormously.

Table 3: Cost-benefit ratios of biological control of *P.manihoti* in Africa

40 years, discounted (6%) with scenario:	CBR	absolute (million US$)
1 Cassava farm gate	1:200	46.9 : 9,371
2 Cassava + transport	1:431	46.9 : 20,226
3 Maize at farm gate	1:170	46.9 : 7,969
4 Maize + transport	1:298	46.9 : 13,971

Sensitivity analysis. Because many data are uncertain, sensitivity analyses could be carried out in many directions. Possible ranges are listed in the following table.

In case the total African cassava area is changed from 6 to 12 million hectares, the total costs per hectare will range from US$ 3.9 (for 12 million hectares) to US$ 7.8 (for 6 million hectares) per hectare.

The results are striking: even with pessimistic scenarios this biological control project will still remain profitable.

Table 4:   Variables for Sensitivity Analysis

Variables	Range		
	Pessimistic	Optimistic	Most realistic
-Interest rate	12%	0%	6%
-Cassava area in Africa (million hectare)	6	12	9 (1995)
-Yields tons/ha	3	20	8
-∅ Damage through P. manihoti	40%	10%	25% (of potential yield)
-∅ Benefit through E. lopezi	10%	40%	30% (reduced loss)
-Local and world market prices (US $/ton)	60	260	100
Cost of transport (US$/ ton and 1.000km)	200	80	140
Duration of analysis (years)	20	100	40

E.g.: For the interest rate, the total amount of benefit might change from US$ 8.98 billion (12%) to US$ 11.87 billion (0%).

4   Discussion

Combined research, as used in this investigation, turned out to be a good method for determining the economic success of a biological control project.

Norgaard (1988) analyzed the same project for the period of 25 years, without detailed country information and with limited ecological background. Norgaard used an interest rate of 10% and as basic year 1982. His results were costs of US$ 14.8 million and benefits of US$ 2.2 billion (cost-benefit ratio of 1: 149).

For the current investigation, the main source for data concerning the distribution and efficiency of *E. lopezi* was the expertise of scientists from IITA. The development of the project was documented in detail from the beginning (Herren et al. 1987; Neuenschwander & Haug 1992).

In Africa there is still an area not infested by CM, producing about 3 million tons cassava. The spread of CM and *E. lopezi* is continuing and within a few decades there will be a general ecological balance between the pest, its exotic and natural enemies, and the cassava plant.

All statistical figures reported and cited are only approximate and have to be interpreted as such. National cassava production and average prices are extremely difficult to estimate, because of the diversity of regional cropping patterns and fluctuations in yield. Real measurements with a scale are rarely found and the cassava price is highly volatile because cassava is traded freely in Africa.

The costs of the biological control. Projects with the dimension of the 'African Wide Biological Control Program' need to be fitted into a comprehensive and applied development work. Therefore secondary costs, like basic research, training, national programs, etc., were incorporated in the economic analysis.

The total costs divided through the 9 million hectares of cassava in Africa would result in a single-treatment-cost US$ of 5.2 per hectare. Divided by the 40 years of the analysis, the yearly costs per hectare are 13 cents. Assumed again that the average African small-scale farmers are growing cassava on about 1/3 hectare, hypothetical costs for each farming family amount to 4 US cents per year.

The benefit of biological pest control in Africa. The main circumstances for the great economic success of the benefit calculation of *E. lopezi* are:
1. *P.manihoti* has a high potential for damaging cassava crops;
2. *E. lopezi* is very effective in combating the pest;
3. The self perpetuating dispersal of *E. lopezi* after introduction is rapid;
4. Costs and benefit were calculated on 8 million hectares of cassava in Africa;
5. Valuation was done over a period of 40 years.

The results reflect the quality of the project idea, the management for finances, personnel and materials. But biological control of insect pests is also subject to factors like weather, ecology and policies, and evaluation is more complex than for purely technical projects. The economic analysis of biological pest control resembles therefore an example of a combined research between economy and natural sciences.

5   Lessons Learned

The economic evaluation of biological pest control needs biological understanding. Therefore the data base of the calculations should contain one's own investigations as well as the data from external experts to compute optimal results.

Biological pest control of insects is a realistic, environment-friendly, and economically effective possibility for plant protection in Africa. The African-wide biological control program of the IITA has proven this by the successful reduction of the cassava mealybug populations.

Any other alternatives – chemical or recurrent biological treatments – are far more expensive than the classical biological control and therefore not competitive.

Acknowledgments

We are grateful for the financial and logistical support from the German Agency for Technical Cooperation (GTZ). We would like to thank the scientists at the International Institute of Agriculture, Benin, and the Institute of Farm Management, University of Hohenheim for their excellent cooperation. Special thanks to Gilbert R. Ombok for permanent help in Kenya.

References

Carter, S.E., Fresco, L.O., Jones, P.G., Fairbairn, J.N. 1992. An atlas of cassava in Africa, CIAT, Cali, Columbia.

CIAT 1993. Cassava: The latest facts about an ancient crop, Cali Columbia.

Dorosh, P. 1988. The economics of root and tuber crops in Africa. Resource and crop management program, IITA, Ibadan, Nigeria, 68pp.

FAO 1975-1995. FAO production yearbooks 1975-95, Rome.

Herren, H. R. 1988. Cassava Mealybug and Green Mite Projekt: A Model for Update Scientific and Technological Aproach to Biological Control. IITA, Biological Control Program, Cotonou, Benin.

Herren, H. R. 1990. Biological control as the primary option in sustainable pest management: the cassava pest projekt. Mitteilungen der Schweizerischen Entomologischen Gesellschaft 63, 405-413.

Herren, H. R., Neuenschwander, p., Hennessey, r.d., Hammond, W.N.O. 1987. Introduction and Dispersal of *E. lopezi* (Hym., Encyrtidae), an Exotic Parasitoid of the Cassava Mealybug *P. manihoti* in Africa. Agriculture, Ecosystems and Environment, 19: 131-144.

Leuschner, K. 1978. Preliminary Observations on the mealybug (Hemiptera, Pseudococcidae) in Zaire and a projected outline for subsequent work. In: Proceeding of the international workshop on the cassava mealybug *P.manihoti* Mat-Ferr.

Lynam, J. 1987. The Cassava Economy of Asia – Adapting to Economic Change. CIAT – Report.

Neuenschwander, P. 1993. Human interactions in classical biological control of cassava and mango mealybugs on subsistence farms in tropical Africa. In: Crop protection strategies for subsistence farmers. Ed. by M.A. Altieri, London, pp. 143-177.

Neuenschwander, P., Haug, T. 1992. New Technologies for Rearing *E. lopezi* (Hym. Encyrtidae), a Biological Control Agent Against the Cassava Mealybug *P. manihoti* (Hom., Pseudococcidae) In Advances in Insect Rearing for Management, edited by T. Anderson & N.C. Leppla, 353-377..

Norgaard, R.B. 1988. The Biological Control of Cassava Mealybug in Africa. American Journal of Agricultural Economics, Vol.70, No.2, 366-371.NWANZE, K.F. 1982: Relationship Between Cassava Root Yields and Crop Infestation by the Mealybug, *Phenacoccus manihoti*, Tropical Pest Management 28 (1) 27-32.

Nweke, F. I., Lynam, J., Prudencio, C. 1989. Status of Data on Cassava in Major Producing Countries in Africa (COSCA, Work. Paper No. 3)

Schulthess, F., Baumgärtner, J.U., Delucchi, V., Gutierrez, A.P. 1991. The Influence of cassava mealybug, *P. manihoti* (Hom., Pseudococcidae) on yield formation of cassava, *Manihot esculenta* Crantz Journal of Applied Entomology 111, 155 -

Technology Transfer Issues in Promoting Crop Diversification

A Case Study of Smallholder Soyabean Production in Zimbabwe

Godfrey D. Mudimu
Department of Agricultural Economic and Extension
University of Zimbabwe
Mount Pleasant Harare, Zimbabwe

Abstract

In the mid-1980s, soyabeans were promoted for diversification to improve cash income and food security in the smallholder farming areas in the high-rainfall zones of Zimbabwe. The present study, covering nine agricultural seasons (1986/87 to 1994/95), was set to investigate factors determining increased soyabean production. It looks at the process and impact of improved technology transfer and adoption and promotion of home processing and use of soyabean products. Home use was intended to contribute to improved household nutrition.

On-farm and demonstration trials showed that improved technologies were viable and fitted into the farming system. Gross margin analysis suggested that soyabean production was profitable with potential to improve household cash income. Home use had the potential to reduce food cash expenditure and contribute to improved household nutrition. The subsequent surveys in 1993/94 to 1994/95, however, show that there was no widespread adoption of soyabean production and home use. One factor was the limited institutional support after the research and demonstration trials to maintain the momentum for adoption. Other constraints were unavailability of improved seed, shortage of working capital and recurrent droughts. The study suggests that technology transfer for crop diversification requires a package of sustained institutional support, accessible input and viable product markets.

Keywords

Technology transfer, crop diversification, food security, soyabeans

1   Introduction

In the mid-1980s, smallholder farmers were encouraged to diversify from low to high value crops as well as from drought prone to drought tolerant crops. Low value crops were the grain cereals, namely maize, sorghum and millets. High value crops were cotton, soyabeans, sunflowers, groundnuts and tobacco. The main reason was that maize was susceptible to droughts and faced unfavourable prices relative to increasing input costs. Thus diversification was seen as critical for sustainable household food security and income and rural development. In 1985, the Department of Research and Specialist Services (R & SS) initiated a project in Hurungwe Communal Area to promote increased production of soyabeans by the smallholder farmers. Several research issues needed to be followed. One was to explore the feasibility of soyabean production within the existing farming system given the prevailing agro-ecological, technological, socio-economic and institutional factors and farmers' management capacity. As soyabeans were a new crop to most of the smallholder farming areas, there was need to evaluate the production and management practices that would promote widespread adoption. This included a comparative economic analysis within the existing cropping system. Secondly, there was need to assess the capacity and options available to specific types of households to diversity by integrating soyabean production, the constraints faced and the strategies to be adopted. Another aspect was assessing the process of technology transfer and institutional support to enhance adoption and crop diversification.

Similar work carried out in several tropical countries (Chanda, *et al.* 1990; Javaheri 1985; Pasaribu and McIntosh 1985; Pasaribu *et al* 1986; Whingwiri 1986; Singh *et al.* 1987) showed that there is potential for increasing small-farm soyabean production through adoption of improved varieties, and management practices such as appropriate nitrogen and phosphorus fertilizer placing and application rates, appropriate planting time and seed inoculation. Weigartner (1987) and Weigartner, *et al.* (1987) considered home processing and utilization as important for promoting adoption by small farmers. The findings from these studies were mostly based on results from agronomic experimental data and on-farm research trials. Longitudinal studies in the post-technology transfer period would shed light on the adoption process and factors influencing the adoption. This study, therefore, contributes to knowledge on the process and impact of technology transfer on crop diversification in the smallholder farming sector.

This case study was part of a larger study initiated to investigate the economics of alternative soyabean production and management technologies, and the potential and constraints for their adoption. The specific objectives were:

1. To determine the relative profitability of improved soyabean production technologies, and their potential for contributing to increasing household income.
2. To identify farm level constraints to increased soyabean production and adoption of improved production technologies.
3. To determine from the preceding analyses whether potential existed for increasing soyabean production in Communal Farming areas.
4. To study the process and impact of technology transfer and crop diversification.

2 Background: Technology Transfer Process

The technology transfer process had two components, namely a) promoting improved soyabean production technologies through on-farm research and demonstration trials, and b) promoting home processing and use of soyabean products through utilization demonstrations.

2.1 On-farm Research and Demonstration Trials

The on-farm research and demonstration trials started in 1986/87 to test and demonstrate the viability of improved varieties under smallholder farming conditions and management. On-farm demonstration trials were intended to demonstrate to farmers the potential of soyabean production under improved varieties and management practices. The trials included comparison of the local variety, "Hurungwe Special," under traditional and improved management production practices. Components of the improved technologies included:

- improved soyabean varieties;
- row planting with appropriate spacing;
- fertilizer application at variable rates;
- proper seed and fertilizer placement;
- inoculation using a commercial inoculant and other cultural practices for introducing the inoculant;
- other improved agronomic practices, such as: early planting, pest and disease control, appropriate harvesting, and practices to avoid crop loss.

The research and on-farm demonstration trials were conducted in the farmers' fields under the farmers' labor with the advice and supervision of the Agronomy Institute Research Officers. In conducting the trials, the standard approach of (a) site selection and description, (b) research design and testing and evaluation were observed.

Dissemination of information on the improved technologies was done through field days held at both the on-farm research and demonstration sites. Competitions were held among farmers participating in on-farm research demonstrations and other farmers growing soyabeans to encourage adoption of soyabean production using recommended practices.

2.2 Utilization Demonstrations

On-farm agronomic and demonstration trials were complemented with promotion and demonstration of home use processing and consumption of soyabean products. The premise was that more farmers would adopt soyabean production if there were immediate household uses for the soyabean. Community Development Workers and Advisers were trained to teach households how to use soyabeans in the house. Recipes were developed. Competitions were held to encourage participation in soyabean use. Soyabean products promoted included meat, milk and coffee substitutes, snack, beverage, protein supplement (in porridge, relish). The use of soyabeans to provide the above translated into cash income saving for the household as it would not need to purchase these from the market. The cash so saved could be channeled to meet other household needs, such as education and acquisition of agricultural inputs.

3   Research Methodology: Data Source and Types

The data for the case study come from two sources and phases of a larger study based on the soyabean on-farm research and demonstration trials undertaken in Hurungwe Communal Area by the Agronomy Institute of the Department of Research and Specialist Services.

3.1   Phase I: On-farm Research and Demonstration Trials

Phase I covered the period of the on-farm and demonstration trials, 1986/87 to 1989/90. There were two data sources, namely (a) the on-farm agronomic and demonstration trials and (b) farm household surveys. Data on inputs and outputs (yields) obtained from research and demonstration trials pertain to the following comparative soyabean production and management technologies:

Case A

Soyabean production based on improved variety Roan and application of all the recommended agronomic practices including use of fertilizer and inoculation with a commercial Rhizobium inoculant. This was done through research and demonstration trials. R & SS managed the trials with the farmers providing labour with advice from extension.

Case B

Soyabean production based on the *local* variety "Hurungwe Special," with use of commercial Rhizobium inoculant and recommended agronomic practices such as appropriate spacing, planting time and fertilizer application. This was done as demonstration trials in selected farmers' fields and under farmers' management with guidance from R & SS and extension workers.

Case C

Soyabean production based on the local variety "Hurungwe Special" as grown by the farmers, that is without fertilizer application, and no inoculation. Data for this came mainly from studying farmers' practices.

Data from the trails were complemented with a survey of farmers participating in the soyabean on-farm research and demonstration trials and a sample of farmers attending the production field days as well as other secondary data sources. The survey involved 70 farm households stratified as follows:

a) 35 farm households being all farmers who participated in the on-farm and demonstration trails, and production competitions since the inception of the Soyabean Project in 1986/87.

b) 35 farm households chosen purposively from farmers growing soyabean but not involved in soyabean trials and demonstrations.

Data collection was initiated in the 1986/87 agricultural season and continued to the 1989/90 season. Pre-coded questionnaires were administered to all the sample farm households to collect data on i) household characteristics, ii) resource inventory, iii) cropping patterns, iv) crop input use and outputs, v) management practices, vi) farmers attitude to and assessment of soyabean production, improved soyabean technologies and constraints to soyabean production.

3.2 Phase II: Post-On-farm and Demonstration Trial

Phase II was a farm survey undertaken in the 1993/94 and 1994/94 seasons. This survey covered aspects relating to the adoption process in the post agronomic and demonstration period, 1989/90 to 1994/95. The focus was the reasons for either continuing, reducing or stopping soyabean production, and utilization by the surveyed farmers and their general perceptions of the district situation.

4 Data Analysis and Results

The analysis is focused on comparative economics of the alternative soyabean production and management technologies and alternative crops and the farmers' perception of these.

4.1 Comparative Analysis of Soyabean Technologies and Crops

The comparative economic analysis of the alternative crops and production technologies is gross margin analysis. The results are summarized in table 1. In terms of net return per hectare and labor day, improved soyabean variety, Roan, under improved management practices (Case A) outperformed the local variety grown under farmers' practices (Case C) and improved management practices (Case B). Comparing returns to land and family labor of all crops and technologies, improved soyabean variety ranked third after cotton and groundnuts. It marginally out-performed maize. Sunflower was outperformed by two of the soyabean production and management technologies (Cases A and C) except Hurungwe Special under the improved management practices (Case B). Net return per labor day of family labor was highest for groundnuts followed by cotton, the improved soyabean variety under improved technologies (Case A), maize, Hurungwe Special under the farmers' current practices, Hurungwe Special under

Table 1: Comparative Analysis of Alternative Crops and Soyabean Technologies

| | | | | | | Soybeans | |
	Maize	Cotton	Ground-nuts	Sun-flowers	Roan improved (A)	Hurunewe improved (B)	Hurunewe local (C)
AVERAGE YIELD	4781.65	1670.29	652.58	926.36	1640.16	1150	855
VALUE OF PRODUCTION							
Cash Sales	808.63	1419.76	0	378.4	613.27	407.4	283.5
Retensions	104.23	–	652.58	19.87	75.6	75.6	75.6
Total	912.86	1419.76	652.58	398.27	688.87	483	359.1
COST OF PRODUCTION							
Non-cash Costs							
Seed			84.7	71.84		45.9	45.9
Land Preparation	70	70	70	70	70	70	70
Cash Costs							
Seed	33.82	7.29			75.6		
Fertilizer	269.83	118.75	0	0	105.1	105.1	
Chemicals	3.24	181.42					
Pesticides			0	0	4	4	4
Inoculant					1	1	0
Hired Labor							
Weeding	0	26.61	0	0	0	0	0
Harvesting	0	46.51	0	0	0	0	0
Seasonal Loan Interest	46.43	115.99	0	41.28	29.93	19.73	18.75
Marketing Costs	135.58		0		40.56	26.94	
Total Cash Costs	488.9	496.57	0	41.28	256.19	156.77	22.75
Total Non-Cash Costs	70	70	154.7	141.84	70	115.9	115.9
Total Costs	558.9	566.57	154.7	183.12	326.19	272.67	138.65
GROSS MARGIN	353.96	853.19	497.88	215.15	362.67	210.33	220.45
Cash	319.73	923.19	0	337.12	357.07	250.63	260.75
Non-cash	34.23	-70	497.88	-121.97	5.6	-40.3	-40.3
LABOUR HOURS (Family)	400	935.67	464	312	406	285.29	280.51
Return/Labor Hour	0.88	0.91	1.07	0.69	0.89	0.74	0.79
Return/Labor Day	5.31	5.47	6.44	4.14	5.36	4.42	4.72
MARGINAL ANALYSIS					(A-B)	(B-C)	(A-C)
Incremental Return to Land					152.35	-10.12	142.22
Incremental Return to Additional One Unit of Labor					1.26	-2.11	1.13
Incremental Return to Additional $ of Production Costs					2.85	-0.08	0.76

Source: Research and Demonstration Trials and Survey

NB: Data averaged over three years (1986/87, 1987/88, & 1988/89)

improved management practices and then sunflowers. These results show that adoption of improved soyabean varieties and management practices would have the potential to increase household family income if farmers were to diversify from maize and sunflowers. Sunflowers could be substituted completely for soyabeans grown under improved production and management practices.

4.2 Farmers' Assessment of the Technologies and Alternative Crops

Table 2 gives the farmers' perception of the improved management practices that contributed to better yields and return. Use of improved seed varieties was ranked high followed by inoculation. High population density, planting in rows, and fertilizer application were sighted as management practices that were not followed with respect to the traditional variety, Hurungwe Special.

Table 2: Farmers' Assessment of Factors Contributing to Improved Performance

Variable factor	Ranking
Use of improved seed	1
Inoculation	2
High population densirt and row planting	3
Fertilizer application	4
Early planting	5
Early harvesting to reduce shattering losses	6

Source: Survey data 1989/90

High returns generated from high producer prices and yields and the potential use of the soyabean products in the home were factors giving incentives for expansion of soyabean production by the smallholder farmers (see table 3). Multiple home use was ranked third indicating that farmers recognized the importance of home use of soyabean.

Table 3: Farmers' Ranking of Factors in Favor of Increased Soyabean Production, Hurungwe.

Variable Factor	Ranking
High producer price	1
High yield	2
Multiple home use	3
Influence of the Soyabean Project	4
Effective field days and demonstration trials	5
Availability of advice from Extension and Research agents	6

Source: Survey data 1989/90

Unavailability of improved seed and other purchased inputs in the local market were the major factors that would constrain increased soyabean production (see table 4). There was competition with established crops for inputs (land, fertilizer, seed). This was a reflection of the general shortage of land, and working capital for purchase of inputs. As soyabeans had to be harvested over a short time to avoid excessive loss due to shattering of the pods, this created a labor bottleneck that was a major constraint for families without adequate labor.

Table 4:   Farmers' Ranking of Major Constraints to Increased Soyabean Production

Variable factor	Ranking
Lack of improved seed inputs	1
Competition for purchased inputs	2
Weather variability	3
Lack of proper management skills	4
Labor intensity at harvesting	5

Source: Survey data 1989/90

4.3   Comparison with Maize, Cotton, and Other Crops

Farmers' opinions on the relative merits of soyabeans versus maize, cotton, sunflowers and other crops were solicited. Farmers considered maize, cotton, soyabeans, and sunflowers to be important cash crops. In terms of the crop that brought in the most money, maize was ranked first, followed by cotton, sunflowers and then soyabeans. This reflected the relative importance in terms of size of land allocated to each crop in the existing farming system. Sunflowers were seen as having the least demand on family labor followed by soyabeans, maize and then cotton. The general practice was not to fertilize sunflowers and do little weeding. Cotton picking and maize harvesting and shelling were considered the most arduous operations and soyabean harvesting was the most intensive.

Compared to other crops, particularly cotton and sunflowers, soyabeans were assessed as better able to conserve the soil. Soyabeans establish a vegetable frame quite early in their growth compared to cotton, maize, and sunflowers. This tends to protect the soil better from wind and water erosion. Soyabean's capacity for nitrogen fixation was regarded favorably, as it reduced, to some extent, application of purchased chemical fertilizers.

4.4   Factors contributing to Trend in Soyabean Production

Table 5 summarizes the reasons for either stopping or reducing production. The difficulties in sourcing improved seed in affordable units for the areas under production, drought or unreliable rainfall that reduced yield and labour shortages appear to have made soyabeans uncompetitive relative to the other crops. This is confirmed in table 6 that gives the main factors given for not expanding soyabean production over the period in question.

Table 5: Reasons for Reducing or Stopping Soyabean Production

Reasons	% of Responses
Improved inputs unavailable	35
Intensive labor at harvesting	23
Drought	18
Other crops preferred	12
Marketing constraints	12
Total	100

Source: Survey 1994/95.

Home use was reported to be rare. For those households growing soyabeans, the reasons were: a) the processing was time consuming, b) there was not much interest by family members and c) non-substitute products were available in the market. For non-growing households, home made soyabean products were considered expensive given availability of non-substitute products and unfamiliar taste of the soyabean products. As a protein source, soyabean was less readily usable compared to groundnuts.

Table 6: Reasons for Not Expanding Soyabean Area

Reasons for Not Increasing Soyabean Area	% of Responses
Labor intensive at harvesting	26.7
Shattering losses at harvesting	33.3
Inappropriate growing season	6.7
No area for expansion	13.3
Low producer price and lack of working capital	20.0
Total	100.0

Source: Survey 1994/95

4.5 Trends in Adoption and Utilization

The Phase II survey revealed that over the period from 1986/87 to 1990/91 there was a 76.77 % increase in the number of farmers growing soyabeans in the study area (compare table 7). Farmers were growing mainly the improved varieties.

Table 7: Trend in Farm Households Growing Soyabeans, in Hurungwe

Season	86/ 87	88/ 89	90/ 91	92/ 93	93/94
Households	1,500	2,003	2,650	1,800	1,560
% Change		34	30	-32	-13

Source: Agritex Hurungwe District Office 1995

Of the 35 farm households participating in the research and demonstration trials, in the initial survey, 15 grew soyabean continuously over the period, 1988/89 to 1993/94; 10 grew intermittently and 10 had stopped after 1989/90. Of the 25 who grew either continuously or intermittently, 16 had expanded the soyabean area by varying proportions. The casualty crops were cotton and sunflowers. The remaining 9 had either not increased or reduced. In the case of area reduction, the benefitting crops were maize, sunflowers and to some extent tobacco. Out of the 35 original non participating subgroup, 12 started production in 1988/90-1990/91. Of these only 5 continued to grow in the most recent season, 1993/94.

5   Discussion

The conclusion from the Phase I survey was that there was potential for increasing soyabean production in the smallholder farming areas in the high rainfall zones. Factors associated with increased productivity were adoption of improved varieties, and management practices such as appropriate nitrogen and phosphorus fertilizer placing and application rates, appropriate planting time and seed inoculation. Farmers could increase household family income if they adopted these technologies and diversified from maize and sunflowers. Soyabeans fitted into the farming system without major adjustment in resource use and requirements. Farmers had positive perception of the improved management practices that contributed to better yields and returns. The results are consistent with the findings of similar work carried out in several tropical countries (Chanda et al. 1990; Javaheri 1985; Pasaribu and McIntosh 1985; Singh et al. 1987). These showed that there was potential for increasing small-farm soyabean production through adoption of improved varieties, and management practices such as appropriate nitrogen and phosphorus fertilizer placing and application rates, appropriate planting time and seed inoculation.

Soyabeans had the potential as a major cash crop for smallholder farmers in better rainfall areas. Expansion of soyabean production was possible given the positive net return to land and family labor compared to some crops in the cropping system. It fitted well into the existing farming practices of the farmer. It offered the opportunity to increase cash income without any serious negative impact on household food security as farmers were unlikely to make a complete substitution of soyabeans for maize.

Training and demonstrations on processing and the development of recipes promoted processing and home use. Home use did not have negative social connotations. Soyabean-based products could be substituted for some purchased commodities and were used to enhance the nutritive content of locally available foods. More importantly, there was no competition with maize, the staple grain. However, it is important to note that the potential for cash income was ranked higher than home use.

The trend in the post 1990/91 seasons suggests that the adoption rate was lower than the rate anticipated in the earlier survey. Several factors appear to have contributed to this. First, the initial support from research and extension was not sustained beyond the first three years. Secondly, farmers had difficulties procuring the improved seed. The seed houses considered seed demand by the small farmers as not significant for their trading account. Seed was available in large units (50 kg bags) yet farmers wanted to purchase smaller quantities. Another factor was the debt that farmers went into as a result of the droughts in 1991/92. Agricultural finance was either no longer available or risky for the farmers. The removal of price controls on inputs in 1991 tended to increase prices of fertilizer and other chemicals. Similar observations have been made by Mombeshora, *et al.* (1993).

Regarding home utilization of soyabean products, the results suggest that this did not take root. One reason appears to be that the labor time for processing was relatively high and could not be fitted into the women's time demands. As a result, home-processed soyabean products were expensive relative to availability of non-substitute products. It appears that, although non-substitutes were more expensive in monetary terms, households had expected the soyabean products to be priced at very low prices. The price differential between the soyabean products and their close non-substitutes was not wide enough to shift interest in the latter. From an institutional perspective, it appears not much was invested in developing less labor-intensive processing technologies. Locally processed products were not able to compete with commercially available close products and soy-products from urban-based industrial firms given the perceptions on taste. A related factor was, therefore, that local demand for locally processed products did not materialize. Most of the soyabeans were marketed outside the growing areas. This is not surprising given that the farmers had rated marketing above home use at the time of the initiation of the soyabean project.

6   Lessons Learned

There are several lessons for technology transfer to enhance crop diversification and food security. This case study illustrates a methodological approach for involving farmers in the assessment of improved technologies to maximize the impact of agricultural technologies in terms of productivity, profitability, and sustainability for crop diversification. Technology availability and institutional support and the participation of the farmers in the process of technology generation and transfer provided a framework for enhancing the impacts of technology transfer and adoption. The factors that offered incentive for technology adoption and crop diversification were:

1. The technology addressed the farmers' needs. This implies that the problems of the target farmers must be clearly identified. The farmers must be facing the problems to an extent that potential solutions are immediately apparent. In this case study, the need was for improvement in farm household income.
2. The introduced technologies proved to work under the farmers' production environment. In this case study, the soyabean technologies worked in the high rainfall zone and were compatible with the farmers' cropping system and did not require unfamiliar farming practices. In other words, the risks were few.

3. The benefits of the new technologies must be clearly identifiable by the farmers and must be better than the farmers' current practices and not introduce other constraints. There were several identifiable benefits, namely:
   a) Soyabeans were identified by the farmers as a high value crops.
   b) Planning of soyabeans in rotation with other crops was viewed as improving soil fertility for the follower crop. This reduced to some extent the farm expenditure on fertilizers.
   c) The use of soyabean products had the potential to reduce household expenditure on those food items that could be obtained from the soyabean products. The use of these products had positive social connotations.
   d) Investment costs for adoption were not high. Therefore the risks were not high.
4. The demonstration trials and field days promoted adoption and were self-targeting. Farmers did not feel compelled to adopt.
5. There was institutional support that was focused on meeting the farmers' training and informational needs.

The follow-up study illustrates a weakness in management of the post-technology transfer process. A sustainable strategy was not developed to support increased adoption. There was lack of institutional support beyond the trial of the technologies. The drought and changes in the input and output markets, brought in by the economic reform program, interfered with the farmers adjustment process. Expansion in production and continued utilization depended on a number of factors. Availability and affordability of improved seed were vital for sustainable production. Other key factors were favorable soyabean prices relative to other crop prices and availability of markets for soyabean products. The policy issue is that there was need to design post-harvesting marketing and utilization strategies that complement agronomic and varietal improvements for continued production of soyabeans.

Acknowledgments

Funding for this research came from the University of Zimbabwe Research Board. The Departments of Research and Specialists Services made available the input and output data from the on-farm and demonstration trials. The Department of Agricultural, Technical and Extension Services (AGRITEX) assisted with the field arrangements and access to reports used for secondary data. Grace Chikowore and Maxwell Chiwashira were valuable with the data entry and analysis. Dr Empraim Whingwiri was instrumental in getting the study done and commented on an earlier draft of the paper. The work on this paper was started while I was on a research visit in the Fachgebiet Ressourcenökonomie, Landwirtschaftlich-

Gärtnerische Fakultät, Institut für Agrarpolitik, Marktlehre und Agrarentwicklung, Humboldt Universität zu Berlin. I am thankful to the facilities and the hospitality I received that facilitated my work.

References

Chanda, K.S., M. Bezuneh, P.T. Gibson, F.J. Olsen and R.E. Hudgens. 1990. "An Agronomic and Economic Evaluation of Soyabean Planting Methods in the Central province of Zambia" **Experimental Agriculture.** Vol. 26:441-445.

Javaheri, F. 1985. "Soyabean Varieties for Small Scale Farmers in Zambia" **Soybean Genetics Newsletter.** Zambia.

Mombeshora, B., M. Mudhara, and S. Chikura. 1993. "A Survey of Soyabean Production in the Communal Lands: Hurungwe and Uzumba." Unpublished Research Report, Department of Research and Specialists Services.

Pasaribu, D., and J. McIntosh. 1985. "Increasing Tropical Soyabean Production With Improved Cropping Systems and Management" in Sundaram, S. and E.W. Sulzberger. (eds.) **Soyabeans in Tropical and Sub-Tropical Cropping Systems: Proceedings.** Tawain. Fortune Printing Co. Ltd.

Pasaribu, D., R.A. Morris, and R.O. Torres. 1986. "Inoculation Methods and Nitrogen Fertilizer Effects on Soybeans in the Tropics: Dry Matter and Seed Yield" **Tropical Agriculture.** Vol. 64 No. 4:323-327

Singh, S.R., K.O. Rachie, and K.E. Dashiell. (eds.). 1987. **Soybean for the Tropics: Research, Production and Utilization**. John Wiley and Sons. New York.

Weigartner 1987. "Processing, Nutrition, and Utilization of Soyabeans" In Singh, S.R., K.O. Rachie and K.E. Daschiell (eds) **Soyabeans for the Tropics: Research, Production and Utilization.** Wiley and Sons, New York, pp. 149-178

Weigartner, K.E. Daschiell and A.J. Nelson. 1987. "Soybean Utilization in Africa: Making a Place for a New Food" **Food and Nutrition**, Vol. 13 No 2: pp. 21-28.

Whingwiri, E.E. 1986. "Soyabean Production in Communal Areas and Small-scale Farming Sectors." Proceedings of the Workshop for the Southern Africa Region on Basics of Soyabean Production and Utilization. Harare, Zimbabwe.

Fruit Tree Integration: An Option to Improve Household Food Security in Nepal's Mountain Region

Devendra Gauchan
Nepal Agricultural Research Council (NARC)
P.O. Box 5459, Kathmandu, Nepal

Abstract

Household food insecurity, which is reported to be caused by poor and unreliable sources of income, is one of the major concerns for Nepal's mountain development. This paper is the basis of a comparative study of two different production systems (fruit tree- and food crop-based) conducted in Nepal's middle mountain region in order to examine the impact of fruit tree (citrus) integration on household income and food security. A farm level multiperiod programming model was employed in various farm groups to find out the impact of citrus integration on household income. The results revealed the significant increment in Net Present Value of household income by the addition of citrus component in their subsistence systems. This study also examined the income-food expenditure relationships in both citrus and non-citrus farm households, categorized according to food availability. The relationship between cash income and food expenditure was strong in citrus-based food deficit households. The important policy implications from this study is that citrus integration in the existing system provides an option for improving cash income, thereby ensuring greater household food security in a mountain environment without sacrificing subsistence autonomy.

Keywords

Household income, citrus integration, food availability, multiperiod programming, food expenditure, food security

1   Introduction

1.1   Background Information

Nepal, with a per capita income of US$ 180 is regarded as one of the least developed countries in the world. Agriculture is the backbone of the Nepalese economy, which provides a livelihood for more than 80% of the population. The country is mainly mountainous and landlocked, located in the cradle of the great

Himalayas between the two giants China and India. Agroecologically, Nepal is divided into high, middle mountain and Tarai (plain) regions.

The middle mountain region extends 800 km east to west from 500 m to about 2000 m above the sea level. It currently figures among the world's most fragile, risk-prone, and impoverished farming areas with 60% of the rural people living below the poverty line. This is the most important region as it covers over 60% of the country's area and supports the livelihood of about 50% of the people, who solely depend on subsistence farming of food crops (APROSC/JMA 1995). However, despite its comparatively large area, arable land is only 36% of the total cultivated area, with very high population density of above nine persons per hectare (Chitrakar 1990). Average per capita availability of cultivated land is so small (< 0.105 hectare), that subsistence food production from rainfed hillslopes is barely sufficient to provide adequate food for more than nine months.

Production systems are highly variable and risk-prone due to irregular monsoon rains, erosion of fragile top soils, deteriorating soil fertility, and lack of suitable innovations to cope with this situation. Furthermore, opportunities for nonfarm employment are very few and demand for labor is highly seasonal. Thus, household incomes are not only low but also extremely variable. This income insecurity in Nepal's mountain region has been reported to be the major cause of household food insecurity.

1.2 Rationale and Objectives

Policies and programs that improve household food security in rural mountains need to be given top priority in Nepal in order to combat chronic hunger, malnutrition, and environmental degradation. Recent evidence from Nepal shows that poor and unreliable sources of income, which are closely interlinked with the complex problems of natural resource degradation and population pressure, have been observed to be the major cause of household food insecurity in this region. In the context of current deteriorating economic and environmental conditions in Nepal's mountain region, a profitable and sustainable innovation such as high-value fruit tree integration, provides an option for improving household income and food security. This region provides a favorable production and marketing niche for growing high-value fruit trees (Jodha 1990).

Among high-value fruit trees, citrus integration into the existing production system has been observed to be the main improvement strategy for sustaining Nepalese smallholder hill farms, where annual crops alone are not stable or economical (Gauchan 1994). Integrating market-oriented citrus production without completely sacrificing subsistence autonomy will protect small farm households from extreme vulnerability to the vagaries of the market economy and natural environment.

The shift towards high value-fruit trees such as citrus integration into the existing subsistence system involves significant reallocation and increased productivity of household resources (particularly land and labor), and is associated with significantly higher household incomes. Total household food availability from home production may not decrease, but access to food may be higher as a result of incremental cash income obtained from citrus sales.

Calkin (1982), in his study of Nepal's Nuwakot district (central middle mountain), reported the positive effect of horticultural cash crops on income, employment, and nutrition. Several other researchers have also pointed out the positive effect of cash cropping on income and household food security (Kennedy and Bouis 1993; Staatz and Bernsten 1992).

This paper is based on a comparative study of two production systems conducted in middle mountains of Nepal, where high-value fruit trees such as citrus integration into the existing system and resource endowments of the households has been observed to be a successful and sustainable innovation as compared to the traditional food crop-based system, in mitigating the problem of food insecurity. The main objectives of this paper are: i) to examine the economic viability of citrus integration into existing crop-based systems, and ii) to analyze the relationship between increased cash income and household food expenditure patterns and food security. Since the mountain people spend the major portion of their income on food items, incremental cash income obtained from the sale of citrus fruits will improve their food entitlement through increased spending on basic as well as complementary food items. This case study differs from other crop commercialization studies, which examine the effects associated with a complete substitution of cash crops for food crops. Instead comparison is made here between two production systems to examine the effect associated with citrus integration.

2   Study Setting and Methods

2.1   Survey and Sampling Methods

This study was undertaken in November to December of 1993 in two villages of the Kavre district (middle mountain region), Nepal, employing both informal and formal survey techniques for collecting data. Rapid Rural (RRA) and Participatory Rural Appraisal (PRA) were the main tools for the informal survey to understand farm household systems, socioeconomic conditions such as resource endowments, household income, food access and availability, food expenditure and consumption patterns, the marketing environment and other general characteristics of the study areas. Information compiled from secondary sources, as well as insights gained from the informal survey, were used in selecting multistage stratified random samples. The field survey consisted of a pretested questionnaire interview of 120 randomly sampled households from two villages: Sankhu (n = 60) and Patlekhet (n = 60), which represent citrus- and non-citrus-based (food crop) systems.

2.2   Analytical Methods

A multiperiod linear programming model with a planning horizon of twenty years, with yearly intervals as periods, was employed in both systems (with and without citrus) to find out the impact of citrus integration on household income under various economic environments and resource endowments of the households. The main objective of the model was to maximize the present value of future income (gross margin) subject to resource constraints (land, capital, peak and slack season labor) and consumption requirements. Econometric techniques were employed to model the consumption behavior of the farm households, incorporated into the programming model, which depended on household income and consumption units.

The economic and food availability outcomes associated with and without citrus fruits were examined among two different groups of farm households, categorized according to food availability (food sufficiency). Market participation among food self-sufficient and food deficit households of both systems were analyzed for basic and complementary food items, as well as other household goods. A Pearson correlation analysis was conducted to find out the relationship between household income and food expenditure patterns in food deficit and sufficient households of both systems.

3   Socioeconomic and Production Characteristics

3.1   General and Socioeconomic Situation of the Study Areas

Sankhu (citrus-based) and Patlekhet (non-citrus-based) villages are located in the Kavre district, 50 km east of Kathmandu, in the central middle mountain region of Nepal. They are situated in upland sloping areas adjacent to each other but separated by a mountain ridge with an altitude ranging from 1200 to 1600 m above sea level. These areas represent the typical middle mountain ecology with similar biophysical and socioeconomic characteristics.

Table 1 shows the characteristics of two groups of farm households: food self-sufficient (FS) and food deficit (FD). Food deficit (FD) households were smallholders with very small farm size, which did not have adequate food available for more than 9-10 months. The percentage of food deficit (FD) households was higher in Patlekhet (72%) than in Sankhu (62%).

The number of food self-sufficient households (FS) with adequate year-round food availability (11-12 months) was low in both the study sites. By ethnicity, households were of two distinct types: Brahmin-Chhetrias (Indo-Aryan origin) and Tamang (Tibeto-Burmese origin), normally Hindus and Budhists, respectively. Small land-holdings with large household size and higher man-land ratios in food deficit households of these villages reflect a situation of excess population pressure on cultivated land.

Table 1: Socioeconomic Characteristics of Food Self-Sufficient (fs) and Food Deficit (fd) Farm Households by Production Systems

Household	Sankhu (Citrus-based)		Patlekhet (Non-citrus-based)	
Characteristics	FS	FD	FS	FD
% Household	38	62	28	72
Farm size (ha)	1.82	0.55	1.69	0.58
Citrus area (ha)	0.36	0.18	-	-
Household size	7.87	6.80	8.55	6.35
Man-land ratio	4.32	12.36	5.05	10.95
Dependants (No.)	3.93	3.12	3.93	2.54
Farm labor force	3.04	2.72	3.80	2.76

Source: Computed from Household Survey 1993

3.2 Agriculture Production Systems

Dry land agriculture is a common practice in both the villages, occupying about 78% of the cultivated area. In Patlekhet, the production system is highly traditional and subsistence-orientated. Maize is a principle rainfed summer crop grown on terraced hill slopes, followed by wheat and rape seed/mustard in the winter. Rice is also an important crop for large farm households under partially irrigated conditions. The return from this subsistence food production system is very low and variable due to unpredictable monsoon rains, soil erosion, and lack of productive and environmentally sustainable technologies.

Citrus integrated with dryland crops such as maize, wheat and mustard is a commonly adopted production system at Sankhu. Surveyed households have integrated citrus in an average area of one-third of their hill slope farms. The average number of productive trees owned ranged from 62 for food deficit to 210 for self-sufficient households, which was highly correlated with land holdings. Intercropping of food crops in between trees during pre-bearing stages was very common among smallholders to meet their subsistence food requirements. Citrus trees offer many advantages in multicropped systems at Sankhu, as they are not seriously affected by low fertility soils and short-term fluctuations in rainfall.

4   Overview of Household Income Sources

Farm households in both the study sites have diversified their earnings from various sources to fit into their food security strategies. They derive their income both from farm and off-farm sources (Table 2). The average annual cash income for the citrus-based system at Sankhu is relatively high compared to the non-citrus-based system at Patlekhet and other similar parts of Nepal's middle mountain region. This is due to the significant contribution of citrus integration on cash income which is over half of the total household income in both food self-sufficient (FS) and food deficit (FD) households.

Crop income in self-sufficient households mainly comes from rice production. Off-farm employment also plays an important role in Sankhu, contributing 24% and 37% of total household income in food self-sufficient and deficit households, respectively. The major source of off-farm income comes from wage labor as well as from remittance and trading.

Table 2:   Different Components of Annual Cash Income (US$) in Farm Household Groups by Production System and Food Availability

Household Income Sources	System with Citrus		Systems without Citrus	
	FS	FD	FS	FD
A. Farm	795.0	425.0	270.0	72.0
- Crop	105.0	-	175.0	-
- Citrus	605.0	336.0	-	-
- Livestock	85.0	89.0	95.0	72.0
B. Off-farm	255.0	250.0	235.0	220.0
- Wage labor	25.0	95.0	45.0	140.0
- Non Wage labor	230.0	155.0	190.0	80.0
C. Household	1050.0	675.0	505.0	292.0

Source: Computed form Household Survey 1993

It is evident from table 2 that income derived from subsistence food crops is low and variable in Patlekhet, which is highly correlated with land holdings. Though the contribution of off-farm activities to total household income is very high, particularly in food deficit (FD) households, the actual amounts are low (US$ 220-255) and also highly seasonal and variable. Wage labor was the major source of off-farm income for food deficit households in Patlekhet, whereas non-wage labor such as remittance and trading were major sources for self-sufficient households.

5   Impact of Citrus Integration on Household Income

A farm-level multiperiod linear programming model was employed to find out the impact of citrus integration on household income in both the study sites. The citrus-based system of Sankhu is compared with the same system without citrus by eliminating the citrus component from the existing situation. Similarly, the existing crop-based system of Patlekhet is compared with the system that integrates citrus by extrapolating input-output coefficients of citrus production from the Sankhu site.

The results obtained from the application of programming models in both the cases indicate the significant effect of citrus integration on Net Present Value (NPV) of household income (discounted by 16% interest rate). The elimination of the citrus component from the present farming activities at Sankhu would cause considerable loss of NPV of income (15%) in both food self-sufficient and deficit households (compare table 3).

Furthermore, by simulating existing crop-based systems with a citrus component in Patlekhet, it gave an average 15% higher NPV of income over the existing situation in both groups of farm households (compare table 4).

Table 3: Impact of Citrus Integration on Annual Household Income (US$) in Sankhu Village, Middle Mountain, Nepal; 1993

Farm household groups	System with Citrus	System without Citrus	Percent Reduction
Food deficit	3.848	3.267	-15.0
Self-sufficient	8,756	7,391	-15.6

Table 4: Potential (Simulated) Impact of Citrus Integration on Household Income (US$) in Patlekhet Village, 1993

Farm household groups	System with Citrus	System without Citrus	Percent Increment
Food deficit	3,116	3,557	14.0
Self-sufficient	8,593	10,007	16.0

From the above results it is clear that there is higher benefit from citrus integration into the existing food crop system. This is because of the incremental benefit obtained from citrus sales and also the reduction in the cost of maintaining the trees during early non-productive years by intercropping with food crops. Evidence from Senegal (Goetz 1992) also indicates that there is significant cost-saving (22.3%) by producing both food and cash crops in the same household, as compared to producing the same quantities in two separate (specialized) households.

6   Household Cash Income and Food Expenditure Pattern

Due to small and unproductive holdings, the majority of the surveyed farm households in Patlekhet and Sankhu suffer from some months of food deficiency. This makes them rely heavily on cash income earnings to purchase food from the market during the pre-harvest hunger season. The reliance of rural smallholders on the market for food is well recognized in Asia (Mellor 1990). As shown in Table 5, there is higher expenditure on food (both staples and non-staples) in food deficit households (FD) of both the systems (with and without citrus) where food takes up nearly 50% of all cash purchases. However, it was low in food self-sufficient households (FS) despite their higher absolute expenditure on non-staples (salt, sugar, spices, cooking oil, meat and vegetables) since they spent nothing for staples such as rice, maize, and wheat.

Table 5: Household Cash Expenditure (US$) and Food Market Participation

Cash Expenditure	System with Citrus		Systems without Citrus	
	FS	FD	FS	FD
Staples	-	190.0	-	130.0
Non-Staples	185.0	125.0	105.0	80.0
Food	185.0	315.0	105.0	210.0
Non-Food	630.0	346.0	394.0	194.0
Total Expenditures	815.0	661.0	499.0	404.0

Source: Computed from Household Survey 1993.

By production systems, absolute food and non-food expenditure (household consumption such as cloth, fuel, ceremony, education, health) was higher in higher earning households with a citrus-based system due to higher cash income obtained from citrus sales. Recently, Kennedy and Bouis (1993) also reported an increase in absolute expenditure on food consumption by cash cropping. In terms of real income, the real expenditure on food, in food deficit households of both sites (if included from their own farm production), could constitute as much as two-thirds of total household consumption expenditure. This is similar in the report by Guru-Gharana (1992), in which the poor in Nepal spend about 74% of household income on food only.

7   Relationship between Household Cash Income and Food Expenditure

Table 6 provides the results of the Pearson correlation analysis, showing positive relationships between cash income and the food expenditure pattern. As compared to livestock and off-farm income, the relationship between citrus income including total household cash income and food expenditure was very strong in food deficit citrus-based households. This means that the expenditure on food, which is taken as a proxy for food security, is strongly related to cash income for households with a citrus-based system.

Several researchers recently have also reported positive relationship between income and expenditure on food consumption and food security by cash cropping (Kennedy and Bouis 1993; Staatz and Bernsten 1992; Von Braun, et al. 1992).

However, food deficit households at Patlekhet were forced to borrow credit from informal sources (e.g. moneylenders and relatives) at an exorbitantly high interest rate (36%) to meet their consumption requirements. Thus, they have adopted a strategy of seasonal migration to urban areas of Nepal and India, to ensure their survival.

Table 6: Relationships between Household Income and Food Expenditure by Types of Farm Households, Middle Mountain, 1993

Household Food Expenditure	Cash Income Sources			Household Income
	Citrus	Off-farm	Livestock	
A. Citrus-based				
Self-sufficient	0.68	0.51	0.45	0.68
Food Deficit	0.88	0.68	0.52	0.84
B. Non-Citrus-based				
Self-sufficient	-	0.49	0.48	0.51
Food Deficit	-	0.71	0.56	0.41

8   Lessons Learned

Considering the very low return from existing technology and production systems, in combination with apparently constrained land access for households in Patlekhet village, means that new sustainable innovation must be available if the majority of the smallholders are to escape the poverty trap in the highly fragile and risk-prone mountain areas of Nepal.

However, the experience gained and lessons learned from Sankhu implies that smallholders in middle mountain areas where, economic and environmental conditions are steadily deteriorating need to diversify their income sources through a profitable and environmentally sustainable innovation such as fruit tree (citrus) integration to improve income and ensure greater household food entitlement.

Food security policies must therefore focus as much on improving access to resources (such as income and land) as on increasing production of food stuffs.

The important policy implication to Nepal from this case study is that in the mountain environment, with risky market and climatic conditions, a sustainable innovation such as the joint promotion and integration of food crops and fruit trees is imperative for reliable income and for ensuring food security to small farm households without sacrificing their subsistence autonomy.

References

APROSC/JMA 1995. *Agricultural Perspective Plan*, Nepal; Prepared for: National Planning Commission, His Majesty's Government of Nepal and Asian Development Bank; Agriculture Project Service Centre (APROSC) and John Mellor Associates, Inc. Washington D.C.

Calkins P. H. 1982. "Why Development Fails: The Evaluation Gaps in Nepal's Subsistence Agriculture". *World Development*, Vol.10, No.5 pp 397-491.

Chitrakar, P. L. 1990. *Planning, Agriculture and Farmers: Strategy for Nepal*. Kathmandu, Nepal.

Gauchan 1994. "An Optimum Planning for Integrating Citrus in Nepalese Hill Farming Systems"; Unpublished Master's Thesis: Agricultural Systems Program, Graduate School, Chiangmai University, Thailand

Goetz, S.J. 1992. "Economics of Scope and the Cash Crop-Food Crop Debate in Senegal". *World Development*, Vol.20, No.5, Pp. 727-734.

Guru-Gharana, K.K. 1992. "Poverty Alleviation and Human Development in Nepal: Macroeconomic and Sectoral Policies and Programmes." Proceeding National Seminar on Poverty Alleviation and Human Development, 22- 24, June 1992, Planning Commission, Nepal, UNDP and the World Bank.

Jodha, N.S. 1990. "Mountain Agriculture Search for Sustainability". MFS Series No.2. International Center for Integrated Mountain Development, Kathmandu, Nepal.

Kennedy, E.T. and O.R., Oniang 1993. "Household and Preschooler Vitamin Composition in Southern Kenya". *The Journal of Nutrition* (USA). May 1993 V. 123(5) pp. 841-846.

Kennedy E. and H.E. Bouis 1993. International Food Policy Research Institute, Washington, D.C.

Mellor, J. W. 1990. "Food Price Policy and Income Distribution in Low -income Countries." In: C.K. Eicher and J. M. Staatz, (eds.), *Agriculture Development in the Third World*, 2nd edition. Baltimore: John Hopkin University Press, pp. 168-188.

Staatz and Bernsten 1992. "Technology Development and Household Food Security". Proceeding of the workshop on Social Science Research and CRSPs. Carnahan Conference Center, University of Kentucky, Lexington, Kentucky.

Von Braun, H. Bouis, K. Shubh and Pandy-Lorch 1992. *Improving Food Security of the Poor; Concept, Policy, and Programs*. International Food Policy Research Institute, Washington, D. C.

Management Strategies in African Homegardens and the Need for New Extension Approaches

Axel W. Drescher
Working Group on Applied Physiogeography of the Tropics and
Subtropics (APT), University of Freiburg,
Werderring 4, D-79085 Freiburg i. Br., Germany

Abstract

In Lusaka, as in many other tropical cities, gardening and cropping receive very little support from local authorities. Indeed, city councils often prohibit these activities. The relationship between urban food production, food security and urban environment has been largely neglected.

The main actors in urban agriculture are often women. It turned out that in all compounds examined in Lusaka, women are to a greater extent involved in cropping and gardening than men. Production of staple food prevails in the wet season, and vegetable production in the dry season. Microfarming obviously contributes to household food security in town, directly by providing food, and indirectly by generating income. People living in the high-density, low-income compounds in Lusaka have the least access to both land and water. Within the high-density squatter areas, vulnerability in terms of food security differs. In some cases, small homegardens help to decrease vulnerability by buffering risks of food shortages and by diversifying the household's sources of livelihood. Other households can do no gardening because they lack sufficient land, water, labor, etc. Those households are more vulnerable, because they depend completely on purchased food, yet they have low purchasing power. In the case of Zambia, it is not the most vulnerable households which practise dry-season cultivation but rather those which have access to the resources essential for this activity. Concepts for agricultural extension in the urban environment are missing due to the fact that "real agriculture" was thought to take place in the rural sector only. Homegardening as an important part of the urban microfarming system was completely neglected in the past not only in the urban but also in periurban and rural areas. Nevertheless there is a great demand and need for extension and advice, especially in the highly sensitive sector of leafy vegetable production. For the welfare of the people it would be advantageous to increase the output of such gardens. Nevertheless past policies of "greening" are not applicable to city gardens.

Three examples show the need for extension in the sectors of pest management, species composition and diversity, and soil fertility, and help to clarify the differences between urban, periurban and rural homegardening.

Keywords

Tropical homegardens, food security, biological pest control, crop species diversity, soil fertility, extension service

Introduction

Hunger and malnutrition in the world are increasing not only due to growing population and loss of yield but also because of the destruction of natural plant resources, the loss of food diversity and structural changes in the environment. Past management strategies of household food security often failed because they where based on the "macro-level" (governments, administrations, ministries). Therefore new strategies focus on the "micro-level" like the individual household (Kampmann 1992).

There is hardly any other field of investigation with such an urgent need for an interdisciplinary approach, like the research on household food security and vulnerability (Drescher 1994). During 1992 and 1993 a research project on homegardening was carried out in Zambia's capital Lusaka, in periurban areas of Lusaka and rural areas of Zambia. The so-called household garden survey concentrated on the household garden activities as an important part of the landuse system. There is a growing consensus that homegardening combined with nutrition education can be a viable strategy for improving household food security for at-risk populations (Marsh & Talukder 1994). This paper focuses on the situation in urban, periurban and rural areas of Zambia and gives some results of the survey. The main objective of the household garden survey was to clarify the role of household gardens for household food security in Zambia and to identify differences and problems in management strategies and their effects on production in the different areas (with respect to urban microfarming see Drescher 1996a).

Three examples may be useful to clarify some problems of smallholder/microfarmers homegardening strategies and extension approaches:
1. The problem of plant protection in tropical homegardens;
2. Practical aspects of calculating crop species diversity in tropical homegardens;
3. The use of fertilizer and compost in tropical homegardens.

1   The Problem of Plant Protection in Homegardens

Not much is known up to now about plant protection strategies and the use of pesticides in homegardens of the seasonal tropics in southern Africa. Especially pesticide abuse is a major problem and heavily underreported, as pointed out by Gura (1995).

The assessment of plant pests and diseases in vegetables requires much knowledge and experience in plant protection and entomology, which could not be made accessible to the members of the field team. Therefore the observed pests where classified roughly as follows:

- aphids
- white fly
- red spider mite
- caterpillars
- beetles, bugs
- grasshoppers, crickets
- thrips

The recognition of thrips was already a problem, because one needs a well-trained eye to do so. It was not possible to distinguish between different species of aphids or caterpillars.

1.1 The Most Important Plant Pests in Homegardens

Pests were observed in 90% of urban, in 72% of periurban and 80% of rural homegardens. There was no need for intervention in all of the observed cases. The most important pest in homegardens is the aphid, which can be observed especially in brassicas like rape *(Brassica napus)* or chinese cabbage *(Brassica chinensis)*.

The assessment of pests during the field surveys comes close to what the farmers estimate themselves. Thrips is not known by most of them and therefore was observed in only 1.1% of their gardens (table 1).

Table 1: Assessment of Pests in Homegardens According to Field Observations and Inquiry of Farmers

Pest	Assessment according to field observation (n=85)	Assessment according to farmers' estimation (n = 87)
Aphids	64.7	60.7
Beetles, bugs	21.2	3.3
White fly	20.0	7.9
Crickets	9.4	7.9
Thrips	9.4	1.1
Spider mites	8.2	15.7
Caterpillars	7.0	15.7

Source: Survey 1992/93

1.2   Alternative Methods of Plant Protection

There are different methods of alternative plant protection practiced in homegardens, including:

- Active measures, e.g. the use of alternative mixtures made of plants, water and ashes. Another active measure is the removing of parts of affected plants or the removing of the pest itself from the plant by hand (picking off);
- Passive measures include rotation of crops, removal of weeds, variation of planting times to avoid pest infection.

The most common method is the use of ash against insect pests, which was done by 20,5% of the respondents. The ash is used either pure or in water solution. One of the farmers uses warm ash against the white fly, by dusting the leaves 3-4 times weekly.

The second important method is the exaggerated use of water. Either the whole crop is flooded, or single leaves or the whole plants are washed (12,5%). The same percentage of farmers practices the method of removing plants or parts of the plants from the garden. The picking off of pests is practiced by 8% of the gardeners.

There are gender-specific differences in the use of alternative methods, but only in periurban areas, where 33% of the men but none of the women practice some kind of alternative protection. In all survey areas 52% of men and 48% of the women practice alternative methods of plant protection (n=83).

1.3   The Use of Chemical Plant Protection in Homegardens

One of the major constraints of homegarden production is the abuse of pesticides and consequently the risk of health hazards for the consumers (Gura 1995; Smit 1995). The use of chemicals is often inadequate in relation to the products utilized, as well as to application methods (Drescher 1996b).

Sixty percent of all the households of the survey use chemical products for plant protection: 61% in urban, 78% in periurban, and 46% in rural areas. Most important is the insecticide Rogor, followed by Fastac and Thiodan. In some cases DDT is still used (table 2). Many of the farmers do not know the name of the product they use, but rather the color of the box or bottle of the product. In Lusaka Town this was observed in over 50 % of the cases.

As table 2 indicates, only insecticides but no fungicides or herbicides are used in homegardens. Often the application is realized with very simple means, and the results are accordingly disappointing. Most of the very poor families are not able to buy expensive pesticides and implements. Therefore in many cases pesticides are not used at all.

Table 2: Insecticides Used in Homegardens

Active Substance	Applicability	Common Name
Dimethoate	Insecticide	Rogor, Salut, Malathion
Lambdacyhalothrine	Insecticide	Karate
Chlorpyrifos	Insecticide	Dursban
Alphacypermethrine	Insecticide	Fastac
Methylcarbamidacid	Insecticide	Carabaryl
DDT	Insecticide	DDT
Endosulfane	Insecticide	Thiodan

Source: Survey 1992/93

1.4 Natural Biological Control of Plant Pests in Tropical Homegardens

Very little activity is to be seen in the field of Integrated Pest Management (IPM) in homegardens of southern Africa. Concepts of other World Regions, as reported by Midmore (1995) and Westermann (1995) for Asia, might not be applicable, due to the low development standard, to the Southern African situation. Because of the great regional disparities in single states and between the different countries, concepts might not even be applicable to the countries as a whole (see Richter, Schnitzler, Gura 1995). The situation in Zambia requires particular approaches. Due to the great economic differences between rural and urban areas and even within the urban centers themselves, a common strategy might not work. First of all, local resources should be protected and used instead of influencing the situation through outside intervention, like rearing and releasing antagonists. In many cases it seems that there is still a very high potential of those local insect resources, partly caused by low impact of pesticides at least up to now. IPM will not work without the participation of the people concerned.

The observation of natural antagonists of plant pests formed an integral part of the field survey. It was difficult to identify and especially to quantify different antagonists because of lack of time. Nevertheless it was possible to concentrate on the biological control of aphids by using the presence of parasitized aphids on leaves as an indicator for the occurrence of parasitic wasps. These parasitized aphids can be identified because they change their color after having been parasitized. Additionally, these aphids show a small hole on their upper backside, which is the loophole of the wasp. In 36% of all homegardens, in 63% of urban, in 21% of periurban but only in 4% of rural gardens parasitic wasps were observed. The parasitation rate was often very high-up to an estimated average of nearly 40%. In some cases all of the observed aphids were killed by the wasps. The results for the rural areas must be put in question because they seem to be very doubtful. The low rate should be seen relative to the schedule of the surveys and the composition of the field team. The field survey in rural areas took place when the vegetable crops where still young and less affected by pests. Therefore no antagonists could be observed. Additionally, it was not always possible to train the members of the team in a short period of time, so that in many cases the beneficial organisms might have been overlooked. Due to the big distances of rural survey areas to the capital, it was not possible to conduct further surveys in these areas.

1.5   The Use of Insecticides and the Presence of Natural Antagonists

It is an interesting question to analyze the interrelation between the use of insecticides and the presence of natural antagonists in the gardens. In 10 gardens antagonists were found and no chemical plant protection was practiced. In 18 cases, in spite of the fact that the gardeners used insecticides, antagonists were observed. In the majority of the gardens (50) where insecticides were used, no antagonist could be observed. In 35 gardens no antagonists could be found although no chemical plant protection was practiced. These findings indicate that the use of pesticides in homegardens at least reduces the activity of beneficial organisms.

1.6   Methods of Plant Protection – Differences between the Survey Areas in Zambia

There are significant differences to be observed in the distinct survey areas of Zambia with respect to methods of plant protection (see figure 1 to 3). In rural areas only 23% of the households use chemical methods, while in Lusaka 36% and in periurban areas even 64% do so. This is connected with the small size of the gardens in urban areas and the subsistence-oriented production in urban and rural areas. Chemical products are available in town but the financial means are very limited. In contrast, very often no chemical products are available on the rural market. Therefore the rural gardeners practice alternative methods of plant protection. Only 14% of the households in rural areas and Lusaka, respectively 10% in periurban areas practice no plant protection at all. Some of the gardeners try both methods, alternative and chemical plant protection, these are about 25% in urban and rural but only 14% in periurban areas.

Pure alternative plant protection is mainly done in rural areas (43%), accounts for 25% in urban, but only for 9% in periurban areas. Due to the market oriented production, most of the periurban farmers practise chemical plant protection.

Gender specific differences were discovered with respect to the use of pesticides and the application of alternative methods of plant protection. In rural areas only 35% of men, but 57% of women use pesticides, but simultaneously more women use alternative methods (86%) than men do (65%). In contrast to the rural situation, in periurban areas no women, but 33% of men practice alternative methods of plant protection.

Figure 1: Plant Protection in Urban Homegardens

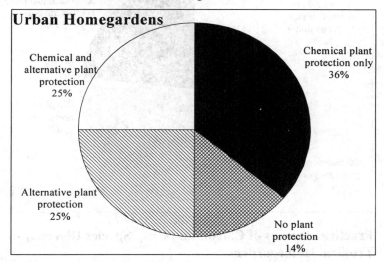

Figure 2: Plant Protection in Periurban Areas

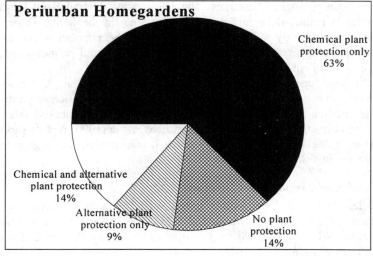

Figure 3: Plant Protection in Rural Areas

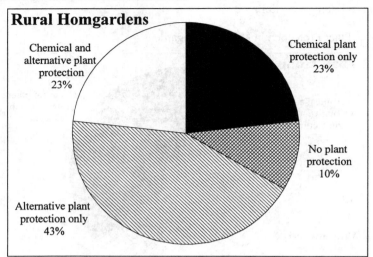

2   Practical Aspects of Calculating Crop Species Diversity in Tropical Homegardens

The contribution of homegardens to the maintenance of species diversity is one of their main ecological functions. The preservation of traditional crops and vegetables is mainly done in homegardens and not in the fields. Those crops contribute significantly to food diversification of the population and to food security. There is urgent need to intensify the research and promotion of these crops, as pointed out by Lewis (1995).

Up to now, interdependence between species diversity and plant protection played no role in homegardening, because there is no market-oriented production. A basic question in this context is whether species-rich production systems are less vulnerable to pests than monocultures. Letourneau (1990) reports successful examples in Mexico and California, where it was proved that higher species diversity facilitates plant protection.

2.1   Index of Crop Species Diversity

Species diversity is determined by two factors: The number of species and the abundance of each species within the community in a given area (compare Shannon & Weaver 1963; Myers & Giller 1990; Begon, Harper & Townsend 1986; Pomeroy 1986; Odum 1971).

During the field survey the following data were gathered for each garden: The total number of species and the number of individuals of each species with respect to crops and trees. The following classes were recorded: Cereals, roots and tubers, grain legumes, fruits, vegetables, spices and condiments, fats and oils, sugar and sweeteners, ornamentals, medicinals and drug plants, raw materials, miscellaneous uses and trees. Weeds were recorded only if they were used as vegetables. These data serve to calculate crop species diversity and probably give an answer to the following questions:

- Is there any correlation between size of the gardens and the crop species diversity?
- Is there any correlation between the sex of the gardener and the crop species diversity?
- Is there any correlation between crop species diversity and the presence of beneficial organisms in the gardens?

For the calculation of the species diversity index the Shannon-Equation was used (Shannon & Weaver 1963). This index is, according to Begon, Harper & Townsend (1986) and other authors, still the most common one.

The Shannon-Index (eq. 1) is calculated as follows:

$$H = - \sum_{i=1}^{S} P_i * \ln P_i \quad \text{(eq. 1)}$$

Source: Begon, Harper & Townsend 1986

H	=	Index of Shannon
S	=	Total number of species
i	=	Single species
P_i	=	Abundance of each species

The Shannon-Index is generally > 0. Only for monocultures it is always = 0. The more species in a garden, the higher the index becomes.

2.1.1 Garden Size and Crop Species Diversity

The Shannon-Index decreases with increasing garden size up to a size of 599 m² (see figure 4). The smallest gardens are located in the urban areas and show the highest crop species diversity. The limited space forces people to concentrate many different species in relatively small numbers on small plots. More space promotes market-oriented production, which causes the decline of crop species diversity in bigger gardens of less than 800 m². The very big gardens between 800 and 1999 m² confirm a positive correlation between size and diversity as was postulated by other authors (e.g. Solar 1985). More space gives more room for different species and allows multipurpose use of garden areas.

2.1.2 Crop Species Diversity and Gender

Comparing the gardens of women and men with respect to crop species diversity, it becomes obvious that women's gardens show higher diversity in rural and periurban areas. In the rural areas the differences are significant: The average Shannon-Index of all women's gardens is 0,99 while men's gardens show only 0,30. This indicates gender-specific differences in the role of men and women in vegetable production in the rural sector: women do more subsistence-oriented cultivation while men concentrate on market production.

Figure 4: Correlation between the Size of the Garden Plots and the Crop Species Diversity Index of Shannon

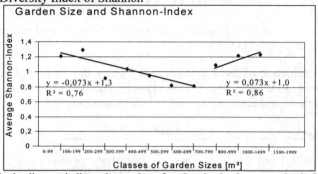

The figures in the diagram indicate the number of gardens having been examined of each class.

In the periurban area the average Shannon-Index is 0,92 for women's gardens and 0,70 for men's gardens. This indicates a similarity to rural areas. Only in urban areas there are, due to the prevalence of subsistence production, no differences with respect to gender and crop species diversity, but the crop species diversity is higher than in the other areas (H= +/. 1,35). The average number of crops and fruit trees occurring in urban gardens is 10, but only 5 in rural and peri-urban areas.

2.1.3 Crop Species Diversity and Plant Protection

Theoretical considerations and practical scientific findings as the above-mentioned ones by Letourneau (1990) indicate that higher species diversity promotes natural antagonists and therefore facilitates plant protection. From the climatic conditions in the survey areas (high temperatures year-round) the presence of pests and predators througout the year can be assumed.

Comparing the crop species diversity index with respect to the presence of predators in the gardens the following can be concluded: Gardens where predators of aphids were observed show a Shannon-Index of 1,34 (n=24), while gardens where no predators were observed show a lower index of only 0,91 (n=39). This means that higher crop species diversity contributes to natural biological control of aphids in tropical homegardens.

3 The Use of Fertilizer, Manure and Compost in Tropical Homegardens

The use of fertilizers shows much differences between the survey areas. The main causes are the motivation of production, which is market-oriented in periurban areas, and the purchasing power of the people, which is generally low in low-income groups of urban and rural areas. The use of fertilizer is additionally gender-specific (compare figure 5). In urban areas only 50% of all respondents use fertilizer, in periurban areas 86%. In periurban areas 100% of men but only 57% of women use fertilizer. The lack of fertilizer for women in periurban areas is compensated by the use of manure. 86% of women use manure, while only 60% of men do so (figure 6). About 55% of gardeners in periurban and urban areas keep chicken while in rural areas only 45% do so. Only 5% of urban gardeners keep cattle. In periurban and rural areas more goats and cattle are kept and more cattle manure is used in homegardens. Goats do not occur among the gardeners in Lusaka, as the survey indicates (figure 8). The use of manure shows a slowly increasing tendency from urban to periurban and rural areas. In urban areas it is still high, with 76% of all respondents. Periurban male producers use more fertilizer, therefore they use less manure. Many of the homegardeners use chicken manure which often causes problems of "burning" of the plants.

Due to the lack of organic matter and knowledge, composting is not common practice in homegardens. Only 32% of the respondents in urban areas practice composting (figure 7), in rural areas even less (24%) and little more in periurban areas (40%). Some of the urban residents buy compost from others because they can't produce their own. Generally the quality of the compost is very low, due to the lack of water and shade as well as of proper waste management.

Soil analysis of 80 garden soil samples proved the high fertility of garden sites compared to rainy season plots in the survey areas. This indicates the possibility for sustainable development of such production sites with low level external input.

Figure 5: Use of Fertilizers in Homegardens

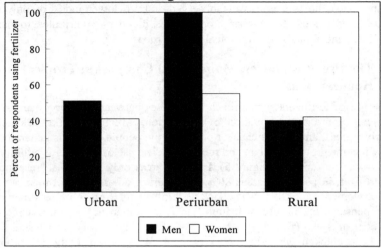

Figure 6: The Use of Manure in Homegardens

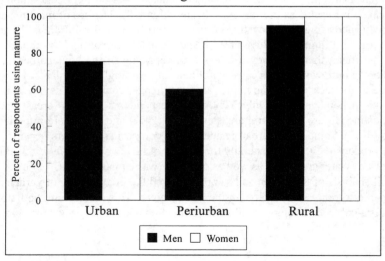

Figure 7:Use of Compost in Homegardens

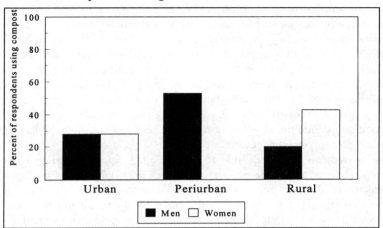

Figure 8: Livestock Keeping of the Respondents of the Survey

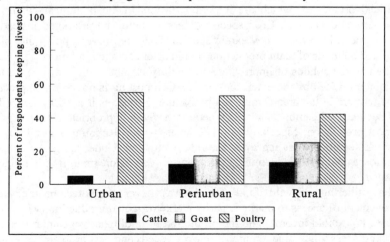

4 Lessons Learned: The Need for New Extension Approaches

With respect to the health of the consumers and environmental impacts **the use of pesticides** in small gardens is not at all desirable. However, 60% of all respondents in Lusaka use pesticides in homegardens, in periurban areas they make nearly 80%. It is very likely that waiting times and dosages are not kept properly, leading to health risks of the consumers. Natural antagonists of aphids were observed in 63% of urban and 21% of periurban gardens. The biological control by parasitic wasps was very effective in many cases. The differences in urban and periurban gardens are caused by a more market-oriented production in periurban areas and they are closely related to a higher input of pesticides in periurban gardens. In general it is assumed that the occurrence of natural antagonists is even higher than the survey findings indicate. Urban gardens show the highest crop species diversity and lowest input of chemical plant protection. Therefore, most of the natural antagonists were observed in these gardens.

Crop species diversity in homegardens contributes to ecological stability and preservation of traditional plant resources. There are manifold advantages of increased diversity in homegardens.

The **extension service**, up to now often quite restrictive in its recommendations, should be made aware of this important role of homegardens. Homegardens do not only contain genetic resources which have widely disappeared, but also provide seeds and cuttings for the production of staple food (e.g. sweet potatoes cuttings). Homegardens provide ecological niches for many insect species which would have disappeared without the "small islands" in the "sea" of monocultures. Homegardens mainly function as preservation areas for beneficial organisms, which are important factors in the biological control of plant pests and diseases. Crop species diversity should be promoted instead of being reduced in favor of few exotic species. Therefore intercropping and other integrated methods of plant production should be encouraged in future.

Alternative methods of improving **soil fertility** is another field of interest that could be promoted by the extension service. Composting is not common practice of the farmers in the area. Traditionally manure is used, as it is still practiced in rural societies of Zambia. There is a need to develop appropriate technology for compost production, especially in urban areas, where declining possibilities for livestock keeping might aggravate the future situation. Under the given climatic conditions, compost production can be done in very short time, if it is properly managed.

The gathering of wild food (which was never promoted in the past), improvement of access to markets, partly market-oriented production (which will increase household income) and the promotion of traditional vegetables (making households less vulnerable to purchased exotic seeds and pest problems) are other sectors of possible impact and positive signals of extension services.

There is a need for **new approaches towards extension** of smallholders on different levels:

- Holistic approach towards the different components of the smallholders agricultural system: This includes farming as well as gardening, livestock keeping, gathering and other activities like hunting. Most components were neglected in the past and extension concentrated exclusively on farming activities.

- New approach on the technical level: With respect to plant protection, the promotion of knowledge of the role of beneficial organisms in small-scale farming systems so far unknown to most farmers and even extension officers.
- With respect to crop species diversity: New findings of different scientific disciplines must be adopted by the extension service in developing countries. The environmental impact of farming practices is obvious but often overlooked by farmers and officials. Technical assistance might be required.
- New approach on the psychological level: Extension must be understood as a service to the people. Consequently interactive learning, participatory extension service, promotion of existing management strategies instead of the introduction of new, unknown, nonadapted and not accepted strategies should be the main goal. The improvement of the quality of existing strategies should be another main target. The impact of currently practiced extension leads in some cases to less crop species diversity in homegardens and nonadapted management strategies, which makes the system more vulnerable to pests and disease attacks and food security.
- New approach towards environmental problems: The avoidance of environmental degradation by environmentally sound land-use strategies to promote the sustainability of agricultural production and resource management should be an integrated part of extension service.
- New approach towards gender-specific agricultural activities: Women tend to have higher crop species diversity in their homegardens and they use different strategies to improve soil fertility in periurban and rural areas. Generally the role of women in food security differs from the role of men. Due to less access to resources compared to men, women use more manure in periurban areas than men do. In some cases women use less chemical fertilisers because they don't have access to credits. Gender-specific differences in agricultural activities need to be paid more attention by extension services.
- Bilateral transfer of knowledge between gardeners and extension officers is required to understand the smallholders land-use system and management strategies properly. Alternative management strategies for homegardens are needed. They can only be developed by participatively elaborating extension strategies in close cooperation between smallholders and extension officers.

5   References

Begon, M., J.H. Harper & C.R. Townsend 1986. Ecology. Blackwell Scientific Publications, Oxford.

Drescher; A.W. 1994. Urban Agriculture in the Seasonal Tropics of Central Southern Africa – A Case Study of Lusaka/Zambia. Contribution to the "International Policy Workshop on Urban Agriculture: A growing Development Tool", University College London (NRI/CPU), 29.06.1994.

Drescher, A.W. 1996a. Urban Microfarming in Central Southern Africa: A Case Study of Lusaka, Zambia. In: African Urban Quarterly (in print).

Drescher, A.W. 1996b. Die Hausgärten der wechselfeuchten Tropen des Südlichen Afrika – ihre ökologische Funktion und ihr Beitrag zur Ernährungssicherung (Fallstudien aus Sambia). APT Reports No. 4., Institut für Phyische Geographie, Arbeitsbereich Angewandte Physiogeographie der Tropen und Subtropen (APT), Universität Freiburg i.Br.

Gura, S. 1995. Vegetable Production – a challenge for urban and rural development. In: entwicklung+ländlicher Raum, Heft 4/95: 3-6.

Kampmann, M 1992. Horizonterweiterung – Frauen in der Ernährunssicherung. In: entwicklung + ländlicher Raum, Heft 4/1992: 1.

Letourneau D.K. 1989. Two Examples of Natural Enemy Augmentation: A Consequence of Crop Diversification. In Gliessman, S.R. (ed.) 1989. Agroecology. Ecological Studies Vol. 78. Springer, New York: pp. 11-29.

Lewis I.U. 1995. Förderung traditioneller Gemüsaearten – Beispiele aus Afrika. In: entwicklung + ländlicher Raum 4/95: pp. 10-11.

Marsh, R.R. & A. Talukder 1994. Effects of the Introduction of Homegardening on the Production and Consumption of Target, Interaction, and Control Groups: A Case Study from Bangladesh. In: System-Oriented Research in Agriculture and Rural Development. International Symposium. Montpellier, France 21 to 25 Nov. 1994. CIRAD-SAR, Montpellier.

Midmore D.J. 1995. Constraints and potentials of periurban Vegetable Production. In: Richter, J., W.H. Schnizler, S. Gura (eds.) 1995. Vegetable Production in Periurban Areas in the Tropics and Subtropics – Food, Income and Quality of Life. Proceedings of an International Workshop held from 14 to 17 Nov. 1994 in Zschortau, Germany. DSE/ATSAF: pp. 64-84.

Myers A.A. & P.S.Giller 1990. Analytical Biogeography – An Integrated Approach to The Study of Animal and Plant Distributions. Chapmann & Hall, London.

Odum E.P. 1971. Fundamentals of Ecology. Saunders College Publ., Philadelphia.

Pomeroy, D. & M.W. Service 1986. Tropical Ecology. Longman Scientific and Technical, Essex.

Richter, J., W.H. Schnizler, S. Gura (Hrsg.) 1995. Vegetable Production in Periurban Areas in the Tropics and Subtropics – Food, Income and Quality of Life. Proceedings of an International Workshop held from 14 to 17 Nov. 1994 in Zschortau, Germany. DSE/ATSAF.

Shannon, C.E. & W. Weaver 1963. The mathematical theory of communication. University of Illinois Press: 117 pp.

Solar, K.M. 1985. The Javanese Mixed Homegarden as a Plant Genetic Resource. Rep. No. 819. Nature Conservation Department, Agric. Uni. Wageningen, The Netherlands.

Westermann, T. 1995. Biologischer Gemüseanbau in den Philippinen – ein Beitrag zur Armutsbekämpfung. In: entwicklung + ländlicher Raum 4/95: pp. 15-18.

Household Food Security through Home Gardening – Evidence from Bangladesh

Robin Marsh
Center for North American Integration and Development
School of Public Policy and Social Research
University of California, Los Angeles, USA

Abstract

A case study methodology was used to conduct a global study of the socioeconomic characteristics of promoted and traditional home gardening, and the contribution of gardens to household food security, for the Asian Vegetable Research and Development Center. This paper presents the results of one case study: a promoted vegetable gardening project in Bangladesh implemented by Helen Keller International.

Key aspects of the HKI project methodology are described: focus on women, training in nutrition education, promotion of low-input, low-cost technologies, and interactive, continuous monitoring. Data are presented on garden production, time allocation, use of inputs, distribution of garden production, income generation and contribution of gardens to family consumption and nutritional status. Benefit/cost ratios calculated at the project and target household levels were estimated at 1.0 and 3.3, respectively.

Regarding development policy, the paper suggests that in areas where food insecurity is a problem, government and NGOs can be successful and cost-effective in promoting nutritional and income-generating gardening, subject to certain preconditions at the local level. Basic criteria for ensuring long-term success and sustainability are offered as a conclusion.

Keywords

Household food security, home/vegetable/mixed gardens, food-based nutrition interventions

1   Introduction

Home gardening is a family food production system widely practiced in developing countries under myriad forms. Its contribution to overall food supply is generally overlooked in national and international consumption statistics. Nevertheless, a review of the literature on gardening and case study research on traditional and promoted gardens in Asia and Central America, reveal that *food production in small quantities close to the house* contributes significantly to household food security (Soleri et al 1991; Midmore 1991). Gardens tended and controlled by women contribute especially to improving maternal/child nutrition and to meeting family food needs during lean periods (Marsh 1994).

Most gardening projects are supported by non-governmental organizations (NGOs) that promote community development and improved food security in low-income rural areas (e.g. UNICEF, UNDP, Helen Keller International (HKI), CARE, Save the Children and many local NGOs). The involvement of governments in support of gardening has been minimal, and to the extent they do get involved, the health and nutrition sectors generally are responsible. Ministries of agriculture (MOAs) tend to discount the actual or potential importance of home gardening as an agricultural or rural development strategy. Consequently, few extension agents are trained in gardening techniques, especially mixed tropical gardening.

Home gardening is also increasingly recognized as an important supplier of food to urban markets, and enhances food security among the urban poor in many of the largest cities of Asia, Africa and Latin America (Soleri and Cleveland 1987; UNDP 1996). Even in the densest populated slums, establishment of container gardens or simple hydroponics require little or no land and minimal cash resources (Urban Agriculture 1993). Access to home grown fruits and vegetables generally ensures a more balanced diet for the urban poor with limited purchasing power, while surpluses can be sold among neighbors and in nearby markets.

This paper evaluates a case study of home gardening in Bangladesh carried out as part of a broader comparative study on home gardening systems for the Asian Vegetable Research and Development Center (AVRDC). The objective of the paper is to present evidence on the production, income-generation, consumption and nutrition effects of a well-designed home gardening project, which can serve as a model for other gardening promotion interventions worldwide. The paper concludes with a section on "lessons learned" and lists criteria for ensuring the sustainability of home gardening for improving household food security.

2   Case study: Home Gardening in Bangladesh

2.1   Justification

In Bangladesh, several factors contribute to the interest by a large number of NGOs, certain government sectors, and international donors in the development of homestead production. Most importantly, is the growing population of landless and near landless (less than .40 ha of land) households in rural Bangladesh, about 9.5 million or 68.8% of total rural households in 1992 (BBS 1992; Venkataraman 1992). Among the landless and near landless, less than 9% have *no* homestead land available for cultivation. Average homestead area equals 150 m^2 and 300 m^2

for the landless and near landless, respectively (*ibid*). This land is typically underutilized.

Widespread protein-energy malnutrition in Bangladesh is clearly related to the high proportion of rural landless. Micronutrient deficiencies are also prevalent. Nutritional blindness among pre-school age children is a persistent problem caused by vitamin A deficiency. Every year, over 900,000 children under 6 years old suffer some degree of xerophthalmia and 30,000 or more children become permanently blind (HKI 1989, 1991). National level statistics show that 90% of rural Bangladeshis' dietary vitamin A is from vegetable sources and that 88% of all households have deficient dietary intake (World Bank 1992).

Women and children disproportionately suffer the effects of malnutrition, largely a function of discrimination in intra-household food distribution (World Bank 1992). Among the children, girls suffer higher levels of malnutrition than boys and the gender disparity increases at higher socioeconomic levels and at higher levels of father's education (HKI 1993). Apparently, somewhat more educated and affluent fathers seek to improve conditions for their sons but not their daughters. However, mother's education level is positively correlated with improved nutrition of girls, underscoring the importance of incorporating education and training of women in nutrition intervention efforts.

2.2 HKI Home Garden Project

Background. Helen Keller International (HKI) is an organization that works globally to reduce the incidence of nutritional blindness and raise awareness of the importance of vitamin A in the diet. In Bangladesh, it is promoting an integrated strategy of nutrition education, home gardening and social marketing to improve nutritional levels among at-risk populations, focusing in particular on vitamin A consumption.

Between 1990 and 1993, HKI implemented a home gardening and nutrition education project in Panchagaor District, northwest Bangladesh. The project incorporated a strong research component to permit a "before and after" analysis of gardening effects on family consumption, nutrition and health (HKI 1993a).

The target group were village households meeting the following criteria: 1) ownership of less than 0.32 ha of land, including the homestead area; 2) not involved in any other NGO promotion activities; 3) with at least one child under six years old; and 4) a woman would represent the household for home gardening training and management. One thousand families were selected from 81 villages. An additional 200 families were selected from nearby villages as a control group. To ascertain any "demonstration" or indirect effects from the project, 100 households were selected from the same villages as the target group to form an "interaction" group. These households did not receive direct assistance from HKI.

Criteria for selection of control and interaction households were the same as for the target group.

Project Extension Methodology. In each target village, working groups of 10 to 20 women gardeners were formed. These women chose among themselves a leader to organize technical assistance and seed distribution for the project. HKI provided training for the group leaders lasting a day every six months for two years. One field officer with an advanced degree, and six extension workers with secondary level education in agricultural science, three men and three women, were hired to work full time in the field with the group leaders and gardeners.

The project provided seasonal vegetable seeds (23 varieties) and seedlings (9 trees) during the first two years at a subsidized cost. "Nursery" women among the group leaders were selected to grow the seeds into seedlings for project-wide distribution. The group leaders facilitated seedling distribution and collection of money, as well as sharing of indigenous vegetable seeds, cuttings and vines. HKI provided technical assistance on seed production and storage techniques to ensure self-sufficiency in seed provision once the gardeners were on their own.

A comprehensive mid-term project evaluation was conducted in December 1992, two years after the baseline survey. The evaluation was conducted by a multidisciplinary team of externally recruited professionals – a medical doctor, an expert in anthropometric measurements, an agronomist, and a social scientist. All households in the target, control and interaction groups were evaluated through detailed questionnaires, observations and measurements. Prior to the evaluation, team members received intensive training from HKI, including pre-testing of questionnaires. Data collected in the field were checked daily and follow-up visits were made when necessary. These procedures, designed by the expert HKI data processing team in Dhaka, were necessary to ensure a reasonably reliable data set.

Mid-Term Evaluation Results

Production. Figure 1 shows the changes, on average, in number of garden varieties, garden production, and garden size from the baseline survey to the mid-term evaluation for the target group of 1,000 families. At the time of the baseline, 50% of the households reported having a home garden of mean size 61 m^2 and an average of 3.1 varieties of vegetables in the ground. Two years later, 100% of the households had gardens of mean size 138 m^2, and the average number of varieties increased nearly five fold to 17. Monitoring round data show that total production of vegetables increased even more steeply than garden size, indicating improving yields over time.

Figure 1: Changes in Number of Garden Varieties, Garden Production and
Garden Size over Time, Target Group

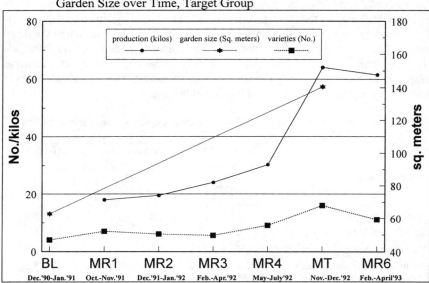

Table 1 compares the same characteristics for the target and control groups at
midterm. Among the control group, only 25% of households maintained gardens,
of about the same average size as the target group. Among target gardeners, the
average number of vegetable varieties grown throughout the previous year, 33,
and in the ground at the time of the midterm evaluation, 17, were several times
greater than for the control group, with 9 and 4 varieties, respectively.

Improvements in garden production, both in terms of number of varieties and
production per unit of land, were possible because of changes in garden
production practices. Extension workers and group leaders recommended reliance
on local materials for soil fertilization and pest management, conforming to
extremely limited financial means. Thus, for both economic and ecological
reasons, use of agrochemicals was discouraged. Seeds were provided at
subsidized rates during the first two years, phasing out seed provision by the third
and last year.

Time Allocation. The midterm evaluation included questions on the time
allocation of the female head of household during a fairly typical day. These
questions were designed to ascertain what time of day gardening is done, and
whether time spent gardening may compete with other important income-
generating or domestic activities. Women were asked to choose among a set of

activities which activity corresponded to their *first* priority during each time period (early and late morning, early and late afternoon).

Most striking is the low priority given to gardening in the control and interaction groups as compared with the target group. Among women in the target group, late afternoon is clearly the preferred time for gardening, with 50% and 48% responding that gardening is their first or second priority at that time, respectively. Gardening does not appear to conflict with "work outside", but may take time away from washing, cooking and child care.

Table 1:   Home Garden Characteristics of Target Group – Comparison of Baseline and Midterm

Variables	Baseline (BL) Dec.'90-Jan.'91		Midterm (MT) Nov.-Dec.'92		MT/BL
Garden last year (%)	49.1		100		
	n=491		n=980		
	mean	SD	mean	SD	
Size of garden (m^2)	61	37	138	113	2.3
No. of vegetable varieties/year	6.2	2.4	33	4	5.3
No. of veg. varieties/year/m^2	.122		.354		2.9
No. of veg. varieties currently	3.1	2	17	4	5.5
No. of veg. varieties currently/m^2	.061		.178		2.9
Use of garden produce last month:	%		%		
- consumption	96		47		
- consumption and sold	4		53		

Principal Constraints. The principal constraints with home gardening, as reported by the target, control and interaction groups at midterm are common among gardeners in developing countries worldwide. For instance, lack of fencing around the garden to keep out farm animals is often cited as *the* major obstacle to successful gardening.

Problems addressed by the HKI Project, such as technical knowledge, seed availability, soil fertility and pest management, are listed as constraints by only a minority of target gardeners, but continue to be principal constraints for the control and interaction groups. However, lack of irrigation, land and fencing, problems not fully addressed by HKI, are still significant constraints for many target gardeners. In fact, as the garden grows in importance for family nutrition and income, the household has a greater interest in protecting it (fencing) and ensuring year-round production (irrigation).

Income. The objective of the HKI Project, as explained earlier, was to enable families to improve their nutrition and health through home gardening, focusing particularly on vitamin A intake by women and children five years and under.

Thus, women were encouraged to preserve the bulk of their produce for home preparation and consumption. Nevertheless, during the first two years of the project, as surpluses became available, there was a shift toward increased sale of garden produce. At baseline, only 4% of target households reported selling some garden vegetables, which increased to 53% at midterm.

Of the 53% of households selling some fruits and vegetables, the average income earned during the thirty days prior to the midterm evaluation was 85 *taka* or about US$2.25. Even this small amount is significant when placed in the context of overall cash income earned. Total cash income earned thirty days prior to midterm was estimated at about 694 *taka* or US$18 for the target group, slightly higher than comparable figures for the control and interaction groups. Therefore, for the subset of target households that sold garden vegetables, income earned was equal to nearly 15 percent of total cash income.

Gender Effects. Evaluation data on *who* decides whether or not to sell garden produce show that among target, control and interaction households the decision is made by women in 65%, 25% and 26% of the cases, respectively. The husbands are more likely to make this decision in the control and interaction groups. Also, women are more than twice as likely to receive and exercise control over income earned from garden sales in the target group (67%), as compared with the control (31%) and interaction (17%) groups. As expected, given the high percentage of total cash income spent on food, most income earned from gardening is likewise spent on food. This may have significant nutritional and health benefits, as discussed later in the paper.

Consumption and Health. A primary objective of many home gardening projects is to improve availability of vitamin-rich vegetables *year-round*. Data shown in figure 2 compare vegetable availability for target, control and interaction households during the three main seasons prior to and including the midterm evaluation. Generally, undernutrition by wasting (low weight for height) is most prevalent between August and October after the mid-year monsoons and prior to the *aman* rice harvest[1] (HKI 1993b). Both rice and vegetable availability are highest during the dry and cool *boro* season.

In no season did target households report vegetables "not available", whereas the control group, and to a lesser degree the interaction group, reported lack of availability as a major problem in the *aus* and *aman* seasons. Over 95% of target households reported that vegetables are "available and adequate" in the *aman* and *boro* seasons, while 37% reported availability "not adequate" in the lean *aus* season. Vegetable growing during the hot monsoon season presents the greatest

---

[1]The largest rice crop corresponds to the *aman* growing season, harvested in November.

challenge to gardeners, a challenge best met by relying on indigenous leafy
vegetables resistant to high temperatures and humidity as well as local diseases.

Figure 2:   Seasonal Vegetable Availability

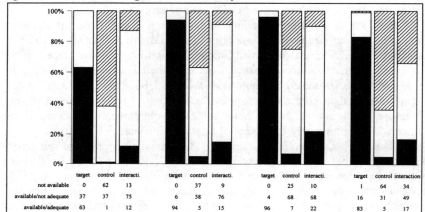

For the target group, vegetable consumption increased from an average of 5.8
kilos to 7.5 kilos per week, or 30%, and 82% of vegetables consumed came from
their home gardens. On a per capita basis this equals nearly 200 grams per day,
which just meets the FAO recommended daily intake of vegetables. During the
same period, vegetable consumption for the control group increased 6% from 5.1
kilos to 5.4 kilos per week (16% from their home gardens), while vegetable
consumption for the interaction group declined by 20% to 5.0 kilos per week.

The midterm evaluation included questions on frequency of vegetable
consumption by young children because of the importance of adequate vitamin
intake for normal physical and mental development in the early years. Figure 3
compares vegetable consumption by children under five years for the target,
control and interaction groups. Among the target group, fewer babies of 6-11
months (55%) and toddlers of 12-23 months (17%) are not eating vegetables at
all, as compared with the control (83%, 40%) and interaction groups (79%, 31%).
Thus, mothers in the target group are beginning to include strained vegetables in
weaning foods, a change from traditional practices. It is still of concern that
nearly 20% of target households appear not to be feeding their toddlers
vegetables on a daily basis, or perhaps not at all.

Both the baseline survey and midterm evaluation included anthropometric measurements to ascertain overall nutritional well-being, as well as specific medical assessments of vitamin A and iron deficiencies. The data indicate that night blindness in children, a sensitive indicator for vitamin A deficiency, declined from 2.3% to 1.2% in the target group, although prevalence beyond 1% is still considered of public health significance. The prevalence of severely underweight children under five (weight for age <3Zscores) declined by 7% in the target group (from 25% to 18%), and by 3% in the control group (from 22.3% to 19.3%).

Figure 3:   Vegetable Consumption by Children

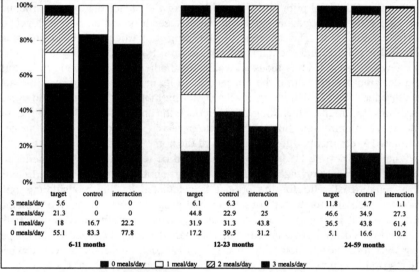

	target	control	interaction	target	control	interaction	target	control	interaction
3 meals/day	5.6	0	0	6.1	6.3	0	11.8	4.7	1.1
2 meals/day	21.3	0	0	44.8	22.9	25	46.6	34.9	27.3
1 meal/day	18	16.7	22.2	31.9	31.3	43.8	36.5	43.8	61.4
0 meals/day	55.1	83.3	77.8	17.2	39.5	31.2	5.1	16.6	10.2
	6-11 months			**12-23 months**			**24-59 months**		

■ 0 meals/day   ☐ 1 meal/day   ▨ 2 meals/day   ■ 3 meals/day

HKI staff interpret the latter finding to be related as much or more to increased consumption of rice, purchased with income or cash savings from home gardening, than to any direct effects of vitamin A intake on growth (HKI 1993a). For the average target household, 90% of calories consumed are from rice, complemented with small amounts of *dal* (lentils), dried fish and cooking oil. Therefore, given the overwhelming importance of rice in the diet and widespread seasonal deficits in rice consumption, it is likely that a significant portion of the income earned from home gardening is spent on rice. Even among gardening households who do not sell vegetables, reduced spending on vegetables frees up cash for purchase of additional rice.

Summary and Conclusion. The preceding data analysis has shown that the HKI Home Gardening Project in Panchagoar District resulted in significant nutritional and economic benefits for participating households. First and foremost, has been the impact of the project on family consumption of vitamin-rich vegetables, especially by young children. Consumption increased overall by an average of 30% after two years of gardening. Considering savings in purchased vegetables as well as income earned from sales of home garden produce[2], the average imputed monetary benefit was 163 *taka* per month, or 25% of average total cash income earned 30 days prior to the midterm evaluation. Most of the additional cash income was spent on food, reducing the prevalence of severely underweight children.

Therefore, the HKI pilot project provides strong evidence that home gardening can be a viable strategy for improving the food security and nutritional levels of at-risk populations. The success of the project, particularly in overcoming formidable cultural and economic barriers in rural Bangladesh, may be attributed to a few key factors: 1) its focus on women as mothers, gardeners, group leaders, and decision-makers within the household; 2) its incorporation of nutrition and health education at all training levels; 3) its promotion of low input, low cost gardening techniques, including seed production; and 4) its use of continuous, interactive monitoring. Furthermore, the research component of the project facilitated a reasonably rigorous analysis of the home gardening experience.

Whether or not the HKI pilot project should be recommended as a model for other development organizations depends in part on its cost effectiveness. In table 2, a benefit/cost ratio for the project is calculated as one, considering only monetary benefits for target households and program costs. Since the principal benefits of the project are non-monetary, actual benefits are substantially underestimated. The program cost for each target family averaged US$39.0 per year over three years, increasing to US$46.0 for each household surveyed when the research component is included.

Table 3 calculates a benefit/cost ratio at the individual household level, taking the monetary benefit shown in table 2 and average operating costs for seed, seedlings and crop protection as well as depreciated capital investment in irrigation and fencing. Labor is not given a positive value since the opportunity cost of family female and child labor during the late afternoon, when most gardening is done, is negligible in this isolated part of Bangladesh. The total cost, at US$11.7 per year, was calculated using the 30% subsidized rate for seed and seedlings. Benefits, as stated above, are only partially accounted for. Subject to these caveats, the ratio comes to 3.3, a very positive outcome.

---

[2] For the 53% of target households that sell produce. For the remaining 47%, only savings in expenditures would be counted.

Table 2: HKI Project Cost per Beneficiary[1], 1990-1993

	US$
Program cost/direct beneficiary (target group, n=980)	
- Total	117
- Average/Year	39
Program cost/direct and indirect Beneficiary (target and interaction groups, n=1,075)	
- Total	107
- Average/Year	36
Program and research cost/household surveyed (target and control and interaction groups, n=1,303)	
- Total	138
- Average/Year	46

Benefit-Cost Ratio = 38.9^2/39 = 0.997

[1] Before overhead charges; [2] Average target household benefit (1US$ = 38 taka):

	Taka/mo	US$/mo*
Cash	85	2.24
Savings	78	2.05
Total	163	4.29

US$4.29 x 12 = $51.5 (for vegetables sellers -53%); US$2.05 x 12 = $24.6 (for non-sellers - 47%)
Average: US$ 3.24 x 12 = **$38.9**

Table 3: Average Annual Home Garden Costs, Target Group

	Taka $
Operating costs	
- Seed	83[1]
- Seedlings	20[2]
- Crop protection	8[3]
- Labor	0[4]
Sub-total	111
Capital investment	
- Irrigation	300[5]
- Fencing	33[6]
- Sub-total	333
Total	444 = US$11.7

Benefit-Cost Ratio = 38.9^7/11.7 = 3.3

[1] Includes price of all varieties (23 in total). During the first two years of the project, seeds were distributed at a subsidized price (30% subsidy); in the third year market prices were employed.
[2] Includes seedlings for five fruit and four multipurpose trees, also subsidized by 30% during the first two years.
[3] Out-of-pocket cost for crop protection was for soap and kerosene; otherwise locally available resources were employed (ash, plant parts).
[4] Since family labor is used exclusively in the gardens, primarily female and child labor during the late afternoon, the opportunity cost of this labor is negligible.
[5] Treadle pump + boring costs an estimated 1,000 taka; a hand tubewell costs about 2,000 taka. Taking an average and depreciating over five years gives 300 taka per year. Not all households invested in irrigation.
[6] The cost of a bamboo fence (100 taka) depreciated over three years. "Live" fencing made of jute stick or trees costs less.
[7] See table 2 for the calculation of household monetary benefits from home gardens.

Largely because of the success of the Panchagaor pilot project, HKI was able to enlist the support of donors, leading Bangladeshi NGOs and the Department of Agricultural Extension for implementing gardening, nutrition education and social marketing activities at a national scale. In order to reach a much larger target population (nearly one million households), HKI developed strategies to work more cost effectively in its current "to scale" gardening project, *The NGO Gardening and Nutrition Education Surveillance Project, 1993-1997* (HKI 1993c).

3   Lessons Learned

3.1   Home Gardening and Food Security

From the literature and case study presented, we can conclude that home gardening contributes importantly to household food security by providing direct access to nutritious foods and additional income for purchasing essential non-garden foods. Furthermore, in women-managed gardens, or where women play an important role in gardening in collaboration with other family members, there is a greater likelihood that garden production will be primarily for family consumption, and that garden foods will be fed daily to very young children (HKI 1993a; Cleveland and Soleri 1991).

In assessing the nutritional impact of home gardening, we need to understand the relationships between availability and consumption, and consumption and improved nutritional status. Decisions regarding harvest distribution and intra-household food distribution determine the first linkage, as well as palatability, especially by children, whereas bioavailability or degree of absorption determine the second linkage. Effective conversion of consumed foods into absorbed nutrients depends on the relative quality of the nutrient source, food processing and cooking techniques, and the presence of promoting or inhibiting factors, e.g. other nutrients, infections, malnutrition (Soleri et al 1991; OMNI/AID 1995). These complex interactions highlight the importance of nutrition education as a complement to gardening activities.

There is also extensive evidence indicating that home gardening plays a special role in enhancing food security during the lean or "hungry" seasons and other times of extreme scarcity. Whereas in periods of relative abundance, garden foods *supplement* field subsistence production and purchased foods, the garden may become the *principal* source of household food and income during stressed periods, e.g. pre-harvest lean season, harvest failure, prolonged unemployment, health or other disabilities suffered by family members (HKI 1993b; Marsh 1994; UNDP 1996).

3.2 Criteria for Success of Garden Interventions

Traditional home gardens of widely varying types exist in thousands of communities around the world. In areas where specific nutritional deficiencies persist or there appear to be unexploited income-generating possibilities, these communities could benefit from the assistance of government and NGOs to improve the diversity and productivity of their traditional gardens. Where home gardening is not traditional, such organizations may play an important role in introducing gardening.

Any garden intervention, however, requires a good baseline understanding of local conditions to be successful, for success is clearly linked to gardening that is *sustainable* under local resource constraints. Although factors affecting sustainability will vary across projects, evidence from the field indicates these general "rules of thumb":

1. Begin by assessing the traditional ways of gardening in the target or neighboring regions – who, what, when, why and why not, and let this knowledge determine the needs and means for garden improvement.
2. Develop a plan for community organization and enhancing nutrition awareness and education.
3. Involve and train local people to be promoters (rather than paid professionals).
4. Work in areas with adequate access to water and family labor for year-round gardening (minimal maintenance of perennials/semi-perennials during the dry season), adopting water conservation techniques as needed.
5. Be flexible with respect to choice of species and cropping patterns, encouraging diversity and cultivation of indigenous or locally adapted varieties.
6. Encourage reliance on local materials for soil and pest management as well as household/community seed production; minimize "give aways".
7. Conduct regular monitoring based on specific but reasonable evaluation criteria, such as: number of garden species, increased consumption of fruits and vegetables, savings on food expenditures, improved social status of women, and sustainability of gardens over time.

References

Bangladesh Bureau of Statistics. 1992. *Statistical pocket book of Bangladesh, 1992*. BBS, Statistics Division, Ministry of Planning. Dhaka, Bangladesh.

Helen Keller International (HKI). 1989. *Vitamin A Deficiency in Bangladesh: Prevention & Control*. Ed. Ian Darnton-Hill. HKI Bangladesh/VHSS. Dhaka, Bangladesh.

HKI. December 1991. *Vitamin A Homegardening and Promotion of Consumption for Prevention of Nutritional Blindness*. Baseline Report. HKI Bangladesh. Dhaka, Bangladesh.

HKI and Institute of Public Health Nutrition. June 1993. Nutritional Surveillance for Disaster Preparedness and Prevention of Nutritional Blindness. *Summary Report on Gender Differentials in Undernutrition*. HKI Bangladesh/IPHN. Dhaka, Bangladesh.

HKI/AVRDC. June 1993a. *Home Gardening in Bangladesh: An Evaluation Report*. HKI Bangladesh. Dhaka, Bangladesh.

HKI. April 1993b. *Nutritional Surveillance for Disaster Preparedness and Prevention of Nutritional Blindness*. Report of Round 19. HKI/IPHN. Dhaka, Bangladesh.

HKI. February 1993c. Home Gardening at the National Level-The NGO Approach. *A proposal to increase the supply and consumption of vitamin A rich foods in Bangladesh*. HKI Bangladesh. Dhaka, Bangladesh.

Marsh, Robin. 1994. *Production and Consumption Effects of the Introduction of Home Gardening on Target, Interaction and Control Groups: A Case Study from Bangladesh*. Presented at the International Symposium on Systems-Oriented Research. November 1994, Montpellier, France.

Midmore, David J., Vera Niñez and Ramesh Venkataraman. 1991. *Household gardening projects in Asia: past experience and future directions*. AVRDC Technical Bulletin No. 19. Shanhua, Taiwan.

OMNI/AID. 1995. *Bioavailability and Bioconversion of Carotenoids: Can Foods Rich in Provitamin A Carotenoids Provide Adequate Vitamin A for Human Needs?* Summary of a Workshop Jointly Organized by The Micronutrient Initiative and OMNI. Washington, D.C.

Soleri, Daniela and David A. Cleveland. 1987. *Household gardens as a development strategy. Human organization*, 46(3): 259-270.

Soleri, Daniela, Cleveland, David A. and Frankenberger, Timothy R. 1991. *Gardens and Vitamin A: A Review of the Literature*. Office of Nutrition, Bureau for Science and Technology, AID. Washington, D.C.

The Urban Agriculture Network. 1993. *Urban Agriculture: A Neglected Resource for Food, Jobs, and Sustainable Cities* (pamphlet). Washington, D.C.

UNDP. 1996. *Urban Agriculture: Food, Jobs and Sustainable Cities*. UNDP. New York, New York.

World Bank. 1992. *Bangladesh Food Policy Review: Adjusting to the Green Revolution*. Washington, D.C. and Bangladesh.

Venkataraman, Ramesh. March 1992. *Household Gardening in Asia: A Review*. AVRDC Working Paper No. 3. Shanhua, Taiwan.

Lessons from North Benin for the Introduction of Animal Traction in Sub-Saharan Africa

Michael Brüntrup

Institute for Agricultural Economics and Social Sciences
in the Tropics and Subtropics
University of Hohenheim (490), D-70593 Stuttgart, Germany

Abstract

The introduction of animal traction in the countries of SSA constitutes in the most cases a revolution for the concerned farming systems that affects elements of plant production, animal rearing, ecology, economy, sociology, extension, and the input supply and output demand markets. In the north of Benin, the most important effect of animal traction is the extension of cultivated area. Animal traction is particularly attractive in the northern savannah zones, favored by low labor input requirements for uprooting land, cropping systems based on mechanizable cotton and cereals and a surplus of family labor during slack periods. Several other conditions were favorable in the study region for animal traction adoption, most of them are linked to the cotton sector which warrants stable prices, commercialization, inputs and credit. The case study shows that a complex technology such as animal traction needs a highly supportive economic, institutional and infrastructural environment to be successfully implemented.

Keywords

Animal traction, farm organization, cotton, Benin

1   Introduction

Animal traction was one of the most important steps of technical progress and intensification of agriculture in the western industrialized world (Binswanger 1984). Mechanization of agriculture in Africa mainly developed since the colonization at the begin of this century. Only in North Africa and Ethiopia traditional forms of animal traction existed (Munzinger 1981). Initially, efforts to introduce animal traction were mainly aimed at increasing export crop production (Eicher and Baker 1982). After independence, many countries considered animal traction as backward technology and focused their agricultural development strategy towards tractor mechanization (Voss 1982). The disillusionment with industrialization in Africa, the development of a philosophy of adapted technology development and the economic shock of the first oil crisis in 1973 led to the rediscovery of animal traction as an interesting alternative by several governments and aid agencies (Munzinger 1982; Starkey 1988).

Meanwhile, a dense net of projects, support- and communication structures has emerged (e.g. the West Africa Animal Traction Network, WAATN) and a flood of research work has been carried out. For instance Starkey et al. (1991) list 1,341 documents on the subject, which demonstrates the high interest in the technology. However, the success of the efforts of propagating animal traction technology in SSA are considered as being only modest (Pingali et al. 1987), only 15% of the farm area is ploughed with animal traction (Matlon 1990).

There are manifold reasons for the low adoption of animal traction in SSA, including physical, institutional, social and economic ones. The objective of the present study is to show how slight differences in the natural environment lead to rather important differences in the economic performance of animal traction. The case study is particularly apt for this purpose since many other factors that can cause differences in the adoption, as ethnicity, institutional environment and markets, are very similar throughout the research area. Under these circumstances it is mainly the relative changes of crop yields and management practices that cause differences in the profitability of investment in traction equipment across agro-ecological zones. In addition, a central aspect of investment decision is the impact of price incentives. This impact is depicted for cotton for which the Benin government is realizing an active price policy which highly influences the profitability of animal traction. Further aspects are discussed which can modify the profitability of mechanization, such as the external labor input, the learning costs and the impact of mineral fertilizer on fertility management.

The different adoption rates of animal traction across the research area are compared with the economic performance of mechanization which allows the assessment of minimum thresholds for a successful introduction of animal traction. Furthermore, mechanization-supporting factors are discussed.

2   Data Basis and Methodology

Farm/household data for this study originate from an extended survey in three of the four agro-ecological zones (AE-zones) of the province Borgou (see table 1). Data were collected during a 16-month cost-route survey on 25 farms conducted in 3 villages, one in each AE-zone. Farmers selection was made by stratified random sampling. Time-series data on structure and production patterns of between 286 and 369 farms over a period of 8 years were available from a survey initiated by a World Bank project and the regional development authority CARDER. Yield data originated from the previously mentioned surveys and the analysis of experiments of the cotton research department RCF (1982-1992) of the national agricultural research institute.

The focus of the presentation lies on modeling of the impact of animal traction in order to isolate the mechanism of changes in the farming systems. Linear programming (LP) models of average farms in each of the three AE-zones were used to estimate the effect of animal traction use versus a non mechanized farm with equal resource endowment. In the models, animal traction is considered as integer variable. The mechanization consists of a plough and two oxen. 81 production processes for the nine principal commodities were formulated, distinguishing between mechanized or manual cultivation, early and late sowing, and for some crops their place in the rotation. For cotton and maize, simple fertilizer response functions were integrated into the models, for the other crops only the traditional and the recommended fertilization technologies were considered. Subsistence production has not been valued since it was assumed that farmers maximize their cash income after satisfying their own subsistence needs rather than maximizing the monetary value of consumed goods. The subsistence target was to satisfy 90% of the caloric needs from staple crops; in addition some restrictions for nutrition pattern and food preference were formulated.

Special attention was given to labor constraints, the conversion of household members in men-equivalents (ME) follows the specific sex, age and occupation status of each household member and differentiates between hard, medium and easy work. Land and cotton credit are, de facto, freely available. Labor capacities and demands were defined on a monthly base during the rainy season (2 sowing and 3 maintenance periods which cover the time from May to September), for the dry season only two periods of 3 and 4 month were differentiated since most of the works effected in these periods, mainly yam planting and harvest, sorghum and cotton harvest do not need very timely realization. Soil preparation both manually and with a plough as well as sowing are only allowed on days in which rainfall accumulated within 3 days equaled at least 20 mm (Sivakumar 1992). The number of these days was determined by analyzing daily rainfall data from the district capitals for the period 1980-1989. Hired labor, when allowed in the models, could be used up to a maximum of 25,000 FCFA.[1]

First, in a static scenario analysis it is supposed that animal traction is already introduced on the farm and only variable costs have to be covered. The impact of animal traction use on farm area, crop composition, income and productivity parameters is discussed. Second, for assessing the profitability of the introduction of animal traction, the change in income is compared to the investment costs. These were 67,000 FCFA for a plough and 110,000 FCFA for a pair of bulls in 1992.

---

[1] 1,000 FCFA before the devaluation in January 1994 equalled about 4.5 US-$.

Three measures of profitability of investment in animal traction are used: the incremental benefit cost ratio (BCR), the internal rate of return (IRR) and the net benefit increase (NBI). They are used to compare the additional benefit of a farm with animal traction to the situation without animal traction, where the additional benefits include the increased use of family labor and cotton credit. The time span was set at t=10. Certainly, iron ploughs last much longer, but it is also possible that the farmers' planning horizon for investment in animal traction equipment is even shorter, given the typically high preference of farmers in developing countries for present consumption. The credits which are granted by official organizations for animal traction equipment have to be repaid in 3 years. In all investment scenarios it was assumed that in the first year only the investment costs, but no additional production are realized. The discount rate for BCR and NBI calculations was assumed to be 12% p.a. Neither replacement costs nor additional benefit from increased weight of animals was considered, it was assumed that on average the loss of animals equilibrates the value increase. The average value of (young) untrained bulls in the central (northern) village was about 45,00 (40,000) FCFA and for adult bulls 55,000 (45,000) which means that on average there is no value loss when investing in draught animals (see also Tyc 1988). Other assumptions about factors which may influence the profitability of the introduction of animal traction are listed in the empirical findings section below.

3   Results

3.1   The Farming Systems and the Spread of Animal Traction

The province of Borgou has a rather low population density with on average 24 persons per km² arable land.[2] The average household size is about 12 persons. There is a clear south-north differentiation in the production systems, particularly due to the lower and shorter rainfalls in the northern agroecological zones (700-900 mm per year over 5 months compared to 1100 mm over 7 months in the south). Natural vegetation changes from a closed to an open tree savannah (Guinea savannah). The yam-based production systems in the south are characterized by short cropping rotations with about 4 years of cropping and an intensive use of fallow. Towards the north, the cropping periods increase, caused by the mineral fertilization of cotton which dominates the rotations. Farming systems are strongly influenced by the ethnic group to which farmers

---

[2] Excluding parks, forest reserves and land unsuitable for agriculture, calculated according to De Hon and Breuker (1989) and population records of the census of 1992 published in CARDER (1994).

belong (Brüntrup 1995). The further calculations are manly valid for Bariba farmers, the main ethnic group in the province.

First attempts to introduce animal traction in the Borgou province were made in the 1930s with donkeys. Since the begin of the 1960s, the use of cattle of a crossing zebu x bos taurus is propagated, first by the French CFDT (Compagnie Française de Développement des fibres Textiles) until 1973, since the communist revolution by the regional CARDERs, and more recently by some NGOs. At the beginning of the 1970s about 1000 traction pairs, at the begin of the 1990s about 30,000 working pairs were counted. Up to now mainly the simple plough is generally used, other implements (18,000 ridgers, 3,780 carts, 526 harrows) are less frequent (Tyc 1988; CARDER 1994). During the 1980s, particularly in the northern agro-ecological zone (AE-zone) the percentage of farms with complete animal traction equipment increased by about 3% p.a. In 1989 in the northern AE-zone almost two of three farms owned their own complete traction equipment, in AE-zone 2 about one third and in AE-zone 1 below 5%.

3.2 The Impact of Animal Traction on the Farm Organization

3.2.1 Empirical Findings

Farmers' opinions on animal traction and an analysis of the impact of animal traction on the farm economy, particularly on farm area and yields, are discussed in detail in Brüntrup (1996). The main findings which are important for assessing the plausibility of the model results are:

- animal traction increases the farm area by about 2-2.5 ha for a single pair of oxen in all AE-zones after having accounted for the differences in household labor capacity.
- the composition of the cropping area on mechanized farms is different from that of manual ones; particularly the share of cotton is increased, whereas those of yam and manioc are reduced.
- yield increases are only moderate and not found for all crops, which is in line with findings in other SSA countries (Pingali et al. 1987).

The empirical findings on the impact of animal traction on the farm organization reflect the preference of Borgou farmers for simple ridging in spite of deep ploughing plus ridging as recommended by the CARDER. By choosing this technique it is possible to exploit the limited working potential of the traction equipment better: few rainy days at the onset of the rainy season are suitable for ploughing and sowing, and animals cannot work more than 3-4 hours per day.

Asked for their reasons for not adopting animal traction, over 70% of the non-owners blamed the lack of credit and capital as the main reason for non-adoption. The others, generally Peul farmers (traditional herders), gave a variety of other reasons mostly expressing lack of motivation. When those farmers actually possessing traction were asked why they had not acquired the equipment earlier, the answers were slightly different: About 40% cited lack of capital and credit, but almost 30% lack of knowledge and almost 20% lack of children to guide the animals.

In the models, several effects of mechanization are considered which derive from the empirical data analysis:

- Changes in the yields of certain crops due to better soil preparation, which were derived by analysis of yields (Brüntrup 1996).
- Reduced time consumption for soil preparation and certain (not all) weeding operations. The early planting helps to achieve better yields for some crops. The reduction of yields for late sowing were estimated to be (in % of early sowing) at 83% for cotton, 90% for maize and sorghum and without effect for other annual crops. Cowpea is always planted late, after June.
- Fixed annual expenditures for spare parts and animal health were estimated at 6000 FCFA/year.
- Labor for maintaining animals, particularly fodder search-respective guidance on pasture, which is especially important in the dry season.
- Mechanized soil preparation needs land without roots, extra labor is needed for uprooting if no such land is already available. At least for maintaining soil fertility by the traditional crop-fallow rotation, some land has to be uprooted annually. By using mineral fertilizer, the cropping period can be doubled from 4 to 8 years (Brüntrup 1994).
- When mechanizing soil preparation, the heavy work of manual ploughing and mounding is replaced by physically easier work for direct ridging for which a higher family labor capacity exists. For yam and manioc which are exclusively planted on mounds only limited possibilities to mechanize cultivation exist.
- All traction work including pasture guidance is exclusively realized by male persons.

3.2.2 Modeling of the Impact of Animal Traction on the Farm Organization

Static comparison of manual and mechanized optimal farm plans. The cash income increase with animal traction versus the manual farm is 23-29% in the south, 31-40% in the center and 65-83% in the north (table 1). A higher income increase is always realized with hired-labor use which can overcome specific labor bottlenecks. Animal traction changes the optimal farm plans in many ways. Most obvious is the increase in farm size. This is linked with a change in the cropping pattern according to the empirical findings: more cotton and cereals and less yam. Cotton yields are higher through the direct impact of deep ploughing on yields, and in the northern AE-zones by the increase of the share of early planting. Land and labor productivity augments only slightly, the most important effect of animal traction is the possible increase of family labor use (measured in ME-hours) through the break of labor bottlenecks and the increase of land use. The same effect is also empirically detectable for the survey farms where on traction farms the labor input per ME increases by about 50% in both the central and northern AE-zones. This is only possible because both land and family labor capacities in slack periods still lie idle. The impact of hired labor on both manual and traction farms is rather high, and can be explained by the same catalyzing effect on family labor. For realizing these benefits, both working capital and external labor have to be available.

The profitability of animal traction as influenced by the output price of cotton. The impact of cotton price policy on the profitability of animal traction depends on the relative competitiveness of cotton with respect to other crops and the possibility of mechanizing the entire farming system. When parametrizing the cotton price over the historical price range of 50-150 FCFA/kg raw cotton, the additional income (NBI) is 10% in the south at low cotton prices and without cotton production, climbing to about 25% with high cotton prices (figure 1). In the north, NBI attains 40% to 60% without cotton and reaches 110% to 180% at a cotton price of 150 FCFA/kg (figure 2). Also, the other parameters of profitability show a steady increase with growing cotton prices, except BCR which has some extreme points at low cotton prices when low additional income increases are coupled with high cost increases caused by the application of fertilizer in cotton production. In almost all scenarios the use of hired labor significantly increases the profitability of animal traction.

Without cotton production a BCR of 2 is passed only in the north and in the central AE-zone when hired labor is employed. In the north, BCR remains low with increasing cotton price because of the steady increase of cotton area and the linked use of fertilizer credits. The high income increases compensate for this low BCR. The depressions of BCR and NBI at cotton prices of about 80-110 FCFA/kg in the north indicate a weakness of traction technology compared to the manual scenario and the important role that price policy may play in supporting technology attraction. The existence of high growth rates for animal traction equipment in AE-zone 3 and the stagnation in AE-zone 2 at actual prices of about 100-110 FCFA/kg cotton since 1986 suggest that a BCR of more than 2, an IRR of more than 1 and an NBI of more than 0.3-0.4, calculated under static assumptions, are necessary for substantially encouraging the investment.

Table 1: Optimal Farm Plans for Manual and Mechanized Farms - with and without Hired Labor

AE-zone		South				Center				North			
Hired labor		without		with		without		with		without		with	
Farm type		man.	mech.	man.	mech.	man.	mech.	man.	mech.	man.	mech.	man.	mech.
Total farm area	ha	3,18	4,39	5,13	5,84	4,79	5,45	6,12	7,45	3,42	4,73	4,31	6,13
- cotton	ha	0,86	1,19	1,49	1,45	2,40	2,88	3,06	3,73	0,73	1,63	1,16	2,22
- maize	"	0,00	0,00	0,00	0,14	0,00	0,00	0,07	0,00	0,00	0,00	0,00	0,00
- maize/sorghum	"	0,69	1,05	1,17	1,69	0,00	0,59	0,39	0,76	1,69	2,37	2,16	3,06
- sorghum	"	0,00	0,00	0,00	1,03	0,41	0,00	0,00	1,77	0,00	0,00	0,00	0,00
- groundnuts	"	0,30	1,30	1,14	0,57	0,00	0,04	0,00	0,00	0,00	0,00	0,00	0,00
- yam	"	0,94	0,53	1,03	0,69	1,25	0,76	1,54	0,88	0,50	0,50	0,50	0,50
- manioc	"	0,39	0,27	0,30	0,27	0,28	0,23	0,38	0,28	0,23	0,23	0,50	0,34
- cowpea	"	0,00	0,05	0,00	0,00	0,46	0,94	0,68	0,03	0,00	0,00	0,00	0,00
- rice	"	0,00	0,00	0,00	0,00	0,00	0,00	0,00	0,00	0,00	0,00	0,00	0,00
- millet	"	0,00	0,00	0,00	0,00	0,00	0,00	0,00	0,00	0,00	0,00	0,00	0,00
Early plantings	% of total area	31	29	37	38	43	42	55	60	30	37	34	41
Fertilizer use	kg	322	445	558	543	899	1080	1148	1397	274	611	433	834
Total cash input use	1000 FCFA	51	77	114	117	143	178	208	253	43	103	94	164
Cotton yields	kg/ha	1486	1660	1652	1992	1512	1724	1624	1884	1583	1771	1583	1833
Cotton production	kg	1276	1968	2456	2884	3624	4966	4972	7018	1157	2887	1828	4075
Total food exports	Mcal	26356	13707	17439	17759	6185	5358	7234	9048	6461	6568	8078	10265
Total cash income	1000 FCFA	255	330	382	471	317	416	417	584	189	312	236	433
- cotton	%	30	38	39	40	69	77	71	78	38	60	44	59
Total farm income	1000 FCFA	353	429	472	570	439	538	540	707	275	398	324	518
- cotton	%	22	29	32	34	50	60	56	65	26	47	33	50
Labor use	MEh	3786	4551	5300	5851	5099	5853	6014	7056	3904	5200	4433	5997
Average land productivity (cash income)	FCFA/ha	80034	75247	74372	80665	65968	76319	68177	78348	55132	65978	54808	70613
Average labor productivity (cash inc.)	FCFA/MEh	67	73	72	81	62	71	69	83	48	60	53	72
Average capital productivity (cash inc.)	FCFA/FCFA	5,0	4,3	3,4	4,0	2,2	2,3	2,0	2,3	4,3	3,0	2,5	2,6

Figure 1: Income Development with the Introduction of Animal Traction
Depending on the Assumption of Adoption

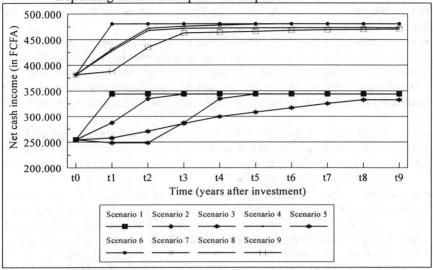

Figure 2: Parameters of Profitability of Introduction of Animal Traction
Depending on the Cotton Price for AE-Zone 1

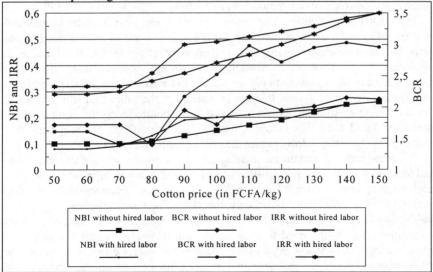

Selected factors influencing the profitability of investment in animal traction.
As was pointed out, the adoption of animal traction is a complex issue and several
factors other than prices can influence the efficiency of its use, particularly in the
first years after acquirement:

- To determine the pace of uprooting when introducing animal traction on a
  farm, the area of uprooted land was determined by recursive dynamic
  modeling technique: the farm is optimized for each individual year, but land
  is uprooted to the possible extent and can be accumulated over the years. This
  scenario assumes that farmers begin to uproot only after they have made the
  investment.
- The farmer needs some time to learn to optimally use the new technology.
  The learning time was estimated to be three years, with 50% of maximum
  working time of the traction equipment in the first year after purchase, 75%
  in the second and 90% in the third year.
- It was tested which effect the use of mineral fertilizer plays in the adoption of
  animal traction. Since without fertilizer use the rotation period is a maximum
  of 4 years, every year considerable amounts of new land have to be cleared
  and uprooted for mechanical ploughing which can constitute a serious
  constraint for mechanization in the south with its dense tree vegetation.

The consequences of these assumptions are analyzed only for AE-zone 1 where
adoption of animal traction is most critical in the Borgou: in the north, the low
tree density and the actually wide spread of and knowledge about traction
technology make the above factors less important.

The results show that the labor input to uproot new land in order to maintain
soil fertility can be a severe handicap for the efficient use of animal traction and
thus for its profitability, particularly when only using family labor (table 2,
scenarios 1-3). Also when assuming a learning process that allows the
employment of the equipment only for a reduced time of its potential (scenario 4),
the income impact of animal traction is reduced to the point that it is preferable
for the innovator to clear fallow for some years before using the equipment. In
scenarios 3 and 4 the IRR falls to critical values below 20%, but in general it is
below 50%. The BCR hardly passes the critical limit of 2 (see below).

When the most important labor peaks are overcome by the use of hired labor
(table 2, scenarios 5-9), the profitability of animal traction increases, but again
high clearing costs reduce it by up to 50%. The effect of fertilizer on the rotation
period has only a low impact on the profitability of mechanization as long as yam
cultivation is highly beneficial for the farmers and thus fallow is cleared for yam
cultivation, not for the need to gain fertile land. However, when reducing yam
gross margins, the shadow price of the rotation-prolonging effect of fertilizer use
rises substantially. This indicates that the combination of animal traction and

fertilizer use is particularly important when the restitution of fertility by fallowing declines and yam, the leading crop of the traditional cropping system which is particularly sensitive to soil fertility, loses its competitiveness. This situation is often found in the south of Benin.

Certainly, other factors influencing the profitability of investment in animal traction on the farm level must be mentioned, the most obvious being the size of the household: small households have difficulties in fully exploiting the production potential of animal traction.

Table 2:   Indicators of Profitability for the Introduction of Animal Traction depending on the Assumptions of Adoption, AE-Zone 1

Scenario	Scenario assumptions	INB	BCR	IRR
	without hiring labor			
1	immediate adoption, rotation 8 years with fertilizer	0.19	2.47	0.49
2	uprooting at 250 MEh/ha, rotation with fertilizer 4 and 8 years	0.15	2.04	0.38
3	uprooting at 500 MEh/ha, rotation with fertilizer 4 and 8 years	0.03	1.14	0.16
4	uprooting at 250 MEh/ha, adoption lag due to learning: use of traction equipment at 50%, 75%, 90% of maximum time in the first years	0.06	1.41	0.20
	with hiring labor			
5	immediate adoption, rotation 8 years with fertilizer	0.15	3.97	0.55
6	uprooting at 250 MEh/ha, rotation with fertilizer 8 years	0.12	2.80	0.44
7	uprooting at 250 MEh/ha, rotation with fertilizer 4 years	0.11	2.17	0.41
8	uprooting at 500 h/ha, rotation with fertilizer 8 years	0.07	1.90	0.30
9	uprooting at 500 h/ha, rotation with fertilizer 4 years	0.07	1.79	0.29

4   Discussion and Conclusions

In contrast to the generally low adoption of animal traction in Africa where it has not been traditionally used, the province of Borgou is an example of a successful introduction. The regional differences in adoption under similar institutional and market, but different ecological conditions gives some hints for the preconditions of successful mechanization policy.

1. In land-abundant regions "the obsession with yield which most agricultural specialists from the developed world or from Asia bring to Africa is as counter-productive in projects as it is in research" (Binswanger 1985 cited in Dommen, 1988). The main effect of animal traction in land-abundant Borgou is an increase of farm area combined with a switch to easily mechanizable crops, mainly made possible by idle family labor capacities during slack periods. Thus, mechanization in this case is not simply labor-saving as often assumed (Ruthenberg 1985) but instead labor-demanding at least in terms of realized hours per active. This effect is not always appropriately taken into consideration in economic analysis (Anderson 1985). The few natural hindrances for mechanization in the northern

savannah and the concentration of the cotton labor calendar on harvest during the dry period induce that there, incomes are higher than those of (non-mechanized) farms in the south, where natural conditions are more favorable for agriculture.

2. The profitability of animal traction greatly depends on the output prices of agricultural production, more specifically of those products which are appropriate for mechanization. Particularly for export crops many African governments have executed an active price policy by which they could influence the incentive system for farmers.

3. The investment in complex, expensive, risky and long-term innovation, as is the case with animal traction, requires better economic performance than small, partitionable and short-term capital binding innovations (Just 1974). A BCR of 2 is claimed for the adoption of fertilizer (FAO 1980) in view of high risk aversion of small farmers. Thus, it is likely that investment in traction technology requires even higher security margins for small farmers (Jaeger and Matlon 1990). The main problem of animal traction in SSA is the risk of animal health and mortality (Runge-Metzger 1991), followed by fodder procurement. The findings suggest a minimum BCR of 2-2.5 and an IRR of 1 for animal traction calculated under static assumptions (without learning and adoption costs) if it is to be adopted by farmers.

4. Several factors can modify the profitability of animal traction, such as fertility management, knowledge, foreign labor availability and working capital. Whereas some constraints may be reduced as the technology gets better known (knowledge, uprooted land), others can even worsen in the pace of agricultural development, particularly the availability of land (Starkey 1988; Jaeger and Matlon 1990).

5. Liquidity or credit availability is not only important for the initial purchase of the equipment of which the costs are near to the total agricultural cash earnings of a manual farm, credit availability for complementary inputs such as fertilizer and hired labor can also greatly improve the profitability of animal traction adoption.

6. The interaction of the above-mentioned factors explains why a vertically integrated cash crop marketing organization such as the cotton marketing board in Benin was able to overcome several of the mentioned constraints, and successfully promoted animal traction technology in contrast to failures in many other situations (Matlon and Spencer 1984). Credits are more easily available when the commercialization is monopolized since then they are warranted by the future output, inputs and comprehensive extension packages are available. Prices are mostly stabilized and announced in advance, commercialization is assured. The disadvantages of such vertical structures, particularly if managed by a government agency, are often a lower performance of public enterprises and the

tendency to tax export crops to generate government earnings. The high performance of the monopolized integrated cotton sectors in the former French colonies versus the low performance in the segmented and often private cotton sectors in the former English colonies (CFDT 1995) advocates the government intervention model at least in this specialized export sector. Reasons for this result are the high technological exigency of cotton production and processing for the world market and high market imperfections in the concerned countries. The successful mechanization of cotton production, which allowed a boost of the production potential of small farmers, is certainly another reason (Bigot et Raymond 1991). Such discrete shifts in resource allocation are unlikely under free market conditions in many developing countries (see also Timmer 1989; Justman and Teubal 1991; Pletcher 1991).

7. Finally, measures must be taken to alleviate the negative impact of animal traction on the environment, particularly the enlarged cropping area and the uprooting of land that can lead to increased erosion and a decline of the fertility-recovering potential of the fallow (Pieri 1989; Brüntrup 1994). These harmful effects have to be counterweighted against the fact that animal traction permits the increased use of mineral fertilizer, thus an intensification of agriculture, and initiates a process of integrating animal husbandry and agriculture which is rarely found in traditional West African farming systems which are generally suffering from soil mining (Dommen 1989; Van der Pol 1993). However, the already complex introduction of animal traction should not be immediately overloaded by additional technical components. As has been shown, the introduction of animal traction already depends on many factors; they should be reduced to the necessary minimum if they are not become prohibitive. Despite this, they should be integrated in a gradual process of technical change. Those mechanization programs have been successful that were able to offer solutions to a degree that the corresponding problems became visible for farmers (Kinsey 1984; Pingali et al. 1987). This strategy takes into account that the adaptation of a technical revolution with impact on the whole agricultural system, as is animal traction, needs, more than anything else, time.

Lessons Learned

Animal traction technology is a prominent case for the type of innovation that is needed for increasing food security in sub-Saharan Africa by increasing labor productivity and fostering the integration of animal husbandry and agriculture. However, the adoption is a highly complex issue which requires high economic incentives, particularly in an initial phase of adoption, and a promoting institutional environment, including credit, marketing and price stability. The cotton sector in the savannah regions of West Africa where such an environment has been provided is one of the few successful examples of widespread mechanization.

Acknowledgment

This study was supported by the Deutsche Forschungsgemeinschaft under project SFB 308.

References

Anderson, F.M. 1985. Draught Animal Power System in SSA: Their Production Impact and Research Needs, in: J.W. Copland (ed): Draught Animal Power for Production, Proceedings of an international workshop held at James Cook University, Townsville, Qld, Australia, 10-16 July 1985

Bigot, Y. et G. Raymond 1991. Traction animale et motorisation en zone cotonnière d'Afrique de l'Ouest, Collection "Documents Systemes Agraires" No. 14, CIRAD, Montpellier

Binswanger, H. 1985. Evaluating Research System Performance and Targeting Research in Land-Abundant Areas of SSA, Discussion Paper No. 31, World Bank, Washington D.C.

Binswanger, H.P. 1984. Agricultural Mechanisation: A Comparative Historical Perspective, World Bank Staff Working Paper No. 673, Washington D.C.

Bruentrup, M. 1994. La production du coton et l'environnement: quelques considerations pour les zones de savane dans le Nord du Benin, in: P. Ton and L. de Haan (eds): A la recherche de l'agriculture durable au Benin, Amsterdam

Bruentrup, M. 1995.: The role of cotton for income and food security in the Borgu, Paper presented at the international Colloq - "Die multi-ethnische Gesellschaft des historischen und heutigen Borgu" (the multi-ethnic society of historic and contemporaneous Borgou), 23.-25. November 1995, Bayreuth

Brüntrup, M. 1996. Zur Ökonomie der Ochsenanspannung in Nord Benin, in: Giessener Beiträge zur Entwicklungsforschung, Reihe I, Band 22, Ernährung und Entwicklung, Wissenschaftliches Zentrum Tropeninstitut der Justus-Liebig-Universität Gießen, Gießen, p. 119-139.

CARDER (Centre d'Action Régionale pour le Développement Rural) Borgou 1994. Plan de Campagne 1993-1994, Parakou

CFDT (Compagnie Française de Développement des fibres Textile) 1995. Filières cotonnières d'Afrique Francophone. Les risques d'un démantèlement, Paris

Delgado, C. and J. McIntire 1982. Constraints on Oxen Cultivation in the Sahel, in: Americ. J. of Agric. Econ. 64: 188-196

Dommen, A.J. 1988. Innovation in African Agriculture, Boulder

Eicher, C.K and D.C. Baker 1982. Research on Agricultural Development in SSA. A Critical Survey, Michigan State University

FAO 1980. Les engrais et leurs application. Précis à l'usage des vulgarisateurs. Collection FAO: Mise en valeur des terres et des eaux, No. 8, 3ème édition, Rome

Jaeger, W.K. and P.J. Matlon 1990. Utilization, Profitability, and the Adoption of Animal Draft Power in West Africa, in: Americ. J. of Agric. Econ. 72: 35-48

Just, R.E. 1974. An Investigation of the Importance of Risk in Farmers' Decisions, in: Americ. J. of Agric. Econ. 56: 14-25

Kinsey, B.H. 1984. Equipment Innovation in Cotton-Millet Farming Systems in Uganda, in: I.
    Aman and B.H. Kinsley (eds), Farm Equipment Innovation in Eastern and Central Southern
    Africa, Hampshire
Munzinger, P. 1981. Handbuch der Zugtiernutzung in Afrika, Eschborn
Pieri, C. 1989. Fertilité des terres de savanes, CIRAD, Paris
Pingali, P., Y. Bigot and H.P. Binswanger 1987. Agricultural Mechanisation and the Evolution
    of Farming Systems in SSA, Washington D.C.
RCF 1982-92. Rapports de Synthese, Cotonou
Runge-Metzger, A. 1991. Entscheidungskalküle kleinbäuerlicher Betriebs-Haushalte in bezug
    auf Wirtschaftlichkeit und Akzeptanz ausgewählter landwirtschaftlicher Innovationen -
    Studie in den Upper Regions von Ghana, Kiel
Ruthenberg, H. 1985. Innovation Policy for Small Farmers in the Tropics, Edited by H.E.
    Jahnke, Oxford
Sivakumar, M.V.K. 1992. Climate change and implications for agriculture in Niger, in: Climatic
    Change Vol 20: pp 297-312
Starkey, P. 1988. Animal Power in West African Farming Systems, in: P. Starkey and F.
    N'Diamé (eds): Animal Power in Farming Systems, The proceedings of the Second West
    African Animal Traction Networkshop Held September 19-35, Freetown, Sierra Leone,
    Braunschweig
Starkey, P., S. Teklu and M. Goe 1991. Animal traction: an annotated bibliographic database,
    Addis Ababa
Tyc, J. 1988. Projet de developpement de l'elevage bovin dans la province du Borgou, Rapport
    d'evaluation, de programmation et d'orientation à long terme, Cotonou
Van der Pol, F., A.C. Gogan and G. Dagbenombakin 1993. L'épuisement des sols et sa valeur
    économique dans le département du Mono, Benin, Cotonou
Voss, C. 1982. Mechanisierung der Landwirtschaft, in: Blanckenburg (Hrsg): Sozialökonomie
    der ländlichen Entwicklung, Stuttgart

Part Three

Policy and Institutional Framework

Part 3.1

Policy and Institutional Framework
Policies

Funding Alternatives for Agricultural Research
– A Key to Global Food Security

Matthias Lichtblau
Institute of Agricultural Economics and Social Sciences in
the Tropics and Subtropics, University of Hohenheim, Germany

Abstract

Agricultural research needs to be promoted to guarantee innovations and development toward a secure food situation for future generations. Although there is a necessity for well funded research institutions and projects, public expenditures are decreasing. This implies a financial re-engineering towards private funding mechanisms for the worldwide agricultural research system. This paper discusses private market financing instruments, after having introduced a conceptual framework categorizing research projects as "private" or "public". By combining private and public elements, a financial market orientated instrument is suggested as a new funding possibility for agricultural research. The objective of the paper is to demonstrate that the current funding crisis could be overcome by innovative financing approaches. Private actors joining in the funding of public research could revive and increase the awareness for agricultural research in the broad public and in the political decision making sector.

Keywords

Public expenditures for agricultural research, private funding for agricultural research, public good, transaction-cost-theory.

1   Introduction

About 4,7 billion people (85% of the world's population) are living in developing countries. Thirty years from now the world population will rise to more than 8,2 billion, assuming that population growth rates continue to decline. If they do not, by the year 2025 our planet could become home to 10 billion people, more than twice as many as today of which at least 90% will live in developing countries. The International Food Policy Research Institute (IFPRI) estimates that over the next 25 years developing countries' demand for meat will rise by 155% and demand for foodgrains by 75% (Frank 1995). Great efforts are required to increase sustainable worldwide agricultural production without endangering the natural resource base. It is especially important that agricultural research is promoted to ensure innovations leading toward a secure food situation for future generations. Consequently increasing the financial resources for agricultural research can be considered as an investment for the survival of the following generations (Bohnet 1995; IFPRI 1995).

2   Funding Alternatives for Agricultural Research

2.1   The Decline of Public Expenditures for Agricultural Research

Although there is a necessity for well funded research institutions and projects, public expenditures for agricultural research are decreasing (see figures 1, 2). Donors significantly cut aid to agricultural research in the 1980s and early 1990s. In some industrialized countries are tendencies to reduce foreign aid further on (Pinstrup-Andersen, Lundberg & Garrett 1995). New investment in research programs is slowing, particularly with regard to financial support for agricultural research in Latin America and the Caribbean and in sub-Saharan Africa. The rapid build-up of research personnel is not paralleled by an equal growth in financial resources. Real expenditures per researcher have continuously declined during the past thirty years (Pardey, Roseboom & Anderson 1991). This trend of decreasing financial support affects international as well as national agricultural research institutions. The stagnation or decline in financial support affect the effective utilization of human and physical research capacities in the agricultural research system. "As a result, the pace of agricultural development and technological change is threatened at the very time new technologies are critically needed to alleviate the problems of hunger, poverty, a diminishing natural resource base, and damage to the environment" (Bonte-Friedheim, Tabor & Roseboom 1994).

Reduced public spending for agricultural research might end up in a vicious circle: low funding leads to low research productivity and a low innovation rate, which lowers the research impact which again provokes lower funding and so on (Pardey, Roseboom & Anderson 1991). Since agricultural research plays a key role in food security (Bonte-Friedheim, Tabor & Roseboom 1994) and as public funding continues to decrease, funding alternatives will have to be found in the future (von Oppen 1982; von Oppen 1985).

Since this paper deals with an exemplary alternative funding mechanism a theoretical framework like the transaction-cost-approach is not discussed in details. However, comparing private and public institutional arrangements in the light of the above mentioned theory may help to decide which arrangement to choose (Ebers, Gotsch 1993).

Figure 1: Public Expenditures for Agricultural Research

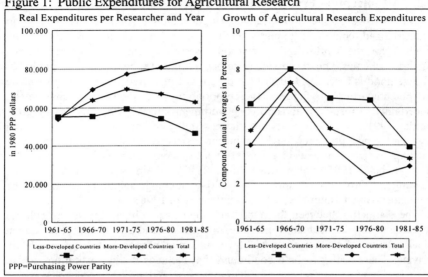

Source: Pardey, Roseboom and Anderson 1991, pp. 198-204

Figure 2: CGIAR (Consultative Group on International Agricultural Research)
Budget Development

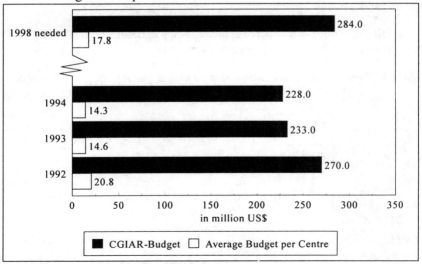

Source: own computations based on CGIAR-data

2.2   A Conceptual Framework for Funding Alternatives

The obvious public donor fatigue (in developing countries as well as in industrialized countries) requires a financial re-engineering towards private funding for the worldwide agricultural research system. Considering private funding schemes, the discussion whether agricultural research is a public or private good is essential. Most of the time it is considered as a public good. Due to potential market failures (inappropriability of returns on investment, uncertainty of results, indivisibility) government intervention is necessary (Roe, Pardey 1991). But there exists also the possibility of government failure (voting and preference problems, lack of incentives, corruption, discrimination, rent seeking) which may lead to a less efficient outcome than an imperfect market does (Schaad 1995; Echeverria, Thirtle 1992). In times of decreased public funding a turn toward more competitive funding solutions seems to be recommendable (Kaltefleiter 1995; Lichtblau et al. 1996).

The distinction between the public and the private dimensions of agricultural research is not clear cut since there are, in terms of funding and execution, only a small number of organizations which can be called entirely public or completely private. There seems to be a continuum that includes public institutions which may be commercial (private) in their behavior and private companies which behave in a non-commercial (public) manner. It is easier to draw a clear line between basic (more public) and applied (more private) research (Echeverria, Thirtle 1992). Even for the high rates of the return on investment it is often not easy to decide whether they are private or public (Rajeswari 1995).

The following three-dimensional approach helps to define the public or private character of each agricultural research project:

Figure 3: Three-Dimensional-Categorization of Agricultural Research Projects

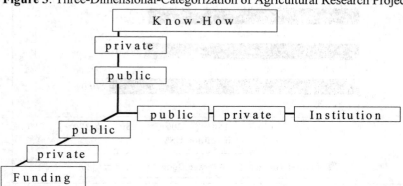

With such a categorization scheme in mind agricultural research projects for a food secure world could be individually defined. Each possible private-public-combination is imaginable for the planning of future international research programs or single village-level research projects. The existing set of research institutions in the agricultural sector can be conceptualized as shown in Table 1:

Table 1: Private and Public Sector Division of Agricultural Research Institutions

Public Sector	- Departments of Ministries of Agriculture, Livestock, Education, Science and Technology, and others - National Research Institutes - Universities - International Agricultural Research Centres.		
Private Sector	Non-Commercial	Private sector targeted aid agencies/Voluntary organisations (NGOs)/Foundations	
	Commercially orientated	Input Companies	Seeds, Feeds, Animal Health Products, Agro-Chemicals, Machinery and Equipment
	Commercially orientated	Farm Sector	Farmers, Cooperatives, Producer Associations, Plantations, Large Firms, Commodity Institutes
	Commercially orientated	Food Sector	Processing and Food Sector Companies
	Commercially orientated	Technical Assistance	Consultants and management companies

Source: Echeverria, Thirtle 1992, p.10

At the moment all the public sector institutions are experiencing budget constraints. Advancing the private funding field may be a way out of the financial dilemma.

2.3   Private Market Financing for Agricultural Research

The possibilities how public sector research institutions can obtain money from the private sector are suggested in the following list:

- Selling research results or research programs;
- Selling agricultural (by-)products;
- Selling non-agricultural goods and services;
- Selling assets.

However each of these money-making activities faces the problem of high transaction costs (high uncertainty and risks, transaction-specific investments required) as well as the undervaluation of research efforts and assets. In fact, no agricultural research institution has at the moment the know-how necessary to keep sustainable research running just by selling their products and results. Selling research results also means that only applied or adaptive research will be paid off.

Basic and strategic research – essential for food security – are still dependent on public funding (Pray 1995). The application of financial market instruments can help to solve the current funding crisis. Private investors invest their money in agricultural research projects with well-known market instruments (e.g. bonds, stocks).

2.4 Private Funding Possibilities for Public Research

An alternative funding mechanism for agricultural research has to combine two models of international development cooperation: the non-governmental/non-profit organizations (NGO/NPO)-funding-schemes as well as (direct) private investment in developing countries. Arguing whether agricultural research should be funded privately (government failure) or publicly (market failure), theories (e.g. "Failure Performance Approach", Badelt 1990) led to the suggestion of a third way: NGOs/NPOs that are voluntarily funded (Heister 1994, Schaad 1995).

In Germany, US\$ 2-3 billion are spent annually on NGOs/NPOs. Private donations to development aid-NGOs/NPOs account for a 30% share of this amount (Heister 1994). In addition to voluntary donations from the private sector there exists a governmental subsidy scheme.

Private financial flows from countries of the Organization for Economic Co-Operation and Development (OECD) almost doubled in the last years to the amount of US\$ 170 billion in 1993 (OECD 1995). Evidence for this upward trend of private investment in developing countries is seen, for example, in the international bond market where an almost fourfold increase of issues took place in just three years (IMF 1995, see Figure 4).

This worldwide financial development indicates that more and more companies, private banks and individuals are willing to invest their money in developing countries. The German Ministry of Economic Cooperation and Development (BMZ) wants to encourage German investors by supporting their private investment "with all the means and instruments available in the operational context of the ministry" (BMZ 1995).

Agricultural research projects must be linked to the international private capital flows with adequate instruments. Additionally, research projects for food security should be connected to the development aid discussion of the NGO/NPO-sector. The example of Germany shows that there are many people willing to pay for development aid beyond their contribution with taxes. New and more donors can be contacted because they invest their money – instead of giving it away as a gift.

There is an existing set of opportunities where people in Germany may invest their money in an ethical, social and ecological way: e.g. bank shares, savings accounts, loans, stocks, investment funds (Deml, Baumgarten and Bobikiewicz 1994). Using one of these market instruments private investors will be gained for agricultural research projects. Since tax incentives and interest rates are still low or not existent (Altendorf 1994), the government should help to build a solid financial base for agricultural research projects (especially those concerning food security). Otherwise, too few investors would be attracted; perhaps only altruistic motivated investors and not the larger number of real profit seeking investors. The latter type of private investor is very important for replacing and exceeding public expenditures for agricultural research. Potential benefits could be, for example, a publicly subsidized interest rate outperforming market interest rates or tax free profits (von Oppen 1982, von Oppen 1985).

The detailed characteristics of the financial market instruments need to be specified according to the type of research project and the expected desires of a broad public. This seems essential since this type of financing must satisfy donor interests as well as agricultural research demands.

Figure 4: International Bond Issues

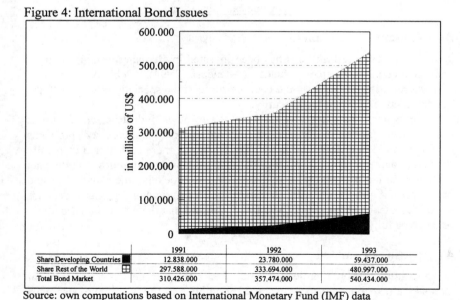

	1991	1992	1993
Share Developing Countries ■	12.838.000	23.780.000	59.437.000
Share Rest of the World ⊞	297.588.000	333.694.000	480.997.000
Total Bond Market	310.426.000	357.474.000	540.434.000

Source: own computations based on International Monetary Fund (IMF) data

Figure 5: Scheme for Private Sector Financing for Agricultural Research

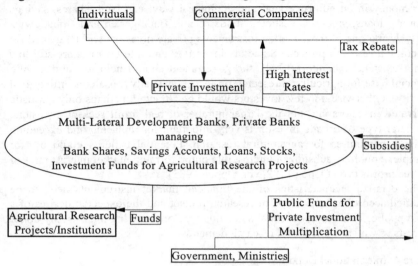

3   Concluding Remarks

Until now US$ 180 millions has been invested in Germany in ethical, social and ecological investment funds (Altendorf 1994). Publicly supported agricultural research funds should be more successful, especially dealing with the important issue of future food security.

Unfortunately, in Germany as well as in other industrialized countries development aid is not on top of the agenda of the perceived problems (Zwingmann 1994). However, as societies becoming more critical and politically or socially active, many individuals will welcome new opportunities to participate in the promotion of worldwide food security and to develop their own ideas and preferences. A program for private investment for agricultural research depends on the acceptance of the public, which will demand that the results of agricultural research be fully explained to the public.

4   Lessons Learned

Agricultural research projects should then be better designed in terms of lessons learned from the successes and the failures in the past. Otherwise most people will refuse to invest in such projects. In other words, referring to successful projects with sustainable, innovative results will significantly increase total expenditures for agricultural research.

Acknowledgment

The idea of alternative funding mechanisms and private investment schemes for agricultural research is a contribution of Prof. Dr. Dr. Matthias von Oppen, Institute of Agricultural Economics and Social Sciences in the Tropics and Subtropics (490), University of Hohenheim, D-70593 Stuttgart, Germany.

References

Altendorf, Kerstin, 1994. Die Verantwortung wird am Bankschalter abgegeben. in: Frankfurter Rundschau, 08. December 1994, p.20.

Badelt, C. 1990. Institutional Choice and the Nonprofit Sector. in: Anheier, H.K., Seibel W. (ed.): The Third Sector – Comparative Studies for Nonprofit Organizations, Berlin/New York, pp.53-63.

BMZ (Bundesministerium für wirtschaftliche Zusammenarbeit und Entwicklung) 1995. Neue Akzente in der deutschen Entwicklungszusammenarbeit während der nächsten Legislaturperiode – Stellungnahme des wissenschaftlichen Beirats beim Bundesministerium für wirtschaftliche Zusammenarbeit und Entwicklung. Bonn.

Bohnet, Michael 1995. Agrarforschung – ein Schlüsselfaktor zur Sicherung der Welt-ernährung und zum Schutz der natürlichen Ressourcen. in: ATSAF Circular No. 42, Juli 1995, pp.34-35.

Bonte-Friedheim, Ch., Tabor, St. R. and Roseboom, J. 1994. Financing National Agricultural Research: The Challenge Ahead. ISNAR Briefing Paper No. 11, The Hague, May 1994.

CGIAR (Consultative Group on International Agricultural Research) 1994. Research for a Food Secure World (Draft).

Deml, M., Baumgarten, J. and Bobikiewicz, L. 1994. Grünes Geld – Jahrbuch für ethisch-ökologische Geldanlagen 1995/1996. Wien.

Ebers, M., Gotsch, W. 1993. Institutionenökonomische Theorien der Organisation. in: Kieser, Alfred (ed.), Organisationstheorien, Stuttgart/Berlin/Köln.

Echeverria, R., Thirtle, C. 1992. Privatisation and the Roles of Public and Private Institutions in Agricultural Research in Sub-Saharan Africa. in: 29th EAAE Seminar, Food and Agricultural Policies Under Structural Adjustment, Hohenheim, pp.1-12.

Frank, Richard 1995. The World at 2025: What Will it Mean for the World Bank and Agriculture, Nebraska.

Heister, Werner 1994. Das Marketing spendensammelnder Organisationen. Köln.

Kaltefleiter, Viola 1995. Die Entwicklungshilfe der Europäischen Union – Rechtfertigung, Effizienz und politische Ökonomie staatlicher Entwicklungshilfe. Heidelberg.

Lichtblau, Matthias, John Lamers, Matthias von Oppen, and Marc Bernard 1996. Private Funding Mechanisms for Agricultural Research in West Africa, Paper presented at the International Symposium, Institutions and Technologies for Rural Development in West Africa, Cotonou (Benin), February 16-22, 1996, forthcoming.

IMF (International Monetary Fund) 1995. Private Market Financing for Developing Countries. Washington, D.C.

IFPRI (International Food Policy Research Institute) 1995. Report about the 2020 Vision Conference held from 13 to 15 June 1995 in Washington D.C/USA. in: ATSAF Circular No. 43, Oktober 1995, pp.14-15.

OECD 1995. Linkages – OECD and Major Developing Economies. Paris.

von Oppen, Matthias 1982. Toward Private Investment Funds for Development Aid. in: Technological Forecasting and Social Change, 22, pp.201-210.

von Oppen, Matthias 1985. Funding Development – With Interest. Andhra Pradesh.

Pardey, Ph. G., Roseboom, J. and Anderson, J. R. 1991. Regional Perspectives on National Agricultural Research. in: Agricultural Research Policy – International Quantitative Perspectives, ed.: Pardey, Ph. G., Roseboom, J. and Anderson, J. R., Cambridge, pp.197-264.

Pinstrup-Andersen, P., Lundberg, M. and Garrett, J.L. 1995. Foreign Assistance to Agriculture: A Win-Win Proposition. in: International Food Policy Research Institute: Food Policy Statement, No. 20, Washington D.C., July 1995.

Pray, Carl E. 1995. Personal conversation: Draft, July 18th, 1995, Private Funding for Public Research, Rutgers University.

Rajeswari, S. 1995. Agricultural Research Effort: Conceptual Clarity And Measurement. in: World Development, Volume 23, Number 4, April 1995, p.617-635.

Roe, T. L., Pardey, Ph. G. 1991. Economic Policy and Investment in Rural Public Goods: A Political Economy Perspective. in: Agricultural Research Policy – International Quantitative Perspectives, ed.: Pardey, Ph. G., Roseboom, J. and Anderson, J. R., Cambridge, pp.7-49.

Schaad, Martina 1995. Nonprofit-Organisationen in der ökonomischen Theorie. Wiesbaden.

Zwingmann, Christian 1994. Sind Mitglieder von Eine-Welt-Gruppen Protagonisten einer konsequenten Entfaltung des Eine-Welt-Gedankens? – Ergebnisse einer Befragung im Bistum Limburg. in: Hoffmann, J. (ed.), Entwicklungsland Deutschland – Ansätze und Erfahrungen kirchlicher Solidaritätsarbeit, Frankfurt a.M.

Agricultural Research Policy in Tropical Africa

Jean Chataigner
INRA (Institut National de la Recherché Agronomique)
2, Place Pierre Viala - 34060 Montpellier, France

Abstract

Experience in both, developed and developing countries, has shown that research can be highly effective in the service of well organized production. Privatization of research or no privatization is not a problem. In developing countries, it is rarely possible to develop private research. Research is necessary for development, both for export sectors and domestic market production. These two orientations, however, clearly integrated into agricultural policies, are able to mobilize available human resources. But it is necessary, too, to develop a very good understanding of intensification and localization of production.

Keywords

Agricultural research, tropical Africa, privatization, rural and urban areas

Introduction

Those who remain impressed by the Green Revolution and the existence of surplus in developed countries do not think it necessary to strengthen agricultural research to maintain food security in developing countries. They are confident that the market economy will arrange research activity and needs. Others are concerned about the increasing world population and the consequences of human activities for the environment. They support the need to redouble our efforts to promote an adaptive research agenda, like the doubly Green Revolution, to satisfy fundamental food security requirements and to preserve natural resources (Griffon and Weber 1995). For them, a collective effort with the supply of public finances is necessary to answer the food question in a situation of rapidly increasing demand.

From our point of view, the urgency to build up strong agricultural research in developing countries cannot be overemphasized; it is as important a priority task as the public effort for industrial research in developed countries is for economic development. Yet, its financing is more difficult because developing countries and international organizations have, in comparison, limited means. At the same time its organization and management has to find compromises with numerous deciding powers, limiting efficiency and effectiveness contrary to industrial researches in developed countries with a strong and clear political will.

Many discussions held recently were focusing on the necessity to mobilize efficiently means and finances for agricultural research. And it is becoming visible, that a large and complex world network for agricultural development, with main links formed by international research centers, universities and special organizations in developed countries, had been formed, with a high human and capital capacity and numerous linkages to developing countries (Uma Lele 1995).

In this context, we wish to analyze the situation in sub-Saharan Africa, particularly in the humid tropical climate zone. In this area, the economic recovery predicted by the World Bank (3.8% per annum for the next five years) will depend, among many other measures, on the intelligent mobilization of research and agricultural services, which remains the surest resource for overall developments. Yet, in the aftermath of the profound crisis in the world markets and the severe economic adjustments that have followed, this mobilization should take into account two majors elements: the urbanization phenomenon and the changing role of the state.

1   Research and Information Systems adapted for the Urbanization Phenomenon

Urbanization and the concentration of a constantly growing population in the coastal zones of sub-Saharan Africa, in West and Central Africa in particular, are without doubt among the most important events in this part of the world. Yet, paradoxically, until now several factors have combined to hinder the rapid transformation of agriculture in the region. These include the availability of unused farmlands, with high potential when newly cleared. It should be recalled, for example, that the average yields in this situation, using traditional techniques, are approximately the same as those in France in the 1950s, both for tubers (5 to 10 tons per hectare) and cereals (1 to 2 tons per hectare). Low revenues from a weak industrial sector, thin urban markets, and the easy access to cheap (subsidized) foodstuffs arising from the structural surplus of developed countries' agriculture play an important role, too. The transformation is, nonetheless, under way giving rise to a diversified and productive agriculture that, at times, is replacing the traditional export oriented model. Research must give priority to this emerging agriculture, both to raise its productivity and to enable it to respond better to the requirements of urban markets.

In this context, research needs to look at the long-term evolutionary process towards a more intensive and better localized production placing emphasis on the understanding of the intensification and localization process and, concurrently, on an adapted information system to support effective agricultural politics.

Intensification

Yield maximization continues to be the main concern of a great number of agricultural scientists. But, in Africa, in the majority of cases, labor and capital are limiting factors; it is, thus, the improvement of the productivity of these two scarce factors that needs priority. The success of the intensification process depends on how seriously these priorities are addressed.

Available indicators of production systems within the Region suggest that the process of intensification, accompanied by a tendency toward sedentarization, is under way almost everywhere. In Cameroon or in Côte d'Ivoire, for example, the cleared land is often used continuously for a longer time, from 2 or 3 years to 4, 5 or more years. This change is accompanied by an introduction of news products or systems. In South West Cameroon, for example, cassava is substituting plantains with the same labor productivity but changing gender roles; women take the place of men. In Côte d'Ivoire, the introduction of cotton allows the continuos cultivation for several more years.

Thus, the intensification process has to be analyzed in a more integrated context. Instead of juxtaposing a high performance intensive system – only mastered on the research station – next to an often poorly understood extensive, traditional system, also occasionally caricatured, it may be wiser for agricultural research to observe, describe and understand the mechanism of intensification and sedentarization that are actually under way including their impact on the environment. These evolutions are generally slow, however, they may accelerate where commercial production is developing. In any event, science based improvements adapted to local settings have the best chances of success.

Localization

The intensification process is closely linked with the changes in the localization of production. In a tropical humid area the geographical patterns of agricultural output follow three complementary pathways which combine in various ways to result in the regional distribution of production observed in a given country, at a given period. The first is the progressive colonization of lands by a population searching to feed itself. This is the dimension of history, constantly changing with the development of new techniques and infrastructure. The second stage results in the development of production for exportation. It depends directly on the availability of lands and labor often connected with migration. Labor migration policies are often decisive for the acceleration and intensification of production.

The geographical concentration of labor that accompanies these export-led dynamics, as long as it is available without constraining food crop production, can lead to the formation of extensive zones of potential surplus production.

Numerous examples show how these zones have been able to respond within a short time to a rapid growth in demand. At the beginning the 1980s, for example, in Côte d'Ivoire, a substantial production of maize emerged from western regions where cocoa production was increasing (Fusiller 1989). This zone was not a traditional zone for maize production, but migrant labor imported for the cultivation period of cocoa was available for maize, too. The surplus of plantains is also directly linked to the extension of cocoa production.

The third factor determining production zones results directly from the increase in demand of urban markets. This appears most strikingly for new products. Production develops closely to consumption centers or along transport routes (Moustier 1994). Fresh vegetables generally develop around the cities. Other vegetables, fruits, chickens and other products are developing dependent on the transport cost. Also many combinations may be observed.

Taking into account these phenomena, and the types of farmers and products which correspond to each case, it is essential to orientate research efforts accordingly. Priority must be given to situations which enable agriculture to respond to market demand. This is important because often there is a large gap between volume and composition of production and the structure of urban consumption. To illustrate this point the reader is referred to the example of the plantain production and consumption in the south west of Cameroon (Temple 1995).

We are facing a typical situation where the structure of consumption in big cities is different from its rural areas because of numerous factors. These include mainly income that allows diet diversification and consumption of higher value products. The market structure which supports the big urban market does not rely on new production systems but simply collects the surplus of existing production systems. Thus, in Côte d'Ivoire, Abidjan is drawing more than 80% of its needs by cocoa based traditional production systems. Also market integration is very weak (Chataigner and Tano 1979). Only in Nigeria can we observe a trend of intensification of plantain production through the development of homegarden production around the main centers. This is a similar phenomenon which can be observed near Djakarta, for example, with fruit production.

In these situations, a price policy trying to encourage diversification has a weak chance of success. In Gabon, for example, the high level of income has led to an increase of prices and plantain consumption imported from Cameroon without involving local production. At the opposite end, the development of plantain production along new roads or a railway in Congo points out the important role of infrastructure.

In humid tropical areas, it is possible to extend this analysis to other tubers crops which represent an important part of food diet.

Cereals follow the same rules. But they are facing a weak labor productivity in comparison with others crops and competition from imports (Ahoyo 1995). Vegetables and fruits are more sensitive to urban market influence because their localization depends less on land access. In conclusion, to supply big cities, there still exist many possibilities from different surplus production systems the localization of which is mainly determined by factors others than urban market characteristics.

Observations and Measures

This inevitable and complex transformation could be better understood today if we had access to relevant statistical information for tracking agricultural output and yields and, in particular, if we could determine the magnitude and evolution of the role of commercialization of food crops.

Until now traditional statistics are mainly preoccupied with the evaluation of total production. This evaluation is not easy with export data, but the task is even more difficult for food production where an important part is directly consumed by farmers and production data are notoriously weak. It is very difficult to verify the sense of evolution of most productions. In spite of serious efforts, insufficient means do not allow to develop a consistent and efficient food policy.

New needs appear with the liberalization of the economy. The observation of markets, prices at different levels (production, wholesale and retail) volumes and qualities are necessary for a good market management (Egg, J. et al.). It is necessary to develop a knowledge about the market structure for each main product to identify the specific chains which link different production systems with different markets. The plantain example in Cameroon shows how to link multidisciplinary research and knowledge about the evolution of market characteristics.

The urbanization phenomenon puts emphasis on the necessity to build statistical knowledge, not only on production but also on the delivery of goods. This necessitates also a good coordination between consumption, commercialization and production statistics. At the same time, particular attention should be given to the mobility of labor, land use and investments. Migration, composition of labor and access to land will determine the localization and diverse combinations of cultivation for a long time. Infrastructure more than prices will play an important role in supplying big cities.

Appropriate statistics based on a solid understanding of the transformations under way in agriculture, unambiguous agricultural policies, and well functioning administrations are necessary for research. This research has to develop itself in a new environmental context where the state is not omnipresent.

2   Agricultural Research and State in Tropical Africa

The transformation of the role of the state vis-à-vis the private economy requires particular attention to understand the consequence for agricultural research. Indeed, experience in both, developed and developing countries, has shown that research can be highly effective in the service of a well organized production, at the level of a product, a sector or the national economy.

In Africa, the withdrawal of the state as a direct actor in the principal agricultural export subsectors marks the end of what has been known as state capitalism. Privatization had already begun to submit these commodity systems to the sole criterion of international competitiveness. Yet their modes of organization, characterized by a high degree of vertical integration, are not likely to change much. Research will have an important role to play in improving their competitiveness, and will need to adapt in order to take into account the acceleration of internationalization. At the opposite end, under any foreseeable circumstances, public sector research will continue to be the principal, if not sole, vehicle for assisting agriculture's adaptation to the requirements of the domestic market or, in other words, for raising the productivity of the agricultural labor force, which continues to decline in relation to the growing numbers of mouths to feed.

In this new context, the priority for agricultural research is to accompany, with the maximum of efficiency, the development of two types of markets: international markets for export subsectors and domestic markets including urban markets under specific conditions defined by an agricultural policy determining income distribution, farm installations and the environment.

The dynamics of these two types of research are different. It is necessary to distinguish them very well, otherwise, like so often in the past, efforts for domestic production are diverted to export production. The content of each organization will be discussed in the following.

2.1   An Integrated Research for Export Crops

In each country, an export crop is one part of an international industry, with its dynamic network of generally integrated research. The level of privatization of this research differs according to the product; the role of importers is the main determinant, either directly or more often through research institutions of their countries.

In developing countries private investment in research is often weak or lacking, except in some cases like hevea in Malaysia. Therefore, the dilemma for producer countries is that they will lose competitiveness if public financing is abandoned. What is the role of public sector national research in these conditions? National governments, though no longer direct economic actors in the commodity systems, still remain the most legitimate partners. They will need to maintain the means to negotiate necessary compromises and to impose, if necessary, measures to ensure the best distribution of profits along the commodity chains, profit being, of course, the gauge of their efficiency. They will also need to impose the measures deemed necessary to ensure that the commodity systems contribute to overall development. Governments must also continue to provide certain services, among them a redefinition of the role and objectives of research seems clearly warranted. Certain modes of international financing can facilitate the linkage between national research, private interests and international partners.

National government financing can also be considered as a compensation for access to the international level of research, on the condition, however, that national researchers are perfectly integrated in international research activities in programs clearly defined and taking into account national priorities. It is important to avoid that national research work be done only for foreign programs.

2.2 A Research for Development of Domestic Market

Concerning the domestic market, we have to realize that international research is mainly focused and organized by products. This orientation reinforces the traditional position of agricultural scientists towards yield maximization or maximization of production for all farmers. But as mentioned above, the priority is also to satisfy the urban demand. It is therefore necessary to organize all efforts towards this goal. This is to say that research, through a good understanding of the complex process of crop intensification and localization, focuses on the development of the products demanded by urban markets with the highest labor productivity as a main criterion.

It is also important to mobilize intellectual resources now available in African agriculture for research. In the US, since the end of the last century, the development of modern agriculture has been built on a strong relationship between training, research and extension services. In France, the spectacular development of agriculture after World War II was based on a close linkage between researchers and a multiplicity of farmers' groups. In Africa, training, research and extension services exist, but they are badly organized. Contacts between research and farmers, for example, rarely exist. Difficulties of financing and managing different services hamper the mobilization of human resources. Traditional conflicts resulting from different project approaches and concepts supported by international financiers, have led to a balkanization of administrations with poor means. Therefore, it is necessary to orientate human resources to build a vigorous administration of agriculture aiming at the development of the urban market where research, training, and extension will work together. In the meantime, it will be necessary to provide dynamic and competent public services acting on well-defined policies and be attentive to the needs of consumers, producers and their intermediaries.

Privatization imposes an additional burden on organization, service and competence for a vigorous development of the market economy. Research alone, competent and well organized as it may be, cannot ensure a green revolution. Indeed, it must be emphasized that the legendary green revolution in Asia was the result, above all, of the application of clearly defined agricultural policies implemented, at times, against the advice of international experts. This was possible, to some extent, because of the existence and support of highly developed agricultural administrations. The sub-Saharan countries today have an impressive number of highly qualified engineers and other agricultural specialists. It is, thus, possible for these countries to put into place effective administrations, a precondition for successful research.

Appropriate statistics based on a solid understanding of the transformations under way in agriculture, unambiguous agricultural policies, and well functioning administrations are, therefore, necessary if research is to be effective. The particularity of research is the need to secure a clear objective. If these conditions are met, results will follow.

Lessons Learned

Experience in both, developed and developing countries, has shown that research can be highly effective in the service of well organized production. Privatization of research is not a problem if it is pursued with reason. Otherwise, there will be no research in sub-Saharan Africa, except for some research supported by developed countries for their own interests.

Research is necessary for development; both for export sectors and for the domestic market. These two orientations clearly integrated with agricultural policies are able to mobilize competence and available human resources. Regarding the financing, developing countries in collaboration with developed countries and international donors can satisfy the needs. But efficiency of this type of financing depends on two conditions: firstly, a clearly separated identification between export sector and domestic market research, the latter having first priority. Secondly, an appropriate structure of financing between investment, personal cost and operating expenses is important; it should be comparable with the structure in developed countries. At present, the funding of most researchers in Africa is far too low, and this leads to a real economic waste (Casas 1995).

Based on experience, it seems advisable to conceive an organization where research is associated with the dynamics of two markets: export and domestic market. In the export sectors, research must be integrated in the international network, it is the guarantee of its efficiency. For domestic markets research must be an active element of a dynamic agricultural administration oriented toward the development of the interior market, closely linked to training and extensive service, and in direct contact with farmers. This research will then be in a good position to benefit farmers and to contribute to international research while avoiding to be just an islet nurtured from abroad (Caracostas 1993).

References

Ahoyo Adjovi, N. 1995. Economie des systèmes de production intégrant la culture de riz au Sud Bénin. Thèse. Université de Hohenheim, 256 p.

Bosc, PM., Hanak Freud E.- Agricultural Research and Innovation in Tropical Africa. Repères. CIRAD-SPAAR. CIRAD-SAR. Montpellier, 133 p.

Carocostas, P. 1993. Recherche et maîtrise sociale: perceptions, approches, expérimentations. Une vue européenne. In Innovations et Sociétés. Tome III. Actes du XIVe séminaire d'Economie rurale. Montpellier. France. pp. 21-37.

Casas, J. 1993. Les systèmes nationaux de recherche agronomique des pays d'Afrique Occidentale et Centrale. Rome, FAO, 229 p.

Chataigner, J. 1989. La production alimentaire africaine en mal de débouchés ou la difficile constitution du marché intérieur agricole dans les pays d'Afrique Sub-Saharienne. Actes du 19ème séminaire européen des économistes agricoles, 29 mai – 2 juin 1989, Montpellier.

Egg, J., Affonda A.S., Engola Oyep J., Harre, D., Igue, J.O., Soule, B.G. 1993. L'intégration par les marchés dans le sous-espace Est: l'impact du Nigéria sur ses voisins immédiats. Paris. France, Club du Sahel (OECD), IRAM, INRA, UNB, 150 pages.

Fusilliers, J.L. 1991. La filière maïs en Côte d'Ivoire. Thèse Université Montpellier I, 297 p.

Griffon, M., Weber, J. 1995. Les aspects économiques et institutionnels de la révolution doublement verte. Séminaire international. Poitiers, 8-9 novembre 1995, 19 pages.

Kuppermincz, O. 1988.Saisonnalité et commercialisation de la banane plantain en Côte d'Ivoire. Fruits, vol. 3.

Lele, Uma. Octobre 1995. Building on the NARS-CGIAR Partnerships for a Doubly Green Revolution: A Framework for the IFAD-LED Initiative. International Seminary, Poitiers, November, 8-9, 1995, 48 p.

Lançon, P. 1991. Circuits commerciaux, marchés et politique d'approvisionnement des villes en Afrique de l'Ouest. L'exemple des produits vivriers au Togo. Thèse en sciences économiques, Université de Paris X.

Moustier, P. 1994. Is the vegetable supply performant in Africa ? Acta Horticulturae, N° 340.

Niweke, F.I., Njoku, J.E., Wilson, G.F. 1988. Productivity and limitations of plantain production in compound gardens in Southeastern Nigeria. Fruits, vol 43, N° 3, pp. 161-166.

Schlemmer, B. 1993. Les principaux acteurs de l'innovation. Présentation. In Innovations et Sociétés. Tome III. Actes du XIVe séminaire d'Economie rurale. Montpellier. France. pp. 21-37.

Temple, L. 1995. Les conditions du développement d'un marché vivrier. Le cas de la banane plantain dans la zone forestière du Cameroun. Université Montpellier I, 305 p. + annexes.

How to Allocate Development Resources for the Promotion of Sustainable Land Use Systems in Developing Countries?

Innovative Approaches

Detlef Virchow
Institute of Food Economics and Consumption Studies
Chair for Food Economics and Food Policy
Christian-Albrechts University of Kiel, Germany

Abstract

Farming is moving from a long era of land abundance to natural resource scarcity with increasing signs of soil degradation on arable land. To develop a concept for the allocation of development resources for sustainable land use systems the causes of soil degradation are analyzed. As main causes anthropogenic effects on soil degradation are identified. They are mainly site specific. The impacts of soil degradation, characterized as costs, are a significant loss of income at the household and national level.

Based on a conceptual framework the paper offers decision criteria for the allocation problem. The allocation of development resources refers to general criteria, the instruments of promotion, and the selection of technology (in hierarchical order).

Besides a geographic decision matrix, which is designed to identify the most seriously affected regions, the importance of so-called marginal lands and their promotion is stressed. Promoting sustainable land use systems will only be effective in connection with other development objectives: poverty reduction, food security, combined with sustainable economical growth.

Keywords

Sustainable land use systems, soil degradation, financial resource allocation, developing countries

1   Introduction

The agricultural frontier is closing as farming moves from a long era of land abundance to natural resource scarcity (Heidhues 1994). In 1961, the amount of arable land was 1.3 billion hectares with a global population of 3 billion people. In 1990, this ratio had declined substantially: the amount of arable land had only increased by 0.1 billion hectares, where as the world population grew to 5.3 billion people (Alexandratos 1994). On the global level, 5 to 7 million ha arable land is lost due to use of inadequate technologies (UNEP 1992). That is 0.3 - 0.5% of the actually used land. 25% of the global arable land is damaged to a great extent by soil degradation, and its productivity is less than it could be (GLASOD 1990). The costs of soil degradation are characterized by significant loss of income at the household and national level. Given the noted problem, on what basis can decisions be made for allocation of scarce development resources for sustainable land use systems? Can a set of criteria be developed to allow a more systematic approach to the problem, rather than the existing ad hoc country or local decision making? These questions are discussed in this paper.

2 Analysis of Impacts and Causes of Soil Degradation

2.1 The Impacts of Soil Degradation

Soil degradation can be defined as a reduction in the land's actual or potential uses (Blaikie et al. 1987). The anthropogenic induced soil degradation, besides natural induced soil degradation, which is not covered in this paper, reduces the potential of land use by destroying the production factor soil through human activities or failed activities.

Man-made water erosion and wind erosion are the major forms of degradation in developing countries (56% and 28% of soil degradation respectively), followed by chemical (12%), physical and biological degradation (UNEP/ISRIC 1991). Soil degradation is often a very slow accumulative process, where the visible damage occurs only in an advanced stage, when it is already difficult to reverse the process.

The on-site damage is the loss of topsoil, available water, mineral and organic soil-components, as well as soil contamination and deterioration of the soil structure. The results of on-site damages are reduced soil-fertility, productivity decline and as a consequence, yield losses.

The off-site damage is destruction of infrastructure (through increased run-off water and soil loss) and contamination of drinking water (through pesticides and nutrients). Soil degradation and the induced productivity loss leads to reduced food production, production expansion on marginal lands, loss of income and employment. Land becomes less able to support the population, with the consequence of poverty increase as well as national and international migration. Through the loss of natural habitats soil degradation has a more indirect consequence on the loss of genetic resources and the change of micro and macro climate.

The global annual costs of soil degradation can be assessed by calculating the on- and off-site costs. A rough estimation by Pimentel et al. (1994) estimates annual costs of about US $ 400 billion.

2.2 The Causes of Soil Degradation

For the allocation of development resources it is important to analyze the causes of soil degradation, which are shown as a complex system in figure 1. There are three levels which cause or reduce the anthropogenic induced soil degradation according to the specific situation and combination of elements:

1. Agricultural and other **land use activities** have a direct impact on the degree and development of soil degradation. Inadequate agricultural techniques, overgrazing, and deforestation are causing complex biological, physical, and chemical processes, which lead to different types of soil degradation, depending on site-specific biophysical characteristics.

2. On **farm-level** the driving force of soil degradation is the fact that farmers achieve short-term higher profits by using non sustainable land use methods, which will increase soil degradation. But in the long run these methods lead to reduced soil productivity, the so-called 'soil-mining.' Depending on the different agro-ecological situation (e.g. type of soil), the process of productivity loss will continue at different rates, but the end of the line will be a situation of irreversible soil degradation. The individual farmer will start reacting by introducing soil improving measures, but not before the costs on farm-level (in terms of forgone profit due to soil degradation) exceeds the benefit of non sustainable land use methods (Lutz et al. 1994). This change in production methods might be too late to stop the irreversible soil degradation, depending on the agro-ecological conditions (e.g. buffercapacity of the soil). Even though the costs on farm-level exceed the benefits there will also be farmers who will not change their production methods. Their action can be explained by insufficient knowledge, lack of capital or labor, and investment-risks, e.g. because of unsecured and/or unforeseeable policies (property rights etc.). These causes are part of the overall framework, which has to be discussed next.

3. The farmers' choice for certain agricultural and other land use activities are a reaction to social, economical, political and institutional **frameworks**, which influence soil degradation more indirectly by influencing farmers' decision-making process. Four groups can be identified:
   1. the socio-demographic complex,
   2. service and general infrastructure,
   3. the situation on the different relevant markets, and

Figure 1: Causes for Induced or Reduced Soil Degradation

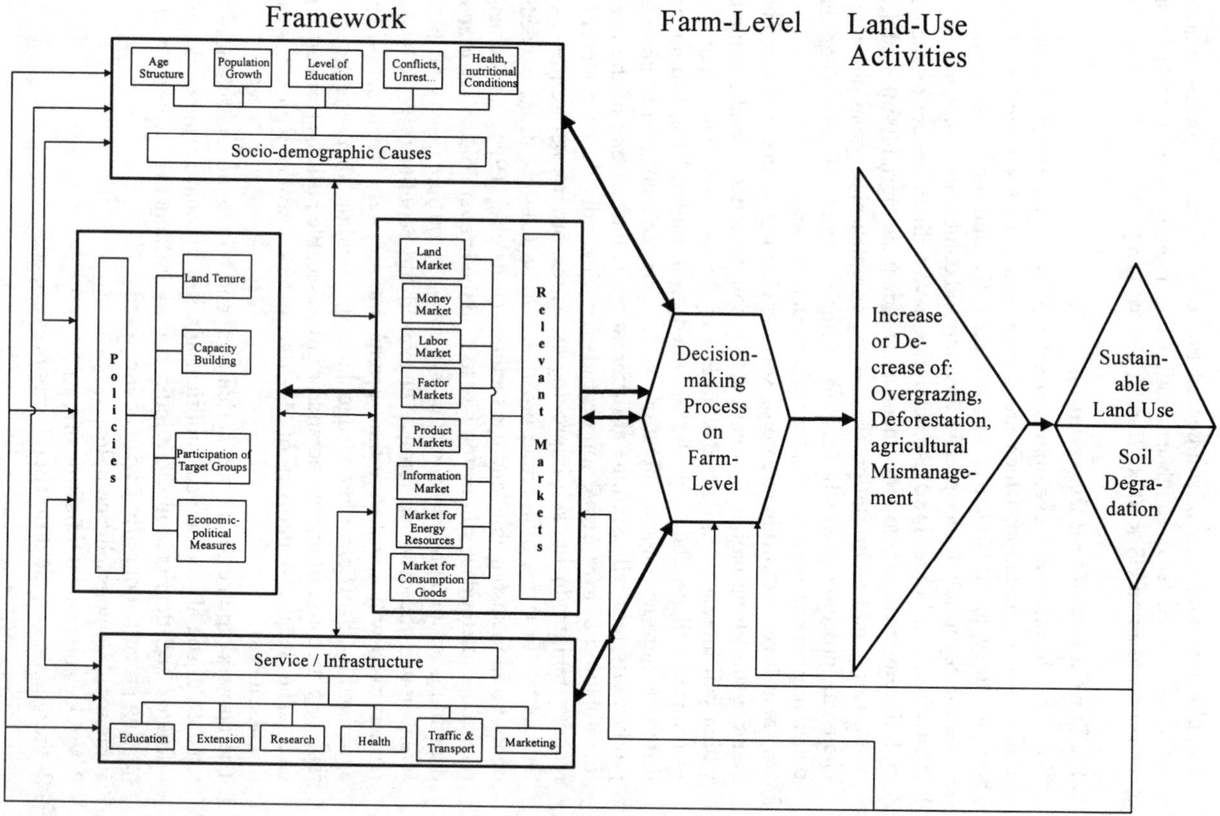

4. policies. According to the regional or country specific situation these criteria influence the farmer's decision for certain land use activities and therefore induce or reduce the process of soil degradation. Given a demand for labor and a supply of adequate technology and its related extension, population increase might be a driving force for innovative, soil-adapted production technologies like the example of the Machakos District in Kenya (English et al. 1994) shows us. But without, a large increase of population will have a significant impact on soil degradation (Panayotou 1994).

Summarizing the causes of soil degradation, it has to be taken into consideration that the farmers are involved in dynamic adjustment processes reacting to changing scarcities or processes of degradation of natural resources. 'Self-correcting' mechanisms, which react to degradation processes are resource shortage and increasing private and social costs, besides market-integration and population pressure, which Ruthenberg (1980) had mentioned. If these mechanisms are successful, they will induce the use of new, adapted methods through local innovative methods or the farmers will adopt external, but adapted technologies (Sherr et al. 1994). But the adoption of new technology for a sustainable land use will take time. Incentives have to be introduced, distorted incentives eliminated to accelerate this process. Whether sustainable land use methods are adopted by the farmers is a site-specific issue. The decision depends on the specific agro-ecological conditions faced, on the available technologies and their potential to meet the farm-level's objectives, and it depends on the overall institutional, political, social, and economical framework.

3   Main Development Objectives

The promotion of sustainable land use systems is only effective in connection with and complementary to main development objectives: poverty reduction, food security, combined with a sustainable economical growth. Sustainable land use is a part of sustainable agriculture, which is a part of a sustainable development. Sustainable development is the 'management and conservation of the natural resource base, and the orientation of technological and institutional change in such a manner as to ensure the attainment and continued satisfaction of human needs for present and future generations' (FAO 1991). Sustainable land use includes all activities which use soil as the production basis and maintain or increase the soil productivity over time. Sustainable land use requires such criteria as: 1. sustainability, 2. production-increase, 3. rentability on farm-level, and 4. compatibility for the farm's production and household objectives.

To promote sustainable land use one has to concentrate not only on the farm-level. To solve certain technology problems without improving the social and political framework will be without success in the long run. But to concentrate

solely on improving the framework, without improving the technologies will also be without reward. Two single factors have to be kept in mind:
The actual average soil productivity in developing countries is not sufficient to sustainably feed a steadily growing population. In 1960 the amount of cultivated land was 0.44 ha per capita. In 1990 the average arable land for each earth's inhabitant was 0.27 ha. Following estimations, in 2025 it will be 0.18 ha (Engelman et al. 1995). Because of limited land expansion, there is a need for technical progress to increase the land intensity.
The increasing pressure of population density on limited land potential should be addressed by programs like family planning and non agricultural employment. Without these measures the actual success of, and investments in, promoting methods of sustainable land use will be neutralized by the increased amount of people.

4   Approaches to Allocate Development Resources

Because of the increasing soil degradation in developing countries the traditional approaches to allocate development resources for promoting sustainable land use systems have to be rethought.

The allocation of development resources refers to 1. the selection of a technology or a set of technologies to reduce soil degradation, as well as 2. the selection of instruments of promotion of these technologies and their optimal combination. It is important to realize the interdependence between the selection of technologies and the adequate promotion systems. Because of limited financial resources for the promotion of sustainable land use system there has to be – in addition to the assessment of technologies and promotion instruments – 3. a set of general criteria to locate the 'hot spots' for promotion.

4.1   Technologies

The selection of adapted technologies refers to the local situation and depends heavily on an appropriate monitoring and evaluation system. Furthermore efficient communication transfer between land users, extension workers, and researchers is of importance, mainly for the development of technologies and their implementation. Technology assessment, including assessment of the cost-effectiveness of proposed solutions, has been widely discussed and their criteria are used for the selection of technologies (FAO 1992).

4.2   Instruments

The success of adapted technologies depends on a framework which allows a farmer to change his production methods in favor of a sustainable land use system. Six different groups of instruments exists, which individually or in combination have the aim of changing the framework: 1. economic incentives could reduce the individual opportunity costs of changing to a more sustainable land use system; 2. improving the service structures will supply the farmers with the necessary technology, knowledge etc. to adopt a sustainable land use system and increase productivity; 3. support of institutional reforms will increase the effectiveness and efficiency of institutions involved in development of sustainable land use systems; 4. horizontal and vertical coordination of national policies to prevent negative incentives on sustainable land use systems; 5. creation of or improving legal and constitutional frameworks could force landowners to invest in sustainable land use systems; 6. creation of international regulations and conventions.

   Which instruments and which combination of instruments has to be promoted to reduce soil degradation and, in the long run, to implement sustainable land use systems depends on a bundle of specific criteria (farm structure, production potential, the degree of organization of the agricultural sector, the agro-ecological zone, the predominant form of soil degradation, the existing and functioning social structures, the economical and political situation etc.). As a means of assessing the efficiency of promotion instruments and in order to compare and optimize a combination of the different available instruments, a cost-benefit analysis is, up to now, not always operational. This is due to the fact that the benefits of some objectives of sustainable land use systems have yet to be monetarized (Munasinghe 1992). In making such an assessment therefore, it is necessary to add alternative economic methodologies.

   To assess the different promotion instruments a **multi-criteria decision support model** can be used (van Herwijnen et al. 1993, Romero et al. 1987). Each feasible promotion instrument will be analyzed and assessed according to the percentage of achievement of the stated objectives.

   Having decided which objectives must be realized these will be described using a number of operational indicators. The feasible instruments to achieve these objectives will be described, and these will be rated according to their potential to succeed in realizing the objectives. This will vary according to the socio-economical framework and ecological situation in which the promotion instruments are operating.

   The cost-efficiency of each instrument and of the combination of different instruments can be assessed by analyzing the costs of each instrument and comparing them with the degree of achieving the different objectives. A matrix, describing the instruments, their degree of achievement and their impacts under different frameworks will be used to identify optimal combinations of instruments to promote sustainable land use.

Besides the decision of a certain combination of instruments, an analysis of problems and weaknesses for each instrument is essential for adapting the instrument to the local conditions and for a cost-efficient utilization. The fundamental problems of implementing a theoretically sound combination of instruments in a socio-economic weak surrounding has to be recognized as well.

4.3 Key-Criteria

To solve the danger of soil degradation and to promote and create sustainable land use systems is a complex problem, containing technological as well as socio-economic elements and relating to specific sites. To allocate funds for promoting sustainable land use to a fixed set of instruments for one agro-ecological zone as a standard solution will not be successful. Even though similar technological problems causing soil degradation are to be found in one agro-ecological zone, different approaches have to be taken to overcome these problems depending on the socio-economical frameworks of each country. Therefore similar problems of soil degradation may have to be solved by different techniques, or by similar techniques but using different instruments to promote these techniques, always taking into account the special overall situation.

There are no standard solutions or blue prints for political decision makers. The same technique cannot always be promoted to overcome a special degradation problem, nor can the same instrument or combination of instruments be used to promote the same technical solution to overcome soil degradation. To allocate scarce financial resources to promote sustainable land use each degradation problem has to be assessed individually, which is not feasible. So there is a need for a bundle of ecological, technological, economical, as well as social criteria to focus on 'hot spots' for promotion. In a pragmatic synthesis of theoretical and conceptional consideration, six general criteria are developed for an objectives-oriented allocation of development resources to promote sustainable land use. Only, where these six criteria can be met, the chance to reduce soil degradation as well as the benefit of investing scarce resources in promoting sustainable land use systems will be high. The six criteria are:

1. Ecological Priority

Special attention has to be drawn to the most seriously affected regions. To identify these regions, a geographic decision matrix has to be designed. The indicators are the three main relevant aspects of soil degradation (Sanders 1994): The status of soil degradation characterizes the actual situation of soil degradation. The rate of soil degradation characterizes the soil degradation over time. Finally the risk of further soil degradation for a certain site depends on the ecological conditions, mainly the risk of further soil erosion. These three indicators are necessary to assess the soil degradation in its whole extent. Table 1 shows the most relevant soil types according to this characterization.

Table 1:   Geographic Decision Matrix

Type I:	Status: >		Type II:	Status: >		Type III:	Status: >	
	Risk:	>		Risk:	<		Risk:	<
	Rate:	>		Rate:	>		Rate:	<
Type IV	Status: <		Type V	Status: <		Type VI	Status: <	
	Risk:	>		Risk:	>		Risk:	<
	Rate:	>		Rate:	<		Rate:	<

Allocating funds to promote sustainable land use is important for those sites which have a high status of degradation, high rate of degradation, and a high risk of further degradation (Type I). The second most important sites to be promoted are those which have a high rate of degradation and a high risk of further degradation, even though their status of degradation is still low (Type IV). To allocate funds according to the ecological importance is promoting curative (the first mentioned type of soil) and also preventive (the second mentioned type of soil) measures.

2. Institutional Practical Application

The potential of technologies are used best when they are integrated into the social surroundings. Funds are not used objective-oriented, if they promote a technology-intensive, but organization-extensive strategy. If different executing agencies have different interests, the adoption of certain technologies will be delayed.

Funds should only be allocated or used, if all participants in the development process of promoting sustainable land use systems actively accept the development objectives and are capable and willing to achieve the goals. To analyze this precondition, key criteria like legitimacy, achieved standard of development, and the socio-cultural heterogeneity should be used (BMZ 1992).

It is essential to know the capacity of the participants and their limits. The more the land users participate in planning and implementing the development activities, the more the land users' needs and possibilities are being taking into consideration. In this way the chances of successfully promoting sustainable land use systems will increase.

Education, information transfer, and an improved self-help organization improves the ability of land users to ask for special public services. The promotion of sustainable land use systems is only effective if the public and private services function adequately, are capable of providing specific services, and if there is a two-way communication flow.

3. Technological Flexibility

Experiences have taught that farmers, offered a whole development package, will seldom take over the whole package, but will select certain methods and will modify them according to their own demands. So methods for sustainable land use have to be developed and offered as innovation modules, to be used flexibly depending on the site and the individual needs of the adopting farmer. A participatory approach of technology development would stimulate the flexibility of the technologies.

4. Monitor and Evaluation and Pilot Measures

Financial resources should only be spent where the activities and the impact of the funds are constantly analyzed and corrected during the development process and evaluated at the end. It is important to use – in addition to quantitative criteria – also qualitative criteria. Only by monitoring and evaluation will long term information be gained about adopted and adapted methods as well as the costs and benefits of sustainable land use. These experiences can be utilized for future promotion approaches and where pilot measures promise broad impacts.

5. Social Acceptance

The main objective of all development activities is to improve welfare of a nation without irreversibly destroying any resources for the next generations. Maintaining natural resources, as well as increasing economic growth has to correspond with this main objective. Maintenance of natural resources and poverty alleviation should not compete for funds. Instead poverty reduction might often be a key element in the maintenance of natural resources for the next generations. Funds should be objective-oriented allocated where the promotion of sustainable land use systems has a positive effect on poverty reduction.

6. Economical Efficiency

Besides the ecological, institutional, technological, and social criteria, allocation of funds has to fulfill economic criteria as well. The above mentioned curative measurements require high financial input to prevent irreversible soil degradation. In contrast to curative activities, preventive measurement can lead to success with far less financial resources. Mainly cost-efficiency methods have to decide, whether promoting curative or preventive measurements will best secure production output.

Furthermore funds should be allocated to promote instruments, which – once implemented – don't need further funding, but still have a positive effect on sustainable land use. Land reform regulates land rights and will have positive effects on sustainable land use in the long run. Once implemented, there will be no demand for further financial resources.

These six general criteria have an impact on the promotion of **marginal lands**. The significant importance of the marginal lands has to be stressed. There will hardly be sustainable land use and no sustainable development if the high potential areas are promoted while neglecting marginal areas.

Without promoting the marginal lands the process of soil degradation will continue. The consequences (e.g. starvation and aggressive migration into high potential areas and urban slums) with their ecological, social, and economical costs and political risks will lead to national and international destabilization.

In general, most of the cities in developing countries cannot afford more immigrants (Lipton 1989). There are no further employment possibilities and the cities are expanding already on fertile agricultural land (Smit 1995). In high potential areas the average yield increase is slowing down and the degradation of natural resources is increasing (Pingali 1992, Ruttan 1994, Pingali et al. 1994), besides the fact that migrants are not always accepted (Knerr 1994). Taking into account the situation in the cities as well as in high potential areas, it seems that promoting marginal lands will reduce far more the potential social, ecological and economical costs in the cities and in high potential areas. So it will be the most cost-effective solution after all.

Concrete development objectives will be, for the short run, to stop the irreversible process of soil degradation by stabilizing the ecological and agricultural production systems. To minimize the migration out of the marginal lands has to be the long-term objective. Even though there are some marginal lands which have only very limited development possibilities, marginal lands will have to fulfill following tasks in future:

1. A more intensive production should be achieved for ecological margined lands by improving technology, mainly in breeding and management skills.
2. By improving the institutional, economical, and political framework, economical margined lands could increase their productivity (e.g. increased market integration due to improved infrastructure leads to higher production).

Carrying-capacity can be increased on the marginal lands with development possibilities. By reducing the migration, this will be a significant contribution to reduce pressure on high potential areas and cities.

The objective should be to profitably combine the potential of the different sites for a common rural development.

5   Lessons Learned

A sustainable agricultural development is in the long run only possible if a sustainable land use is under way. Even though soil degradation was the first of the natural resource issues discussed, it is still one of the major ongoing threats, because the land available for agriculture is still decreasing.

The experiences have taught that soil degradation will be reduced in the long run if all influencing criteria are well harmonized. But these 'self-correcting' mechanisms react to individual threats, whereas the social threats of loosing too much productive land is much higher. Where short-term incentives have been introduced and distorted incentives eliminated, the process of adopting sustainable land use systems was accelerated.

Reflecting the limited financial resources available, efficient use for the promotion of sustainable land use systems can only be made by allocating and concentrating the financial resources according to the introduced bundle of criteria. An isolated promotion of sustainable land use will not be successful. Only an overall concept can take advantage of the synergistic and complementary effects. Main areas of funding should be:

- poverty reduction: for economical and ecological reasons poverty reduction (e.g. rural employment programmes) is an important part for a sustainable development (von Braun 1992) and contributes essentially to reduce soil degradation;
- training programmes: to improve the educational level of the poor is not a sufficient condition for reducing poverty, but it is an essential precondition;
- agricultural research: only through ongoing research activities is there a chance to keep pace with the increasing food demand through increasing average yields, e.g. through improved technologies for sustainable land use;
- institutional reforms and improvement of rural services: besides their main impact on food security, the positive effects for promoting sustainable land use systems has been shown.

The promotion of sustainable land use systems will mainly depend on the political priorities of the governments of the developing countries and the influence of the rural population on the decision-making process. Without participation in the programme approaches, the objective to implement sustainable land use systems tend to fail, even with external development resources.

Acknowledgments

This paper is based on the author's report 'Allokation von Fördermitteln für die ressourcenschonende Bodennutzung in Entwicklungsländern – Ein Strategiepapier' for the GTZ. The author is particularly indebted to Dr. Kurt G. Steiner, project manager of 'Ressourcenschonende Landnutzungssysteme' of GTZ for providing excellent support. Advice and background documents were kindly provided by GTZ-staff, Prof. Heidhues and his staff at Stuttgart-Hohenheim, and by FAO's agricultural Department. Finally, intellectual guidance from Prof. von Braun, Kiel, is most gratefully acknowledged.

References

Alexandratos, Nikas 1994. World Agriculture: Toward 2010. FAO, Rome.

Blaikie, P., Brookfield, H. 1987. Land Degradation and Society. Methuen, London.

BMZ 1992. Sozio-kulturelle Kriterien für Vorhaben der Entwicklungszusammenarbeit. Rahmenkonzept. In: Sektor- und sektorübergreifende Konzepte II, Materialien 85. p.20. BMZ, Bonn.

von Braun, Joachim 1992. Improving Food Security of the Poor. IFPRI, Washington, D.C.

Engelman, Robert, Pamela LeRoy 1995: Conserving Land: Population and Sustainable Food Production. Population and Environment Program. Population Action International, Washington, D.C.)

English, John, Mary Tiffen, Michael Mortimore 1994. Land Resource Management in Machakos District, Kenya 1930-1990. World Bank Environment Paper No. 5. The World Bank, Washington, D.C.

FAO and Gov. of Netherlands 1991. The den Bosch Declaration and Agenda for action on Sustainable Agriculture and rural Development. Report of the Conference. Rome, p.2.

FAO 1992. Technology Assessment and Transfer for sustainable Agriculture and rural Development in the Asia-Pacific Region. Highlights of a FAO Expert Consultation, Kuala Lumpur, Malaysia, 14-18 December 1992.

GLASOD 1990: Global Assessment of Soil Degradation. World Maps (4 sheets). Wageningen, Netherlands, ISRIC and UNEP

GTZ (Gesellschaft für technische Zusammenarbeit) 1994. Sachstandsbericht. Ursachen der Bodendegradation und Ansätze für eine Förderung der nachhaltigen Bodennutzung im Rahmen der Entwicklungszusammenarbeit. GTZ, Eschborn.

Heidhues, Franz 1994. Probleme internationaler Arbeitsteilung in der Agrarwirtschaft. In: Agrarwirtschaft 43 1994), Heft 4/5. pp. 191 - 197.

van Herwijnen, M., R. Janssen, P. Nijkamp 1993. A multi-criteria Decision Support Model and Geographic Information System for sustainable Development Planning of the Greek Islands. In: Project Appraisal, Vol. 8, No. 1 1993, Surrey, England. pp. 9-22.

Knerr, Béatrice 1994. EU-Agrarreform, Migration und ländliche Beschäftigungssituation in Entwicklungsländern. Vortrag auf der 35. Jahrestagung der Gesellschaft für Wirtschafts- und Sozialwissenschaften des Landbaus vom 5. bis 7. Oktober 1994 in Hohenheim.

Lipton, Michael, Richard Longhurst 1989. New Seeds and Poor People. Unwin Hyman, London.

Lutz, Ernst, Stefano Pagiola, Carlos Reiche 1994: The Costs and Benefits of Soil Conservation: The Farmers' Viewpoint. In: The World Bank Research Observer, Vol. 9, No. 2, pp. 273-295.

Munasinghe, Mohan 1992. Environment Economics and Valuation in Development Decisionmaking. Environment Working Paper No. 51, The World Bank, Washington, D.C.

Oldeman, L.R., R.T.A. Hakkeling, W.G. Sombroek 1990. World Map of the Status of human-induced Soil Degradation: An explanatory Note. ISRIC (International Soil Reference and Information Centre. Wageningen), The Netherlands.

Panayotou, Theodore 1994. The Population, Environment, and Development Nexus. In: Robert Cassen (ed.) 1994. Population and Development: Old Debates, New Conclusions. U.S.-Third World Policy Perspectives No. 19, Overseas Development Council, Washington, D.C., pp. 149-180.

Pimentel, David, C. Harvey, P. Resosudarmo, K. Sinclair, D. Kurz, M.McNair, S. Crist, L. Shpritz, L. Fitton, R. Saffouri, R. Blair 1994. Environmental and Economic Costs of Soil

Erosion and Conservation Benefits. College of Agriculture and Life Sciences, Cornell University, Ithaca, N.Y. Draft.

Pingali, Prabhu L 1992. Diversifying Asian rice-farming systems: a deterministic paradigm. In: Trends in Agricultural Diversification: Regional Perspectives. Barghouti, Shawki, Lisa Garbux und Dina Umali (Hsg.), World bank Tech. Paper No. 180. The World Bank, Washington, D.C., PP. 107-126. Zitiert in: Pingali, Prabhu L., Mark W. Rosegrant 1994).

Pingali, Prabhu L., Mark W. Rosegrant 1994. Confronting the Environmental Consequences of the Green Revolution in Asia. EPTD Discussion Paper No. 2, IFPRI, Washington, D.C..

Romero, Carlos, Tahir Rehman 1987. Natural Resource Management and the Use of Multiple Criteria Decision-Making Techniques: A Review. In: European Journal of Agricultural Economics. Vol. 14 1987. pp. 61-89.

Ruthenberg, Hans 1980. Farming Systems of the Tropics. Oxford.

Ruttan, Vernon W. 1994. Sustainable Agricultural Growth. In: Ruttan, Vernon W. (Ed.) Agriculture, Environment & Health. Sustainable Development in the 21st Century. Minneapolis. PP. 3-20.

Sanders, D.W. 1994. A global Perspective on Soil Degradation and its socio-economic Impact: the Problems of Assessment. 8th International Soil Conservation Conference, 'Soil and Water Conservation: Challenges and Opportunities', New Delhi, India.

Scherr, Sara J., Peter B.R. Hazell 1994. Sustainable Agricultural Development Strategies in Fragile Lands. EPTD Discussion Paper No. 1, IFPRI, Washington, D.C..

Smit, Jac 1995: Urban Agriculture prospects in Africa, Latin America and Asia. In: Richter, Jürgen, Wilfried H. Schnitzler, Susanne Gura (eds.) 1994. Vegetable Production in Peri-urban Areas in the Tropics and Subtropics - Food, Income and Quality of Life. Proceedings of the International Workshop held from 14 to 17 November 1994 in Zschortau, Germany.

UNEP 1992: Saving our planet. The state of the environment (1987-1992).

UNEP, ISRIC (United Nations Environmental Programme, International Soil Reference and Information Centre) 1991. GIS evaluation of GLASOD map (cf. Oldeman et. al. 1990), Nairobi.

Virchow, Detlef 1995: Allokation von Fördermitteln für die ressourcenschonende Bodennutzung in Entwicklungsländern. Ein Strategiepapier. Abschlußbericht für die GTZ. Institut für Ernährungswirtschaft und Verbraucherlehre der Universität Kiel, Lehrstuhl für Ernährungswirtschaft und Ernährungspolitik.

Promoting Sustainable Capital-led Intensification in Sahel Agriculture Following Macroeconomic Policy Reform

T. Reardon,[1] V. Kelly,[1] B. Diagana,[1,5] J. Dioné,[1,4]
E. Crawford,[1] K. Savadogo,[2] D. Boughton[3]
[1]Dept. of Agricultural Economics, Michigan State University, USA
[2]FASEG, Université de Ouagadougou, Burkina Faso
[3]ICRISAT/Malawi
[4]PRISAS, Institut du Sahel/CILSS
[5]BAME, Institut Sénégalais de Recherches Agricoles, Senegal

Abstract

*Rapid, sustainable intensification is needed in Sahel agriculture. In both favorable and unfavorable agroclimatic zones, intensification is already proceeding as population density increases and extensification options disappear. The **first key issue** is what kind of intensification can meet pressing needs for agricultural products yet be environmentally sustainable? We contend that "capital-led intensification" is the best option to meet this dual need. This path involves significantly increased use of chemical fertilizer, manure, bunds, and animal traction. (We illustrate from the cotton zones of Mali and Burkina Faso.) Capital-deficient intensification is unfortunately more common, involving merely an increase in labor per hectare and a reduction in fallowing. Moreover, where capital is used it is often "partial capital-led intensification" which is unsustainable. We illustrate with the case of peanuts in Senegal, where seeding density has been increased without accompanying use of fertilizers to protect soil fertility. This exhausts the soil and leads to lower yields and incomes, and a vicious circle of more capital-deficient intensification or even extensification onto fragile marginal lands. (We illustrate from the Peanut Basin of Senegal.) Hence, low-capital agriculture or intensification with key missing capital inputs is not sustainable under conditions of high population pressure.*

*The **second key issue** is how to replace the public credit, input supply, and extension systems that were eliminated in the 1980s. Although these systems had high budgetary costs, their elimination sharply increased input costs to farmers and led to a decline in input use. Public or private alternatives to these systems are not yet in place. The main task ahead is to overcome structural constraints to capital investment, and specifically to: 1) redesign and reintroduce agricultural support programs; 2) tackle the taboo subject of subsidies to fertilizer and soil conservation investments; 3) remove bottlenecks to private investments by making complementary public investments, e.g., in roads, trucks to haul laterite for bunds,* *culverts to protect farmland, wells to water windbreaks, etc.; 4) promote smallholder cash cropping in vertically integrated systems that reduce risk and provide inputs, credit, and attractive prices; and 5) link nonfarm enterprise and employment programs to farm investment goals, especially where spinoffs from agriculture are possible. An illustration is the manufacture and repair of animal traction equipment.*

Keywords
Sub-Saharan Africa, intensification, soil fertility, macro policies

1   The Key Issues

The key issue is how to promote sustainable capital-led intensification. The key problem is that capital-deficient intensification is now common and is unsustainable and impoverishing. Moreover, "partial" or unbalanced capital-led intensification is also practiced and is unsustainable.

Due to rapid growth of population and slow growth of agricultural productivity, the Sahel has passed from land abundance to land scarcity. For example, Binswanger (1986) classes Niger with Bangladesh in the group of countries that are most densely populated in terms of persons per unit of "carrying capacity," a standardized unit of land.

Farmers are less able to meet growing food and fiber demand by "extensifying" (cultivating new land). Increasingly, farmers must "intensify" by using more labor and nonlabor inputs to raise yields. Here, for simplicity, we use the term "capital" for nonlabor inputs other than land (e.g., fertilizer, animal traction equipment, bunds).

Boserup (1965) maintains that as population density increases and arable land per capita declines, fallow periods must be shortened, and land-substituting technologies must be adopted. Yet intensification to date in the Sahel has merely meant the use of more labor per hectare and shorter fallow times – without accompanying investments in land conservation and in soil fertility. This can be termed *"capital-deficient intensification"* to focus on the lack of capital in the process. Without sufficient use of fertilizer and organic matter, intensification of land use causes soil erosion and loss of fertility.

To break this vicious circle, Sahel farmers need to pursue *"sustainable capital-led intensification."* This means using inputs and capital which provide net gains in productivity, but which also protect land and water, and enhance soil fertility over time. Sustainable capital-led intensification is the balanced increased use of a full set of complementary capital inputs[1] on a given unit of land: 1) fertilizers

---

[1] These inputs and practices were identified in the MSU synthesis paper on determinants of agricultural productivity in Africa (Reardon et al. 1994b).

(chemical fertilizer, manure, mulch); 2) seed; 3) water; 4) animal traction; 5) soil conservation infrastructure (bunds, windbreaks, terraces);[2] 6) human capital (economic and agronomic management)[3].

This balanced increase in use of a set of capital inputs will require three critical sets of investment: 1) investments by farmers in these capital inputs; 2) investments by input producers and merchants, and product merchants and processors; 3) investments by governments in complementary public infrastructure such as roads, wells, irrigation perimeters, and enactment of policies that spur the private investments 1) and 2). Note that 2) and 3) will be critical in providing the incentive and capacity for farmers to invest, by lowering transaction and transport costs, and by making farm investments affordable and profitable. Making the set of investments 1-3 can be thought of as "intensifying the entire system" both on the farm and in the food and fiber system in general. Below we will illustrate from the cotton zones of Mali and Burkina Faso successes in combining these investments for "sustainable capital-led intensification."

Nevertheless, one needs to be on guard against a problem that has been exacerbated with structural adjustment – that of "*partial or unsustainable capital-led intensification*." This is the unbalanced use of one or more capital inputs within the set of capital inputs listed above. We illustrate this below with the case of the Senegalese peanut basin, where seeding density per hectare is increasing to offset yield decline from soil degradation – but without complementary use of fertilizers to protect soil fertility. This creates a vicious circle and is unsustainable. Hence, it is crucial that the full set of relevant complementary inputs be used, which brings us back to the need for the three sets of investments listed above.

The main implication of the paper is that macroeconomic policy reform during the decade of structural adjustment was necessary but not sufficient to induce sustainable capital-led intensification. Addressing structural constraints to raising the incentives and capacity of farmers to invest in capital is key. This requires complementary public investments in infrastructure, private investments in marketing of inputs and outputs, and in processing of outputs, farm and nonfarm sector programs, and emphasis on promotion of cash cropping where feasible and profitable.

We proceed as follows. Section 2 presents evidence of the manifestation of these paths in Sahel agriculture and what structural conditions and policy contexts have led to each, drawing on MSU case studies in collaboration with ISRA (Senegal),

---

[2] Introduction of perennial crops or integration of forestry/fruit trees/livestock with cropping are other ways of ensuring that intensive farming is sustainable.

[3] Such management could, for example, lead to timely application of fertilizers, proper plant spacing, and so on.

IER (Mali), and the University of Ouagadougou (Burkina Faso).[4] Section 3 discusses policy and program implications. The main arguments are presented in bold type, and are then illustrated and discussed.

2   Evidence and Discussion

2.1   The Path to Sustainable Capital-Led Intensification

2.1.1 Agricultural Diversification into Cash Crops (Food and Nonfood)

Cash cropping provides incentive for farmer investment in capital-led intensification. In our case studies we find that farmers usually apply the bulk of productivity-enhancing inputs and resource conservation investments to cash crops either because profitability is higher than for subsistence crops or because there is credit or input provision in cash crop schemes (Reardon et al. 1994b). In Burkina Faso for example, Savadogo et al. (1994 and 1995) found that the payoff (in terms of marginal value product) to use of animal traction, manure, and fertilizer was much higher on cash crops (cotton and maize) than on semi-subsistence food grains (millet and sorghum); farmers were much more likely to use capital and inputs on the cash crops.

Cash cropping increases farmers' capacity to make capital investments. This point can be illustrated with the case of animal traction investments in Senegal. From 1960 through 1980 a liberal credit program encouraged farmers in Senegal's Peanut Basin to invest in animal traction equipment. The equipment credit program was seconded by other input policies (fertilizer and seed subsidies and input distribution programs) and output marketing programs (guaranteed prices and markets) that helped farmers earn the level of net returns necessary to reimburse the equipment credit. Adoption was very high during this period, so that virtually every farmer in the Peanut Basin now uses some form of animal traction.

Dione (1989) found for Mali that cash cropping increased the ability of farmers to buy inputs for food cropping, thus setting off a "virtuous circle." Cotton farming (in a vertically integrated system) provided the cash and the institutional platform to have access to the formal credit market that allowed farmers to buy animal traction equipment, which in turn increased productivity of cotton *and* of maize production.

---

[4] The studies used primary data from surveys of rural households in the 1980s and 1990s. The empirical results and conclusions are discussed in more detail in Diagana et al. (1995), Dione (1989), Kelly et al. (1995), Savadogo et al. (1994 and 1995), and Reardon et al. (1994b, 1995).

2.1.2 Income Diversification into Noncropping Activities

Noncropping sources of income can complement cash crop income and contribute to capital-led intensification, particularly where credit markets function poorly.

For example, in the Guinean zone of southern Burkina Faso, where agroclimatic conditions are good, Savadogo et al. (1994 and 1995) show that noncropping earnings (mainly from local and migratory nonfarm activities and from livestock sales) are reinvested in expensive animal traction packages. Noncropping income and farm size were important determinants of adoption of animal traction. Noncropping income (controlling for farm size) was particularly important in this zone because credit was not generally available, so the household's own liquidity-mainly from noncropping income-was crucial to the animal traction investment.

Also in Burkina Faso, Reardon and Kelly (1989) show that fertilizer use is positively related to noncropping income in the Sudanian zone – but not in the Guinean zone where the presence of SOFITEX (the cotton parastatal) makes fertilizer available to farmers regardless of village location and household cash sources.

In Senegal, Kelly et al. (1995) show that noncropping income is used to purchase tools and (occasionally) fertilizer, repair animal traction equipment, and obtain peanut seed. The source of noncropping income appears to influence the method of peanut seed acquisition. Those with large shares of livestock income tend to use the income for down payments to obtain peanut seed credit. Credit permits these farmers to keep more of their capital assets in livestock during the cropping season, rather than turning it all into seed. This spreads risk across different farm activities. Those with large shares of noncropping income are more likely to purchase peanut seeds for cash, by-passing the deferred payment option associated with credit because the peak period for noncropping liquidity is at the end of the dry season rather than at the end of the rainy season.

We are worried, however, because in much of the Sahel, participation in nonfarm activities is inequitably distributed – poorer households depend more on their farms and thus are vulnerable to the vicissitudes of weather, while richer households have much more diversified incomes. The poor must content themselves with labor-intensive jobs that have low capital entry barriers. Richer households can start relatively capital-led nonfarm enterprises, because they are less bound by cash and credit constraints (Reardon et al. 1994a).

2.1.3 Devaluation – Accompanied by Proper Conditions

Devaluation can have an incentive effect on capital-led intensification in cases where it increases net returns.

In Mali, after devaluation of the franc CFA in January 1994, there was a rise in the profitability of Malian irrigated rice, the output price of which was allowed to rise faster than input costs. Net returns per hectare rose 10-35 percent according to the zone and level of intensity of input use (Mendez del Villar and Diakité 1995; Coulibaly et al. 1995). Note, however, that further expansion of this intensified system is constrained by limited complementary public investments (irrigated perimeters). State investments in extending infrastructure would allow the intensified rice system to expand; investments in rehabilitation of infrastructure would allow the system to function more efficiently and profitably.

2.2   The Path to Capital-Deficient Intensification

2.2.1 Structural Adjustment and the Decline in Use of Capital

With the decline in government support for agriculture during structural adjustment, fertilizer use has declined, traction equipment is deteriorating – and this is leading to capital-deficient intensification and partial capital-led intensification that are unsustainable.

Fertilizer use declined substantially in two MSU case study countries – Senegal and Burkina Faso – when subsidies were removed and/or access to credit was made more difficult (Kelly et al. 1995; Savadogo et al. 1994).

In Senegal, decades of continuous peanut/millet cultivation with limited use of fallow, organic matter, and chemical fertilizers has increased soil degradation through erosion and nutrient loss. Following the sharp drop in fertilizer consumption during the 1980s (due to changes in subsidy and credit policies), soil degradation accelerated. Farmers began increasing peanut seeding densities to compensate for the declining soil quality which they believed was slowing down the growth of peanut ground cover and, therefore, increasing weed problems. The practice has become widespread; survey data show that many farmers are using more than two times the recommended quantity of seed per hectare. Although this appears to be a logical short-run solution which increases yields and net returns (Kelly et al. 1995), agronomic research suggests that it is not a sustainable practice (Gaye and Sene 1994). Without supplementary fertilizer and organic matter, increased seeding densities will not only lead to further soil mining but also have negative repercussions on seed quality. This is an illustration of the "partial capital-led intensification" path – where critical complementary capital inputs are missing.

Moreover, in the domain of animal traction equipment, the current dilemma in Senegal is that the credit program was halted in the early 1980s and then replaced by a program which made access to credit much more difficult. At the same time, there has been substantial inflation in the cost of factory-made equipment. This has fostered the production of traction equipment by local blacksmiths who sell their products at a fraction of the price demanded for industrial-quality equipment. The extent to which artisanal production of traction equipment can provide a sustainable solution in the long-run needs to be examined quickly, as the current stock of factory made equipment is, on average, more than 20 years old-well beyond the 10-15 year lifetime used in most calculations of depreciation.

2.2.2 Devaluation and Agricultural Profitability

Devaluation has increased gross returns of most tradeable agricultural products – but there is evidence in some areas of negative impacts on incentives for sustainable capital-led intensification due to increases in input costs.

A case in point is Senegalese peanut production since the January 1994 devaluation of the franc CFA. Despite two producer price hikes representing a combined increase of 71 percent over pre-devaluation levels, and smaller increases in the cost of peanut fertilizer (47 percent by May 1995), economic incentives to intensify peanut production with fertilizer remain inadequate. Linear programming analysis confirms that the "optimal" peanut production technology at present is to forego fertilizer and increase peanut seeding densities well beyond recommended levels – this provides maximum yields and maximum net income (Diagana et al. 1995). The lack of incentive for fertilizer use lies in the worsening price ratio between peanut and fertilizer prices, as well as liquidity constraints at the farm level for purchase of fertilizer.[5] In turn, we hypothesize that these demand-side constraints are among the factors undermining the successful take-off of private fertilizer marketing.

That the profitability of peanuts increased relative to other crops such as millet, sorghum, maize, and cowpeas (both with and without fertilizer) contributed to the sharp 21 percent increase in land planted to peanuts immediately following the devaluation. The linear programming results simply confirm that the devaluation has not reversed the pre-devaluation problem of low fertilizer use and movement toward higher peanut seeding densities-both of which lead to soil exhaustion and ultimately, lower yields.

The devaluation also lowered incentives to produce irrigated rice and to use urea in the Senegalese River Basin. Unlike peanut fertilizer, which is produced using large amounts of local phosphates and smaller amounts of imported nitrogen and

---

[5] For Senegal, Gaye (1992) shows that farmers' demand for fertilizer is more sensitive to changes in output/input price ratios than to net returns. Sharp declines in the ratio in the mid-1980s led to drastic reductions in fertilizer consumed by farmers in the Peanut Basin despite economic analyses showing that fertilizer remained profitable in the southern Peanut Basin with average value/cost ratios greater than 5 (Kelly 1988). Farmers' reliance on fertilizer output/input price ratios can be explained by the difficulty of estimating net returns for this input which exhibits highly variable interannual yield responses. Where farmers' reliance on input/output price ratios does not foster input use decisions that maximize net returns over time, policy interventions may be required to improve the farmgate appeal.

potassium, urea is entirely imported. As a result, its post-devaluation price represented a 90 percent increase due to the combination of the devaluation and changes in world market prices. The increase in urea costs, when combined with smaller but important increases in seed, pesticide, and irrigation costs (primarily imported fuel for pumps), caused net income per hectare of irrigated rice to fall from a pre-devaluation level of 139,000 FCFA to a post-devaluation level of 69,000 FCFA (BAME/ISRA 1995).

3 Lessons Learned: Implications for Policy

(1) There is a pressing need to improve access to soil-fertility enhancing inputs and incentives to use them. Input use in the Sahel has historically been promoted in ways that are not economically sound or fiscally sustainable in the long run. Yet the reduction of government programs and subsidies associated with structural adjustment appears to have discouraged the use of modern inputs (improved seed, fertilizer, animal traction), by raising cost and reducing availability.

The upshot is that farm input costs must be reduced without returning to fiscally unsustainable and generalized subsidies. We advocate a "middle path" between fiscally unsustainable government outlays and complete government withdrawal from support to agriculture. This middle path implies substantial public and private investment in agricultural research, human capital, and production and market infrastructure. In certain situations, where it is fiscally possible and justified by risk considerations and potential net benefits to farmers and to society, the reinstitution of selected subsidies for fertilizer use and soil conservation investments should be considered. Thus the debate should be reopened on identifying cost-effective ways of increasing access to inputs, by improving the delivery of inputs and enabling farmers to acquire the means to pay for them. This effort is especially appropriate in the countries of the Sahel, whose macroeconomic environment has become more favorable through structural adjustment.

(2) Macroeconomic policies are not enough to spur sustainable capital-led intensification. To improve the incentives for farmers to invest, improved political stability and improved macroeconomic conditions – "getting prices right" – the two foci of policy attention in the past 15 years, are *necessary but not* sufficient to induce the crucial farm investments outlined above, and to spur higher agricultural productivity. Governments are wrestling with policy changes associated with structural adjustment, which usually is a mixed bag of new incentives and disincentives from the farmers' perspective. But a long-term policy perspective is needed by governments in order to promote rural capital formation over the long haul. A strategic vision to promote investment will require greater coordination of agricultural, employment, and industrial policies.

Impacts from prices of outputs and inputs must be considered in tandem. If more investment in sustainable intensification is the goal, policymakers must ensure that devaluation does not make "extensive" cultivation more profitable than intensive cultivation. There is a strong risk of this as modern inputs tend to be imported and prices will rise with devaluation.

Innovations that aim at decreasing risk and increasing affordability of the investments, and the incentive and capacity of farmers to undertake them are important – especially in the domain of infrastructure, credit, and institutional policy.

(3) Ensuring adequate soil fertility is a sine qua non of sustainable intensification. The availability and affordability of the following three sources of fertility need special attention.

Chemical fertilizer. Reduction of the fertilizer subsidy in various study countries (Burkina, Senegal) over the 1980s coincided with a decrease in its use. Because fiscal constraints prohibit a return to the days of large fertilizer subsidies, programs and policies are needed to get cheaper fertilizer to farmers in a more cost-effective manner.

A key way to do this is to reduce transport costs and improve the quantity and quality of rural infrastructure. For example, a study of potential impacts of devaluation in Burkina Faso by the Prime Minister's Office (1993) shows that fertilizer costs can be greatly lowered through improving the transport system and infrastructure.

Other complementary public investments can also reduce the risk and increase the profitability of fertilizer use – for example better water management and associated infrastructure.

Moreover, country-specific studies of selective fertilizer subsidies are needed (a taboo subject in the 1980s but a debate that needs to be revisited now). Agronomic research on fertilizer response (particularly the possibility of using locally produced phosphates) needs to be updated. Cost/benefit analyses are needed of the subsidy levels that would be required to increase fertilizer use to more agronomically and economically appropriate levels. Both the agronomic and the economic analysis should take into account the risk associated with fertilizer use, to avoid overestimating the beneficial effects. Both private and social costs and benefits must be considered.

There is a strong need to address fertilizer issues with national programs rather than many disparate programs sponsored by bilateral and multilateral donors.

Study and promotion of the fertilizer/lime subsector are needed. The focus should be on constraints to private sector production and marketing of inputs. Government regulations and licensing requirements that inhibit fertilizer imports should be examined and, if need be, eased or eliminated.

Organic matter. Manure is an important complement to fertilizer for restoring soil fertility in areas undergoing intensification. Moreover, research in Africa has shown the merits of green manure and forage crops. Their introduction into agropastoral systems leads to better integration of farming and livestock husbandry, and greater soil fertility.

Animal traction programs. Animal traction is very important in many parts of the Sahel because of its value in reducing on-field labor requirements and allowing area expansion – and its value in increasing yields and pursuing intensification and facilitating incorporation of manure and fertilizer (illustrated in the MSU productivity study in Burkina Faso, Savadogo et al. 1994 and 1995).

As discussed for Senegal, there is a need to reexamine the state of animal traction equipment and repair in areas that had successful programs in the 1970s; there is need for new manufacture and repair capacity locally, which can be tied into small enterprise and rural employment programs.

(4) Improving farmers' capacity to invest is crucial. Farmers need cash to buy materials, to buy animals, and to hire labor for productivity and conservation investments. In practice, the three major sources of cash are noncropping activity, cash cropping, and credit. Individual sources of cash have become *critical* after the dismantlement of many public credit programs in rural areas of Africa in the 1980s.

Rural income diversification into noncropping activities. Promotion of small rural nonfarm enterprises and the rural labor market is important for several reasons. First, such enterprises provide rural employment; they can also provide farm inputs. Second, noncropping activities increase the demand for crops through downstream production linkages. Third, the income provided by noncropping activities reduces pressure on the land by relieving households of the need to earn a livelihood entirely from farming. Fourth, noncropping income can be an important source of cash for farm investments.

Reardon et al. (1994a) show that in the Sahel, noncropping income constitutes roughly one half of rural incomes, and some two-thirds of cash income. Unfortunately, noncropping income is poorly distributed and the poor need help to start off-farm businesses or find off-farm employment. Industrial location and small enterprise promotion policies should focus on providing greater noncropping income-earning opportunities in fragile zones experiencing severe land constraints and soil degradation, and to the poor. In agroclimatically more favorable zones where agriculture is more dynamic, such policies could promote nonfarm enterprises linked to agriculture. For example, in Senegal, Kelly et al. (1995) recommended programs promoting animal traction equipment manufacture and repair, processing of peanuts and cotton, and livestock feeding enterprises that sell manure and hides for local processing. Input delivery could also be improved by supporting microenterprises that provide inputs and services (e.g., repair services for animal traction).

Agricultural diversification into cash crops (food and nonfood). We found in our case studies that cash cropping is crucial to both the incentives and capacity for farmers to make productivity and conservation investments in both cash crop and food staple production. Moreover, credit programs organized by cash crop schemes, and cash income from cash cropping, allowed farmers to: (1) acquire fertilizer in Burkina Faso through cotton cropping; (2) acquire animal traction equipment in Mali through cotton cropping; (3) acquire equipment in Senegal through peanut cropping.

Improving access to credit. Innovative credit programs are needed. Improving capital/credit markets will increase access to farm and nonfarm activity inputs for the poor. To take advantage of farm/nonfarm linkages in areas where nonfarm income is reinvested in the farm, credit could be provided for nonfarm activities. This is especially attractive given that experience has shown that it is difficult to design economically viable financial institutions to directly fund agricultural projects; the covariate risk problem is at the heart of this difficulty. Note, however, that whether a credit program for a specific crop can be successful depends on the returns, risk, and sustainability of the market for that crop. Crops with strong external demand, and that are profitable (e.g., cotton, horticulture) have had successful credit programs associated with them.

Credit programs that help cushion farmers from risk (e.g., by allowing variable interest rates or rescheduling after bad harvests), should also be investigated. An innovative approach would be to *link input use and natural resource management programs*, perhaps with the help of extension services. For example, one could tie fertilizer credit to evidence of improved natural resource management practices, such as composting.

(5) Public investment in complementary infrastructure is critical to make farm capital investments affordable and attractive.

Complementary investments by villages, NGOs, national governments, and donors in physical infrastructure at the village or regional level can be crucial in facilitating profitable on-farm investments. Critical infrastructure includes roads, culverts, and wells. Investment bottlenecks due to lack of such infrastructure need to be identified and addressed (Reardon 1995).

Public interventions that demonstrate to farmers the practical payoff to conservation investments are critical to reducing the perception of riskiness. Moreover, community institutional arrangements to reduce the problem of externalities undermining private incentives to investment are important.

Some new practices that are not strictly capital investments at the farm level (say, integrated pest management), may be relatively cheap (in cash) for the farmer, but only if there are prior outlays by the community or the State for extension and other "soft infrastructure" and possibly substantial increases in labor outlay on the farm (Reardon et al. 1992).

We are worried, however, that the current focus by donors and NGOs on the "local participation" approach carries with it the danger of not addressing directly the key incentive and structural constraints on farm investment. Community action and local participation can be useful and successful *if* they address underlying infrastructural and economic constraints that households and communities face in pursuing their primary objectives – attaining food security and avoiding income shortfalls – especially when they are poor and do not have any "margin to maneuver." *If not*, even if they are aimed at objectives that can benefit local communities and the outside world in the long run, they will fail.

Moreover, combining programs that meet immediate food security goals with construction of these complementary investments is key: a case in point are local *food-for-work* projects if the community lacks sufficient resources (von Braun et al. 1992). Relief programs could be designed to provide farm inputs and complementary infrastructure rather than just food aid.

Acknowledgment

We thank the United States Agency for International Development (AFR/SD/PSGE/FSP and AFR/WA) for funding this work under the Michigan State University Food Security II Cooperative Agreement managed by the AID/Global Bureau, Office of Agriculture and Food Security.

References

BAME/ISRA. 1995. "Etude de l'impact de la dévaluation du franc CFA sur les revenus et la sécurité alimentaire au Sénégal: contribution du BAME/ISRA" mimeo, presented at the Atelier Régional du PRISAS sur Impact de la Dévaluation du Franc CFA sur les Revenus et la Sécurité Alimentaire en Afrique de L'Ouest, July, Bamako.

Binswanger, H.P. 1986. "Evaluating Research System Performance and Targeting Research in Land-abundant Areas of Sub-Saharan Africa." *World Development,* Volume 14, Number 4. April, pp. 469-476.

Boserup, Esther. 1965. *The Conditions of Agricultural Growth: The Economics of Agrarian Change Under Population Pressure.* Chicago: Aldine.

von Braun, T. Teklu, and P. Webb. 1992. Labour-intensive public works for food security in Africa: Past experience and future potential. *International Labour Review.* Vol. 131, no. 1. pp. 19-33.

Coulibaly, B.S., O. Sanogo, and D. Mariko. 1995. "Cas du coûts de production du paddy à l'Office du Niger," mimeo, paper presented at the Atelier Régional du PRISAS Sur l'Impact de la Dévaluation du FCFA sur les Revenus et la Sécurité Alimentaire en Afrique de l'Ouest, July, Bamako.

Diagana, B.N., V. Kelly, and A.A. Fall. 1995. "Dévaluation du franc CFA et décisions de production agricole: une analyse empirique de l'impact de la dévaluation du franc CFA sur les choix de culture et de technologies de production par les ménages ruraux du Bassin Arachidier du Sénégal" mimeo, presented at the Atelier Régional du PRISAS sur Impact de la Dévaluation du Franc CFA sur les Revenus et la Sécurité Alimentaire en Afrique de L'Ouest, June, Bamako.

Dione, J. 1989. *Informing Food Security Policy in Mali: Interactions Between Technology, Institutions, and Market Reforms*. Ph.D. Thesis, Michigan State University.

Gaye, M. 1992. "Les recherches sur l'économie de la production agricole dans le Bassin Arachidier: synthèse des acquis de 1986 à 1992." Kaolack: Institut Sénégalais de Recherches Agricoles.

Gaye, M. and M. Sene. 1994. Les fortes densités de sémis de l'arachide au Sénégal: motivations paysannes et interprétation agronomique. Kaolack: ISRA. Mimeo.

Kelly, V.A. 1988. *Factors Affecting the Demand for Fertilizer in Senegal's Peanut Basin*, Ph.D. Dissertation, Michigan State University.

Kelly, V., B. Diagana, T. Reardon, M. Gaye, E. Crawford. 1995. *Cash crop and foodgrain productivity in Senegal: Historical view, new survey evidence, and policy implications*. MSU Staff Paper No. 95-05, January.

Mendez del Villar, P. and L. Diakité. 1995. "Impact de la dévaluation du franc CFA sur la filière irrigué au Mali," mimeo, paper presented at the Atelier Régional du PRISAS Sur l'Impact de la Dévaluation du FCFA sur les Revenus et la Sécurité Alimentaire en Afrique de l'Ouest, July, Bamako.

Premier Ministère. 1993. L'impact probable de la dévaluation du Franc CFA sur l'économie du Burkina Faso, Ouagadougou, Burkina Faso. December.

Reardon, T. 1995. "Sustainability Issues for Agricultural Research Strategies in the Semi-Arid Tropics: Focus on the Sahel," *Agricultural Systems*, Vol. 48, no. 3, pp. 345-360.

Reardon, T., and V. Kelly. 1989. "Impact of Liquidity Sources on Chemical Fertilizer Use in Semi-Arid West Africa," Select Paper, mimeo, AAEA 1989 Meetings.

Reardon, T., A.A. Fall, V. Kelly, C. Delgado, P. Matlon, J. Hopkins, and O. Badiane. 1994a. "Is income diversification agriculture-led in the West African Semi-Arid Tropics? The nature, causes, effects, distribution, and production linkages of off-farm activities," in A. Atsain, S. Wangwe, and A.G. Drabek (editors) *Economic Policy Experience in Africa: What Have We Learned?* African Economic Research Consortium, Nairobi, Kenya.

Reardon, T., V. Kelly, E. Crawford, K. Savadogo, T. Jayne. 1994b. *Raising Farm Productivity in Africa to Sustain Long-Term Food Security*. MSU Staff Paper no. 94-77.

Reardon, T., E. Crawford, and V. Kelly. 1995. *Promoting Farm Investment for Sustainable Intensification of African Agriculture*. International Development Paper no. 18. Michigan State University.

Reardon, T., Islam, N., and M. Benoit-Cattin. 1992. "Questions sur la durabilité pour la recherche agricole en Afrique," *Les cahiers de la recherche developpement* (CIRAD, France), no. 30, June.

Savadogo, K., T. Reardon, and K. Pietola. 1994. Farm productivity in Burkina Faso: Effects of animal traction and nonfarm income. *American Journal of Agricultural Economics* 76(August).

Savadogo, K., T. Reardon, and K. Pietola. 1995. "Mechanization and Agricultural Supply Response in the Sahel: A Farm-Level Profit Function Analysis," *Journal of African Economies*, vol. 4, no. 3, December, pp. 336-377.

Part 3.2

Policy and Institutional Framework
Institutions

Financial Innovations Combat Food Insecurity of the Rural Poor: The Case of Cameroon

Gertrud Schrieder
Institute for Agricultural Economics and Social
Science in the Tropics and Subtropics
University of Hohenheim, 70593 Stuttgart, Germany

Abstract

Cameroon's overall food self-sufficiency rate equals 96 %. Nevertheless, chronic and transitory food insecurities still exist. Natural calamities and population density are the prime causes for Cameroon's food insecurity problem.

The underlying hypothesis of this paper is that notwithstanding natural constraints and population pressure, the food security of Cameroon's rural population can be improved by accessible financial markets. This implies the existence, adoption and diffusion of financial innovations.

The role of technical innovations and their diffusion in the process of economic development has long been recognized. Institutional innovations, and among them innovations in the financial system, have received greater attention in development economics only during the last three decades. This paper highlights the food security improving effect of innovations in the financial system. It also assesses the adoption and diffusion process of specific financial innovations in the formal as well as informal financial sector and different organizational forms.

The paper shows that access to financial services can improve the food security situation of the rural poor. It also demonstrates for the country case of Cameroon, how financial organizations of the formal and informal sector adapt, adopt and diffuse financial innovations. The paper concludes by formulating financial market policies that allow for innovations, particularly in relation to rural finance and food security aspects.

Keywords

Financial market innovations, rural financial services, food security, Cameroon

1   Introduction

Cameroon's overall food self-sufficiency rate equals 96 %. Nevertheless, chronic and transitory food insecurities still exist. Natural calamities and population density are generally accepted as the primary causes for Cameroon's food insecurity problem.

The underlying hypothesis of this paper is that, notwithstanding natural constraints and population pressure, the food security of Cameroon's rural population can be improved by accessible financial markets. The term accessible financial market implies the existence, adoption and diffusion of financial system innovations, especially financial organization and product innovations.

For the mass of the rural poor, the formal financial sector is inaccessible due to its exclusive institutional infrastructure and financial products. This has two effects on the food security of the rural poor. First, having no access to financial means to bridge temporary, often seasonal food shortages results in deficient human productivity due to mal- and undernutrition. Lower labor productivity and income losses are the consequence. This can lead to chronic food insecurity if human productive capacity is lost in the long run. Secondly, an income shortfall and inaccessibility to financial services can undermine the ability of rural households to invest in agriculture which may sap long-term food security. Non-investment in agriculture or alternative income-earning rural activities reduces future income streams and consecutively endangers food security in the long run.

The role of technical innovations and their diffusion in the process of economic development has been recognized since the works of Marx, Schumpeter and Kuznets. Institutional innovations and among them financial system innovations have received greater attention in development economics only during the last three decades. This paper highlights the food security improving effects of financial system innovations. It also assesses the adoption and diffusion process of specific financial innovations in the formal as well as informal financial sector.

First, this paper presents a literature review of financial services aimed at improving the food security of the rural poor. It then continues to examine empirical evidence, indicating that access to financial services has a positive effect on food security. With respect to Cameroon, the paper progresses in demonstrating how financial intermediaries from the formal and informal sector adapt, adopt and diffuse financial innovations at the institutional and product levels. The conclusion comprises recommendations for financial system policies that allow for innovations in relation to rural finance.

2   Literature Review of Financial Innovations Aiming at Food Security

It is now recognized that financial innovations are crucial in the economic development process. The transitions in financial engineering as well as the revised attitude of rural financial institutions (RFI) towards poor clients' financial service demands prompted RFIs to cater financial innovations to the poorer clientele segment.

2.1 Definition of Financial Innovation

Generally, innovations are defined as new ideas, behaviors, or products that are substantially different from existing ones (Engel 1993; von Stein 1991). Financial innovations in the sense of technical progress comprise the development of new products (services) or changes in the process, organization and market systems that raise efficiency. The cost decreasing effect of financial innovations, in practice, may be difficult to assess, particularly if the costs are shifted from the finance institutions to the client (Burkett 1988).

2.2 Categories of Financial Innovations

Financial intermediation is influenced by the macro, organization, and micro levels of the financial system. Accordingly, development economics can categorize financial innovations as (1) financial system, (2) organization, (3) processing, and (4) product innovations (Schrieder and Heidhues 1995; von Stein 1991). Due to the pertinence of environmental issues and the possible contribution of financial engineering for sustainable resource management, innovations in (5) environmental banking, may also become more important.

Each of these five financial innovation categories has the potential to improve food security. Financial system innovations can improve market integration and expand customer coverage; organization innovations can ameliorate service accessibility for the poor; process innovations are cost reducing and increase efficiency; product innovations can ameliorate the banking institution's orientation towards customers' demands; and environmental banking innovations can promote investments in sustainable economic development and resource management (Schrieder and Heidhues 1995; Schrieder 1996).

2.3 Financial Innovations' Contribution to Food Security

Access to adequate food in quantity and quality at the household level is largely governed by income and purchasing power. Thus, households frequently apply the following four strategies to improve their food security: income generation and diversification, saving and dis-saving (in kind and in cash), borrowing, and inter-household gift exchange. Financial services play an important role in the first three of these strategies (von Braun 1992).

Financial engineering that is adapted, accessible and sustainable can contribute to clients' income generation and food security by offering:

- production credit to finance income/wealth-creating investments and inputs,
- consumption credit to maintain and expand human productive capacity,

- quality savings schemes to manage year-round liquidity, and
- insurance schemes to cope with personal and local covariate risks (Schrieder and Heidhues 1995; Zeller 1995).

Innovative financial engineering for the rural poor has common characteristics. The following review of RFIs with an innovative financial engineering concept shows that they almost always comprise savings programs, diverse credit services and client adapted collateral schemes (Schrieder and Heidhues 1995; Zeller et al. 1996).

Financial system innovations: Financial innovations can relate to the finance system as a whole. Innovations of this category that may affect the food security of the rural clientele are, for example, changes in the legal and regulatory framework, the establishment of new finance organizations and alterations of existing operations and service structures (Schrieder and Heidhues 1995; von Stein 1991). An effective financial system innovation that is likely to improve food security is the incorporation of group finance schemes[1], a new organizational form of formal financial intermediation in poverty-oriented banking enterprises. Successful examples of the group finance approach (e.g. the linkage banking of AFRACA) show that the integration of informal financial banking outlets is not only a method to effectively reach the poor but also to improve the financial viability of the formal intermediary (Christen et al. 1994; Hossain 1988; Wolff 1994). Also, group financing replaces capital assets with group liability as loan collateral. In not requiring capital assets, it is particularly suited for the poor and food insecure clientele. Furthermore, the group lending package is frequently tied to contractual savings mobilization (Ellsäßer and Diop 1990; Hossain 1988; Christen et al. 1994; Krahnen and Schmidt 1994).This increases the self-financing potential and raises credit access by expanding the debt capacity of the clientele. Scholars in development economics have long stressed this effect as the best indication for effective financial intermediation (Adams et al. 1984).

Financial organization innovations: The term financial organization innovation refers to changes in the structure and legal form of an organization. The transformation of an informal financial association into a registered and officially recognized association or formal financial organization is such an innovation (e.g., Izumida 1992). There are several promising examples of such innovations, e.g., the Grameen Bank, the village banks in Mali and Burkina Faso, and the Mutuelles Communautaires de Croissance (MC2) in Cameroon (Ellsäßer and Diop 1990; Hossain 1988; Schrieder 1995). The Burkinabé village bank program, for example, accomplished a measurable increase in savings capacity

---

[1] For a more detailed description of the advantages and risks of group lending refer to Holt and Ribe 1991; Hossain 1988; and Schmidt and Zeitinger 1994.

among its clientele that was totally decapitalized prior to the program. This is a clear indication for improved food security, since part of the financial income can now be set aside for future consumption or investments instead of immediate consumption.

Processing innovations: Processing innovations focus on improving administrational, organizational and service distribution aspects of financial organizations. Processing innovations in rural finance include simplifying financial transactions. A processing innovation in the area of improved marketing would be a participatory client approach (Heidhues 1992). To ensure that process innovations are beneficial to the rural poor, the target group ought to be included in the design of rural institution building (Schrieder and Heidhues 1995).

A recently tested analytical tool to adapt financial service profiles to the actual demand of the rural target clientele is the Conjoint Analysis (CA). CA is a consumer and marketing research method that has proven its potential to effectively model a demand oriented future reality of financial services that could improve the income and food security of the poor (Schrieder 1996). The introduction of personal computers to facilitate the task of administration and monitoring in micro-finance programs for the poor is a classic processing innovation. A micro-enterprise lending program in Egypt run by the Alexandria Business Association is completely computerized. This keeps lending costs down and allows a tight control of loan recovery. Due to the computerized administration, loan officers can leave their desks in the late morning to follow up with their clients (Adams 1995b).

Product innovations: Financial product innovations are defined as new or modified financial services that have not existed in the market before or differ substantially from existing ones (Engel 1993; Franzen 1988; von Stein 1991). Product innovations play a critical role in rural financial engineering that aims at alleviating rural poverty (Schrieder 1996; Zeller et al. 1996). An often emphasized product innovation is the introduction of flexible savings facilities in rural financial intermediation. At the household level, savings schemes reduce the risk of seasonal income shortfalls since stress periods can be bridged through dis-saving. Rural finance schemes that offer savings contracts are important in improving the capital and income situation of the poor (World Bank 1989 and 1990). Micro-finance programs that offer insurance services, such as BRAC in Bangladesh (Jahangir and Zeller 1995), adopted a product innovation that is more and more asked for by the rural population (World Bank 1989). Furthermore, there is a market opportunity to develop contractual savings arrangements that can function like life and health insurance or pension provision. Premature use of contractual insurance and pension funds should be discouraged but not foreclosed (Schrieder and Heidhues 1995).

Environmental banking innovations: Environmental banking innovations fall most often into one of the above categories. Due to the particular importance of sustainable economic development and resource management, however, innovations in environmental banking are presented separately. Investment has a vital role to play in correct resource management. Through appropriate financial engineering, the environmental direction and thus the productive sustainability of investments can be influenced (Gudger and Barker 1993). An environmental banking innovation at the level of a banking organization is the introduction of an environmental cost-benefit analysis or the less stringent environmental impact assessment (EIA). EIA is an analytic tool that evaluates the likely environmental effects arising from a planned activity. By this means, a financial intermediary could assess the social, economic, and environmental consequences of its lending decisions. Introducing a system of environmental cost-benefit analysis into banks' operating procedures would clearly have far-reaching practical and theoretical implications. With regard to the former, there is the problem of mitigating the inherent clash between commercial gain and social need. In the long run, however, banks would clearly benefit from a broader investment approach since a well managed environment gives rise to a healthy economy and population (Gudger and Barker 1993; UNEP 1993).

3   The Effect of Rural Financial Services on Food Security: Empirical Evidence[2]

Access to appropriate rural financial innovations induces purchasing power and a higher risk capacity. Thus, it promotes the rural poor's access to innovative technology. Subsequently, it generates income and alleviates poverty and food insecurity.

This section describes the impact of diffused financial services from the formal and informal sector on the rural poor's food consumption, based on data from an empirical study in Cameroon.[3] Schrieder and Heidhues (1995) show that the adoption of financial services has a mixed impact on food security, depending on short- or long-term time-frames. On a short-term basis (season by season), debt servicing obligations tend to reduce consumption, although not significantly. On a longer-term basis (year by year), loan access has a positive, but not consistently significant impact on food consumption. Thus, access by the poor to credit facilities must be conceptionalized on a lasting basis to be effective in terms of

---

[2] This section draws strongly on Schrieder and Heidhues (1995).

[3] In the framework of the IFPRI/University of Hohenheim Project 'Credit for the rural poor in sub-Saharan Africa', a detailed micro-economic survey was conducted from October 1991 to September 1992 in Cameroon. Among other econometric analyses, the consumed calories per adult-respondent were put in causal relation to socio-economic explanatory variables.

food consumption stabilization. Based on the Cameroon study, this reasoning is supported by the fact that sustainable access to informal sources of credit increase consumption at a significance level of at least 15 %. Participation in informal institutions is generally based on a long-term commitment. Therefore, the seeds of debt and risk capacity planted by financial and insurance services have time to flourish.

Women appear to invest an important share of their loans in family nutrition which causes a positive effect on calories consumed (5 - 12 % significance level). This is a compelling finding, considering that the share of women's income in total household income does not necessarily influence consumption positively (Schrieder 1996). It also indicates that women are generally liquidity constrained and that rural financial intermediation must account for the female customer segment when diffusing its services.

Loan financed human capital investments, such as education, food and health have a significant and positive impact on long-term food consumption. Human capital investment has a positive effect not only on future consumption but also on income. Under such circumstances, consumption loan schemes ought to be integrated in financial programs aimed at improving the living standards of their clientele.

The empirical analysis of the relationship between financial intermediation and food consumption indicates that households with a high dependency ratio and sickness occurrence consume significantly fewer calories than others. This suggests that a poverty oriented financial intermediation framework should also track the improvement of the social and health security of its target clientele. This could be done by experimenting with innovative insurance schemes (Schrieder and Heidhues 1995).

The empirical results presented in this section support the hypothesis that food security relates to financial market access and the adoption level of innovations in the financial system. Access to sustainable and appropriate financial services improves income and, in turn, income has a positive and significant impact on the rural households' food security.

4 Adaptation, Adoption and Diffusion of Financial Innovations: The Case of Cameroon

The financial systems in developing countries have undergone substantial changes over the last two decades. Apart from the lessons learned from formal financial sector failures and the thriving of the informal sector, the rapid transition in financial engineering prompted most developing countries to reshape their approach to financial system development, particularly their attitude towards poverty-oriented microfinance.

4.1 Informal Finance

Informal financial organizations use different financial intermediation strategies than formal ones. Financial services from informal intermediaries are indigenously developed and thus closely adapted to the demands of their clientele. In contrast to formal financial services, they are continuously and flexibly adjusted to the changing socio-economic environment and client demands.

Schrieder (1996) interviewed 109 leaders of Cameroonian informal financial associations (IFA) in 1991/92 regarding organizational changes to assess whether IFAs are actually as flexible as they are often quoted to be in the literature. Almost 25 % of the group leaders stated having changed their organizational structure or adopted a new service at least once, and 11 % mentioned two changes/innovations during the past five years. Table 1 depicts the financial innovations recalled by the group leaders.

Table 1 shows that the majority of the innovations mentioned by the group leaders fall into the category of innovations related to the organization. More than 45% (17 groups) of the IFA sub-sample introduced financial innovations by changing their organizational structure. Pure savings associations adopted credit services, meaning they became savings and credit associations (27 %; 8 groups). This may be an indication that the members of the association demanded access to a loan facility to supplement their own resources. About 16 % (6 groups) of the associations changed their organizational structure from rotating (RoSCA) to non-rotating savings and credit associations (Non-RoSCA). This structural change mitigates a disadvantage of RoSCAs, namely, their inability to provide continuous access to member loans. A RoSCA only provides a loan to a member once in a group's cycle. A Non-RoSCA is more able to satisfy multiple loan demands by one member (Tankou and Adams 1995). This organizational innovation allows increased flexibility of the group's credit service, eventually a more efficient allocation of its funds, and finally larger incremental income gains through high return investments.

The most prominent product innovation concerns the insurance service of the groups. More than 15 % of the IFAs that had reported to have adopted innovations, changed their mutual aid service from in-kind to in-cash assistance. This means that the disbursement form of the insurance service changed. One can conclude that the group members had expressed a more acute demand for cash than physical insurance.

Table 1: Financial Institutional and Produce Innovations in Cameroonian IFAs

Type of innovations	First change		Second change		All changes	
	N=26	% of groups	N=12	% of groups	N[a]	% of groups
From in-kind mutual aid to in-cash	6	23.1	...	...	6	15.8
From RoSCA to Non-ROSCA	5	19.2	1	8.3	6	15.8
From savings-only to Non-RoSCA	7	26.9	1	8.3	8	21.1
From Non-RoSCA to RoSCA	1	3.8	...	...	1	2.6
Introduction of emergency fund, fine system or joint business	5	19.3	6	50.0	11	29.0
Transitory emergency fund or fine system	1	3.8	2	16.7	3	7.9
Acceptance of women members	...	...	1	8.3	1	2.6
Community level registration	...	...	1	8.3	1	2.6
Reduction of loan term	1	3.8	...	...	1	2.6
Total	26	99.9[b]	12	99.9[b]	38	100.0

Source: University of Hohenheim/IFPRI, Credit for the Poor in Cameroon, Own Data, 1991/92
Notes: ... = not applicable;
[a] 'N' refers to the total number of organizational changes, not to the absolute number of groups that had changes.
[b] Numbers may not add up to 100 % because of rounding.

IFAs in Cameroon frequently administer premia funded insurance funds (62%), the so called emergency and mutual aid funds (Schrieder 1989 and 1996, Tankou and Adams 1995; Zeller et al. 1996). The emergency fund covers unexpected and urgent expenditures of members. It is primarily called upon to cover personal risks such as sickness, death, and other social expenses. Furthermore, it is used to cover contributions of group defaulters and to assist members that are temporarily unable to meet their savings obligations. The mutual aid fund provides help for the same circumstances as the emergency fund. Financial assistance from the emergency fund, however, ought to be repaid, although mostly interest free, in contrast to mutual aid. While the emergency fund is mainly an insurance substitute, the mutual aid fund is a genuine form of member-financed insurance. Schrieder (1996) found that 61 and 13 % of the associations (N = 109) insure personal risks by providing mutual aid or emergency funds, respectively.

Also more sophisticated Cameroonian RoSCAs overcome the financial intermediation inefficiency, namely their incapacity of allocating funds most efficiently, by applying a bids-technique to determine the rotation of their funds (Schrieder 1989; Tankou and Adams 1995). Funds are allocated most efficiently if they go to the group member who has the highest expected marginal return from the use of additional cash. However, the simpler RoSCAs typically determine the allocation of their funds by lot or on the basis of need perceived by the group leader, There may be a mismatch between those who receive the funds in a given rotation and who has the investment opportunity with the highest expected rate of return (Tankou and Adams 1995).

4.2   Formal Finance

Formal financial institutions, such as commercial banks and cooperatives, have begun only recently and tentatively to adjust their organizational and product profiles to the demands of the rural clientele. Often these services are somewhat adopted from the informal sector. Nevertheless, several financial innovations and their impact on the clientele of three formal Cameroonian institutions – the Crédit Agricole du Cameroun (CAC), the Caisse Communautaire de Crédit et d'Epargne (CCEI Bank), and the Cameroon Cooperative Credit Union League (CamCCUL) – are more closely assessed. While CamCCUL offered rural financial intermediation right from its foundation in 1968, the relatively new universal banks CAC and CCEI introduced their rural banking only in 1991. The financial depth (available banking outlets per 10,000 persons) of CamCCUL compared to Cameroon's banking sector is 0.319 credit unions (in 1993) to 0.137 bank branches (in 1990) per 10,000 persons. Due to the near collapse of commercial banks since 1990, the financial depth relation of credit unions to banks must have shifted even more towards CamCCUL (Schrieder 1996).

CAC: CAC has launched a pilot project for rural financial institution building. It founded its first CAC village bank (Caisse Locale: CL) in 1991. The CLs build on already existing local organizations and elites, and must register with the governmental authority at the sub-division. The CLs comprise multiple savings and credit groups that unite the individual village bank members, and design then financial and organizational regulations according to specific demands. This may include the provision of productive and consumption loans. The CAC intervenes in the transactions of the CLs only in the sense of monitoring and technical assistance. Although the concept appears promising, there exist just a couple of CLs to this day that are affiliated to CAC. While in the beginning the results were encouraging, these CLs are mal-functioning in terms of loan repayment and self-administration. CAC has attempted to adapt this concept by designating special staff to this task and by cooperating with local NGOs that are experienced in working with village groups. According to CAC, one problem of the CLs is their "ethnic isolation". This is to say that bank staff that enjoys the trust of CLs in one region will not necessarily associate successfully with CLs in a different region due to ethnic animosity.

In May 1994, the CAC started to operate its own professional training center, similar to the German apprenticeship system with 25 apprentices that were trained in the banking business. The training period is two years, thus, the first lot should have started working full-time in 1996. CAC expects to obtain qualified and loyal bank personnel by means of this outstanding institutional innovation.

CCEI Bank: The CCEI Bank has adopted financial organization as well as product innovations. One of the organization innovations, the Mutuelles Communautaires de Croissance (MC2), has good potential to diffuse demanded financial services to the rural target population. In addition, CCEI has a Research & Study Division in its headquarters to follow up the new developments in financial engineering.

In 1995, 10 MC2 already existed and 14 were in the planning phase (Bomda 1995).The MC2 are micro-banks that are linked to the central bank through their affiliation to the CCEI. This is a major advantage as compared to the credit unions affiliated to CamCCUL since the latter operate under the cooperative law and, thus, have no access to the credit refinancing lines of the central bank (Schrieder 1995). The MC2 are generally launched by the CCEI together with the urban elite in their village of origin. The CCEI subsidizes its MC2 through technical assistance. The urban elite generally buys shares of the MC2 to make it operational, knowing that the operation will experience losses in the first 3 to 5 years. Furthermore, it subsidizes the micro-banks financially and through in-kind donations (e.g., furniture). Bomda (1995) found in a survey of the four MC2 in the West Province of Cameroon that already 84 % of the savings account bearers (1225) are rural and that 70 % of the mobilized shares and savings balances are of rural origin (US $ 242,90). Women constitute 16 % of the membership, 50 % of whom are rural women. Almost 100 % of the loans disbursed go to rural applicants. Presently the repayment ratio is 100 % and the investment activities are predominantly business and agriculture.

CCEI diffuses also a financial product innovation, the Flash Cash Checks (FCC) to its customers. According to bank officials, this product was designed in association with local businessmen. Based on the amount deposited in the client's Flash Cash checking account, the CCEI Bank issues FCCs of the same amount to the client. The checks have many features of traveler's checks and credit cards (Adams 1995a). As with traveler's checks, the issuing branch of CCEI registers each number of the FCCs for security purposes. Since the FCCs can be deposited to any MC2 account, urban Cameroonians with relatives in MC2 villages start to send remittances in the form of a FCC. The rural remittee must have a MC2 account to which the amount of the FCC is deposited. This transaction may take a week since each FCC is verified by CCEI headquarters. Afterwards the money can be withdrawn. This reduces traveling and accommodation expenses as well as other transaction costs since neither the remitter nor the remittee has to travel.

CamCCUL: Its cooperative structure enables CamCCUL to be close to the heartbeat of its members, to their financial service demands and to their changing socio-economic situation. Thus, CamCCUL has frequently adopted financial innovations to improve its service. Due to the popularity of Non-RoSCAs in Cameroon and their need to safeguard members' savings, CamCCUL always accepted collective group clients, even if they were not registered. The commercial banks started only in recent years to adopt this organizational innovation. A novel development is CamCCUL's application to the Ministry of Finance to open its own bank, the Union Bank (Schrieder 1995). Its members appear to have grown economically and their financial service demands have changed with their upgraded economic status. Particularly the urban clients demand more financial market integration, such as money transfer services that only a bank, not a cooperative, can furnish. CamCCUL intends to satisfy these demands by opening its own bank.

On the product side, CamCCUL offers flexible credit services that allow loans for productive as well as consumption purposes. Savings mobilization is basic to the concept of savings and credit cooperatives. Thus, CamCCUL has closely observed the financial transactions of IFAs and, a prerequisite of successful product diffusion and market success, namely compatibility. Compatibility refers to the concept that newly introduced services should be consistent with the existing values and past experiences of potential clients. CamCCUL's financial products are consistent in this sense.

Presently, CamCCUL also cooperates with the Food and Agriculture Organization (FAO) and the World Council of Credit Unions (WOCCU) regarding the installation of a computerized accounting system (processing innovation) in two of its larger credit unions. The league is already computerized (WOCCU 1994).

5   Lessons Learned

A better understanding of the complex interactions of poverty oriented financial engineering and income and food security provides guidance for financial policy and food security programs.

Cameroon's formal financial market is rich in experiences in innovative rural financial engineering. Therefore, it is surprising that the coverage of potential rural bank customers is still weak. Nevertheless, access to financial services can stabilize the poor's food consumption through the possibility of adjusting disposable income by borrowing or dis-saving. Access to adapted financial engineering services can be an efficient support instrument to complement conventional food security policies such as food prices, income and farm diversification, and food-for-work policies. Financial services may be even more efficient as they can be designed in a flexible way and customized to particular market segments.

The following comprises lessons learned regarding financial engineering in rural environments and its potential effect on food security.

Empirical evidence from all over the world has shown that innovative financial engineering in the rural microenterprise sector must account for the target clientele's demand for attractive savings schemes. However, livestock-in-kind-savings frequently generate a higher profit rate for the saver than microfinance. Therefore, microfinance programs must thrive to successfully compete financially and sociologically with in-kind savings schemes to attract customers and their savings.

Women's enterprise and household occupations and responsibilities are closely related and intertwined. Therefore, their demand for financial services is distinctly different from the male market segment. Since women are often cash-constrained, they tend to spend cash revenues on productive purposes and finance urgent consumption needs through loans. Despite their tight budgets, women honor their debt obligations. Cameroonian women, contrary to men who tend to mainly demand production loans from formal finance programs, prefer to have the option of either production or consumption loans. It is vitally important that women's service preferences are taken into account when adapting and diffusing rural financial services, especially as they produce 70 % of the staple food in sub-Saharan Africa.

It must be emphasized that the existence of a financial system and the diffusion of appropriate and poverty-oriented financial services do not substitute for public health and social insurance. Nonetheless, risk insurance is a financial service demanded by the rural poor, confirmed by informal financial sectors world-wide which often establish a complementary mutual aid/emergency member service to protect their clients from personal risks that could undermine their repayment capacity and credit worthiness. A parallel policy strategy of the public and private sector, both offering insurance services, could generate synergetic effects and the greatest benefits for the rural poor in improving their food security, health and economy.

Acknowledgement

The GTZ (Gesellschaft für Technische Zusammenarbeit) financed the research for this paper within the framework of a special project. It was carried out in close collaboration with IFPRI (International Food Policy Research Institute) in Washington, D. C. The author gratefully acknowledges the GTZ and IFPRI for their support. Furthermore, the author wishes to thank all commentators of earlier versions of this paper, particularly Dr. Kropp of the GTZ and Prof. Heidhues of the University of Hohenheim.

References

Adams, D.W. 1995a. Flash Cash in Cameroon. Columbus, OH, USA: Internet Development Finance Discussion List.

Adams, D.W. 1995b Microlending technology. Columbus, OH, USA: Internet Development Finance Discussion List.

Adams, D.W, Graham D.H. and J.D. Von Pischke (eds.). 1984. *Undermining rural development with cheap credit*. Boulder, CO, USA: Westview Press.

Bomda, J. 1995. Projet pilote de "Linkage" entre les banques et les groupes d'auto-promotion au Cameroun. Report prepared for the GTZ. Stuttgart, Germany: University of Hohenheim.

Braun, J. von. 1992. Rural credit in sub-Saharan Africa: Enabling smallholder production growth and food security. Paper prepared for the workshop on Agricultural development policy options for sub-Saharan Africa, Airlie, VA, August 23 - 25, 1992. Washington, DC, USA: International Food Policy Research Institute (IFPRI).

Burkett, Paul. 1988. Informal finance in developing countries: Lessons for the development of formal financial intermediaries. Coral Gables, FL, USA: University of Miami.

Christen, R.P., E. Rhyne, and R.C. Vogel. 1994. Maximizing the outreach of microenterprise finance: The emerging lessons of successful programs. Arlington, VA, USA: IMCC Washington Operations.

Ellsäßer, K. and M. 1990. La banque expérimentale de Banh: Une démarche de recherche-développement sur le crédit en milieu rural sahelien. Montpellier, France: DSA-CIRAD, Sahel-Action, and CNCA-Burkina Faso.

Engel, J.F., Blackwell, R.D., and P.W. Miniard. 1993. *Consumer behavior*. Seventh Edition. Fort Worth, TX, USA: The Dryden Press.

Franzen, Christopher. 1988. Finanzinnovation – was ist das? Die Bank (1): 18-20.

Gudger, W.W. and D.C. Barker. 1993. *Banking for the environment*. FAO Agricultural Services Bulletin No. 103. Rome, Italy: Food and Agricultural Organizations (FAO).

Holt, S.L. and H. Ribe. 1991. Developing financial institutions for the poor and reducing barriers to access for women. World Bank Discussion Papers No. 117. Washington, D.C., USA: The World Bank.

Hossain, M. 1988. Credit for alleviation of rural poverty: The Grameen Bank in Bangladesh. Research Report No. 66. Washington, D.C., USA: International Food Policy Research Institute (IFPRI).

Hospes, O. 1992. Evolving forms of informal finance in an Indonesian village. In *Informal finance in low-income countries*, 225-238, ed. D. W Adams and D.A. Fitchett. Boulder, CO, USA: Westview Press.

Izumida, Y. 1992. The Kou in Japan: A precursor of modern finance. In *Informal finance in low-income countries*, 165-180, ed. D. W Adams and D.A. Fitchett. Boulder, CO, USA: Westview Press.

Jahangir, A. S. M., and M. Zeller. 1995. Overview paper on rural finance programs for the poor in Bangladesh – A review of five major programs. Washington. D.C., USA: International Food Policy Research Institute (IFPRI).

Krahnen, J.P. and R.H. Schmidt. 1994. *Development finance as institution building. A new approach to poverty oriented banking*. Bolder, CO, USA: Westview Press.

Schmidt, R.H. and C.P. Zeitinger. 1994. Critical issues in small and microbusiness finance. Paper presented at the seminar on financial services and the poor: U.S. and developing country experience. Washington, D.C., USA, September 28-30, 1994. Washington, D.C., USA: The Brookings Institution.

Schrieder, G. 1996. *The role of rural finance for food security of the poor in Cameroon.* Ph.D. Thesis. Frankfurt, Germany: Peter Lang Verlag.

Schrieder, G. 1995. Innovations and TCs. Columbus, OH, USA: Internet Development Finance Discussion List.

Schrieder, G. 1989. Informal financial groups in Cameroon: Motivation, organization and linkages. M.S. Thesis. Columbus, OH, USA: The Ohio State university (OSU).

Schrieder, G. and F. Heidhues. 1995. Rural financial markets and the food security of the poor: The case of Cameroon, Savings and Development (1-2): 93-130.

Stein, J.H. von. 1991. Finanzinnovationen. Das Wirtschaftsstudium (1): 43-47.

Tankou, M. and D. W Adams. 1995. Sophisticated rotating savings and credit associations in Cameroon. *Savings and Development* (1-2): 81-92.

United Nations Environment Program (UNEP). 1993. Concepts and principles in "A statement by banks on the environment and sustainable development". Geneva, Switzerland: UNEP.

Wolff, P. 1994. Der Linkage-Ansatz im ländlichen Finanzwesen: Fallbeispiell Indonesien. Diplomarbeit. Stuttgart, Deutschland: Universität Hohenheim.

World Bank. 1989. *World development report 1989: Financial systems and development.* New York, NY, USA: Oxford University Press.

World Bank. 1990. World development report 1990: Poverty. New York, NY, USA: Oxford University Press.

World Council of Credit Unions (WOCCU). 1994. Togo & Cameroon provide leadership in computer technology. Perspectives – Monthly news. Madison, Wisconsin, USA: World Council of Credit Unions (WOCCU).

Zeller M. 1995. The demand for financial services by the rural households – Conceptual framework and empirical findings. Quarterly Journal of International Agriculture 34 (2): 149-170.

Zeller, M., Schrieder, G., Braun, J. von, and F. Heidhues. 1993. Credit for the rural poor in Sub-Saharan Africa. Financial Report to the German Agency for Technical Cooperation (GTZ). Washington, DC, USA: International Food Policy Research Institute (IFPRI).

Zeller, M., Schrieder, G., Braun, J. von, and F. Heidhues. 1996. Review of rural finance for food security of the poor: Concept and implications for research and policy. Washington, D.C., USA: International Food Policy Research Institute (IFPRI), forthcoming.

Determinants of Repayment Performance in Group-Based Credit Programs: The Cases of Bangladesh

Manohar Sharma and Manfred Zeller
International Food Policy Research Institute
17th Street, N.W., Washington, D.C. 20036, USA

Abstract

This paper analyzes the repayment of credit groups belonging to three group-based credit programs in Bangladesh: the Association for Social Advancement (ASA), the Bangladesh Rural Advancement Committee (BRAC), and the Rangpur Dinajpur Service (RDRS).

Hypotheses are drawn from economic theory relating group responsibility, and the resulting monitoring by peers, to a more effective enforcement of contractual obligations as well as to improved ability of the group as a whole to repay loans. Specific tests are performed on the following hypothesized determinants: group size, size of loans, degree of loan rationing, enterprise mix within groups, demographic characteristics, social ties and status, and occurrence of idiosyncratic shocks. Analysis is conducted using TOBIT maximum likelihood procedures. Implications for policy and institutional design are discussed.

Keywords

Credit groups, financial institutions, institutional design, Bangladesh

1 Introduction

Lending is an inherently risky enterprise because repayment of loans can seldom be fully guaranteed. For this reason, lenders devise various institutional mechanisms aimed at reducing the risk of loan default. In this context, providing credit to the rural poor who generally lack assets requires institutional innovation that combines prudent and sustainable banking principles with effective screening and monitoring strategies that are not based on physical collateral, such as land. A good example of this kind of innovation is found in Bangladesh where nongovernmental organizations have designed credit programs that employ group responsibility and peer monitoring as core principles guiding financial transactions. This has resulted in repayment rates that are very high compared to traditional collateral-based financial institutions. However, they are not uniformly high for all groups or for all institutions. What important factors affect group repayment rates within these new financial institutions? This paper attempts to provide some answers to this question and shed light on ways in which further innovation can improve the cost-effectiveness and, hence, the ultimate sustainability of these new institutions. The rest of this paper is divided into four sections. Section 2 briefly reviews repayment performance of traditional state-owned banks and those of group-based institutions in Bangladesh. Section 3 outlines the institutional structure of three such institutions – Association for Social Advancement (ASA), Bangladesh Rural Advancement Committe (BRAC), and the Rangpur Dinajpur Rural Service (RDRS) – while Section 4 presents the results of an econometric analysis of repayment behavior of a sample of 128 groups who obtained credit from these groups. Conclusions and recommendations are presented in Section 5.

2   Financial Services for the Rural Poor: Institutional Responses, Setbacks, and Reengineering

A full appreciation of the recent innovations in Bangladesh's rural financial sector is not possible without an understanding of past efforts, actions, and failures. This section describes repayment rates of traditional commercial banks and the newer group-based lending organizations, and highlights factors that have enabled group-based systems to achieve high rates of repayments even when traditional commercial banks failed miserably.

2.1   Rural Branches of Commercial Banks: Lessons on How Not to Do it

During the 1970s as well as in the 1980s, a basic assumption driving government policy seemed to be that replicating the traditional urban-based banking structure in rural areas, and fortifying it through a package of banking legislation and subsidized capital would be sufficient to kick-start a viable financial sector in the rural areas.

In 1977, for example, the replication effort took the form of the so-called "two-for-one" banking policy requiring commercial banks, all government-owned, to open two rural branches for every urban branch (Khalily and Meyer 1993). This period also saw the establishment of two specialized agricultural development banks – the Rajshahi Krishi Unnayan Bank (RAKUB) and the Bangladesh Krishi Bank (BKB) – that had specific mandates to deliver agricultural credit. Implicit in this latter decision was the realization that *some* change in banks' organizational structure was indeed necessary to make the carry-over to the rural sector. However, in reality, the basic principles of banking remained more or less unchanged: loans continued to be strictly collateral-based, incentive structures within banks allowed little incentives for managers to screen borrowers for creditworthiness, evaluate loan projects objectively, or enforce contract compliance. In addition, the ready and continuous availability of cheap funds from the central bank combined with their oligopolistic hold of the market encouraged inefficiency and impeded innovation at the institutional level. As a result, recovery rates on rural sector loans were not only low, but were steadily declining through the 1980s: from about 51% during 1981-82 to under 19% during 1992-93 (Khalily and Meyer 1993, World Bank 1995).

There were other factors exogenous to the banking system that were contributive to this environment of lax credit discipline. First, legal recourse to foreclose and liquidate collateral was, in practice, nearly impossible (World Bank 1994), especially in the agricultural sector; this greatly encouraged strategic default. Second, confusing signals created by frequent announcements of loan amnesty and interest remission programs – results of direct political interference (Khalily and Meyer 1993) – increased incentives to default even among creditworthy borrowers. Third, non-economic considerations in routine lending decisions coupled with high transactions costs made formal banks less attractive long-term partners for most small and marginal farmers. This perceived short-term association provided further incentives for strategic default. Because of these reasons, the end of the 1980s found rural branches of the state-owned banks utterly failing to carry out their mandates. Instead, the entire network of branches had metamorphosed into a structure that was no longer sustainable.

In the late 1980s, a series of actions were taken by the government to liberalize and reform the financial sector, especially under the Financial Sector Reform Project initiated in 1989. Though the impact of these reforms are not fully clear, some improvements are now starting to be discernable. For example, some check seems to have now been imposed on the unwieldy expansion of lending volume (World Bank 1995), and provisional data for 1993-94 for nationalized commercial banks indicates that recovery from the *current* year's realizable loan from the agricultural sector had increased to 56.7%. In spite of this, traditional commercial banks continue to be financially weak, largely due to their earlier reckless expansion, their inefficient organizational structure, and their lack of expertise in making sound project loans.

2.2 Innovative Group-Based Lending Organizations: Common Threads and Repayment Rates

In the late 1970s, even as the traditional commercial banks were making huge losses, a few group-based credit institutions like BRAC and the Grameen Bank were already beginning to challenge the basic paradigm of rural finance in Bangladesh. In fact, by the end of the 1980s, a number of such institutions had already gone a significant way toward demonstrating that the task of financing the poor could indeed be made feasible and sustainable. The basic institutional structures of three group-based banking systems are described in some detail in the next section. Below we point out four common threads that weave around the institutional structures of most NGO-based credit organizations.

First, credit is always provided to small groups of borrowers on the basis of joint liability and without the pledging of any physical collateral. Second, at any time, the entire group is denied further credit when outstanding arrears exist for any one of the members. Third, lending activities are supplemented by training activities in areas ranging from entrepreneurial skill development, management of micro enterprises like shop-keeping, crafts production, etc., to education on social awareness and family planning activities. Fourth, groups are required to contribute to an emergency fund that may be used when members experience household and other emergencies.

Loan recovery rates of such group-based institutions are astounding when compared to those of the commercial banks. Jahangir and Zeller (1995) have noted the recovery rates for six of them during the period 1992-93: 100% for ASA (1993); 98% for BRAC (1933) and the Grameen Bank (1993); 93% for PROSHIKA (1993); 77% for Swanirvar Bangladesh (1993); and 100% for UDDIPAN.

2.3   Why are Repayment Rates of Group-Based Organizations so Good?

Fairly recent work in institutional economics has shed considerable light on why the new group-based institutions have been able to perform so well when others failed. Drawing heavily from Zeller (1995), this is reviewed below.

In group-lending programs, the functions of screening, monitoring, and enforcement of repayment are to a large extent transferred from the bank's agent to the borrowers – the group members themselves. It is argued that groups accomplish these tasks better than the banks and therefore lead to higher repayment rates. Stiglitz (1990) and Varian (1990) discuss these perceived advantages of collective action in screening of loan applicants and monitoring of borrowers. The incentives for screening and monitoring the actions of peers arise from joint liability and the potential loss of access to future loans. The main argument is that, compared to socially and physically distant bank agents, group members can obtain, at low cost, information regarding the reputation, indebtedness and wealth of the loan applicant, and about his or her efforts to ensure the repayment of the loan. Zeller (1994) shows that members of formal groups – like informal lenders – consider a peer's indebtedness to the informal market to be a major determinant of credit rationing. Thus, group members are found to be able to access complex and sensitive information just like informal lenders. In addition, groups may also have a comparative advantage in the enforcement of loan repayment. While the formal lender usually has limited options to compel repayment from delinquent borrowers, group members can potentially employ social sanctions or seize physical collateral of the defaulter (Besley and Coate 1995). In many rural societies, including the ones in Bangladesh, nonresident bank agents have little leverage in actually going to a village and seizing collateral. Furthermore, group members appear to be in a better position to assess the reason for default, and to offer insurance services to members experiencing shocks beyond their control while sanctioning willful defaulters.

However, it is important to note that group lending may not ensure higher repayment rates at all times. First, since the risk of loan default by an individual is shared by his peers, a member may choose a riskier project compared to the project chosen in case of an individual contract. This is because the individual borrower may count on other members to repay his/her loan in their efforts to secure future loans. Bratton (1986) analyzes the repayment record of credit groups in Zimbabwe and shows that expectations about a peer's probability to repay a loan influences the loan repayment of an individual member: group loans performed better than individual loans in years of good harvest, but worse in drought years. As argued by Varian (1990), such domino-like effects may be mitigated if group members are able to exclude potentially bad borrowers. A similar line of reasoning underlies the suggestion of Stiglitz (1990) and Devereux and Fishe (1993) that there is incentive for individuals facing a similar magnitude of risk to form groups. There is also the problem of covariate shocks, especially after a drought or a flood, when impaired repayment capability of some members coincides with the equally impaired capacity of other members to bail the former out. For this reason, as Zeller (1995) emphasizes, individuals may attempt to exploit economies of risks by grouping with others whose income streams are negatively correlated with theirs. Also, sustainability of group-lending programs in areas with high covariate risks depends on the ability of the financial intermediary to reschedule the loan of defaulting members or to raise funds from borrowers during a normal year to cover such contingencies. Lastly, there is also the question of optimal group size, since groups beyond a certain size may experience increased difficulty of informational exchange and coordination; further, disincentives attached to reneging on contracts diminish as each member may expect that the effect of his/her action on other members will be diluted (Glance and Huberman 1994).

3   Structure of Group-Based Systems: the Cases of ASA, BRAC, and RDRS

This section provides some pertinent information on key institutional characteristics of the three group-based lending programs whose repayments structures are analyzed in the next section.

Credit services provided by ASA, an NGO with a large and diversified portfolio of activities, is administered through its Income Generation through Credit Program (IGDP) that was launched in 1989 (ASA 1992,1993). Only members of ASA's village groups qualify for loans. Membership of such groups is restricted only to the landless poor and borrowers are generally female. Loans are of a one-year term, repayable in fifty equal weekly installments. The size of an individual loan ranges between Tk[1] 1,000-Tk 5,000, with the average being Tk 2,500. All loans are charged an interest of 15 percent per annum, repayable along with principal. Further, borrowers are required to contribute 1 percent of the loan amount to an Emergency Fund maintained with ASA. This fund is used as a buffer against future delinquency; however, the loan recovery rate currently stands at 100 percent. As with credit programs of other NGOs, there is a strong emphasis on savings. Saving a minimum of Tk 4 per week is mandatory.

BRAC, one of the largest NGOs in Bangladesh, initiated its credit program in 1976 (BRAC 1991). The cumulative amount of loan disbursed from 1990 through 1992 stood at Tk 1,745 million. Special priority is given to women: 80 percent of the borrowers were female. As of June 1993, 70 branches of RCP were in operation with a coverage of 379,000 members. Loan recovery was 98%. An interest rate of 20 percent per annum is charged to all loans. Membership of a BRAC's Village Organization (VO) is mandatory to attain eligibility. Only the landless poor, defined as people owning less than 0.5 acres of land, are eligible for membership to such organizations. Though each VO has 45 to 55 members, they are split into a number of functional groups comprising five to seven members each. There are also other stipulations; important among them are rules regarding compulsory savings that are collected along with weekly loan repayment installments. An important part of the savings mobilized goes to an emergency fund, accessible to groups or households under special stress.

The credit program of RDRS is the product of a collaboration between the Government of Bangladesh, Deutsche Gesellschaft Für Technische Zusammenarbeit (GTZ), and the International Fund for Agricultural Development (IFAD). Unlike other lending organizations, RDRS does not lend from internal funds; rather, the program serves as a "link" between borrower groups and branches of four commercial banks. The current form of the program was

---

[1] Tk 40 is equal to US$ 1

initiated in 1989 and the first 300 groups were declared to have reached their "bankability status" in 1991. Loan disbursement started in 1992. Total outstanding loans by the end of June 1994 was Tk 25 million. After a group is formed, RDRS trains and eventually certifies them as being bankable. The interest rate is linked to market rates and was 12.5 percent per annum during December 1994. Considerable emphasis is placed on savings. A minimum Tk 1,000 needs to be deposited in the bank before the first loan application is made. An additional four percent up and above the interest rate is collected on loan until a special fund, the group-owned guarantee fund reaches 10 percent of outstanding loans.

4 Empirical Analysis

4.1 Data

During 1994, the International Food Policy Research Institute (IFPRI) conducted a survey of 128 groups participating in group lending programs of BRAC, ASA, and RDRS (Zeller, Ahmed, and Sharma 1995). These groups were randomly selected from 41 villages in 11 *Thanas* and a formal questionnaire was administered to the chairperson of each group. Information was collected on a range of group and community characteristics including all loans procured by the group. For this study, a subset of the data set including only those transactions for which the repayment date had passed at the time of the interview were chosen: these totaled 868.

4.2 Econometric Specification

The dependent variable used in this study is the default rate (DEFAULT) defined as the proportion of the total loan amount in arrears at the date when complete repayment was promised. DEFAULT = 0 implies complete repayment on time whereas DEFAULT = 1 would imply complete default. There were no cases of the latter. The default function is defined as follows:

$$DEFAULT = f(LNSIZE, \mathbf{X}, \mathbf{Z}, \mathbf{M}) \qquad (1)$$

where, LNSIZE is the loan size, $\mathbf{X}$ is a vector of group characteristics, $\mathbf{Z}$ is a vector of community characteristics, and $\mathbf{M}$ is a vector of lender characteristics. Note that this function is defined only for LNSIZE > 0. To accommodate this concern in a practical way, we specify a function with the property that $\lim_{\text{Lnsize } 0}$ DEFAULT = 0. This is a reasonable assumption since defaults on small amounts of loans are indeed likely to be zero. When equation (1) is specified as a linear function, this is achieved by interacting $\mathbf{X}, \mathbf{Z}, \mathbf{M}$ with LNSIZE as in equation (2).

A corollary of this assumption is that the effects of **X**, **Z**, **M** on the default rate are, quite reasonably, made conditional on the loan size, i.e.,

$$\frac{\partial(Default)}{\partial X} = g^x (LNSIZE)$$

and similarly for **Z** and **M**.

Also, because the dependent variable is truncated at zero (group decides not to default) the estimating equation is specified more generally as (for the i-th group):

$$DEFAULT_i{}^* = \beta_1 (LNAMT) + (LNAMT)\mathbf{X}\,\beta_2 + (LNAMT)\mathbf{Z}\beta_3 \quad (2)$$

$$(LNAMT)\mathbf{M}\,\beta_4 + e_i ,$$

where $DEFAULT_i = 0$ if $DEFAULT_i{}^* \leq 0$

and $DEFAULT_i = DEFAULT_i{}^*$ if $DEFAULT_i{}^* > 0$.

In this framework, $DEFAULT_i{}^*$ is a latent variable observable only when it takes a positive value. Equation (2) is estimated by using the TOBIT maximum likelihood technique (Maddala 1983) after correcting for heteroscedasticity based on the method proposed by Greene (1993).

4.3   Regressors, Hypotheses, and Discussion of Results

Table 1 provides the means of variables used and also presents the results of the TOBIT maximum likelihood estimation of the default equation. Below, we define regressors, present hypotheses, and interpret results.

GROUPSIZE This is defined as the average size of the subgroup in a group. In case there are no subgroups in a group, this is equal to the size of the group. **Hypotheses**: The bigger the group, the more imperfect are flows of information likely to be between members. Hence problems arising out of asymmetric information makes monitoring and enforcing costly and less effective. Rates of default are therefore expected to increase with group size (+). **Result**: The sign of the coefficient is positive as expected; however, it is marginally insignificant at the 10% confidence interval.

LNAMNT and **(LNAMNT)**^{2} This is the value of loan in Taka, and its square. **Hypotheses**: We see two factors at work. First, the greater the loan size, the greater the probability of UNWILLING default (+). However, the bigger the loan, the higher is the cost of default [=(1+r+p)*LNAMNT], where p is the incremental penalty rate of interest. The second factor puts pressure on the borrower to reduce the amount defaulted. Consideration of the latter is important since default, in our context, mostly consists of arrears that are eventually paid, even if late. (As opposed to complete writeoffs). It is for this reason that a squared term is included. **Result**: The coefficient on LNAMNT is positive and significant in both the models and therefore supports the first part of the hypotheses. Though the sign of the coefficient on the squared term is as expected (-), it is not significant.

Table 1: Determinants of default on group loans (TOBIT)

Variable[1]	Mean	Coefficient	T-Ratio
LNAMNT	12.031	0.11×10^{-4}	4.922**
$(LNAMNT)^2$	25.5×10^7	-0.35×10^{-11}	-0.23
GROUPSIZE	12.5	0.18×10^{-7}	1.48
M_LAND	0.50 acres	-0.14×10^{-7}	-2.06**
VARLAND	1.62	0.33×10^{-6}	-0.73
RATION	25.0%	0.54×10^{-7}	-3.85**
$(RATION)^2$	5140.0	0.46×10^{-10}	2.26**
RELATIVES	51.5%	0.19×10^{-7}	1.82*
STOCKS	22.0	-0.46×10^{-7}	-2.68**
AG_PROP	0.3%	-0.56×10^{-5}	-2.88**
M_DRT	0.35%	-0.19×10^{-4}	-4.43**
PCFEMALE	87.0%	-0.57×10^{-7}	-6.73**
DUMINTD	0.30	0.15×10^{-5}	3.60**
LN_AGE	1.55	-0.35×10^{-7}	-0.15
DISTANCE	12.0	-0.18×10^{-6}	-2.19**
SAMITY	0.23	0.97×10^{-6}	1.612*
FFW	0.23	-0.11×10^{-5}	-1.63*
IRRI	30.0%	0.18×10^{-7}	1.88*
PARTRATE	200.0	-0.69×10^{-8}	-3.86**
DUMGTZ	0.013	0.18×10^{-5}	-0.26
DUMBRAC	0.71	0.41×10^{-5}	2.71

Log likelihood = -438.27

Note: ** and * indicate that the parameter is significant at the 5 and 10 percent, confidence intervals respectively.

[1] Each variable is interacted with Loan size.

M_LAND This is the mean level of land owned by the group. **Hypothesis**: Since it reflects ownership of an important asset it was expected that it would enhance capacity of the group to repay loans on time (-). **Result and interpretation**: The effect of land ownership on the default rate is found to be negative and significant, as expected. This indicates the importance of even *marginal* difference in land owned, since all three programs, specially BRAC and ASA, limit lending to persons belonging to households that own less that 0.5 acres of land. This result may be partly due to the high marginal productivity of land at such low levels.

VARLAND This is the variance of the land owned by members of a particular group. **Hypothesis**: This variable was used as one indicator of portfolio diversity among members of a group. It was hypothesized that the greater the diversity, the less covariant the incomes. Hence, a higher variance was expected to be associated with a lower rate of default as it would enable better pooling of risk among members. **Result and interpretation:** The coefficient is not significantly different from zero, indicating probably that it was not a good indicator of portfolio diversity. It may also be due to the fact that both ASA and BRAC use a strict criterion for land ownership of 0.5 acres or less as one of their eligibility requirements and this reduces the variable's variability in the sample.

RATION, (RATION)^2 RATION is computed as the difference between the value of loan applied for and the actual value of the loan received expressed as a percent of the total loan amount. **Hypotheses:** Higher degree of rationing implies a higher level of unfulfilled credit demand. If this generates a greater concern for future borrowing privileges, groups can be expected to increase efforts to lower default rates (-). However, if the degree of rationing is too high, it is likely to render the loan amount more and more trivial (in comparison to the needs of the groups) so that the lender may not be considered a feasible long term partner. This may increase incentives to default (+). **Result and interpretation**: The coefficients of both variables are significant and carry the expected sign, supporting both the hypotheses.

RELATIVES This is proportion of members in the group that are related to each other. **Hypothesis**: Since information flows are expected to be better among relatives, there would be less moral hazard associated with bailing out a relative who is unable to meet repayment requirements (-). However, cultural factors are important and this may limit screening and enforcement among relatives (+). **Result and interpretation**: The coefficient is positive and significant, implying that the latter effect outweighs the former.

SHOCKS This is the number of different types of shocks (family emergencies, crop/income loss, measure social events) in the last 18 months reported by members of the group. **Hypothesis**: This is obviously positive (+). **Result**: Negative and significant, and therefore contrary to expectation. This result is most likely due to the fact that the SHOCKS variable contains only incomplete information on the shocks received by groups. What is as important as the number of shocks, it seems, are their magnitudes, and SHOCKS does not contain any information on magnitudes.

AG_PROP This is the proportion of members reporting agriculture as the principal occupation. It is therefore another indicator of asset portfolio diversity within groups. **Hypothesis**: An important eligibility criterion used especially by ASA and BRAC is that the members do not posess land in excess of 0.5 acres.

The base scenario is therefore one where most members derive a major part of their income from agricultural wages or profits from off-farm microenterprise (Zeller, Ahmed, and Sharma 1995). Hence, as AG_PROP increases from this base scenario, incomes within groups are likely to be less covariant, making it easier to bail out errant members (-). Further, since most households generally own very little land, those that report agriculture as their main occupation are likely to be tenant farmers who rent land. Given this, they are likely to have other borrowing privileges (e.g. from landlord) that may be used to meet the repayment schedule of group loans. Also, non-agricultural incomes are likely to be more risky, especially income from casual laboring. Therefore, unwilling default, on the average, is likely to be greater for those groups that have a greater share of non-agricultural income. **Result and interpretation**: The coefficient is strongly significant with (-) sign.

M_DRT This is the group wise mean dependency ratio (proportion of children in total household size). **Hypothesis**: In general, the higher the dependency ratio, the more risk-averse the household, since the consequence of adverse shock is likely to be relatively serious as it affects children who are more vulnerable. Hence, ceteris paribus, the higher the dependency ratio, the less likelihood the default, since such groups would want to avoid risking reduced future borrowing privileges or reduced access to special emergency funds (-). **Result**: The coefficient is significant with expected sign, supporting the hypothesis.

PCFEMALE This is the percentage of group members who are female. **Hypothesis**: It is expected that the higher this percentage, the lower the default rate (-). **Result**: Result is supportive of the hypothesis.

DUMINTD Dummy variable which equals one when the group is initiated by an NGO agent, zero otherwise. **Hypothesis**: It is difficult to place an a priori expectation on the sign, and the interest here is to examine whether the manner in which the group was formed makes a difference at all. **Result and Interpretation**: The coefficient is significant and positive indicating that default rates are lower for groups that form on their own. One explanation may be that screening is more effective within such groups than within those that depend on the intervention from an outside agent.

LN_AGE This is the number of years from the date of the interview that the loan was procured. **Hypothesis**: If each subsequent transaction reinforces the value of the credit service to the borrower, one may expect default to decrease at each successive transaction. If this is indeed so, default on more recent loans would be lower than ones in the past (+). However, if borrowers perceive the relationship to be only transitory, then one can expect default on later-date loans to increase (-). Hence, prediction on the sign of the coefficient is ambiguous.

Result and Interpretation: The coefficient is negative but very insignificantly different from zero.

DISTANCE This is a community level variable computed as the mean distance from the village to nine types of service centers ranging from post office, health post to the nearest agricultural input dealer. **Hypothesis**: The closer the village to the service centers, the less remote and more buoyant the local economy. Hence, default rates are likely to be low (+). **Result and interpretation**: The coefficient is negative and significant and therefore does not support the hypothesis. A possible explanation is the following: the more remote the village, the more value is placed on the credit services of the group programs since other alternatives are less available (e.g. like loans from traders, employers); default rates therefore are low to avoid loss of future borrowing privileges from this important source.

SAMITY This is the number of self-help groups in the village. **Hypothesis**: The less the number of self-help groups, the more the value of an outside agency that provides insurance services. Therefore, lower default rates can be expected (+). **Result**: The coefficient is positive and just significant at the 10% level.

FFW This is a dummy variable that equals one if the village has a food-for-work (FFW) program in place. **Hypothesis**: Since FFWs are generally placed in relatively depressed areas, poverty-related unwilling default is likely to be relatively large. However, the more impoverished the village, the greater will be the value placed on continued access to these credit programs. Hence net effect on default is not clear. **Result**: The coefficient is negative and significant at the 10% confidence interval, implying that the second effect is dominating. It implies that areas with above-average poverty rates can have better repayment records.

IRRI This is the proportion of the cultivated area in the village that is irrigated. **Hypothesis**: Higher levels of irrigation not only increase income levels but also reduce riskiness of agricultural incomes. Hence, unwilling default is likely to be lower (-). **Result**: The coefficient is positive and significant. Though this is a result that cannot be satisfactorily explained, it should be noted that poorer households may actually own little irrigated land, even in villages that have high irrigation rates.

PARTRATE This is another community-level variable indicating the number of persons participating in group-based institutions per 1,000 inhabitants of the village. **Hypothesis**: The greater the participation rate, the greater the demonstrated benefits of the group-based lending in the community. This contributes importantly to the viability and the perceived permanence of participating institutions. Hence, default rates are likely to be low as groups act to preserve transactions well into the future (-). **Result**: The coefficient is negative and significant.

Lastly, DUMGTZ and DUMBRAC are dummies for RDRS and BRAC, respectively, indicating whether default rates vary across the institutions even when all the other variables are controlled. Our results show that while there is no significant difference between ASA and RDRS, BRAC has a significantly higher default rate than the two, at least in the sample of group selected for the analysis.

5   Lessons Learned

Several lessons can be drawn from the study. First, there is a costly lesson from history. Expansion of rural financial institutions cannot be based on an easy formula that attempts to replicate institutional structures of urban-based commercial banks in the rural areas. The cost of adopting such a formula is especially high when market power is concentrated in a few state-sponsored institutions. This is because assured market power provides almost no incentives for managers to undertake organizational reforms necessary for providing cost-effective and profitable financial services to the rural poor. It also provides political leaders with a ready apparatus that can be easily used to advance their own interests. As in many other developing countries, the cost of such meddling by the political leadership – evident in the sheer amount of unrepaid loans – has been quite high in the case of Bangladesh. Of course, this does not mean that the traditional commercial banks do not play any role in the development of rural financial institutions. Given autonomy in management, sound banking regulations, and an environment that promotes healthy competition, these banks have the potential to make considerable gains in rural finance, especially by taking advantage of their huge network of branches to diversify risks. Evidence of this potential is just emerging, and repayment rates for some institutions have started to make a turnaround. Also, as we noted earlier, some of these banks have joined hands with group-based institutions to form a mutually profitable institutional alliance. This is indeed positive development.

Second, there is a heartening discovery in repayment records of group-based financial systems, namely that once the right institutional structures are in place, there need not be any major conflict between prudent financial management and lending to the asset poor. We observed that repayment rates of group-based systems are especially good in relatively remote communities, and even in communities that are likely to have higher than average rates of poverty. The secret seems to lie not just in innovations that reduce the cost of screening, monitoring, and enforcing loan contracts, but also in the successful demonstration to small rural communities that these innovations and institutions were not transitory phenomena, that they addressed their financial concerns, and that it was worthwhile for them to invest in a profitable long term association. In fact it is precisely this realization among borrowers that has contributed to the building up of a critical mass of social capital that support these institutions. Without this critical mass, the concept of joint liability would quickly flounder. Understanding the financial concerns of the poor is therefore indispensable; after all, there is little incentive for borrowers to build lasting relationships with institutions that do not address their requirements. Also, when new activities or new technologies are introduced, it is important that steps are taken to ensure that they are properly understood by borrowers. The general practice of the NGO institutions to combine lending services with a range of personal, social and entrepreneurial education is a good example.

Third, steps should be taken to make the process of group formation more endogenous to the members themselves and less subject to external rules. Our analysis indicates that factors such as portfolio diversity within groups significantly affect repayment rates. In general, potential members are in a better position to screen and select right partners for group formation giving due consideration to factors such as potential risk-pooling benefits. A good mix of income activities, including agricultural production activities, is likely to lead to better repayments; hence, change in eligibility conditions that increase the maximum allowable land ownership from its current low level of about 0.5 acres needs to be considered.

Finally, the experience of group lending shows that the basic principles of prudential banking has to be adhered to at all times. Delivering finance to the poor should not be taken to mean that loan evaluation or rationing can be entirely dispensed with. On the contrary, loan size has to take into consideration limited investment capacities and the limited risk-taking abilities of the rural poor. In fact, our analysis indicated that default rates do appear to increase with loan size. Hence, objective and realistic project evaluation is necessary prior to loan approval. However, it is important to ensure that this evaluation not be based on traditional forms of gender or age bias. As the result of our analyses indicates, these biases, however deep- rooted, are totally misplaced.

Acknowledgment

The authors wish to thank the Ministry of Economic Cooperation (BMZ) of the Federal Republic of Germany for funding this research through the Deutsche Gesellschaft für Technische Zusammenarbeit (GTZ).

References

Besley, T. and S. Coate. 1995. Group lending, repayment incentives and social collateral. *Journal of Development Economics*. 46: 11-18.

Bratton, M. 1986. Financing smallholder production: A comparison of individual and group credit schemes in Zimbabwe. *Public Administration and Development*. 6:115-132.

Devereux, J. and R. Fishe. 1993. An economic analysis of group lending programs in developing countries. *The Developing Economies.* 31: 102-121.

Glance, N. and B. Huberman. 1994. The dynamics of social dilemmas. *Scientific American.* March Issue.

Greene, W. 1993. *Econometric Analysis.* Prentice Hall.

Jahangir, A. and M. Zeller. 1995. Overview paper on rural finance programs for the poor in Bangladesh: A review of six major programs. International Food Policy Research Institute, Washington, D.C.

Khalily, M.A. and R. Meyer. 1993. The political economy of rural loan recovery: Evidence from Bangladesh. *Saving and Development.* 17(1):23-38

Maddala, G. 1983. *Limited dependent and qualitative variables in econometrics.* Cambridge:Cambridge University Press.

Stiglitz, J. 1990. Peer monitering and credit markets. *World Bank Economic Review.*4:351-366

Varian, H. 1990. Monitoring agents with other agents. *Journal of Institutional and Theoretical Economics.* 146: 153-174

World Bank. 1994. Bangladesh: From stabilization to growth. Report No.12724bD Washington, D.C.

World Bank. 1995. Bangladesh: Issues in rural finance. Mimeo. Washington, D.C.

Zeller, M. 1995. Determinants of loan repayment in group lending: The role of intra-group risk-sharing and social cohesion. Mimeo. International Food Policy Research Institute, Washington, D.C.

Zeller, M., A. Ahmed, and M. Sharma. 1995. Credit for the rural poor: Country case Bangladesh. Interim Report Submitted to German Agency for Technical Cooperation (GTZ). International Food Policy Research Institute, Washington, D.C.

Dairy Development Policies in Kenya and the Implications for Research Strategies and Priorities

M. Hitzel[1] and A. N. Mbabu[2]
[1]International Service for National Agricultural Research (ISNAR), The Hague, The Netherlands
[2]Kenya Agricultural Research Institute (KARI), Nairobi, Kenya

Abstracts _____

This paper presents findings from an empirical analysis of subsector and macro-level policies influencing dairy research in Kenya. The first step in the study is a review of the past and present national dairy research policies. The study then discusses development objectives as defined in policy documents, factual observed objectives, and perceptions of dairy stakeholders. Policy objectives have been distinguished in final policy objectives and intermediate objectives. Final objectives are, for example, identified as equity or economic efficiency. Intermediate objectives could be seen as research thrusts, e.g. fodder production. Past and present policy objectives were obtained from a review of documents about the development of the dairy sector.

Stakeholder objectives were obtained using the Analytic Hierarchy Process (AHP). Afterwards, the objectives, as obtained from the different analyses, are compared. Objectives diverge largely, thereby complicating their use for the purpose of dairy research management.

Keywords _____
Kenya, dairy development, priority setting

1   Introduction

The research presented here is performed within the framework of the KARI/ISNAR/HUB project on linking adoption studies and priority setting for dairy research. This project aims to refine priority setting methods for dairy research by improved integration of adoption information. It studies different aspects that influence priority setting for dairy research. It analyzes and quantifies the factors influencing technology adoption, correlates technology diffusion and adopters' characteristics, and integrates the estimated adoption rate into decision-making models for research priority setting.

The project consists of five different modules. Module 1 deals with the policy context of agricultural research, and will be elaborated in this paper. Module 2 deals with the impact of technology characteristics on adoption and diffusion. Module 3 tries to identify the user demand for technology. Module 4 aims to develop a decision support model for priority setting, that integrates the previously collected information. Module 5 concerns the design of a participatory and transparent procedure for priority setting that integrates the results of the other modules (figure 1).

1.1 Background

Agricultural research must make a strong effort to meet the demands of agriculture in sub-Saharan Africa. Population pressure and political and economic instability form a difficult environment for agricultural development. Financial resources for research at international institutes and national agricultural research systems (NARS) are no longer increasing. This is especially the case for the NARS of developing countries. The result is a serious imbalance in which NARS are faced with concerns and demands by society on the one hand and a declining budget on the other. Research priorities must be set and resources must be allocated in such a way that benefits are maximized. In order to do this, the research objectives and alternative research projects with their expected outcomes and diffusion should be known.

The present paper discusses how research objectives were elicited and compiled for dairy research in Kenya. The challenging question for this task was how to identify the most important policy objectives and how to make these operational for the priority setting process. The module discussed in this paper must address the "target-cocktail dilemma" (Jahnke 1995), i.e. how to tackle a multi-dimensional problem. The results of this research policy module should be a weighted set of operational research objectives that show the importance for dairy research of different policy dimensions.

1.2 Objectives and Hypotheses

This paper links the development of the dairy sector with the objectives for research in Kenya. It then describes a method to define the weights for research priority setting criteria. These weights should reflect the importance of policy objectives. The most important objectives for dairy production in Kenya will be described. The objectives to be analyzed and compared, originate from three different sources:

1. objectives stated by policy documents;
2. objectives elicited by the stakeholders interviewed;
3. factual objectives as observed in the implementation.

Once the historical analysis of dairy development has been concluded and the objectives weighted, we will test the following hypotheses:

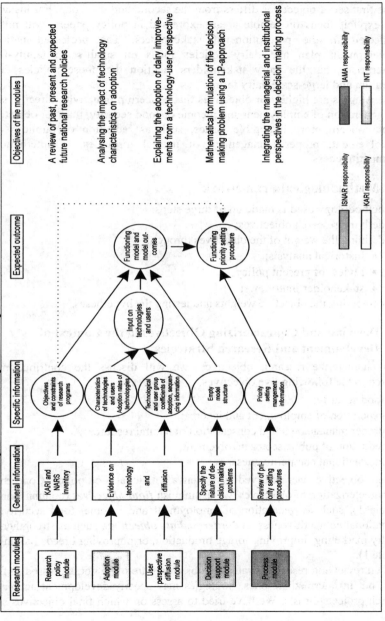

Figure 1: Project Structure, Objectives, and Expected Outputs of the 5 different Modules

Research modules	General information	Specific information	Expected outcome	Objectives of the modules

Research policy module → KARI and NARS inventory → Objectives and constraints of research programs

A review of past, present and expected future national research policies

Adoption module → Evidence on technology and diffusion → Characteristics of technologies and users / Adoption rates of technologies

Analysing the impact of technology characteristics on adoption

User perspective diffusion module → Technological and user group coefficients of adoption, sequencing information

Explaining the adoption of dairy improvements from a technology-user perspective

Decision support module → Specify the nature of decision making problems → Empty model structure

Mathematical formulation of the decision making problem using a LP-approach

Process module → Review of priority setting procedures → Priority setting management information

Integrating the managerial and institutional perspectives in the decision making process

Input on technologies and users → Functioning model and model outcomes

Functioning priority setting procedure

ISNAR responsibility KARI responsibility IAMA responsibility INT responsibility

1. The first set of objectives differs from the second and third one. For instance, an explicit focus on remote areas, expressed in policy papers, will not be reflected in the perception of stakeholders. The professed national development plan and dairy policies focus on small-scale family-farm enterprises, but the dairy stakeholders mention that these policies favor medium and large-scale dairy farms.
2. The weights are higher for objectives that concern productivity directly, such as generation of employment and income or food security, than for objectives that concern more intangible issues, such as reduction of public sector involvement, proper management of natural resources, or international competitiveness.

2   Methodological Framework

The methodology used is made up of three steps:
  1. deriving research objectives;
  2. defining the weight of the objectives through:
     - historical analysis;
     - review of present policy;
     - stakeholder interviews;
  3. comparing the objective weights and testing the hypotheses.

2.1   Deriving and Characterizing Objectives in the Context of Development and Research Strategies

To characterize research objectives, we will discuss the contribution of research to the following five objectives:
  1. food security;
  2. generation of employment and income;
  3. proper management and conservation of natural resources;
  4. reduction of public sector involvement;
  5. international competitiveness.

These objectives were derived from Kenya's national food policy. Concerning the characterization of objectives, we distinguish *final objectives* (column 2 and 3 of table 1), such as generation of employment and income, food security, or international competitiveness, and *intermediate objectives*, such as strengthening of dairy marketing, improving forage production, or improving breeds (column 1 of table 1).

When reviewing research strategies, objectives are often not expressed in final terms, but in intermediate ones. Strategies may specify development actions or research projects/thrusts. We have tried to assess on which final objectives such actions would impact positively or negatively, in order to be able to derive factual final objectives.

For example, a focus on certain regions may be taken with an equity concern in mind, and price control measures may have been implemented to favor food security, though often with a negative effect. A focus on large farms was often take for efficiency reasons. Intensification has often had negative consequences on natural resource management but was supposed to foster efficiency (see table 1).

An important issue is that objectives are not necessarily independent. There is definitely a trade off between the different objectives. Therefore, an excessive number of program objectives makes them difficult to handle in a research strategy. Formulating the program strategy may become cumbersome and time consuming and the result may be ambiguous.

Table 1:   Historical Development Activities and Research Thrusts with Effects on Development Objectives

Development action	Favored objectives	Disfavored objectives
Increasing milk production	Food security, generation of employment and income	Proper management and conservation of natural resources
Import of milk	food security	Reduction of public sector involvement, international competitiveness
Production for export	Generation of employment and income, food security, international competitiveness	Reduction of public sector involvement, proper management and conservation of natural resources
Controlled dairy prices	Food security	Generation of employment and income, international competitiveness, food security, reduction of public sector involvement
Search action/ thrust		
Intensification of fodder production	Food security, generation of employment and income, proper management and conservation of natural resources	Proper management and conservation of natural resources
Animal health	Food security, international competitiveness	
Artificial insemination	Food security	Reduction of public sector involvement
Animal breeding, genetic resources	Food security, international competitiveness	Proper use and conservation of natural resources

2.2 Eliciting Weights of Final Research Objectives Using the Analytic Hierarchy Process (AHP)

AHP was developed by Saaty in the late 1970's. It enables decision makers to structure a complex decision as a hierarchy of smaller decisions. AHP is based on three principles: decomposition, comparative judgment, and synthesis of priorities (Saaty 1980). Decomposition occurs while determining the hierarchy of the problem elements (goal, criteria, and alternatives). The alternatives are compared in a pairwise fashion, according to the criteria. In complex hierarchies, the weights and priorities need to be synthesized (Saaty 1980). Inconsistencies in judgment can be evaluated. AHP has been used as a method for defining the weights for priority setting criteria. In a multi-objective priority setting the weighted objectives are used as indicators in the performance assessment of research alternatives (Dyer & Forman 1992). AHP is used to facilitate the weighting of a complex comparison of objectives.

3   Empirical Analysis

3.1   Historical Analysis of Dairy Research in Kenya

Mbabu et al. (1993) reviewed the history of dairy research in Kenya to reveal how policy and economic changes influence agricultural research. The history of agricultural research at Kenya Agricultural Research Institute (KARI) was deeply influenced by political decisions of the respective times.

Dairy Research Before 1945

Formal agricultural research has been recorded since 1895, when Kenya became a British protectorate. At the time, activities only consisted of training the agricultural extension service in order to improve farming methods. Later, research was directed towards large-scale farms owned by European settlers. A research system as such did not exist and the policy framework was determined by colonial power. The settlements of the European farmers in the "white highlands", with an abundance of land, were in strong contrast to the small farms in the overcrowded African reserves of the lowlands. Labor productivity on the African farms was low.

The Years Following World War II

This marked a time of new orientation and opening for the African farmers. The main part of agricultural research undertaken was meant for commercial large-scale farmers. Before independence, agricultural research was directed towards the production of large-scale farming systems. Crops such as coffee, tea and wheat were given first priority over small-scale peasant crops. This was in conformity with the agricultural development policy at the time. The research activities in dairy were in forage production. Africans could now establish mixed farms in the white highlands, though these were smaller than those of their white counterparts. At the time around the "Mau Mau" rebellion, development policy was directed towards a transfer of land from large- to small- holders as a strategy to maintain peace in rural areas. In the end, more land was provided to African farmers with positive effects on employment. The introduction of mechanization (tractors, etc.) counteracted this trend and led to unemployment of many Africans.

After 1961

Occupation of the white highlands by African farmers was legalized. Agricultural policy now focused on the development of independent small-holder agricultural production systems, to create income potential and employment in the rural areas. At this time, the commercial farms focused on export production. The research projects concerning dairy research dealt with experiments in animal husbandry and milk issues. Policies started to pay attention to subsistence subsectors, but the issue was once again minimized in the 70's in favor of commercial large-scale and small-scale farmers. In the mid 70s, as the oil crisis was affecting the world, Kenyan policy focused on small-holder farms in order to increase distribution of national income. The research policy supported research on high value commodities. There was only a slight interest in subsistence milk production, but an increasing interest in family farm enterprises. It was determined that animal feeding was a more serious constraint to milk production than the genetic potential of the animal. In the national livestock research system, programs on economics, rural sociology, development, and post harvest technology were implemented.

The 80s and early 90s

Policy emphasized a welfare orientation to assist the marginalized populations. The farming-systems approach and development of the arid and semi-arid areas were emphasized, and attention was given to high-value commercial crops. This period saw a renewal of priorities in dairy research. Important research activities were in animal science protection and production. The greatest number of experiments were meant to target family-farm enterprises. As in all the previous time periods, research failed to give priority to dairy production in subsistence subsectors. The three development plans in this period were directed towards alleviation of poverty, with special emphasis on arid and semi arid land (ASAL). The emphasis on environmental degradation was increasing. Research policy put emphasis on farming systems research. Dairy research was seen as an equity tool. Within dairy research, the focus was placed on fodder issues. The government also facilitated adoption of research results and recommendations by improving infrastructure and supplying technical support. It was also government policy to direct input suppliers towards providing complete packages required for certain technologies.

Table 2 provides a summary of the previous analysis. Food security, employment and income have been the most significant, and most stable objectives over time. The other objectives have had lower and variable importance throughout the different periods.

Table 2:   Factual Dairy Development Objectives, Conclusions for Research
           Objectives

	1895-1945	1946-1960	1960-1978	1979-1992
Food security	*[1]	**	**	**
Generation of employment and income	***	***	***	**
Proper management of natural resources	-	-	-	*
International competitiveness	**	*	**	*
Reduction of public sector involvement	-	-	-	*

[1] * = not very important; ** = important; *** = very important

3.2   Review of Present Dairy Policy

Successful technology generation depends largely on the policy framework. To identify the most important policies and policy instruments, policy papers were screened and stakeholders were interviewed.

Since 1992

The principal policies that affect dairy development (besides technology development and diffusion) are:

- marketing;
- infrastructure;
- processing;
- input supply;
- credit policy.

Marketing Policy

The main findings of ILRI (International Livestock Research Institute) sector and macro-economic policy studies on Kenya (Ehui 1995) show the possible benefits of price liberalization, but also that other structural reforms are needed to improve competition and reinforce the positive effects of price deregulation.

Producer profits and welfare were improved by the deregulation of 1992, but producer disincentives still exist. A principle difficulty is that a powerful marketing monopoly cannot be broken through price liberalization alone (Staal & Shapiro 1994).

Infrastructure Policy

The Staal and Shapiro study mentions the problems dairy farmers face in remote areas, with no access to all-weather roads, and therefore a weak collection, cooling and transport system. As the road system not only depends on political willingness among dairy farmers but on public (and perhaps also private) large-scale investments, it lies outside the direct influence of the dairy stakeholders in Kenya.

Input Supply Policy

Fodder production and feeding problems in dairy production have received special attention in dairy development policies. This is particularly important for the dry season, when fodder becomes scarce and the production decreases. The response has been to emphasize research on dry-season feed sources. For other inputs, recent policy changes have heavily influenced the dairy sector. In 1991, the Government started a gradual cost-sharing process with eventual liberalization. Some veterinary services, such as dipping and clinical services, started to be privatized in 1993/94.

Processing Policy

Though dairy markets have been liberalized, there has been little effect on price formation and farm income. This is because alternative marketing opportunities were restricted by the lack of processing capacity. Lately, small-scale processors have been able to construct their own plants and leading to more competition. This is a field where the Government should certainly encourage competition, e.g. by providing credit for building dairy plants.

Credit Policy

The conditions attached to loans and the types of loans granted by institutional credit sources tend to favor large livestock producers over small holders and to emphasize short-term projects over long-term projects (Ehui 1995). Costly technologies will not be adopted by farmers without access to credit.

It is not easy to draw conclusions from recent development actions on the factual policy objectives (table 3). The liberalization efforts tend to emphasize the importance of employment generation and income. The reduction of public involvement in input services, shows that the Government is seriously committed to reducing its role. The main divergence between the stated objectives and the observed objectives as factually expressed, lies in natural resource management. It is not clear where this objectives is emphasized in development actions.

Table 3:   Review of Factual and Stated Dairy Development Objectives Stated in Policy Papers, 1992-1996

	Factual objectives	Stated objectives
Food security	**[1]	**
Generation of employment and income	***	***
Proper management of natural resources	*	**
International competitiveness	*	*
Reduction of public sector involvement	**	**

[1] * = not very important; ** = important; *** = very important

4   Deriving Research Objectives for Dairy Production in Kenya

It was assumed that the most important objectives for dairy development in Kenya, would also determine dairy research. Objectives for the livestock subsector are determined partly by an overall political philosophy and partly through an assessment of the direction and speed at which change in the current functions of the subsector is desired (ILRI 1995). These objectives should also guide research and are therefore important for research priority setting.

We investigated how stakeholders assess the relative importance of the five selected policy objectives. AHP was used to weight the objectives in a pairwise comparison. The interviewed persons conducted a pairwise comparison of the five selected policy objectives.[1]

Persons from the following institutions were interviewed:
- Ministry of Agriculture, Livestock Development and Marketing (MALDM)
  - Animal Production Department
  - Dairy Production
  - Provincial Livestock Production
  - Research Extension Liaison
  - National Dairy Development Project (NDDP)
- Egerton University, Policy Analysis Matrix
- Kenya Agricultural Research Institute (KARI)
  - Livestock Research Department
  - Animal Production Unit

[1] The major national objectives in Kenya's development policy are: food self-sufficiency, food security, employment creation, income generation, generation of foreign exchange earnings, rural-urban balance, overall growth (Republic of Kenya 1994).

- Socio-economics Unit
- International Livestock Research Institute (ILRI)
- University of Nairobi
- Meru Dairy Cooperative

The comparison of the objectives was carried out according to the following scale:

equally important	moderately more important	more important	much more important	extremely more important

The comparison values used are recommended by Saaty (1980 and 1987), and stand for fundamental scale values, respectively (1, 3, 5, 7 and 9). These values can be processed by computer software and result in objective weights. The weights in table 4 indicate how the stakeholders thought about the relative importance of the compared objectives for dairy production. The objective *generation of employment and income* was identified as the most important objective.

Table 4: Weighted Macro-Policy Objectives

Rank	Objective	Average pairwise comparison weights
1	Generation of employment and income	0.34
2	Food security	0.31
3	Proper management and conservation of natural resources	0.15
4	International competitiveness	0.13
5	Reduction of public sector involvement	0.07
	Total	1.00

Six out of 18 interviewed persons gave the highest weight to the objective *Generation of employment and income*. Ten out of 16 gave the second highest weight to this objective. That means 16 out of 18 persons weighted this objective very high. The objective *Food security* was given the highest weight by 8 out of 16, and second highest by 4 out of 16.. This objective is put in first or second place by more people than any other objective. However, the final weight is less than that for *Employment and income generation*, because, among the people who didn't put it in first place, it received very low scores. These two objectives are by far the most important, followed by *Proper management of natural resources, International competitiveness*, and *Reduction of public sector involvement*.

5   Analyzing and Comparing Objective Structures

Table 5 shows how different the objectives emerge from the three sources discussed. Official documents, like the national development plan or the national dairy policy, often do not sufficiently consider the changing policy framework and may quickly become outdated. The question is, how much these policy papers should guide research policies, and whether planners of research programs have to rely on them. To a certain extent, policy has to combine proclaimed objectives with long-term vision because research results may be difficult to implement within a 2-3 year horizon. Research must definitely address the stated goals, but must also take the future into consideration, in order to keep research programs relevant.

Table 5:   Comparison of Factual Objectives, Stated Objectives and Stakeholder Objectives of Dairy Development Objectives

	Factual objectives	Stated objectives	Stakeholder objectives
Food security	**	**	**
Generation of employment and income	***	***	**
Proper management of natural resources	*	**	*
International competitiveness	*	*	*
Reduction of public sector involvement	**	**	-

The stated emphasis on small scale farms, given their importance for dairy production (80% of the marketed milk in Kenya comes from small holder farms, Staal & Shapiro 1994), is not reflected in the development actions. The stakeholders mentioned that a focus on medium- or large-scale farms can be observed in the policy framework but not in reality. Additionally, the flexibility of larger farms to adjust to changing environments was considered higher. The prevailing policy framework seem to disfavor the small-scale farmers. This observation has also been confirmed by others (Muthee 1995).

Objectives that directly concern productivity (generation of employment and income; food security) are more important than more intangible objectives (proper management and conversation of natural resources; international competitiveness; reduction of public sector involvement). This is valid for all three sources of assessment (see section 1.2). The most controversial objective was *international competitiveness*, which was seen by some stakeholders as important, but not by the majority. Dairy exports played a bigger role in the past then at present.

6 Lessons Learned: Identifying Research Objectives for Priority Setting

Research objectives strongly define the priority-setting framework and guide performance assessment. It is therefore important to define them carefully. An important issue is whether to use a multiple-objective approach instead of a focus on economic efficiency only (which would be easier to execute). A main argument for a multiple-objective approach in research priority setting is that it best approximates development-policy reality, even if it takes more resources. In a single-objective approach the danger exists of omitting important development objectives and, consequently, emphasizing the wrong research activities. In all policy documents that we received multiple objectives were stated.

When talking about priority setting at the national level, policy information on macro and subsector levels is essential. The objectives defined at these levels, guide the research program. Most often, not one, but, several objectives are defined for the development of a subsector. However, the difference between stated objectives and what is being done is large. This may be due to the fact that policy makers overestimate their ability to modify the thinking of the principal stakeholders involved in executing policies.

Another lesson from this study is the emphasis on production oriented objectives such as food security and income and employment generation. It is not that other objectives are unimportant, but their importance varies over time whereas food security and income questions were important at all times. This would suggest that, if a single objective method to priority setting is chosen, a production perspective (e.g., through an economic surplus model) is justified.

Which objectives to use in a priority setting process needs to be carefully analyzed. Decisions on the use and weights of objectives should be based on the analysis of policy documents, but cannot be derived directly from them. However, the final decisions will be taken by stakeholders and decision makers in the priority setting process, since they are the responsible implementing the priorities.

Acknowledgment

The activities were carried out in a collaborative special project by the International Service for National Agricultural Research (ISNAR), Kenya Agricultural Research Institute (KARI), and Humboldt University of Berlin (HUB). The project is funded by the *Bundesministerium für wirtschaftliche Zusammenarbeit und Entwicklung* (BMZ) of Germany.

References

Dyer R. F. and Forman E. H. 1992. Group Decision Support with the Analytic Hierarchy Process. In: Decision Support Systems, 8 (1992). Elsevier, Science Publishers.
Ehui, S. 1995. ILRI's Perspective on Public Policy Research, mimeo.
ILRI (International Livestock Research Institute). 1995. Livestock Policy Analysis. ILRI Training Manual 2. Nairobi, Kenya: ILRI.
Jahnke, H. E. 1995. Personal communication.
Muthee, A. M. 1995. The adjustment gap, constraints on development of privates sector delivery systems for animal health services and inputs in Kenya's dairy production districts.
Republic of Kenya 1993. Kenya Dairy Development Policy, A Strategy towards the Development of a self-sustaining Dairy Sector. Ministry of Agriculture, Livestock Development and Marketing, Nairobi.
Republic of Kenya 1994. Sessional Paper No. 2 of 1994 on National Food Policy, Government Printer, Nairobi.
Saaty, T. L. 1980. The Analytic Hierarchy Process. New York, NY, U.S.A.: McGraw-Hill.
Saaty, R. W. 1987. The Analytic Hierarchy Process - what it is and how it is used. In: Mathematical Modeling. Vol. 9. No. 3-5, pp. 161-176. Great Britain: Pergamon.
Staal S. J., and B.I. Shapiro. 1994. The effect of recent price liberalization on Kenyan peri-urban dairy, Food Policy 1994 19 (6) 533-549.
Worldbank 1995. Kenya, Economic Update, February 1995. Washington.

The Impact of Market Access on Agricultural Productivity: Lessons from India, Kenya and the Sudan

M. von Oppen[1], B. K. Njehia[2] and Abdelatif Ijaimi[3]

[1] Institute for Agricultural Economics and Social Sciences in the Tropics and Subtropics, University of Hohenheim, Germany
[2] Department of Agricultural Economics and Agribusiness Management, Egerton University, Njoro, Kenya
[3] Planning and Agricultural Economics Administration, Ministry of Agriculture and Natural and Animal Resources, Khartoum, Sudan

Abstract

Improved access to markets and clear price signals induce farmers to specialize (or diversify) according to comparative advantage and to intensify input use in production. The resulting increase in production leads to more marketed surplus and economies of scale in handling, which – under competitive conditions – bring about better prices; these in turn induce farmers to further specialize and intensify.

Market induced increases in agricultural productivity have been investigated. The impact of physical market access on local agricultural productivity on the basis of cross-sectional farm level data from India, Kenya and Sudan has been quantified and its distribution by farm size assessed.

Quantification of efficiency and equity effects of market access permits policy makers to draw conclusions about the needs for, and the pay-offs from investments into physical and institutional infrastructure of agricultural markets.

Keywords:

Market access, agricultural productivity, infrastructure, economies of scale

1   Aim and Scope of the Study

The overall objective of this paper is to assess the impact of physical market access on agricultural productivity and to develop recommendations and policy implications. The specific objectives are:

- to assess how market access influences farmers' decisions with regard to land use, input use, and how these effects are reflected in aggregate productivity and market surplus in different farm size groups.

- to examine whether improved market access would have a desirable effect on the distribution of market generated gains.

This paper addresses the above objectives on the basis of analyzing cross-sectional farm level data from India, Kenya and Sudan.

2   Methodology

The paper summarizes results of three studies which essentially followed the same methodology: the estimation of production functions (in partial analyses as well as simultaneous equation systems), expressing aggregate productivity as a function of inputs, resources and market access, and simultaneously expressing input use as a function of market access and resources.

2.1   The Data Sets

The data sets were collected in India, Kenya and Sudan. In India the data base was created from surveys of 300 farmers in the two regions of Mahbubnagar and Nagpur during 1978-79. In each region 20 villages of an average type were purposely selected at varying distances from market networks. In each village 15 farmers were selected from a stratified population 5 small (<4 ha), 5 medium (5 - 8 ha) and 5 large (>10 ha).

In Kenya cross-sectional data were collected from 144 sample farmers in Nakuru District during the years 1991/92. The farmers were selected at varying levels of access to Nakuru Market. The sample was stratified in 3 farm size groups – small (< 8 acres), medium (13-30 acres) and large (>50 acres).

The data base in Sudan was created from a survey of 201 farmers (100 small and 101 large) in 21 villages covering an area stretching about 400 km along the river Nile north of Khartoum. Small and large farmers were distinguished based on farm size. In addition, all large farmers selected own a water pump. The villages were purposely selected in pairs, one on the east and the other on the west of the river Nile, with different access to a number of markets of different types. The field survey was conducted in the 1991/92 cropping season.

2.2   Analytical Methods

In the case of India, where bullock carts were by far the most common mode of transport, market access was presented by the road distance to the nearest market. In the Kenya and Sudan studies, the average transport time it takes a farmer to move produce from the farm to the market or inputs from the market to the farm, using his most common mode of transport, has been used as a more reliable measure for market access. The choice of time as an index of access to markets has the advantage of incorporating and capturing the full effects of the many qualitative aspects of the transport system in a quantitative measure. In the three studies aggregate productivity refers to the overall productivity of a farm per hectare (or acre) in constant monetary terms.[1]

Two analytical approaches are used in the three studies in a complementary way: partial analysis and simultaneous equation analysis.

2.2.1 Partial Analysis

The impact of market access was assessed by studying its relationship with the variables representing land use, input use, aggregate productivity and market surplus. The analysis is by farm size and accessibility to the market. For the purpose of this partial analysis, data are presented in the form of averages by categories, grouped by easy, medium and difficult access to the market.

2.2.2 Econometric Analysis

Market access affects agricultural productivity at two levels: directly through farmers' decisions on land use (specialization), and indirectly, through the level of input use (intensification). Since input use directly affects productivity, the relationship between market access and agricultural productivity must be estimated simultaneously in a system of equations. To quantify the direct and indirect impacts of market access on agricultural productivity, the three-stage least squares technique was used.

The model can be summarized in the following equations:

$$TP = f_1(IN, RES, MA) \qquad\qquad IN = f_2(RES, MA)$$

where:

TP = the sum of aggregate farm productivity expressed in constant monetary terms per hectare/acre;

IN = inputs such as fertilizer, pesticides and high yielding seed varieties;

RES = resources such as credit, land and labor

MA = market access expressed in terms of distance or time to transport goods to the market

The application of the Three-Stage Least Squares Method (3.SLS) requires that the model has to be identified. For the entire model to be identified, it must be in a form that enables the unique estimation of its parameters made subsequently from the sample data. After specifying the detailed models used in the three

---

[1] Aggregate productivity was computed at constant village prices (average prices). Thus market access effects measured below are net of the price gradient. Aggregate productivity is obtained by multiplying the quantity of each product by its price, adding up over all products and dividing by the total land under use.

studies, it was found that the system of equations in each model was overidentified and thus solvable.

3 Results and Discussion

3.1 Results of Partial Analysis

3.1.1 India

Tables 1 and 2 show important features and cropping patterns of the sample farmers in Mahbubnagar and Nagpur districts, respectively. In the case of Mahbubnagar, it was found that the area under commercial crops decreases with increasing distance to the market, while the area under food crops increases. This tendency was found in all farm size groups but it is stronger as farm size increases. In Nagpur District the effect of access to the market on the cropping pattern tends to be similar, but not so significant, i.e. more commercial cropping in the vicinity of markets.

Table 1: Cropping Patterns, Input Use, Total Productivity and Marketable Surplus of Sample Farmers by Farm Size and Market Accessibility in Mahbubnagar Region, India

Group of villages	Nearby (up to 15 km)				Middle (16 to 25 km)				Far (Above 25 km)			
	Small	Medium	Large	All	Small	Medium	Large	All	Small	Medium	Large	All
No. of Farmers	40	40	40	120	35	35	34	104	25	25	25	75
Farm size (acres)	4.8	5.7	7.0	5.8	4.3	5.5	7.3	5.7	5	6.5	6.7	6.1
% HYV area	1.6	4.8	9.6	7.4	1.2	2.9	7.7	6.7	5.5	2.3	1.6	2.3
% food crops	75.0	56.0	56.8	58.1	75.6	65.4	59.0	62.4	73.6	67.0	64.1	66.0
% commercial crops	23.2	36.9	31.1	32.2	20.9	26.8	27.6	27.4	12.2	21.4	26.4	22.7
Fertilizer use (Rs/acre)	10.4	33.2	57.7	33.8	20.6	33.0	46.3	33.2	16.4	16.5	20.2	17.7
Pesticide use (Rs/acre)	0.4	2.0	4.6	2.3	0.2	2.0	1.9	1.4	0.2	0.1	0.5	0.3
Manure (Rs/acre)	26.9	15.5	23.9	23.4	28	16.5	15.4	20.7	38.8	14.5	12.8	19.4
Tot. Productivity (Rs/acre)	419	507	622	516	367	544	528	479	423	387	396	402
% Market Surplus	37	53	60	52	29	48	54	45	35	43	49	42

The use of commercial inputs (fertilizer and pesticides) generally decreases with increasing distance to the market in both regions and for all farm size groups. It is further observed that in both regions, small farmers use more non-commercial inputs than do large farmers and vice versa large farmers use more commercial inputs than do small farmers. Aggregate productivity and market surplus have a positive relationship with farmers' accessibility to market.

Table 2: Cropping Patterns, Input Use, Total Productivity and Marketable Surplus of Sample Farmers by Farm Size and Market Accessibility in Nagpur Region, India

Group of villages	Nearby (up to 15 kms)				Middle (16 to 25 kms)				Far (Above 25 kms)			
	Small	Medium	Large	All	Small	Medium	Large	All	Small	Medium	Large	All
No. of Farmers	75	75	65	215	25	25	25	75	-	-	-	-
Farm size (acres)	2.9	8.5	25.6	11.7	2.8	8.0	22.0	10.9	-	-	-	-
% HYV area	15.6	10.1	12.5	12.7	16.6	8.5	8.3	11.2	-	-	-	-
% food crops	58.7	49.8	45.5	47.7	55.5	48.7	46.5	47.8	-	-	-	-
% commercial crops	33.5	38.4	40.6	39.5	34.8	33.8	37.0	36.0	-	-	-	-
Fertilizer use (Rs/acre)	54.8	49.9	78.9	60.4	64.2	27.9	49.4	47.2	-	-	-	-
Pesticide (Rs/acre)	17.1	16.9	30.6	21.1	17.2	6.5	14.6	12.7	-	-	-	-
Manure (Rs/acre)	31.9	25.2	25.5	27.6	46.8	10.6	26.2	27.9	-	-	-	-
Tot. Productivity (Rs/acre)	481	399	513	462	456	224	416	366	-	-	-	-
% Market Surplus	53	59	60	57	50	49.5	66.3	56	-	-	-	-

- not applicable

3.1.2 Kenya

Partial analysis of land use shows that there is the tendency to allocate more land to crop production as access to the market increases (Table 3). On the other hand, the percentage of land allocated to milk production tends to increase as access becomes more difficult.

Three major inputs were considered in the study – fertilizer, high yielding variety of seeds (HYV), and pesticides. Credit was included as a factor facilitating the use of these inputs. The analysis shows that there is a clear and significant decreasing trend in the use of each of these inputs as access to markets becomes difficult.

3.1.3 Sudan

The percentage share of all perishable high value products in the area cultivated increases with increasing accessibility to the market, while at the same time the percentage share of the area devoted to dry low value crops decreases (Table 4). This tendency was found to be more or less the same for small and large farmers. Therefore, it could be concluded that the accessibility of markets enables the farmers to produce perishable products such as fresh vegetables, fruits and fodder which need to be marketed daily in order to reduce losses. Farmers with difficult access to markets will concentrate more on non-perishable, home consumption products. Hence, market access seems to play a decisive role in farmers' choice of cropping patterns.

Table 3:   Cropping Patterns, Input Use, Total Productivity and Marketable
          Surplus of Sample Farmers by Farm Size and Market Accessibility in
          Nakuru District, Kenya

Access = Item	Easy (up to 0.5 hour)				Middle (0.5 -1 hour)				Far (>1 hour)			
	Small	Medium	Large	All	Small	Medium	Large	All	Small	Medium	Large	All
No. of Farmers	17	16	16	49	17	17	18	53	14	14	14	42
Farm size (acres)	5.7	21.9	65.6	30	6.3	20	64.4	30.5	6.6	21.9	63.6	6.1
% HYV area	69.5	61.4	53.4	61.6	52.2	42.7	49.9	48.2	48.3	42.5	30.6	40.5
Fertilizer (Kg/acre)	28.9	29.1	26.2	28.2	24.5	18.9	26.1	23.1	25.2	22.3	16.3	21.3
Pesticide (KSh/acre)	18.7	19.4	18.6	18.9	14.1	13.9	16.6	14.9	12.5	12	11.2	11.9
Credit (KSh/acre)	794	840	1063	897	779	700	1314	934	679	375	379	477
Cropped area(%)	78.4	75.6	66	70.3	72.6	55.6	63.7	65	74.9	57	58.8	61.4
Dairy Area (%)	21.6	24.4	33.9	26.6	27.4	44.4	36.3	36.2	25.1	43	41.2	36.4
Tot. Productivity (KSh/acre)	4016	3936	3314	3494	3341	2738	3179	3145	3047	2766	1958	2868
% Market Surplus	68.6	84.1	91.6	78.9	60.6	73.2	93.2	71.3	61.6	80.8	81.9	42

Table 4:   Cropping Patterns, Input Use, Total Productivity and Marketable
          Surplus of Sample Farmers by Farm Size and Market Accessibility in
          the Area North of Khartoum, Sudan

Group of villages	Easy access (< 5 hours)			Medium (5-10 hours)			Difficult (> 10 hours)		
	Small	Large	All	Small	Large	All	Small	Large	All
No. of Farmers	35	35	70	34	34	68	31	32	63
Farm size (ha)	2.2	6.0	4.1	3.2	13.8	8.5	2.4	11.6	6.9
% HYV area	13.0	8.5	10.8	2.9	12.0	7.5	4.7	4.0	4.4
% Farmers contacted by Ext. Agent	26	17	21	9	15	12	6	9	8
% Perishable crops	29.2	31.7	31.2	13.3	11.8	12.0	3.3	6.7	5.7
% Dry crops	70.8	68.3	68.8	86.7	88.2	88.0	96.7	93.3	94.3
Fertilizer use (Kg/Ha)	200	208	204	117	144	130	61	72	66
Pesticide use (Ls/ha)	773	887	830	690	1073	881	71	268	171
Total Productivity (in 1000 Ls/ha)	107	108	107	69	77	73	55	55	55
% Market Surplus	98	98	98	94	94	94	91	92	91

The use of mineral fertilizer, pesticides and high yielding seed varieties
increases significantly with market access. This implies that accessibility of the
market induces the farmers to intensify production through the use of modern
inputs. Aggregate productivity and market surplus have a significant positive
relationship with farmers' accessibility to market. Average aggregate productivity
and market surplus of the farmers with relatively easy access to markets are about
twice as high as those of farmers with relatively difficult access, without
significant differences between small and large farmers.

3.2   Results of the Simultaneous Equation Analysis

3.2.1 The Indian Case

Table 5 displays the variables considered in the model and their mean values in the two regions in India. The multivariate regression results are shown in Table 6. The results obtained for Mahbubnagar show in Equation 1 that market distance has a negative effect on productivity for all farm size groups; however this is significant at 10% level for large farmers only. This relationship reflects the specialization effect of market access on productivity through the allocation of cropping patterns, as inputs and other production factors are kept constant. The relationship between market distance and the use of fertilizer as well as HYV show the expected negative signs. However, the impact of market distance on HYV is significant in the case of medium farmers while in the case of fertilizer use, the relationship is only significant for small farmers. Market distance shows the expected negative effect on pesticide use only in the case of small and medium farms and here also is not significant.

Table 5:   List of Variables Considered in the Regression Equations and their
             Mean Values in the two Selected Regions, India

Abbreviation	Description of the variable	Unit	Mean value	
			Mahbugnagar	Nagpur
TP	Total productivity value per acre	Rs	478	437
FER	Fertilizer value per acre	Rs	30.7	57
FYM	Farm yard manure value per acre	Rs	21.5	27.7
PEST	Pesticides value per acre	Rs	1.6	18.9
HYV	High yielding varieties area	%	5.1	12.3
NAL	No. of attached laborers	No.	0.47	0.98
HLAB	Human labor value per acre	Rs	77.7	136
FS	Family size per household	No.	5.8	6.5
CR	Carts per acre	No.	0.07	0.12
IRR	Irrigated area	%	23.8	27.9
CT	Cattle	No.	5.3	6.9
SMK	Nearest market distance, small farmers	Km	20.4	10.9
MMK	Nearest market distance, medium	Km	20.4	10.9
LMK	Nearest market distance, large farmers	Km	20.4	10.9

In Nagpur District, the impact of market distance on productivity through specialization is negative as expected but insignificant for all farm size groups. Fertilizer and pesticide use are significantly influenced by market distance but only in the cases of small and medium farmers.

Table 6: Simultaneous Equation Model and Estimated Parameters of Aggregate Productivity and Input Use as a Function of Resources Given and Market Access by Farm Size, Mahbubnagar District and Nagpur District, India

Variable	Equations (Nagpur)					Equations (Mahbubnagar)				
	1	2	3	4	5	1	2	3	4	5
TP	DEP	-	-	-	-	DEP	-	-	-	-
FER	1.53 $(3.8)^{***}$	-	DEP	-	-	2.26 $(9.2)^{***}$	-	DEP	-	-
FYM	2.43 $(4.5)^{***}$	-	0.03 (0.4)	DEP	-	1.67 $(4.1)^{***}$	-	0.118 (1.4)	DEP	-
PEST	-0.68 (1.0)	-	-	-	DEP	5.7 $(2.7)^{***}$	-	-	-	DEP
HYV	1.77 $(2.2)^{***}$	DEP	1.23 $(8.5)^{***}$	-	0.066 $(0.8)^{***}$	2.16 $(2.9)^{***}$	DEP	0.78 $(3.8)^{***}$	-	0.252 $(10.7)^{***}$
CR	-42.8 (-0.8)	-	-	-2.27 (-0.4)	-	50.1 $(2.1)^{***}$	-	-	0.091 (0.03)	-
IRR	1.47 $(2.4)^{***}$	0.004 (0.1)	0.68 $(8.6)^{***}$	-	-	3.37 $(7.3)^{***}$	0.187 $(8.6)^{***}$	0.896 $(11.1)^{***}$	-	-
HLAB	1.55 $(6.2)^{***}$	-	-	0.238 $(13.0)^{***}$	-	0.51 $(2.2)^{***}$	-	-	0.065 $(2.4)^{***}$	-
FS	_	2.3 $(2.6)^{***}$	-	4.09 (-3.3)	-	_	-0.58 $(-1.6)^{*}$	-	0.99 (1.2)	-
CT	-9.3 (-1.0)	-	-	6.16 $(6.4)^{***}$	-	-20.3 (-1.3)	-	-	15.3 $(6.9)^{***}$	-
SMK	-4.4 $(-1.4)^{*}$	0.018 (0.1)	-1.12 $(-2.0)^{**}$	-	-0.58 (-1.7)	-1.12 $(-1.4)^{*}$	-0.05 (-0.9)	-0.405 $(-1.9)^{*}$	-	-0.03 (-1.1)
MMK	-3.97 (-1.3)	-0.23 (-1.0)	-1.13 $(-1.9)^{*}$	-	-0.81 (-2.4)	-0.62 (-0.8)	-0.11 $(-1.9)^{*}$	-0.289 (-1.4)	-	-0.01 (-0.4)
LMK	-0.6 (-0.2)	-0.48 (-0.2)	-0.008 (-0.01)	-	-0.04 (-0.1)	-1.31 (-1.8)	-0.075 (-1.3)	-0.089 (-0.4)	-	0.009 (0.3)

Figures in parenthesis are t-values; DEP = dependent variable, - = variable not included. Significant levels: *, ** and *** are significant at 10%, 5% and 1% respectively. Adjusted R2 is not applicable in three-stage least square. Source: Survey observations.

3.2.2 The Kenyan Case

Table 7 displays the variables considered in the model, their mean values in Nakuru District, Kenya, and the regression results. Distance to the market for the three classes of farmers is (expectedly) negatively related to the level of total productivity. Even though the estimated coefficients of market access variables for small and medium farms are weak, however, they are significant in the case of large farms. This implies that market access influences specialization in farm production.

Low significance of the impact of other variables in the equations is probably an indicator of a generally weak level of differentiation among the sample farmers. It would seem that differences in market access between 10 and 20 minutes for "good" access and 40 to 50 minutes for "poor" access are not sufficient to cause significantly different behavior and production patterns; in other words, all farmers have a relatively good access to the market and therefore their decisions are not significantly different.

Table 7: Simultaneous Equation Model, Descriptive Statistics and Estimated Parameters of Productivity and Input Use as Functions of Resources and Market Access, Nakuru District, Kenya

Var.	Description	Unit	Mean	S.D.	Eq 1	Eq 2	Eq 3	Eq 4	Eq 5
TP	Total productivity	KSh	3169.4	1521.8	(DEP)	-	-	-	-
HYV	High yielding varieties	% of land	50.5	25.6	39.050 (1,708)**	(DEP)	0.267 (4.85)***	-0.045 (0.674)	-
FERT	Fertilizer	Kg/ acre	24.3	11.1	6.374 (0.076)	-	(DEP)	-	-
PEST	Pesticides	Ksh /acre	15.4	11	-24.614 (0.843)	-	-	(DEP)	-
CREDIT	Formal and informal Credit	Ksh/ acre	788.1	1493.7	0.146 (0.456)	0.029 (8.744)***	0.009 (4.261)***	0.004 (2.236)***	(DEP)
MAS1	Small farms access to local market	min.	11	4.3	-	-	-0.004 (0.025)	-	-
MAS2	Small farms access to central market	min.	44	26.2	-1.433 (0.468)	-0.095 (0.907)	-	-0.088 (2.261)***	-1.96 (0.337)
MAM1	Medium farms access to local Market	min.	18	11.1	-	-	-0.037 (0.532)	-	-
MAM2	Medium farms access to Central Market	min.	47	25.8	-1.401 (0.4675)	-0.127 (1.270)*	-	-0.07 (1.805)**	-3.745 (0.738)
MAL1	Large farms access to local market	min.	18	11.2	-	-	-0.062 (0.798)	-	-
MAL2	Large farms access to central market	min.	49	25	-3.497 (1.201)*	-0.263 (2.63)***	-	-0.067 (1.592)*	0.457 (0.076)
FS	Farm size	Acres	30.6	26	-	-	-	-	-3.879 (0.584)
FZ	Family size	No	6.1	1.8	-	-	-	-	1.499 (0.028)
LBR	Total Human Labor used	Man-days	89.5	48.3	11.619 (2.482)***	-	-	-	-
COWS	Cows per household	No	4.7	3.6	7.435 (0.416)	-	0.006 (0.028)	-	14.699 (0.482)
EXT	Extension service	Contacts/ year	1.4	104	-	-	-	0.415 (2.179)*	-

Figures in parenthesis are t-values; DEP = dependent variable, - = variable not included. Significant levels: *, ** and *** are significant at 10%, 5% and 1% respectively.

3.2.3 The Case of Sudan

A four-equation model describing the direct and the indirect effects of market access on aggregate productivity was specified. Table 8 displays the variables considered in the model and their mean values, while in Table 9 the multivariate regression results are shown.

Table 8: Variables Considered in the Regression Equations and their Mean Values, North of Khartoum, Sudan

Variable	Description of the variable	Unit	Mean value	S.D.
FERQ	Fertilizer use per hectare	Kg	136	134
PEST	Pesticide use per hectare	Ls	641	1064
PHYVA	High yielding varieties area	%	7.6	21
TL	Human labor per hectare	man-days	102.9	73
FS	Family size	Number	8.4	3.4
CFI	Farmers receiving credit from formal institutions	number	0.23	0.42
EXT	Extension visits to the farms	number	0.21	0.61
SQ	Soil quality (1 for silt loam, 0 otherwise)	index	0.83	0.38
KMAS	Transport time to Khartoum for small farmers	Hours	8.0	5.2
KMAL	Transport time to Khartoum for large farmers	Hours	8.0	5.2
NMAS	Transport time to the nearest market for small farmers	Hours	1.6	1.1
NMAL	Transport time to the nearest market for large farmers	Hours	1.6	1.1
FZ	Farm size	Ha	6.5	8.1
TP	Aggregate total productivity per hectare	Ls	79221	54974
MKS	Market surplus per hectare	Ls	76085	56190

S.D. = standard deviations.
Source: Own survey.

Generally speaking, all the market access variables were found to be significant. This implies that market access significantly affects specialization and intensification of farms. Concerning the specialization effect (equation 1) market access variables are significant at 2.5 % and 5 % for large and small farmers, respectively. The relationships between market access and fertilizer and HYV use were found to be significant at 1 % probability level for all farm size groups. In the case of pesticide use, its relationship with market access was found to be significant at 1 % for small farmers and at 5 % for large farmers.

Table 9: Simultaneous Equation Model and Estimated Parameters of
Productivity and Input Use as a Function of Resources and Market
Access by Farm Size, North of Khartoum, Sudan

Variable	Equations			
	1	2	3	4
TP	DEP	-	-	-
FERQ	185.3 (1.6)*	DEP	-	-
PEST	45.6 (3.7)***	-	DEP	-
PHYVA	27.7 (0.03)	6.7 (6.4)***	-9.9 (-1.2)	DEP
TL	348.0 (3.6)***	-	-	-
FS	_	-	-	0.4 (1.1)
EXT	_	-	-	8.8 (4.5)***
SQ	_	-7.3 (-0.4)	-	-
CFI	_	-	-	3.2 (1.2)*
KMAS	_	-11.2 (-5.3)***	-50.8 (-2.7)***	-
KMAL	_	-12.1 (-5.8)***	-36.3 (-2.0)**	-
NMAS	-7835.0 (-1.8)**	_	-	-3.8 (-2.8)***
NMAL	-10807.7 (-2.0)**	-	-	-3.6 (-2.6)***

Figures in parenthesis are t-values; DEP = dependent variable, - = variable not included.
Significant levels: *, ** and *** are significant at 10%, 5% and 1% respectively.
Source: Survey observations.

4   Comparison of the Results Obtained from the Three Studies

In this section, a comparison of the results obtained from the three studies on the impact of market access on agricultural productivity is presented. The focus is on the impact of improved market access on agricultural productivity with regard to efficiency as well as equity across farm size groups. Based on the regression analyses shown in Section 3, elasticities are derived and the impact of a 10% improvement in market access on agricultural productivity is computed and presented in Table 10.

4.1 The Efficiency and Equity Effects of Market Access

In the case of Mahbubnagar Region of India, large farms tend to be affected relatively more through the allocation effect of market access, the medium and small farm groups tend to respond stronger to market distance through changes in input use. The 10 % improvement in market access has an aggregate effect of 0.83 % increase in productivity. In Nagpur District a 10 % market access improvement results in a 1.6 % increase in aggregate productivity on average; small and medium farm groups are significantly affected while for large farms the effect is insignificant.

Table 10: The Impact of 10% Improvement in Market Access on Farmers' Aggregate Productivity in the Study Area

Category	Impact on aggregate productivity (%)		
	Small farms	Medium farms	Large farms
India:			
Mahbubnagar Region:			
(a) specialization effect	0.500	0.300	0.600
(b) input effect	0.508	0.404	0.177
Total effect (a+b)	1.008	0.704	0.777
Nagpur Region			
(a) specialization effect	1.500	1.400	0.200
(b) input effect	0.650	0.740	0.300
Total effect (a+b)	2.150	2.140	0.500
Kenya:			
(a) specialization effect	0.199	0.208	0.541
(b) input effect	0.255	0.573	1.346
Total effect (a+b)	0.454	0.781	1.887
Sudan:			
(a) specialization effect	1.60	-	2.10
(b) input effect	4.40	-	4.00
Total effect (a+b)	6.00	-	6.10

- not applicable.

In Nakuru District of Kenya, a 10 % improvement in access to markets results in an increase of 1.5 % in the aggregate productivity, of which 0,4 % is achieved through specification and 1.1 % through intensification. These low values with low significance levels indicate that the improvement in access to markets does not very strongly affect specialization. However, the improvement has a significant impact on the use of inputs which in turn positively affects productivity.

In Sudan, the market access estimates imply significant specialization and intensification effects: improvement of market access by 10 % would increase aggregate productivity through specialization by 2.1 % in the case of large farmers compared to 1.6 % in the small farmers' case. With regard to the intensification effect (input effect), 10 % improvement in market access would increase the use of inputs (fertilizer, pesticide and high yielding varieties) which, in turn would cause aggregate productivity to increase by about 4.4 % for small farmers compared to 4.0 % for large farmers. That means, a 10 % improvement of market access would increase aggregate productivity through specialization plus intensification by almost the same magnitude of 6.0 % and 6.1 % for small and large farms respectively.

5 Lessons Learned

The three studies from India, Kenya and Sudan show very clearly that market access affects aggregate productivity of farms in all three countries in a similar way:

1. With improved market access aggregate productivity increases.
2. Specialization and intensification effects both contribute to this increase; in India the specialization effect appears to be stronger than the intensification effect; in the two African countries the opposite is found, i.e., the intensification effect contributes about two thirds and the specialization effect only one third of the overall effect.
3. These efficiency gains apply to small as well as to large farmers, but the distribution varies. While in India small farmers tend to gain relatively more than large farmers from better market access, in the African countries it is the group of large farmers that appears to gain relatively more.

The empirical evidence produced by these studies lends support to the request for improving markets in developing countries; institution and infrastructure investments into improving rural marketing systems will significantly increase productivity.

As these efficiency gains go to small *and* large farms, markets per se are not generating a necessarily inequitable distribution of such gains. In India small farmers tend to gain more than large farmers from better market access.

This research on physical market access has laid important ground work. It should lead to further research to include institutional aspects, especially the role of credit, but also the impact of market information, training and education on the performance of the agricultural sector. As much as this study supplies information to prove the positive impact which market improvement exerts on aggregate productivity, it can also be used to predict the negative effects of a deterioration of markets or of a sudden expansion of market activity without a corresponding infrastructure.

In many countries today, markets tend to be opened and liberalized by replacing formerly state controlled systems with systems where little or no control exists and where the organizational and institutional infrastructures are not sufficiently developed to efficiently cope with the task. Not surprisingly, under these conditions inefficient marketing depresses productivity. This aspect requires attention at highest priority, in order to assure that the potential contribution which efficient marketing systems can contribute to agricultural development will indeed be realized to the benefit of small and large farmers as well as consumers in developing countries.

References

Antle, John M. 1985. Measuring Returns to Marketing Systems Investment for Agricultural Development, in: von Oppen, M.: (Ed.); Agricultural Markets in Semi Arid Tropics. Proceedings of the International Workshop 24-28. October 1983, ICRISAT Center, India

Heidhues, F.; Schrieder, G. 1993. The Role of Infrastructure Components for Rural Households Access to Financial Market: A Case Study of Cameroon. In: Thimm, Heinz Ulrich; Hahn, Herwig (Eds.); Reinhard, I.; Schultz, D.: Regional Food Security and Infrastructure (Volume 11). Münster-Hamburg.

Ijaimi, Abdelativ, A. M. 1994. Efficiency and Equity Effects of Market Access on Agricultural Policy in Sudan: A Case Study for Smallholders along the River Nile, North of Karthoum. In: Schriften zur internationalen Agrarentwicklung, Band 12, Köster, Berlin.

Liang, Ernest P. L. 1981. Market Accessibility and Agricultural Development in Prewar China, University of Chicago.

Lipton, M. 1985. The Fear of Trade: Equity Considerations in the Analysis of Marketing 1985. In: von Oppen, M: (Ed.); Agricultural Markets in Semi Arid Tropics. Proceedings in the international Workshop 24-28. October 1983, ICRISAT Center, India.

Mittendorf, H. J. 1993. Organization of Viable Agricultural Marketing and Rural Financial Systems with Particular Reference to Least Developed Countries, 1993. In: Thimm, Heinz Ulrich; Hahn, Herwig (Eds.); Reinhard, I.; Schulz, D.: Regional Food Security and Infrastructure (Volume 11). Münster-Hamburg.

Njehia, B. K. 1994. The Impact of Market Acces on Agricultural Productivity: A Case Study of Nakuru District, Kenya. In: Schriften zur internationalen Agrarentwicklung Band 13, Köster, Berlin.

von Oppen, M.; Parthasarathy Rao, P.; Subba Rao, K.V. 1985. Impact of Market Acces on Agricultural Productivity in India. In: von Oppen, M: (Ed.); Agricultural Markets in Semi Arid Tropics. Proceedings in the international Workshop 24-28. October 1983, ICRISAT Center, India.

von Oppen, M.; Parthasarathy Rao, P.; Subba Rao, K.V. 1984. The Role of Agricultural Marketing for Development. Paper Presented at the IV th European Congress of Agricultural Economists, Kiel,Germany, 3-7 September 1984.

von Oppen, M. 1978. Agricultural Marketing and Aggregate Productivity: A Dimension to be Added to Agricultural Market Research. Economic Program Discussion Paper 3. ICRISAT, India.

von Oppen, M. et. al. 1982. Equity and Efficiency Effects of Market Access for Farmers in two Regions of India. Conference Paper No. 155, ICRISAT. Presented at the International Conference on Improving the Geographical Accessibility of Rural Services, Indian Institute of Management (IIM), 19-21 July 1982, Bangalore, India.

Wanmali, S. 1985. Rural Household Use of Services: A Study of Mirayalguda Taluka, India, Research Report No. 48, International Food Policy Research Institute.

Technological Choices for Sustainable Land Use and Food Security at Farm Household Level

H. Hengsdijk, G. Kruseman, R. Ruben and J. Bade
Agricultural Research Department,
Research Institute for Agrobiology and Soil Fertility (AB-DLO),
Agricultural Economics Research Institute (LEI-DLO) and
Department of Development Economics
Wageningen Agricultural University, The Netherlands

Abstract

A farm household modeling approach is presented that identifies microeconomic responses to the introduction of various technological land use options. In this approach, production and consumption decisions are analyzed simultaneously, permitting an appraisal of the impact of technological change on farm household welfare, land use, and the natural resource base.

The modeling framework is based on the linkage of modules with agro-technical and socio-economic information. It includes separate modules for prices, expenditures, production activities, savings and investments, and resource endowments of farm households.

The model is applied to assess technological options at farm household level in the Koutiala Cercle in Southern Mali. Four types of farm households are defined according to their resource endowments and objectives to acknowledge different directions of responses. The results show which technological options are preferred by which type of farm household and what the effects of the choices are in terms of net revenue, and the balance of soil organic matter, nitrogen and food at farm household level.

Keywords

Farm household model, technological choice, sustainable land use, Mali

1 Introduction

Food production per capita stagnated or declined in large parts of Sub-Saharan Africa over the past two decades (Pinstrup Andersen 1994). Although opportunities to increase food productivity are available, yield performances remain poor (Wolf *et al.* 1991). Moreover, current production systems exhaust natural resources and degrade the production potential of land in a rapid pace. Introduction and dissemination of land use technologies in Sub-Saharan Africa to increase and sustain productivity failed in many cases. Various explanations have been given in literature why new technologies have had such little impact. Possible causes range among others from limited profitability of new technologies, risk aversive behavior of farmers, to an insufficient economic infrastructure (Anderson 1992).

An analytical framework is lacking that permits the appraisal of the impact of technological changes to increase and sustain agricultural production. Such a framework should take into account the agro-ecological possibilities and limitations of land resources and the socio-economic objectives of farm households (Hengsdijk & Kruseman 1992). For policy purposes, three major issues arise regarding technological options: 1. which are the critical components of the technological 'package' that contribute simultaneously to highest net return and maintenance of the natural resource base, 2. which types of farm households are most interested in each of the components of the technological package, and 3. under which market and institutional conditions are farmers able to select these different components? This paper focuses on the first two issues, although the framework proposed is also suited to contribute to the third issue (Ruben *et al.* 1996). Assessment of technological packages on farm household welfare, land use, and natural resources supports policy-makers and extension services in taking decisions on which options are appropriate to introduce and to support with additional policy measures. Moreover, it allows setting priorities for the agricultural research agenda.

The paper presents a framework for the assessment of technological options at the farm household level. A Farm Household Modeling approach using Linear Programming techniques is applied to analyze the responses of farm households in the short and medium term (1-5 years) to the introduction of technological options which are in this context characterized as well-defined ways of converting inputs into agricultural products (Van Keulen 1993). The analyzed technological options in this study refer to changes in agricultural production methods that combine productivity increases with conservation measures, which are considered crucial for sustainable land use in the semi-arid tropics (Reardon 1995).

The Farm Household Modeling framework analyses the impact of technological changes on farm household objectives, production structure, and agro-ecological sustainability indicators for four farm household types in the Koutiala *Cercle* in southern Mali. Agricultural production in this region is based on food crops (millet, sorghum and cowpea), cash crops (cotton and groundnuts), and livestock (cattle, sheep and goats). Average annual rainfall is about 780 mm. Soils can be characterized as loamy sand (50% of all soils), gravely (40% of all soils) and clay depressions (10% of all soils), with low organic matter and nutrient stocks. Besides soil depletion, runoff and erosion are considered as major factors limiting production (Berckmoes *et al.* 1990). Due to a high population growth, pressure on land rapidly increased during the last decades resulting in an over-exploitation of fragile natural resources. As land becomes a scarce factor, attention should be placed on technologies that enable an increased production per unit area (Van Keulen & Breman 1990; Reardon 1995).

2 Methodology and Model Structure

The approach applied is an adaptation of the farm household model described by Singh *et al.* (1986). This model includes linked production and consumption decisions of farm households, which implies maximization of expected utility of consumption subject to budget and time constraints. The budget constraint is linked to the net returns and is derived from a production function. In the present analysis the production decisions are modeled using linear programming techniques, in which production activities are described in terms of discrete technological packages, based on the complex interactions of inputs required to obtain outputs. In this way econometrically derived relations guide the optimization procedure in which the production structure of farm households is determined.

The structure of the farm household model is schematically presented in figure 1. The model includes six separate modules for 1. prices, 2. expenditures, 3. production activities, 4. farm resource endowments, 5. savings and investments and 6. objectives and goal weights. This modular structure permits the linkage of information from agro-technical (e.g. input-output coefficients of production activities generated by crop growth simulation models) and socio-economic (e.g. budget and market surveys, farming systems research) sources.

Figure 1: The Structure of the Farm Household Model

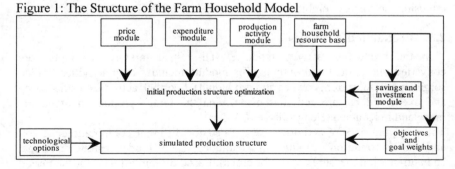

The framework includes separate and subsequent optimization procedures. In the first optimization the initial production structure and allocation of savings of the farm household under 'normal' weather conditions is attained. The resource allocation of this optimization forms the basis for the following optimizations in which in sequential steps technological options are submitted to the model under 'weighted average' weather conditions. The latter accounts for the unknown weather conditions farmers face at the start of the growing season. In these multi-objective optimization steps the effects of technological options on the production structure, farm household objective values and sustainability indicators are analyzed. All optimizations are carried out with constant expected market prices. In the following paragraphs the different modules of the framework are presented.

2.1 Prices

The model makes use of expected market prices, based on a weighted average of real farm-gate prices during the last three years, with coefficients of expectation set at levels of 0.5 for year (t-1) and 0.25 for years (t-2) and (t-3) respectively. Transaction costs are defined as a margin between farm gate and market price, subject to available transport infrastructure and market information. Using hedonic price analysis, these margins are set at 50 %. Statistical records of market prices are only available for tradable commodities. Prices for non-tradable commodities (land) and the terms of trade for reciprocal exchange transactions (family labor, animal traction) are based on implicit prices (Goetz 1992).

2.2 Expenditures

The relationship between household income and consumption utility is estimated using a cross-sectional budget survey (DNSI 1991). Marginal utility of consumption for different expenditure categories (cereals, meat, milk, non-agricultural commodities) is converted into utility making use of a negative exponential function (Ruben *et al.*, 1994). Linearization of this function is carried out using the convex combination constraint (Hazell & Norton 1986).

2.3 Production Activities

In the production activity module, well-defined mixtures of inputs are converted into agricultural outputs. The module includes crop activities (millet, sorghum, maize, cotton, cowpea and groundnut), livestock activities (cattle, sheep and oxen) and pasture activities quantifying the forage production of natural rangeland in Koutiala (Hengsdijk *et al.* 1996).

The crop and pasture activities are defined for different combinations of soil and rainfall conditions, production techniques, use of fodder residue or forage, and anti-erosion measures (only for crops). Based on rainfall data for the period 1950-1981, three types of rainfall years are identified, a 'dry,' a 'normal,' and a 'humid' year, representing the 10% driest, the middle 45% and the wettest 45% of the rainfall years, respectively.

Besides 'current' production activities quantifying the current means of production in Koutiala, technological packages are defined that combine higher productivity with conservation measures (see also section 3). Agro-ecological sustainability in the crop activities is operationalized using a (i) soil organic matter balance defined as the difference between the annual supply of organic matter and the organic matter decomposition in the soil, and (ii) a nutrient balance for N, P and K defined as the difference between the annual supply and withdrawal of these nutrients from the system. Both indicators allow monitoring changes in the organic matter and nutrient stock of the soil. In Koutiala where soil depleting crop activities are currently dominant, crop activities with a positive or equal organic matter and nutrient balance are considered agro-ecologically sustainable.

2.4 Farm Household Resource Endowments

As responses of farm households to technological options depend on their objectives and resource endowments (land, labor, livestock and equipment) four types of farm households are identified in the Koutiala *Cercle*. This classification was developed by the regional development agency *Compagnie Malienne pour le Développement des Textiles* (CMDT 1994) and is mainly based on the availability of animal traction at the farm households, as prospects for agricultural intensification depend to a large extent on access to animal traction and related equipment. Other variables like farm size, labor availability, farm size and land use are highly correlated with animal traction as shown by Brons *et al.* (1994). In table 1 the characteristics of the four farm household types are shown. Farm household types A and B, the largest farm households, represent 46% and 40% respectively of all farm households in Koutiala. They combine food and cash crop production and attain food security with own production, while income growth is attained through investment in cattle and/or intensification of cropping activities (Van der Pol 1993). The smaller households with less equipment (type D) have less diversified production systems and depend on purchase of food to guarantee self-sufficiency. These households rely on hiring of animal traction against payment with labor.

Risk behavior of farm households is characterized by different time discount rates taking into account the valuation of nutrient losses (see also section 2.6). Cropping activities are subject to the available land with prevailing soil types which are distributed over the farm households proportional to the regional soil distribution. The cotton area is limited to a quarter of the total farm area to control soil born diseases. Constraints on oxen and labor availability can be elevated by exchange of these production factors among farm household types.

Table 1: Characteristics of the Identified Farm Households

Farm household characteristic	Type A	Type B	Type C	Type D
Family size (pers.)	25.1	11.9	8.5	5.5
Labor force (pers.)	11.8	5.7	3.9	2.5
Land (ha)	17.8	10.1	5.8	3.3
Cattle (no.)	23.1	3.0	0.6	0.1
Oxen (no.)	5.8	2.7	1.0	0.2
Goats (no.)	4.7	2.5	1.1	0.4
Sheep (no.)	9.6	3.7	1.0	0.1
Donkeys (no.)	1.5	0.7	0.2	0.1
Ploughs (no.)	4.2	2.2	0.9	0.1
Sowers (no.)	1.0	0.3	0.1	0.0
Small equipment (no.)	5.0	5.0	5.0	5.0
Small carts (no.)	1.2	0.7	0.2	0.1
Time discount rate (%)	5	10	18	25
Fixed savings coefficient (%)	20	10	5	1
Number (N)	9092	7905	2383	401

Source: DLV calculations based on CMDT (1994)

2.5 Savings and Investments

Savings and investment decisions are modeled by means of an optimization procedure in which full income is maximized in a normal rainfall year. Transitory savings are used to purchase livestock as a buffer stock to maintain expenditures in periods with adverse weather conditions (Deaton 1990; Rosenzweig & Wolpin 1993). Fixed savings are used to maintain or enhance the resource base through the purchase of additional livestock, equipment, or investments in anti-erosion measures. They vary among farm households expressed in different fixed savings coefficients. Returns for alternative allocations of savings are discounted to allow comparison between farm households.

The savings and investment module permits a dynamic analysis of farm household behaviour, as the recursive modelling framework allows for a separate specification of production and investment decisions. Production decisions are based on the availability of resources and specified fixed and transitory savings coefficients. The fixed savings depend on the income level, while transitory savings represent 80 percent of the difference between (i) the expected income under 'normal' rainfall conditions, and (ii) the effective income under weighted average weather conditions. Work capital is not required, since production costs are financed post-harvest.

2.6 Objectives and Goal Weights

Because it is impossible to elicit farm household objectives directly it is assumed that farm households maximize (i) net expected full income and (ii) consumption utility. Consumption utility is derived from the expenditure module (see section 2.2). Full income is defined as the difference between net revenue and the monetary value of nutrient losses (Van der Pol 1992). An implicit risk objective is applied as different fixed savings coefficients and discount rates taking into account the valuation of nutrient losses. Smaller households tend to be risk aversive (Binswanger 1980; Hazell 1982) as expressed in higher time discount rates and lower fixed savings coefficients (see table 1). In other words, these farm households prefer present consumption before investments for maintaining future consumption.

Goal weights are generated permitting the specification of the relative importance of each objective for the farm households. Following Romero (1993), these goal weights are determined through a confrontation of the calculated values of the specified objectives under partial optimization with only actual production activities and current prices, with the actual objective values as derived from farm survey data for farms with the same resource endowments (DRSPR 1992). Calibration of the model with relative goal weights of .75 for consumption utility and .25 for full income (including monetary value of nutrient losses) provides a reasonable good fit.

3 Technological Options

Eight technological packages are defined in which the impact of farm household objective values, production structure and agro-ecological sustainability indicators are analyzed. The technological options include changes in the production methods to increase productivity and to maintain soil organic matter or nutrient stocks. Moreover, some technological options reduce soil erosion. In table 2 the technological options are summarized as scenarios. The first four scenarios (I, II, III and IV) relate to the cropping systems of farm households, while three other scenarios (V, VI and VII) relate to the livestock component of households. The last scenario VIII combines all preceding technological options.

The defined technological options are not new in the sense that they can be currently practised. However, they are not widely applied in Koutiala.

The defined technological options relate to development objectives formulated by the Malian government (MAAE 1992):

- Reduction of cultivated area under cotton and intensification of cotton production techniques;
- Improvement of integration between cropping and livestock activities;
- Control of erosion and stimulation of soil conservation;
- Intensification of livestock production systems, i.e. increase of value added per animal; and
- Crop and income diversification.

Table 2: Scenarios for the Model Simulations

Scenario:	Characteristics:
I	The introduction of cropping systems using manure and fertilizers in amounts that compensate the annual withdrawal of soil organic matter and nutrients.
II	Scenario I plus the introduction of tied ridging in cropping systems. In this scenario cultivation techniques are taken into account that improve the surface storage capacity by construction of physical barriers. It increases the available water for crop production and reduces soil erosion.
III	Scenario I plus the introduction of mulching in cropping systems. This scenario includes activities in which crop residues are distributed over the land after the harvest of the main produce. The crop residues contribute to the soil organic matter stock and reduce soil erosion. Activities depend less than in scenario I and II on the availability of manure to supply soil organic matter stocks.
IV	This scenario combines the three preceding scenarios (I, II, and III).
V	The production of cowpea straw for feed purposes. This scenario includes activities with cowpea producing high quality fodder. In this scenario feed rations of a better quality can be produced diminishing the pressure on common pastures. The cowpea activities use manure and fertilizers to compensate the annual withdrawal of organic matter and nutrients.
VI	The introduction of animal systems with a higher productivity attained by the introduction of feed rations with a higher percentage of high quality feed.
VII	This scenario combines scenario V and VI.
VIII	All technological options as described in the preceding scenarios.

Integration of livestock and cropping systems can be mutual beneficial: Cropping systems can produce residues and high quality fodder crops (cowpea) for feed, while manure for soil organic matter and nutrient cycling can be used in cropping systems. However, even in such integrated systems supply of fertilizers is a prerequisite to sustain production in the long run as shown by van Keulen & Breman (1990). Therefore, only technological crop options are taken into account in which the annual organic matter and nutrient withdrawal is compensated by manure and fertilizers.

First the model is optimized with activities representing the current production systems. Subsequently, the technological options as defined in Table 3 are incorporated in the model in sequential steps after which optimization takes place with these alternative production activities. Besides alternative technological options in each scenario current (in general soil depleting) cropping activities are offered to the model.

4   Impact of Technological Change

Table 3 shows the impact of the eight technological packages on the net revenue, organic matter balance, nitrogen balance and food balance of the four farm household types. The results are presented as a percentage change in the indicator value compared to the actual situation. Table 4 presents for the four farm household types and for each scenario the area distribution of the technological options among actual and alternative activities, the share of high quality feed in livestock rations, and the share of feed used for high productivity animals.

The net revenue increases in all scenarios compared to the actual situation, except for farm household type D for which scenario I and III do not result in higher net revenues. The latter two scenarios also show the lowest gain in net revenue for the other three households due to continuation of actual activities (see table 4). The net revenues attained in scenario IV in which the technological options of scenario I, II and III are combined closely correspond with the revenues attained in scenario II. The higher net revenues in scenario II and IV are attributed to the application of tied ridges improving the water availability for crop production. Consequently, the increased yields result in higher net revenues than in the other two scenarios I and III. In table 4 the positive response of farm households on the availability of tied ridges is shown. The majority of the alternative activities chosen in scenario II, IV and VIII include activities with tied ridging. This option combines a productivity increase with soil conservation measures best because also erosion is more reduced than in other scenarios (not shown in the table).

The revenues attained in the scenarios V, VI and VII related to the livestock component of the households correspond to a large extent with the number of animals per household. The more animals per household, the larger the impact of these technological options on the net revenue. This is supported by the observation that the share of high quality feed in the livestock rations and the share of feed used for high productivity animals at farm households of type A is generally higher than at the other households (table 4).

The food balances, defined as the difference between production and consumption per capita, decline for all farm household types in most scenarios. Only in scenario II the food balances of farm household type A, B and C increase compared to the current level. In general, the production structure shifts from the production of cereals towards cash crops resulting in higher net revenues which are used to meet household food requirements.

All technological options result in a reduction of the deficient organic matter and N-balances of the households. However, in none of the scenarios technological options can prevent soil depletion. In scenario VIII where all technological options are available, farm household A reduces the organic matter and nitrogen deficit with ± 50%, in contrast to farm household D in which the balances decrease only with ± 15%. This can be explained by the higher time discount rates of farm households of type D.

Table 3:   Impact of Technological Change on Net Revenue, Organic Matter, Nitrogen and Food Balance

Indicator	Farm household type	Actual situation	Scenarios (percentage change in the indicator value compared to actual situation)							
			I	II	III	IV	V	VI	VII	VIII
Net revenue	FH-A	54,812	8	18	8	19	14	14	20	32
(FCFA)	FH-B	41,780	9	25	9	25	11	15	16	33
	FH-C	25,188	8	26	5	25	9	12	12	30
	FH-D	16,768	0	19	0	20	1	3	3	26
OM-balance	FH-A	-1,106	35	46	38	51	38	39	38	54
(kg C ha^{-1})	FH-B	-1,293	31	12	36	37	33	35	34	41
	FH-C	-1,356	30	25	51	31	39	30	39	32
	FH-D	-1,075	27	13	35	10	28	25	28	13
N-balance	FH-A	-38	16	44	21	41	21	23	22	52
(kg N ha^{-1})	FH-B	-45	21	28	22	37	28	26	29	44
	FH-C	-43	11	24	21	22	18	11	18	25
	FH-D	-38	0	15	6	12	2	2	3	15
Food-balance	FH-A	44	-58	32	-37	-75	-21	-14	-24	-73
balance	FH-B	199	-34	31	-43	-34	-46	-18	-53	-48
(kg cereal	FH-C	66	-68	18	-123	-77	-101	-69	-102	-78
per capita^{-1})	FH-D	-68[1]	-61	-73	-56	-83	-65	-66	-72	-108

[1] A negative food balance in the actual situation means a cereal deficient farm household relying on market purchase to meet household food requirements.

Scenario I, II and IV can be considered as serial developments in land use technology. Farm household A increases both net revenues and organic matter balance in consecutive steps. Farm household type B and C increase in scenario II their net revenues at the expense of their organic matter stocks. In scenario IV the net revenues of farm household types B and C remain stable at a high level and the organic matter balance is slightly higher than in scenario I. Net revenues of farm household type D increase at the expense of the organic matter balance in scenario II and IV compared to scenario I.

Closer examination of table 3 reveals the occurrence of trade-offs between net revenues and sustainability indicators. Net gain and losses in the organic matter balance are valued against future effects using farm household type specific time discount rates in the calculation of full income. Even though discount rates go down as the available assets increase, the effects of the trade-offs are visible for all households. The organic matter balance of farm household C increases significantly between scenarios I and III while the net revenue drops. The other households maintain income levels with lower improvements in the organic matter balance. Comparing scenarios VI and VII shows trade-offs in favor of income for farm households A and B, and in favor of the organic matter balance for farm households C and D. The existence of these trade-offs in the comparison of scenarios indicates that the response of farm households to technological changes is sensitive to exogenous parameters (e.g. time discount rates) and variables (e.g. distribution of resources).

Table 4: Area Distribution of the Technological Options, the Share of High Quality Feed in the Livestock Rations, and the Share of Feed Used for High Productivity Animals for the four Farm Households.

Farm Household type	Type of activity	Actual situation (ha)	Scenarios (in ha)							
			I	II	III	IV	V	VI	VII	VIII
FH-A	actual activities	17.9	11.8	7.8	10.8	7.6	11.6	11.0	11.6	7.1
	total alt. activities[3]	-	6.1	10	7.0	10.1	6.3	6.8	6.3	10.7
	- tied ridges	-	-	5.2	-	6.7	-	-	-	7.9
	- mulch	-	-	-	1.8	4.9	-	-	-	2.5
	% Q8 menus[1]	-	-	-	-	-	33	-	43	48
	% P4 systems[2]	-	-	-	-	-	-	71	73	60
FH-B	actual activities	10.1	7.8	5.7	7.1	4.9	7.1	7.3	7.1	5.4
	total alt. Activities	-	2.3	4.4	3.1	5.2	3.0	2.8	3.0	4.8
	- tied ridges	-	-	3	-	3.3	-	-	-	3.5
	- mulch	-	-	-	2	3.2	-	-	-	2.5
	% Q8 menus	-	-	-	-	-	25	-	18	6
	% P4 systems	-	-	-	-	-	-	31	26	28
FH-C	actual activities	5.8	4.3	3.7	3.0	4.0	4.0	4.4	4.3	4.0
	total alt. Activities	-	1.5	1.5	2.8	1.8	1.8	1.4	1.5	1.8
	- tied ridges	-	-	1.2	-	1	-	-	-	1.4
	- mulch	-	-	-	2.1	0.8	-	-	-	0.7
	% Q8 menus	-	-	-	-	-	52	-	34	25
	% P4 systems	-	-	-	-	-	-	54	12	38
FH-D	actual activities	3.3	3.2	3.0	3.2	2.9	3.2	3.2	3.2	2.9
	total alt. activities	-	0.1	0.4	0.1	0.4	0.1	0.1	0.1	0.4
	- tied ridges	-	-	0.4	-	0.4	-	-	-	0.4
	- mulch	-	-	-	0	-	-	-	-	0.1
	% Q8 menus	-	-	-	-	-	0	-	1	11
	% P4 systems	-	-	-	-	-	-	40	28	11

[1] % menus Q8 = the percentage of feed with a high quality (Q8) fed to the animals.
[2] % P4 systems = the percentage of feed fed to high productivity animals (P4).
[3] Alternative activities can include activities as defined in scenario I, mulching (scenario II) and tied ridging (scenario III). The latter two activities can occur simultaneously. Therefore, the areas with tied ridging and mulching can exceed the total area with alternative activities.

5   Discussion

The approach presented offers an analytical framework for the appraisal of technological packages on farm household welfare, land use and the natural resource base. The model approach takes into account the multiple and divergent objectives and differences in resource endowments of farm households, while agro-ecological relationships are quantified in the cropping, livestock and pasture production activities. Although the results of this study should be used with care they illustrate the type of information generated by the model which is especially suited to identify technological packages contributing to the revenue of farm households while at the same time maintaining the natural resource base.

The results indicate that the technological options analyzed in this study differ in their impact on farm household welfare, production structure and natural resource base. The impact of technological change increases with the size of the farm household. This can partly be explained by the assumed time preferences expressed in the discount rates of farm household types valuing a reduction of the soil nutrient and organic matter depletion. Another part can be explained by the size of the resource base (available equipment, number of animals, etc.) of the larger farm households which allows them to adopt technological options more easily.

The impact of the analyzed technological options in this study can not be equated with the actual adoption process by farm households. The speed of adoption depends on adopter-specific characteristics, e.g. knowledge, access to markets, infrastructure, presence of institutions etc., factors which have not been taken into account. Moreover, results of the individual four types of farm households should be aggregated to analyze the interaction among farm households and its effect on various markets (input, produce, labor, etc.).

The farm household modeling approach presented in this paper integrates econometric techniques, based on continuous functions, with linear programming techniques, based on discrete technological options. Its modular structure allows the adaptation of relevant modules in case of improved data availability. Particularly, the specification of more detailed empirical evidence with respect to decision making on various aspects of the households (consumption, labor use, etc.) can improve the results. To determine contributions of off-farm employment to on-farm investments, linkages with the non-agricultural sector must be incorporated in the model. With respect to the production activity module a more dynamic definition of the activities is required to acknowledge the effects of changes in the natural resource base and to gain insight in the competition between investments in conservation measures to improve the production potential of land and investments in (on-or off-farm) activities that may have higher short-run pay-offs (Reardon 1993).

6   Lessons Learned

To analyze the impact of new technologies in Sub-Saharan Africa integration of agro-ecological and socio-economic aspects of households is required because sustainable land use and food security are affected by their combined effects. Although the approach presented can be improved at several points the results indicate that introduction of (sustainable) technological options alone is insufficient to offset depletion of the natural resource base in Koutiala. Additional policy measures will be required to reverse the soil degradation process. Moreover, most scenarios showed declining food balances of farm households compared to the current situation indicating a shift from cereal production towards cash crops. This implies a higher market dependency which is only possible when regional cereal markets are functioning well. Although not applied in this way, the framework presented is suitable to analyze the effectiveness of policy measures, such as price instruments as well as in the field of institutional reform to support the introduction of new technologies and to attain agro-ecological sustainable land use (Ruben *et al.* 1996). Research efforts have to continue to sketch the choices at stake so that policy formulation with respect to land use and food security can be improved.

Acknowledgments

The DLV research project is financed by the Netherlands Ministry of Agriculture, Nature Management and Fisheries (LNV) and the Directorate-General for International Cooperation (DGIS) of the Ministry of Foreign Affairs. We thank the *Institut d'Economie Rurale* (IER), the *Projet Production Soudano Sahélienne* (PSS-Niono) and the *Equipe Systèmes de Production et Gestión de Ressources Naturelles* (ESPGRN-Sikasso) for their cooperation and sharing data.

References

Anderson, J.R. 1992. Difficulties in African Agricultural Systems Enhancement? Ten hypotheses, Agricultural Systems 38 (1992) 387-409.

Berckmoes, W.M.L., E.J. Jager & Y. Koné 1990. L'intensification agricole au Mali-Sud: souhait ou réalité?, Amsterdam: Royal Tropical Institute. Bulletin No. 318. pp. 40.

Binswanger, H.P. 1980. Attitudes towards risk: experimental measurement in rural India, American Journal of Agricultural Economics 64, 391-393.

Brons, J, S. Diarra, I. Dembélé, S. Bagayoko & H. Djouara (1994) Diversité de Gestión de l'Exploitation Agricole: Estude sur les facteurs d'intensification agricole au Mali Sud, Sikasso: IER-DRSPR Document No. 94/33. pp 70.

CMDT 1994. Annuaire Statistique - Résultats de l'Enquête Agricole Permanente 93/94, Bamako: Suivi Evaluation CMDT.

Deaton, A.S. 1990. Savings in Developing Countries: Theory and Review, World Bank
    Economic Review (4): 61-96.
DNSI 1991. Enquête Budget Consommation (1988-1989), Bamako: DNSI/PADEM/DSA
DRSPR 1992. Commision technique sur les systemes de production rurale. Synthese des
    resultats de la campagne 1991/1992, DRSPR/Sikasso, 199 pp.
Goetz, S.J. 1992. A Selectivity Model of Household Food Marketing Behaviour in Sub-Saharan
    Africa, American Journal of Agricultural Economics (64): 444-452.
Hazell, P.B.R. 1982. Application of risk preference estimates in farm household and agricultural
    sector models, American Journal of Agricultural Economics 64: 384-390.
Hazell, P.B.R. & R.D. Norton (1986) Mathematical Programming for Economic Analysis in
    Agriculture, New York: MacMillan. pp. 400.
Hengsdijk & G. Kruseman 1992. Operationalizing the DLV-program: an integrated agro-
    economic and agro-ecological approach to a methodology for analysis of sustainable land
    use and regional agricultural policy, DLV-report no. 1, Wageningen, 107 pp.
Hengsdijk, H., W. Quack & E.J. Bakker 1996. A Land Use System and Technology Generator
    for the Koutiala Region in South Mali, DLV Report No. 5, Wageningen (in prep.)
Keulen, H. van & H. Breman 1990. Agricultural Development in the West African Sahelian
    Region: a cure against land hunger?, Agriculture, Ecosystems and Environment (32): 177-
    197.
Keulen, H. van 1993. Options for agricultural development: a new quantitative approach, In:
    Systems approaches for Agricultural Development, 355-365 (F.W.T. Penning de Vries et al.
    (eds.)). Kluwer Academic Publishers, The Netherlands.
MAEE 1992. Schema Directeur du Secteur Developpement Rural, Bamako: MAEE
Pinstrup-Andersen, P. 1994. World Food Trends and future food security, Food Policy Report,
    The International Food Policy Research Institute. Washington D.C. 25 pp.
Pol, F. van der 1992. Soil mining. An unseen contributor to farm income in Southern Mali,
    Amsterdam: Royal Tropical Institute Bulletin No. 325., 47 pp.
Pol, F. van der 1993. Profits de l'Intensificacion, Amsterdam: Royal Tropical Institute, 38 pp.
Reardon, T. 1993. Cereals Demand in the Sahel and Potential Impacts of Regional Cereal
    Protection, World Development (21), 3: 17-35.
Reardon, T. 1995. Sustainability issues for agricultural research strategies in the semi-arid
    tropics: Focus on the Sahel, Agricultural Systems (48): 345-359.
Romero, C. 1993. A research on Andalusian farmers' objectives: methodological aspects and
    policy implications, Paper presented to VII EAAE Congress, Stresa, Italy.
Rosenzweig, M.R. & K.I. Wolpin 1993. Credit Market Constraints, Consumption Smoothing,
    and the Accumulation of Durable Production Assets in Low-income Countries: Investments
    in Bullocks in India, Journal of Political Economy (101), 2: 223-244.
Ruben, R., G. Kruseman & H. Hengsdijk 1994. Farm Household Modelling for estimating the
    Effectiveness of Price Instruments on Sustainable Land Use in the Atlantic Zone of Costa
    Rica, DLV-Report No. 4., Wageningen, 44 pp.
Ruben, R. G. Kruseman, H. Hengsdijk & A. Kuyvenhoven 1996. The impact of agrarian policies
    on sustainable land use in Koutiala Cercle of Mali, International symposium on Systems
    Approaches for Agricultural development, IRRI, Los Baños, 1995. (in press)
Singh, I.J., L. Squire & J. Strauss, (eds.) 1986. Agricultural household models: extensions,
    applications and policy, Baltimore: The Johns Hopkins University Press. 335 pp.
Wolf, J., H. Breman and H. van Keulen 1991. Bio-economic capability of West-African
    drylands, CABO-DLO Report 147, 83 pp.

Part Four

Diffusion and Adoption of Innovations

Part 4.1

Diffusion and Adoption of Innovations
Research Issues

Making Farmers Full Partners in the Diffusion and Adoption of Innovations

Barbara Huddleston
Food Security and Agricultural Projects Analysis Service
FAO, Rome

Abstract

This paper presents the experience gained and lessons learned by the FAO in the field application of participatory methods for the diffusion of improved agriculture technology. The two presented methods are Farmers' Field Training Schools and Problem-Specific Extension Campaigns. Building on this experience, FAO has recently developed a framework paper for a Special Program on Food Production in Support of Food Security in Low-Income Food-Deficit Countries which proposes the systematic application of a participatory approach on a wide scale to promote more rapid diffusion of available technologies to enhance productivity and increase food production.

Keywords

Extension campaigns, diffusion techniques, FAO, participatory training

1 Introduction

Over the years FAO has gained considerable experience in the field application of participatory methods for the diffusion of improved agriculture technology. Experience gained and lessons learned from the application of two of the more successful of these methods (Farmers' Field Training Schools and Problem-Specific Extension Campaigns) is reported in Sections 2 and 3. Building on this experience, FAO has recently developed a framework paper for a Special Program on Food Production in Support of Food Security in Low-Income Food-Deficit Countries which proposes the systematic application of a participatory approach on a wide scale to promote more rapid diffusion of available technologies to enhance productivity and increase food production. The Special Program concept, and challenges facing FAO in its implementation, are described in Section 4.

2 Farmers' Field Schools

The two diffusion techniques reported in this paper have been selected because they have been found to be effective for encouraging widespread adoption of new technology, at the scale necessary to promote significant aggregate increase in productivity and production. The first is the Farmers' Field Schools.

Concept

Farmers Field Schools (FFS) were introduced as an innovative participatory training technique for integrated pest management (IPM) concepts and methods. They were first used in Indonesia and subsequently in other national IPM programs.

A Farmers' Field School is a group of about 25 farmers who agree to meet once a week for an entire crop season. This means from 12-16 weekly meetings of at least half a day each. On a typical day, the 25 farmers will break into five small field teams and spend one to two hours in the field making observations, counting population densities of different species, assessing crop physiological condition, and recording observations. Each team then assembles outside the field and discusses, analyzes and interprets its data. The interpreted data are then summarized, often in an agro-system diagram, and presented to the entire field school.

IPM Field Schools are forums for community action. Farmers who live in a village share both its ecological location and a social and political community. IPM Farmers' Field Schools are forums where farmers and trainers debate observations. They apply their previous experiences and present new information from outside the community; the results of the meetings are management decisions on what action to take. Thus, IPM is a dynamic process that is practiced and controlled by farmers. It is not a passively adopted product or technology. IPM training assists farmers to transform their observations to create a more scientific understanding of their agro-ecosystem.

The stronger and more positive interactions between extension workers and farmers benefit extension systems as a whole. Instead of chasing farmers with packages of inputs and collecting loans given out to enable farmers to use those packages, extension trainers become partners in a joint discovery process. This process carries mutual respect for the persons and experiences of farmers and extension staff. IPM triggers a transformation of extension agencies starting from the local level, up to the sub-national level.

Extension workers must become skilled facilitators of groups; this means that the training of trainers, which is much more intensive for IPM than normal agricultural extension, must include group dynamics and group strengthening. Eventually, the extension workers become able to take initiatives inside the agency in planning, monitoring and evaluating, and ultimately in owning the process of extension.

Demand for higher quality technology makes farmers better clients for researchers. It also makes them more articulate. These farmers are in a position to evaluate new technical options presented by agricultural researchers. They are more critical of new proposed technologies. Being more critical does not mean being resistant to change. In fact, it may mean changing faster and changing in a more fundamental fashion. Training-driven research focuses on local problems and concentrates farmers' attention on the processes that contribute to making technology work.

The discovery-based learning process reduces farmers' dependence on outside technology and increases their self-reliance, strengthens indigenous investigations that farmers have carried out through millennia and makes them more active, stronger partners who can make the research and extension system responsive to local needs and priorities.

Experience

While research in IPM has a longer history in Europe and North American than in any other region, Asia is the region where more farmers use IPM. The central accomplishment of Asian IPM Programs has been the steady increase in rice production and in rice yield per hectare without increasing, and usually reducing, the use of insecticides. However, after the first crop season, focusing on IPM and rice, FFS groups have also become interested, through their own observations in the field, in IPM for rotation crops of rice such as vegetables and legumes. They have gone on to experiment with rice-fish culture and considered the use of aquatic resources for the culturing of shrimps, snails, frogs and other aquatic protein.

Experience in Asia is that Integrated Pest Management as a policy and as a training process results in markedly increased benefits of rice farming. IPM is the first example of a rapid technological change that makes the agricultural production system not only higher-yielding but more sustainable. The use of imported inputs that require scarce foreign exchange has declined. At the same time, production continues to increase as farmers understand crop ecology better and, therefore, improve management.

There are good possibilities for using FFS as a vehicle for discovery-based learning for diffusion of other innovations. The initial training cost may be high, but the potential payoff may also be high. To succeed on any significant scale, FFS have to be integrated in national agricultural extension programs as an accepted training technique.

3 Problem Specific Extension Campaigns

Concept

In the context of agricultural extension, a campaign is one of the methods of extension which can reach a large number of target beneficiaries in a short time period. It is not meant to replace other existing programs of a national agricultural extension service, but rather to complement and improve upon them. It generally exhibits the following characteristics:

- A strategic extension campaign focuses on a specific issue or recommended technology.
- Its goals are consistent with, and guided by, the overall agricultural development policies and extension program objectives.
- Campaign objectives are formulated based on intended beneficiaries' felt needs and problems, identified through a baseline survey of their Knowledge, Attitudes and Practices (KAP) vis-à-vis the recommended technology.
- A specific extension campaign strategy is developed with the aim of solving problems that caused non adoption, and/or inappropriate or discontinued practice, of the recommended technology.
- A strategic planning approach is applied in the processes of target audience segmentation, multi-media selection, message/information positioning and design, and packaging, development and production of extension and training materials, with a view of obtaining maximum impact with the minimum effort, time, and resources.
- Field pretesting of prototype multi-media campaign materials is conducted before they are mass-produced.
- Campaign management plans spell out implementation procedures and requirements, including for monitoring and supervision.
- Special briefing and training for all personnel who are involved in the extension campaign activities must be undertaken to ensure that they understand their specific tasks and responsibilities and have the necessary skills and support materials to perform such tasks effectively.
- Tools such as Management Monitoring Survey, Information Recall and Impact Survey, and Focus Group Interviews, are used to improve on going performance, and to determine results and overall effectiveness, as well as to draw lessons from such experiences for future replications.

Experience

Empirical evaluation studies of strategic extension campaign methods (using information recall and impact surveys, focus group interviews and management monitoring surveys), have been prepared for a number FAO-supported problem-specific extension campaigns, conducted, for instance, in Bangladesh and Malaysia (on weed management), Zambia (on maize production), Malawi, Jamaica and Morocco (on population education). These studies all reported positive changes in farmers' knowledge, attitudes and practices vis-à-vis the recommended technologies, as well as significant economic benefits.

As an example, during 1990-1992, Strategic Extension Campaign activities on maize production were undertaken in Zambia.

Provincial and District Crop Husbandry Specialists of the Department of Agriculture in Southern Province were given training on effective methodology of field inquiry and reconnaissance surveys, with a view to identifying farmers' main problems and constraints and consequently to provide solutions, through development of area specific problem-solving oriented agronomic, livestock, post-harvest losses practices and messages. An instrument for a survey of the farmers' Knowledge, Attitudes and Practices vis-à-vis maize production was completed in November 1990.

Extension personnel were trained in KAP survey implementation techniques in February 1991, and they conducted the KAP/baseline survey on maize production through personal interviews and focus group interviews with farmers from March to July 1991.

The findings from the KAP/baseline survey were analyzed and utilized in Strategic Extension Campaign (SEC) workshops in October and November 1991 and again in February and September 1992. These workshops aimed at planning and developing a campaign strategy and designing prototype messages and multi-media materials based on the identified problems for the SEC on Maize Production in Southern Province. Additional aims of the workshop were: to provide extension workers with a theoretical and practical understanding and conceptual framework of strategic planning and management; to demonstrate how to formulate objectives and strategies for extension program planning, including problem identification, objective formulation, strategy development and audience segmentation; to impart skills and techniques on multi-media campaign planning, strategy development, message design, and pretesting of prototype multi-media materials.

At least eight provincial and district Crop Husbandry Specialists, 55 Block Supervisors, 48 Subject-Matter Specialists, and 202 Camp Officers, were trained on various SEC activities in Southern Province. A wide variety of multi-media materials covering 17 different types of messages were developed, pretested, and reproduced in large quantities in 1991. The Maize Production Campaign was conducted in 1991-1992, and later, in mid-1992 new campaign topics, such as livestock (i.e. cattle), sorghum, sunflower and post-harvest practices were also introduced.

One of the results of the SEC activities that has important implications on future extension program planning was that campaign messages created additional demand for information and education. Thus farmers are now requesting more frequent and specific extension and training services from extension workers. Once stimulated or made aware of the campaign issues or messages through multi-media channels or materials, farmers in Southern province sought additional information from neighbors, friends, extension workers, and/or progressive farmers in the area. Farmers and other interested groups approached agricultural camps, blocks, district and provincial offices requesting more copies of extension support materials and more messages to be developed. Fortunately, there were enough copies of the campaign media materials in local languages and their distribution was also timely. The experience of the project has been that the demand from farmers and extension workers for more extension and training activities was greater than expected, as a result of the campaign activities.

An in-depth evaluation in March 1992 found that the project has been successful in its implementation. The project was highly commended for the strategic extension campaign (SEC) methodologies used, high implementation rate (average 98 percent), monitoring and evaluation activities, and over-all technical and operational soundness.

4 Partnership Philosophy in the FAO Special Program on Food Production in Support of Food Security in Low-Income Food-Deficit Countries

Concept

Upon assuming office in January 1994, the new Director-General of FAO introduced a new Special Program to give high priority to helping LIFDCs improve their national food security through rapid increases in productivity and food production as well as through reduction in year-to-year variability in production on an economically and environmentally sustainable basis.

The Program intends to achieve its aims through dissemination of existing and proven agricultural technology, and the removal of constraints which hinder its adoption. Building on lessons learned from past experiences such as those described above, it proposes to make systematic use of participatory on-farm demonstrations as an entry point for identifying the actions necessary to create a socio-economic environment conducive to the sustainable increase of production. It will also follow a participatory and integrative approach in order to assure sustainability and equity.

In each participating country, the Program starts with the Formulation of a National Program through a participatory process of identification of staple foods, areas and technological aspects which would be the basis for determining Program activities in the country. A national formulation team acts as a bridge between FAO, government, farmers, the private sector agents and external partners in developing the details of Special Program activities in the context of the specific country situation.

National Program Implementation commences with a Pilot Phase which is an action-oriented, participatory process of consultation, problem identification and planning. The Pilot Phase features on-farm demonstrations of improved, sustainable farming and water management technologies and practices; and constraints and opportunities analyses at both local and national levels.

The demonstrations serve as a point of entry for beginning a process of ongoing dialogue between farmers, private sector agents and government officials on the potential benefits of the technologies and practices being demonstrated, the constraints to their more widespread adoption, and the actions needed to overcome these constraints. A successful Pilot Phase is followed by a wider-ranging Expansion Phase covering technical solutions, policy measures, investments and capacity-building programs which will address identified problems impeding sustained increases in food production. A National Plan of Action for the Expansion Phase is formulated and the mobilization of resources necessary to implement the Plan of Action is begun during the Pilot Phase.

The Special Program will be adjusted in the light of experience and progress. It is meant to be flexible and holistic, gender-sensitive, participatory and multi-disciplinary. All its activities are to be rooted in community participation, particularly of producers and their association, and the private sector agents. Special emphasis is placed on getting active participation from women's groups and associations. The aim is to ensure that all the elements for success are in place in an integrated, timely and coherent way at community, regional and national levels before engaging in large investment programs.

Challenge Ahead

The Special Program requires the systematic integration of participatory methods to deal with at least four different aspects of the overall approach:

- first, for identifying farmers' problems in selected sites and planning demonstrations which respond to these problems;
- second, for interacting with farmers to identify constraints to widespread adoption of desired technologies and possible solutions to these constraints;
- third, for understanding the socio-economic impacts of adoption of a recommended innovation in the local area, and for planning complementary measures to preserve social equity, if required;
- fourth, for fostering greater awareness of and support for Program goals and activities at all levels of society, and for promoting an understanding of and political support for policy reforms needed to create an enabling environment for agricultural innovation to succeed.

In the 15 countries initially invited to participate in the Program field application of these methods was somewhat uneven at the start. FAO's strategy for providing technical support for implementation of this approach on the scale required by the Special Program, includes the following elements:

- cataloguing participatory and data-gathering methods and tools, as well as experiences of fostering people's participation and conducting socio-economic, demographic and gender analysis, known to FAO;

- conducting field research on participatory and data-gathering approaches, methods and tools used in the Special Program countries;
- convening regional and Rome-based workshops to evaluate the applicability of various participatory and data-gathering methods and tools for the needs of the Special Program in specific country situations;
- training national teams in the use of participatory techniques to plan and implement Pilot Phase demonstration activities, in the conduct of participatory constraints and opportunities analysis in the Pilot Phase demonstration areas, in the conduct of socio-economic and gender analyses, and so forth;
- conducting national information campaigns and participatory fora for the Special Program.

In summary, the Special Program does not base itself only on the level of a Ministry of Agriculture looking down at the farmer, trying to solve his or her problems from above. Instead, it bases itself at the side of the farmer, looking out on the opportunities and difficulties in his or her immediate environment, and offering access to innovations which enable the farmer to take greater advantage of the former and overcome the latter. In this task FAO believes we must all work together to become better partners.

5   Boxes

Box 1: Rapid Rural Appraisal

RRA is a qualitative diagnostic study which uses a variety of data-gathering techniques such as case studies, in-depth interviews with key informants, group interviews, participant observation, secondary data sources and semi-structed interviews with a number of households to permit comparison of different farming systems or socio-economic groups.

Its core features include: (i) interdisciplinary teamwork; (ii) use of indigenous knowledge; (iii) triangulation of information (using different methods, sources, technical disciplines and a range of informants for cross-checking); (iv) the use of purposive sampling; (v) flexibility; and (vi) use of conscious judgment.

The purpose of this method is to enable outsiders to gain information and insights on constraints and opportunities from local people.

Box 2: Participatory Rural Appraisal

The PRA refers to a diagnostic process that empowers local people to change their own condition and situation by conducting their own analysis and planning and taking action. A PRA field exercise is not only for collection of qualitative information and idea generation, but is about analysis and learning by local people. It is about building the process of participation, of discussion and communication, and of constraint resolution.

The focus of analysis in PRA is not just the data collection but is part of the process of development and empowerment and as such an integral part of long-term dialogue and sustained interaction. The PRA does not offer quick solutions to complex problems. It is a learning process that develops and promotes new methods and changes to prevailing attitudes, skills, technologies and procedures.

PRA-techniques include: (i) people's mapping and modeling on the ground; (ii) transect walks with key informants through an area, observing, asking, listing, discussing and learning about different zones, local technologies, introduced technologies, seeking problems, solutions, opportunities and mapping resources and findings; (iii) timeliness and trend and change analysis of major local events; (iv) seasonal and crop calendars; (v) institutional diagramming (identifying individuals and institutions important for the community); (vi) wealth ranking; (vii) matrix scoring and ranking (e.g. to compare different soils, irrigation methods, varieties, technologies etc.).

Box 3: Problem Census/Problem Solving

In a number of countries top-down extension approaches have recently been successfully replaced or augmented by participatory Problem Census/Problem Solving (PC/PS approaches). In essence the approach is to use extension staff as facilitators, or coordinators who help groups of farmers help themselves by first identifying their priority problems and then focusing their attention on solving these problems. The methodology is simple but for best results needs to be carried out with some rigor. A summary of the approach follows:

(i) Coordinators make it clear to participating farmers (groups) that their task is to stimulate and record any discussions, their task is not to impose solutions.

(ii) Coordinators initiate discussion by asking each farmer to consider the problems they have related to specific, important farming activities.

(iii) The group is then divided into sub-groups of 4-6 members, and each sub-group discusses the problems identified by its members. One member of the sub-group is given responsibility to report on the sub-group's main concerns.

(iv) All members of the group then reconvene in a plenary session and each group in turn reports on ist main concerns. After all sub-groups have reported, the plenary group ranks the problems/constraints identified.

(v) The coordinator then initiates a discussion about how the main problems identified by the group could be addressed, e.g. better access to inputs, better marketing and prices, use of the constraints such as the need for better access roads, may not be easy to address. However by discussion it should be possible for the group to select a number of actions that could be undertaken locally during the next cropping season to show how some of the priority constraints can be addressed. At the same time, those requiring action at a higher political level can be referred to local authorities in the name of the group.

Box 4: Knowledge, Attitude and Practice (Kap) Survey

In many countries, extension resources (i.e. funds, facilities, staff, and time) are limited, and thus the effective and efficient use of such resources is imperative. A strategic planning approach by employing a KAP survey, can help in identifying critical extension/education intervention areas which are important and likely to create a significant impact. The KAP survey is used to analyze which specific elements of the technology package are not known to the majority of farmers, what the reasons for their negative attitudes are, how and why they have practiced recommended technologies inappropriately, etc.

In most instances, it is unnecessary to provide all farmers with a complete set of technology recommendations as some of them may already know, have agreed with, and/or acted on, the necessary information. Problem-solving and strategic extension planning basically follows the principle of "start with what they know, and build on what they have."

KAP surveys try to understand and assess farmers' local indigenous knowledge, values and belief systems on farming systems which may be good, need to be improved, or perhaps need to be discouraged.

References

Adhikarya, Ronny 1994. Strategic Extension Campaign: A Participatory-oriented Method of Agricultural Extension, FAO, Rome.

FAO, Agricultural Technology and Dissemination Project for Nepal, Annex 10: "Farmer Group Operations Manual: A Manual for Use by Extension Workers in the Formation and Management of Farmers' Groups."

FAO, APRC/94/3. "Sustainable Agriculture through Integrated Pest Management," May 1994.

FAO, SPFP/DOC/..., "Advisory Note on the Planning and Conduct of Participatory Demonstration," Working Draft, Rome, October 1995.

FAO, SPFP/DOC/4-Rev.1, "Special Programme on Food Production in Support of Food Security in LIFDCs (SPFP): Rationale, Objectives and Approach," Rome, February 1996.

Strengthening of National Research Organizations through the CGIAR-System

Christian Bonte-Friedheim
ISNAR, The Hague, The Netherlands

1   Introduction: NARS, NAROs and NARIs

There is a difference between NARS (National Agricultural Research System), NAROs and NARIs. NAROs and NARIs are individual organizations and institutes within the System. Contrary to today's topic, this contribution to the Hohenheim International Symposium will concentrate on national systems.

2   The Diversity of our World

It is widely assumed that NARS of different countries are similar, and can easily be compared. Such assumptions do not recognize the diversity of our world.

Figure 1:   World Map

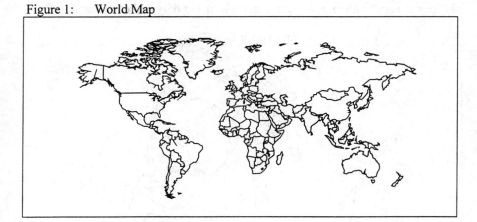

This is the traditional world map, identifying continents and oceans, as well as country boundaries.

Our world, its different continents and countries, different people, cultures and other aspects can be shown in many ways. For several problems linked to agricultural development, the following four maps have been selected to provide a different picture of our globe.

Figure 2:   Anamorphosis of the World: Population Density

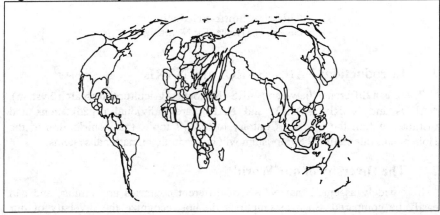

The population density is a very important factor, unfortunately, it is very difficult to show with regard to agricultural land, but only to the total area.

Figure 3:   Anamorphosis of the World: Total Cropland

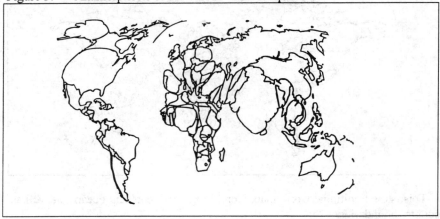

The total share of the world's cropland for each country highlights unexpected situations. Some countries have more crop land than generally expected, although, again the population density should be taken into account.

Figure 4:   Anamorphosis of the World: Renewable Internal Water Resources

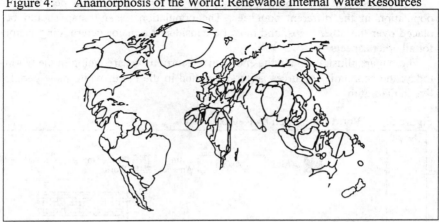

For the future, our water resources are likely to be of much greater importance then cropland. Water will become a limiting factor in many countries. Several countries and regions are already facing shortages.

Figure 5:   Anamorphosis of the World: Gross National Product

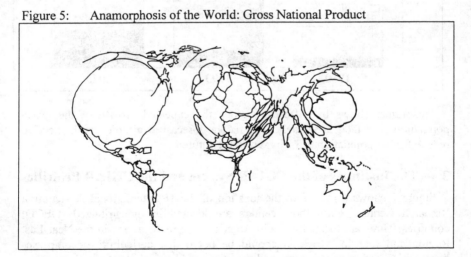

The globe's gross national product when distributed over the different countries is a very revealing map. Of course, it was expected that the OECD countries will have the lion's share of the world's wealth. However Africa, especially when disregarding Nigeria and South Africa, has become very tiny.

Unfortunately, it is impossible to show the resource endowment per head of population in the different countries. The population density map should be placed over the other maps, and must be considered a major determining factor for all other aspects.

These maps illustrate again the enormous distortions we are facing in the world today: the economic resources are concentrated in the North while most people live in the South.

Figure 6:   World Population by Region

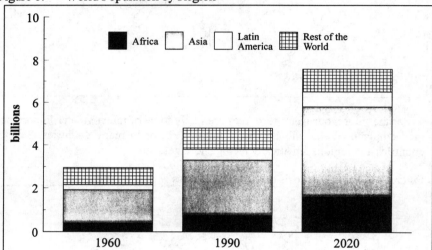

This figure shows by different regions the expected growth of the world population. The facts are widely known. The forecast also indicates the need to reduce further population growth rates in the future.

3   The Institutes of the CGIAR System and the CGIAR Priorities

Figure 7 shows a map with the location of the 16 International Agricultural Research Centers. Only three centers are located in industrialized (OECD) countries. Three are located in Latin America, five in Asia, one in the Near East Region and four in Africa. It should be noted that agriculture encompasses livestock, fisheries, agroforestry and forestry and also includes natural resources management. In addition, food policy and strengthening NARS are important subjects, mandated to two separate institutes.

Figure 7:   The 16 CGIAR Centers

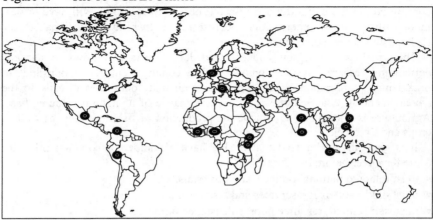

Figure 8:   Priorities in the CGIAR

	Allocation of total CGIAR resources
Increased productivity: a. Germplasm enhacement and breeding (21%) b. Production system development and management (24%) i. cropping activities (15%) ii. livestock systems (6%) iii. tree systems (2%) iv. fish systems (1%)	45%
Protecting the environment	16%
Saving biodiversity	10%
Improving policies	11%
Fortifying NARS: a. Training (7%) b. Information/communications (7%) c. Organization/management counseling (2%) d. Networks (2%)	

This table highlights the distribution of the CGIAR resources by major programs. The percentages are rounded off and relate to the average share of the total allocation for the last few years. Presently, the Technical Advisory Committee of the Committee is discussing the CG Priorities for the period 1998-2000.

4   NARS and NAROs

Originally, a national agricultural research system was understood as a public-funded research institution. This has changed and will continue to change. As a result the research directors will have less time in future to allow them to concentrate on the public-funded research per se. Instead they will have to deal more with the many other actors and research partners at the national, at the regional and at the global level.

The widely accepted new and enlarged definition is as follows: A national agricultural research System comprises all a country's entities responsible for organizing, coordinating, or executing research that contributes directly to the development of its agriculture and the maintenance of its natural resource base. Agriculture is understood to include the production of fish and trees, as well as crops and livestock.

It is generally recognized that NARS have a number of common priorities More than ever before in future, NARS:

- must relate to national policies and programs,
- must link to extension services and farmers, and
- must serve small, resource poor, subsistence farmers.

5   The Tasks of NARS

There are many additional tasks of all NARS. Especially the small NARS cannot concentrate on research only, but they have policy as well as advisory and other functions. In many countries the extension service is very weak and researchers have to take on some of the important extension functions.

Figure 9:   Researchers and Types of Research

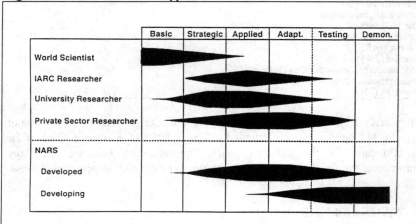

There are five types of research: basic, strategic, applied, adapted and testing. It has also to be recognized that "demonstrations" are closely linked to research, at least in agriculture, and can be regarded as research-related activities. Figure 9 indicates the allocation of research tasks to different researches and institutions.

Most of the different types of research are undertaken in different types of institutes and are the main tasks of different researchers or scientists. It is clear that in developing countries the NARS must concentrate on adaptive research, testing, and demonstrations.

6   The Diversity of NARS – Examples from Africa

The next figures illustrates the difficulties in treating NARS as a homogeneous group. Even neighboring countries differ in their NARS organization, in the number and functions of scientists employed, in research partnerships, in the role of the farmers in determining the research agenda, and in the importance of natural resource management, just to name a few factors. There is a need to develop a classification of NARS, identifying a typology indicating their strength and weaknesses.

Figure 10: Agricultural Research Expenditures as Percent of Agr. GDP 1981-85

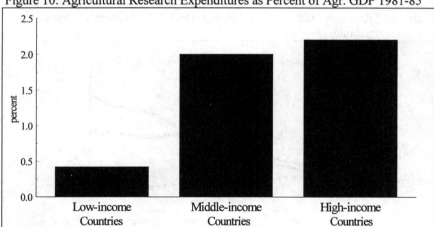

Figure 10 clearly shows that the low income countries are unable to provide the necessary budgetary provisions for agricultural research Based on experience, it can be concluded that low-income countries should spend a minimum of 2% of the value of national agricultural. GDP for their agricultural research

Figure 11: Annual Average Growth in Agricultural Research Expenditures of
            African NARS

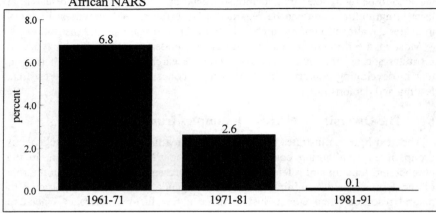

As Figure 11 shows the annual expenditure growth for agricultural research in
Africa has decreased dramatically during the last three decades.

Figure 12: Research Staff and Expenditures, 1961-91: 19-Country African
            Sample

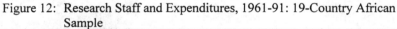
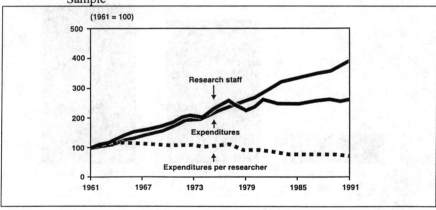

Figure 12 indicates that the number of researchers has increased during the last
three decades while research expenditure has hardly grown at all. As a result the
expenditure per researcher and with it the effectiveness of research has declined.
This situation is best described as "brain waste", which can be even worse than
"brain drain".

Figure 13: Expenditures as a Percentage of the Agricultural GDP (1991)

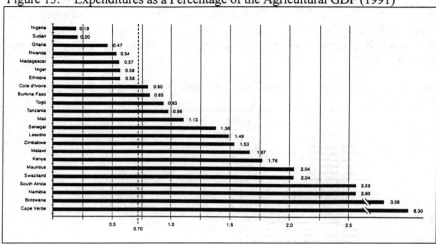

The figures indicating the share of research expenditures in agricultural GDP for African countries. The differences between the African countries are very large. They differ by a factor of more than ten. Especially some of the large countries are providing insufficient funds for research

Figure 14: Researchers per million Farmers (1991)

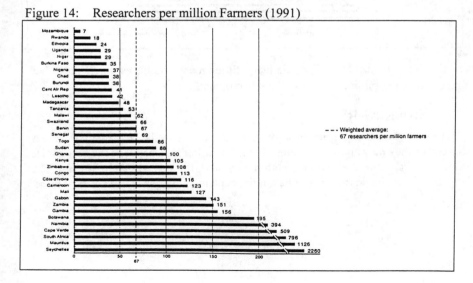

The services that researchers can provide to the farmers also differ widely (Figure 14). Small NARS can have a small absolute number of scientists, but small NARS can also have a small number of scientists per million farmers. In this case it is a factor of more than 20, for example between Mozambique and Zambia.

Figure 15: Number of Researchers per Millions of Hectares Permanent and Arable Cropland

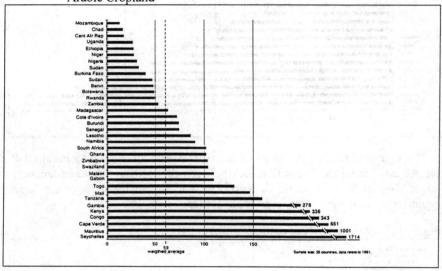

Figures 14 and 15 differ relatively little, many countries have only few researchers per million hectares of arable cropland.

7   Strong NARS

The public-funded agricultural research systems may be locked in a vicious circle, or they may enjoy a virtuous circle. The difference between the two circles are important for the farming community and for the research system. The difference can be described as a threshold, depending on quality and critical mass.

Figure 16: Public-funded Agricultural Research

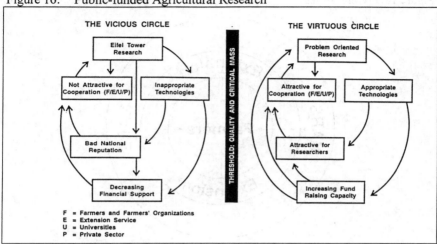

Figure 17: The Threshold: Quality and Critical Mass

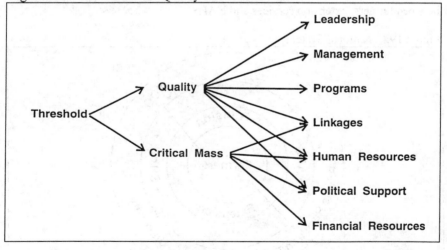

The quality of the threshold is linked to: leadership, management, research programs, linkages, human resources and political support. All NARS depend on a critical mass of financial resources, political support, human resources, and linkages.

Figure 18:   Core System

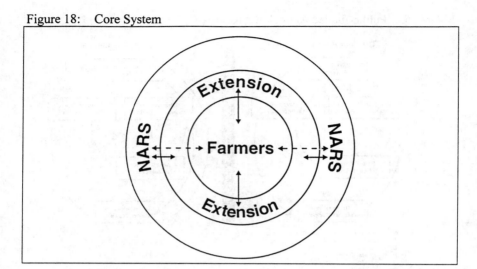

At the national level, the core system provides the most important linkages between farmers, extension services and NARS.

Figure 19:   National System

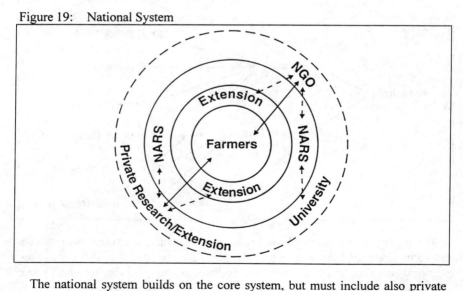

The national system builds on the core system, but must include also private research and its own extension, the universities, and the NGOs.

Figure 20:   Linkages of Farmers and NARS with Partners

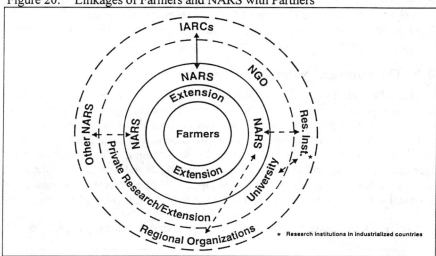

This figure highlights the fact that national agricultural research is also linked at the regional and global level to researchers and advanced research institutions, many of them in industrialized countries.

8   Strengthening NARS – Selected Aspects

What can the CGIAR System do or can do better than other institutions or potential partners? Furthermore, the need is so great that no single partner of NARS has the financial or research-related capacity to help all of them in all their needs. In addition to the known weaknesses and needs regional organizations are also demanding external assistance. There are clearly a number of NARS aspects, which have benefited already and which can benefit further from support through collaboration with the CG system. Some of the aspects are listed and will require further explanations:

a. importance of agriculture and of agricultural research at the national level
b. institution building
c. research financing
d. capacity building, training
e. linkages
f. information systems (knowledge)
g. priority setting

h. transfer of research results, not only in the form of genetic material, but also in most fields identified as part of the national research agenda.

i. partnership in research planning, implementation, monitoring and evaluation, sharing of finances and experiences in success and failures.

9   The Future of National Agricultural Research

The following figure clearly indicates the considerable decline of external assistance to agriculture in the last ten years. There are signs that some of the donors (including the World Bank) have recognized this and are attempting to influence the national political leaders to adopt pro-agriculture and rural development policies. It is hoped that the forthcoming "FAO Summit" will highlight the need to give the necessary political and financial priority to agriculture in the economic development process. Only then is there a chance for sustainable food security at the national, at the regional and at the global level.

Figure 21:   Commitments of External Assistance to Agriculture (in 1985 U.S. dollars)

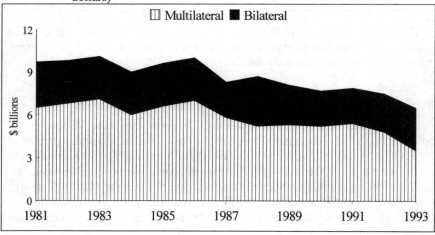

Considerations in Assessing the Impact of Agricultural Research in Developing Countries

Amram Ashri
The Hebrew University of Jerusalem
Faculty of Agriculture
Rehovot 76100, Israel

Abstract

Innovations in agriculture and their adoption followed different routes and have been very meaningful in improving food security at the family, village and national levels. However, they are also difficult because of the need to identify the critical and relevant problems in the framework of the environmental, climatic and socio-economic conditions, solve them and then reach thousands of farmers who are often isolated, poor, uneducated and lacking access to inputs. This though can also be the reward: reaching and improving the lives of thousands of families in one region after another.

In order for the research, extension and adoption by the small farmers to be successful, the projects must be relevant, appropriately designed, sensibly evaluated, involving local participants where possible, and including suitable outreach considerations.

Impact assessment is fraught with problems. Measurement criteria should be chosen carefully, noting that statistics on small-holders in developing countries are often unreliable. Direct and indirect benefits should be quantified and given relative weights. The timing of the assessments and the selection of the evaluators should be carefully considered.

In order to achieve a higher rate of success in R&D as measured by outreach, the following should be considered: suitable training for R&D projects coordinators, encouragement of pairing arrangements between laboratories of NARSs in developing and developed countries and the establishment of an international database of qualified researchers, extension advisors and administrators from developing countries who can serve as reviewers and evaluators.

Keywords

Research, innovation, adoption, GIFRID

Introduction

In planning this symposium the organizers did well to focus on enhancement of food security through innovations. In the past, much of the increased agricultural production resulted from higher inputs of land, labor and capital. Thus, in nine Latin-American countries 60% of the increased agricultural output between 1950 and 1980 were due to the above and only 40% of the growth resulted from technical improvements (Wiggins 1988). Evenson and Kislev (1975) arrived at the same general conclusion. However, in view of the limited availability of water and of the economic and/or environmental constraints on the application of inputs such as fertilizers or pesticides, food production must be increased mainly through innovation. This paper emanates to a large extent from the author's experience with generation of agricultural knowledge and its adoption in developing countries through his long service with the governmental fund for research in developing countries, GIARA (German-Israel Agricultural Research Agreement) and Agridev (an Israeli government-owned international agricultural development company) and as a consultant to agricultural R&D projects for the FAO and IAEA (International Atomic Energy Agency) in many developing countries in Asia, Africa and Latin America. Last but not least, the author served for the past ten years as chairman of the board of the NGO, GIFRID (German-Israel Fund for Research and International Development), which is partially supported by German Agro-Action (Deutsche Welthungerhilfe). The main goal of GIFRID is to transfer to developing countries the agricultural experience gained in Israel's agricultural development. A summary of GIFRID's activities in its 20 years of operation is presented in tables 1 and 2.

This paper will deal mainly with setting priorities in agricultural research for and in developing countries and with the adoption of innovations by "smallholders." These are short to medium term objectives. It should be noted however, that long-term research, often termed basic, should also be considered. The acute need for it is clearly demonstrated (figure 1) by the fact that the world's population depends for most of its food (carbohydrates and proteins) on just ten crops, viz. wheat, rice, maize, potato, barley, sweet potato, cassava, soybean and sugar cane (Kochhar and Singh 1989). There is an acute need to increase the yields of these crops in more sustainable agrosystems. It is encouraging that analysis of the yield increases of maize in the USA shows that for the period 1930-1980, 81% of the increased yield potential was due to enhanced genetic potential (Huffman and Evenson 1993). Similarly, the same authors reported that 67% of the yield increase in soybean and 40% in wheat were due to enhanced genetic potential. Still, efforts should be devoted to the development of new crops, or new uses for existing ones, as was the case with soybean over the past fifty years or so.

Table 1: A Summary of GIFRID's Activities, 1975-1995

Activity	Number
Projects, total	156
Research	90
Training	66
Researchers & extension advisers, total	101
Israeli principal investigators (PI's)	46
Israeli cooperators	22
Developing countries PI's & cooperators	33
Developing countries involved, total	32
With research projects	26
Other	6
Training courses participation	29
" " participants	554
" fellowships, individual	93

Table 2: GIFRID's Research and Training Projects by Main Areas, 1975-95

Area	Number
Crop management in arid zones	21
Plant protection	17
Plant genetic resources and breeding	16
Irrigation and soils	17
Forestry and agroforestry	9
Animal husbandry and aquaculture	13
Grain storage	5
Nutrition	4
Agricultural economics	4

Innovation and its adoption in agriculture are often quite difficult, but they have been very meaningful in improving food security at the family, village and national levels. The difficulty lies in the need to reach thousands of farmers who are often poor, uneducated and without access to inputs. However, this can also be the reward – the potential to reach and improve the lives of thousands of families across wide regions. The author has much respect for the "small farmers" in developing countries (often women), for the way in which they try to optimize their meager resources and labor in order to feed their families. These farmers, by necessity, are more interested in food production throughout the year, than in maximum yields at a peak season.

Figure 1: World Production (1980) of the 30 Major Food Crops

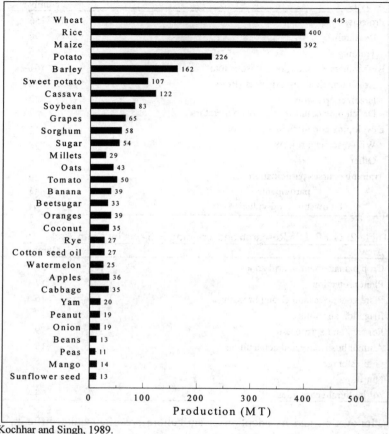

Source: Kochhar and Singh, 1989.

Project Design and Adoption

An assessment of the impact of agricultural research on improving food production or other socio-economic benefits may be quite problematic, except for a small proportion of clear-cut cases of success or failure. Collinson and Tollens (1993) estimated that a 20-year period may be needed from the initiation of strategic research to adoption and full benefits in the field. Alston and Pardey (1995) note that many years may elapse from the time the research is initiated until the findings are widely adopted. They describe three potential lag periods, namely research lag, development lag and adoption lag, each lag being of several years (Alston and Pardey 1995). Shortening one or more of these lag periods can be very meaningful. The process of acceptance of agricultural innovations is often slow because they must reach many farmers who follow age-old traditions, in outlying communities, over wide areas. Such lag periods may result also from economic or government policy matters which are usually beyond the sphere of influence of the innovators, disseminators or farmers (Abt 1995). Therefore, the assessment of the impact of any given project may depend to a considerable extent on its timing. Contradictory conclusions can be drawn at different points along the process.

Although innovation in agriculture can and has been very meaningful in increasing the production of food and other commodities, it has not always resulted in improved food security at the family, village or national levels. In order to maximize the probability of success in agricultural innovation – in terms of its adoption by the farmers and impact in the field – several issues should be weighed during the reviewing process.

A. Obtaining Suitable Research Proposals

Obtaining well-thought out, appropriate and relevant research ideas is difficult even in developed countries, and all the more so in developing countries. The difficulty can be well illustrated by the history of the R&D and adoption of hybrid maize in the USA and Canola rapeseed in Canada. Huffman and Evenson (1993) reported that when in 1916-1919 an economic way was found to produce seeds of high-yielding hybrid maize varieties (after about two decades of research) the director of the USDA maize breeding program and several directors of maize research in Corn Belt state agricultural experiment stations "were convinced that hybrid corn had no practical importance." This considerably delayed hybrid corn research in the USA. The extent of the beneficial impact of hybrid maize on food security in the world via yield increases is shown in figure 2. It also opened a whole new and significant breeding approach.

The transformation of rapeseed with its industrial quality oil to Canola with edible quality oil and good quality meal changed agricultural production in many parts of Canada, changed market demand for other commodities and set a pattern for the development of this crop and others in the world. This process entailed close cooperation of scientists in different areas, processors, growers etc., and received much support from the Canadian government. Yet, it had ups and downs and took some 20 years (Busch *et al.* 1994).

Many qualified researchers in the developed countries are not interested in the problems of developing countries; and often those who wish to be involved do not have the necessary background. On the other hand, turning primarily to scientists from developing countries is not always helpful; some may be willing to cooperate with any project for the funds and prestige, others may prefer to do more academic research which may be deemed more basic. Good research and development ideas should be solicited actively. Even under favorable conditions the rate of success in applied agricultural R&D projects may be as low as 1 in 20 (Alston and Pardey 1995). In less favorable situations the rate would tend to be even lower, hence soliciting very good ideas is even more critical.

The pool of qualified interested researchers in both the developed and developing countries should be enhanced. Still, the adoption or non adoption of an innovation may have only limited relationship to the excellence of the research.

Figure 2: Mean Yearly Maize Yields in the USA, 1865-1985

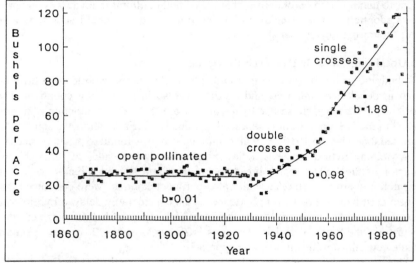

Source: Troyer 1990.

B. Priority Ranking for Projects

Support for research projects should follow national and regional priorities. The NARSs can and should be involved in the process. Successful adoption of foreign-generated research depends on strong national research and extension (Evenson and Kislev 1975; Collinson and Tollens 1994). The validity of this conclusion was noted by the author in missions to various countries.

Furthermore, farm level issues should be considered during the research planning phase and the farmers and extension advisers should be consulted whenever possible. This though may be difficult to do, because in many countries the priorities have not been established (and even where established, often they are not followed) and suitable representatives for the farmers may not be known or available. This difficulty may be even more pronounced in international transfer of improved agricultural technology. This would be the case in collaborative bilateral projects as well as with material transfer and capacity transfer from developed countries (Pinstrup-Andersen 1982).

C. Peer Reviews

Peer reviewing is a well-accepted approach for the evaluation of project proposals. Outside reviewers should not be too far geographically or too far upstream or downstream, technically (Huffman and Evenson 1993). Thus, peer reviews from developing countries' scientists would be very desirable. However, often they are not known to those who select the reviewers. Furthermore, while they may retain the client-responsive climate (Huffman and Evenson 1993) their knowledge may be too region-specific.

D. Availability of Infrastructure, Support Systems and Inputs

The innovation should fit within the culture and agricultural system in the intended region of cultivation. The timely availability of infrastructure and various inputs for the projects should be ascertained. The rapid development of greenhouses and the accelerated adoption of trickle irrigation in the Gaza area in the 1970's and 1980's, where inputs, extension and markets were available (Yaron 1996), underscores the importance of the supports noted above.

Labor distribution should be considered in order to assure that the innovation will be accommodated with the available family labor. In Nigeria, promising earlier productive maize cultivars were not adopted by the growers because the earlier harvest period coincided with the harvest of chili peppers which are important as a cash crop (Efron, personal communication).

The availability of logistic and other support may be very critical for the adoption of innovations. They may lapse for lack of infrastructure, e.g. a successful breeding project will have no impact if seeds of the improved variety cannot be produced reliably or in sufficient quantities.

E. Local Participation

The close involvement of the NARSs, the extension services and the growers should be promoted. Thus, it is important to motivate and train researchers and extension advisers, involve the latter in setting the research agenda, solicit feedback from them, arrange on-farm trials and demonstrations and obtain farmers' responses. A fine demonstration of such a comprehensive approach is the introduction of low pressure trickle irrigation developed in a GIFRID project in

Israel, to an apple orchard in China (Shani 1996). A few examples of farmers' contributions were described for Zaire by Mulumu (1995).

Local identification with externally-funded projects should be sought. Some local or national contribution, in funding or in kind, is essential. They should then be more involved also in the evaluation.

F. Additional Considerations

Generally, preference should be given to innovative approaches that would require low inputs. If somewhat higher inputs would be called for, then low-cost credit should be made available to the small farmers. Thus, the initial phases of the adoption of trickle irrigation by Bedouins in the Jordan Valley were facilitated by interest-free long-term loans from a charitable NGO (Rymon and Or 1991).

Impact Assessment

A. General

Monitoring agricultural innovation projects during their implementation and evaluation of their impact upon completion require much thought. They are problematic for several reasons. First, the criteria for impact quantification should be carefully chosen. Possible criteria for crops are:

- Yield increment;
- Improved yield stability and reduced risks;
- Land area (ha) where the innovation is adopted;
- Number of farmers adopting the innovated variety or technique;
- Cost reduction or net benefits.

The above criteria can be useful but as noted by Collinson and Tollens (1994), data for crops which are grown primarily on small plots of small-holders can be very unreliable.

B. Nature of Impact

Optimally, the impact evaluation should encompass both the direct benefits (e.g. a new improved variety) and the more indirect benefits (e.g. capacity building through staff training and/or laboratory establishment). Quantifying both types of impact is difficult and their relative weights may vary from case to case.

C. Evaluators

Selecting suitable evaluators can be very difficult. Expertise in a given specific scientific area is not sufficient. Assessors should be well acquainted with the conditions and problems of the region, open-minded, and able to communicate and interact with a wider community, not only with researchers. Participation of evaluators from developing countries is very important. However, often those who are charged with choosing the evaluators are not acquainted with a range of suitable experts.

D. Timing of Evaluation

The time lags noted above are common in agricultural research and should be taken into consideration. Assessment should be made after sufficient time has elapsed. At times, an evaluation a few years after the termination of the project may give a more valid assessment of its impact. For example, GIFRID helped fund a workshop in Buenos Aires in the mid-eighties on the use of *Azospirillum* bacteria to improve plant development and yields. Immediately after the workshop, an impact evaluation would not have found evidence for beneficial impact. However, some five years later we found that after a lag of several years commercial bacteria-producing laboratories were established to supply the bacteria to wide areas. Evaluation at the later time would have shown a truer measure of the impact.

Proposed Action

From the preceding discussion and as stated by Bonte-Friedheim (1995) it is evident that appropriate projects and closer contacts between researchers and R&D specialists in the developing and the developed countries, and contacts with the farming communities will lead to better project design, evaluation and implementation. To this end several approaches are proposed, as follows:

A. Training of Agricultural R&D Coordinators

At present in the developed countries, there are still quite a few agricultural researchers and development coordinators, especially among the older ones, who grew up on farms, or otherwise acquired much practical experience. Because of the shrinking farm populations many of the younger researchers in agriculture lack farm experience while the agricultural sciences are becoming more basic and sophisticated. Also the gaps in know-how between the scientists in the developed and developing countries are growing. A way should be found to train experts who would be well attuned to the needs of the developing countries. Similarly, ways must be found to involve researchers and farm advisers in the developing countries as real partners in the intricate process of technology generation, dissemination and application.

B. Pairing Arrangements

Encourage pairing arrangements between NARS's laboratories in the developing countries and laboratories in the developed countries. The benefits will be several. Expensive equipment will not be duplicated and researchers from the developing countries will be able to work periodically in the developed ones. Likewise, scientists from developed countries will be able to make short visits to the developing ones. This will lead to closer acquaintance with the problems and the pool of motivated, "sensitized" researchers in the developed countries will be enlarged. Finally, better research results will be obtained, with better cost-effectiveness.

C. International Roster of Qualified Experts

Establish an international roster of qualified experts (researchers, extension advisers, administrators) from developing countries who can serve as peer reviewers and evaluators. Such a roster should include information on fields of expertise (disciplines, and organisms), language spoken, previous experience etc. At present this information is scanty and scattered. Such a database could be very helpful to various organizations which support research and development in developing countries. This workshop could perhaps suggest a supporting body for such a roster. It appears to the author that ISNAR with its close contacts in the NARSs of the developing countries would be suitable.

D. Funding of Rejected Projects

Recommend to bodies funding research and outreach to set a small portion of their budget, say 5%, to fund some projects that were rejected in the reviewing process. The justification for this is that some very original ideas will not be accepted by the reviewers because they break new grounds.

Lessons Learned

In order for agricultural research and extension projects to be relevant, thus enhancing their adoption on the farm, the end-users and the local facilitators should be consulted. This is even more valid for bilateral or multilateral international collaborative projects. For impact evaluation suitable assessors who know the local conditions should be chosen and the timing should be carefully considered. A list of qualified potential project reviewers and evaluators from the various developing countries should be prepared, by countries and area of expertise. Finally, where more sophisticated and expensive research equipment is needed, and/or where the know-how evolves very rapidly (e.g. genetic engineering) pairing arrangements of laboratories in developing and developed countries is advocated.

Acknowledgments

The author is grateful for stimulating discussions over the years, to staff members and colleagues of the following: German Agro-Action, ATSAF

(Germany), Joint FAO/IAEA Division (Vienna), CINADCO (Israel), Agridev (Israel) and GIFRID.

References

Abt, I. 1996. The Israeli experience in technology transfer. In: Ashri, A. (Ed.) Agricultural Technology Transfer to Developing Countries and its Adoption. Proc. GIFRID 20th Anniv. Workshop, Bet Dagan, Israel, 1995: 15-17.

Alston, J.M. and Pardey, P.G. Making Science Pay, the Economics of Agricultural R&D Policy. International Food Policy Research Inst., Washington DC (unpublished).

Ashri, A. 1996. GIFRID's approach and achievements. In: Ashri, A. (Ed.) Agricultural Technology Transfer to Developing Countries and its Adoption. Proc. GIFRID 20th Anniv. Workshop, Bet Dagan, Israel, 1995: 3-5.

Bonte-Friedheim, C. 1996. National agricultural research and its partners. In: Ashri, A. (Ed.) Agricultural Technology Transfer to Developing Countries and its Adoption. Proc. GIFRID 20th Anniv. Workshop, Bet Dagan, Israel, 1995: 10-13.

Busch, L., Guntor, V., Mentele, T., Tachikawa, M. and Tanaka, K. 1994. Socializing nature: technoscience and the transformation of rapeseed into Canola. Crop Sci. 34:607-614.

Collinson, M.P. and Tollens, E. 1994. The impact of the international agricultural centers: measurements, quantification and interpretation. Expl. Agric. 30:395-419.

Evenson, R.E. and Kislev, Y. 1975. Agricultural Research and Productivity. Yale Univ. Press, New Haven, CO.

Huffman, W.E. and Evenson, R.E. 1993. Science for Agriculture. Iowa State Univ. Press, Ames, IO.

Kochhar, S.L. and Singh, B.M. 1989. Plant resources for AD 2001. In: Swaminathan, M.S. and Kochhar, S.L. (Eds.). Plants and Society. Macmillan Publishers, London, p. 556-617.

Mulumu, S.M. 1995. Kivu farmers and researchers get together. Spore 58:7.

Pinstrup-Andersen, P. 1982. Agricultural Research and Technology in Economic Development. Longman, London.

Rymon, D. and Or, U. 1991. Accelerating technology transfer by means of ATTA (Advanced Technologies in Traditional Agriculture). J. Sustainable Agric. 2:103-118.

Shani, U. 1996. Transfer of simple drip irrigation technology to China. In: Ashri, A. (Ed.) Agricultural Technology Transfer to Developing Countries and its Adoption. Proc. GIFRID 20th Anniv. Workshop, Bet Dagan, Israel, 1995: 5-7.

Troyer, A.F. 1990. A retrospective view of corn genetic resources. J. Heredity 81:17-24.

Wiggis, S.L. 1988. Thirty years of agriculture, a review of Latin America. Span 30.3:102-106.

Yaron, D. 1996. Innovation and development in the Gaza Strip since 1967. In: Ashri, A. (Ed.) Agricultural Technology Transfer to Developing Countries and its Adoption. Proc. GIFRID 20th Anniv. Workshop, Bet Dagan, Israel, 1995: 7-10.

Can the Rural Poor Participate in Setting the Agenda to Eradicate Hunger? Do NGOs have a Role?

Aloysius Prakash Fernandez
MYRADA, Karnataka, India.

*Abstract*_____

Farmers, especially those who inhabit and cultivate semi arid areas and marginal soils, who comprise a significant percentage of those in poverty in India, are becoming increasingly vulnerable to sharp increases in cost of food grains and agricultural inputs, decreasing productivity and area of land, declining investment from Government, inadequate research and inappropriate extension strategies. A burgeoning population and declining trends in world food output are potential threats which will increase their vulnerability over the next 25 years unless there is adequate political will, a radical change in attitudes and systems and adequate resources for investment in these critical areas. A thorough overhaul of the agricultural support system from research to marketing with a strong bias towards farmers in dryland areas should be some of the basic hall marks of the new strategy. Some NGOs who have a comparative advantage in terms of participatory extension techniques and strategies as well as in fostering the process of institution building at the local level, which have the potential to ensure sustainability of the investment, can play a significant role in the process for change in all these sectors.

*Keywords*_____

NGO, marginal areas, participatory extension, institution building

As a representative of the NGOs (who have a reputation for making several provocative statements, a few that are objective and even these at the wrong time) may I claim the freedom to make a few sets of statements based on the perceptions of an observer, since I am an outsider to the agricultural research family.

Having spent over 25 years in development in various capacities, may I start off with a set of statements based on personal experience as well as on reports from others, ranging from the people who have been involved in the development process to academics and scientists who have contributed to it. The context of these statements is limited to i) India, ii) rural India, iii) rainfed rural areas with erratic rainfall from 300 to 600 mm, and iv) undulating terrain with high soil erosion and poor soil quality, and to a society which is not homogeneous but is comprised of groups with varied access to and control of economic, political and social power. Myrada has been working in partnership with the Swiss Development Cooperation, German Agro Action, EZE, PLAN International and with Canadian Organizations like CIDA, HOPE and the Canadian Hunger Foundation in these arid areas for several years. Many of the observations in this paper are drawn from this experience

The first set of statements sets the context and provides the reasons that demand a sustained commitment from all of us to ensure that the poor play a role in decisions regarding investment in future agricultural strategies.

a) Though at the global level there is evidence that the prices of food grains (cereals) has shown a declining trend over the past ten years, this is not reflected in the rural areas where the prices of cereals (rice, finger and pearl millet, sorghum), as well as of fuel and cooking oil have registered an annual average increase of approx 15% to 20% between 1985 to 1995. This is the case in four rural areas across three states in Southern India where Myrada is working. The proportion of daily wages spent on food has also increased significantly during this period. This is why people who were reluctant to join "food for work" programs (outside drought situations)in the early 1980s were willing to do so in the early 1990s. A future agricultural strategy must focus on increasing the productivity of dryland areas on which the poor depend for their food.

b) A recent statement by the Finance Minister of India that the number of people under the poverty line has decreased from 25% in 87-88 to 19% in 93-94, has been accepted with a degree of skepticism by many. I am, however, inclined to accept his figures but with the proviso that there has been significant improvement only in certain parts where the number below the poverty line has fallen even below 15%. There is evidence, however, that in arid areas there has been little improvement and even a rise in the number below the poverty line. Even in areas where there has been significant improvement in livelihoods, the gap between the poorest and others has increased. A new strategy is called for therefore, which is adequately diversified to cope with issues specific to the area and to the local configuration in society. Surveys also indicate that those who have succeeded attribute their success to their own initiative. Government services (like agricultural extension in rice and wheat producing areas), which some found useful in the past, is viewed increasingly as irrelevant to further progress. Though infrastructure provided by the Government like roads, electricity and markets have played a significant role, it is not being expanded or maintained at the level required to cope with demand; this is an additional cause of frustration. Besides, scarcity of these resources reduces the access of the poor to them, since political and economic power and social status, which the poor do not enjoy, play a major role in ensuring access to resources in a situation of scarcity.

c) Researchers inform us that the population will exert an extraordinarily heavy pressure on food supply. Even if current productivity growth rates continue, a world-wide shortfall in cereal production of 700 million tons is expected by 2025. The shortfall in oilseeds, fuel and other items in the food basket will probably be higher. We are also told that there will be a dramatic increase in population between 2005 and 2025, and a decline after that. Whether this increase and decline will be uniform throughout, or whether the increase will be greater and the decline slower in developing countries when compared to the developed (taking into account both natural increase and the potential to migrate which globalization should promote) is not clear. If it turns out to be so, then the stress on the poor will surely increase, especially if the projected productivity increases in cereals do not materialize in these countries and if the purchasing power of the poor does not register a significant rise.

d) We are also told that on a global scale, grain production per person is showing signs of stagnation due to reduction in productivity increases and other factors like water logging in irrigated areas, salinity and increasing extension of cultivation into marginal lands. Studies in India, for example, show a marked increase in areas affected by high sodium content of the soil and a significant decline in lands held by Government which were allocated for pasture and grazing since they were not fit for cultivation. The decline over a period of ten years (1975-85) is in the range of 5 million ha.

e) Researchers also warn us that the size of land holdings will continue to decline; it is expected to be one tenth of a hectare per person by 2025 in South Asia. Can we expect productivity increases to compensate for this loss, or will the marginal farm family have to depend almost entirely on the market for their food?

f) Is there any need to point out the proportionately heavy erosion of soil from marginal lands on higher slopes which are usually cultivated by the poorer farmers? In Myrada's Gulbarga project, a number of experts were surprised when the richer farmers cultivating lands lower in a watershed objected to soil erosion control measures higher up, on the grounds that their harvest of soil would be reduced. This is only one example, among many others, that draw attention to the importance of social configuration in development strategy.

g) There has been no investment in government owned lands even though they have a close interaction with agricultural lands and impact significantly on their productivity. A similar situation prevails with degraded forest lands; there is no strategy to relate the health of these degraded forest lands with sustained productivity in adjacent dryland farms. One has only to read the National Forest Policy of 1988 and various other policy and administrative guidelines to see that the concept of this interrelationship does not hold a significant place. In Myrada projects covering arid areas of Anantapur District in Andhra and the eastern part of Chitradurga Dt. in Karnataka, the price of one bag of biomass (not farm yard manure) is equivalent to the price of half a bag of urea. The forest lands are bare, except where eucalyptus or acacia auriculiformis plantations have survived; yet people make an effort to meet their food needs in an environment that is decreasingly supportive.

h) Increases in agricultural productivity during the past 30 years have been largely restricted to irrigated areas and confined to rice and wheat and, to a limited extent, to major millets. In rainfed areas there have been limited increases in a few areas; declines in productivity have been a far more common feature. This has directly affected the livelihoods of the poor.

i) The prices of materials used in food production(like seeds, fertilizers except urea, animal feeds and fuel) have increased sharply in the context of liberalization and the removal of subsidies. One must note, however, contrary to the claims of a few local politicians, that small farmers who are able to manage their water requirements are happy with the improved quality of seeds supplied by some private companies and even to produce hybrid seed on contract. The sharp increase in prices of fertilizers (except urea) has had a serious impact on productivity in dryland areas. In some parts of South India, like Kerala, where horticulture is a major livelihood source, farmers have shifted from P and K based fertilizers after the prices shot up, to farmyard manure which is being imported in large quantities from Southern parts of Karnataka and Tamil Nadu. With the prices of farmyard manure rising, farmers in these areas have opted to sell rather than apply to their own farms. With decreasing farmyard input, the productivity of dryland farms is bound to decline. The use of P and K based fertilizers in these areas has also declined sharply with urea remaining the only inorganic input; this unbalanced use of fertilizer will further decrease the quality of soils in these areas which are already highly vulnerable.

The second set of statements represents largely my beliefs; some are strongly influenced by my vision of society and will therefore be disputed, others have been accepted by and large.

a) Development strategy needs to focus investment on the regeneration and management of natural resources mainly because success in this area creates the greatest potential for improving livelihood opportunities for the poor. The recent focus on productivity of labor, therefore, needs to be matched with a sustained investment in and commitment to the productivity of lands under the Forest, Revenue and other departments, water bodies and Biosphere Reserves. Management systems appropriate to each area and asset need to evolve with the support of strategic interventions where required.

b) For productivity in dryland agriculture to become sustainable, all lands in a micro watershed must come under one management (not ownership)which reflects all interests. Experience in Myrada's projects indicates that for such a management system, involving several groups as well as government representatives, to emerge and to be effective, requires adequate investment in time and resources. Experience also indicates that for the poor to benefit, they need to be organized into self-help groups which are based on affinity and homogeneity and which can mobilize their own resources and build networks and linkages. Together these factors provide them with the support they need to gain the skills and confidence required to change their lives for the better. Experience also indicates that outside intervention (possibly from an NGO which has a comparative advantage in these areas) will be required to initiate the process and to intervene strategically as it progresses, leading towards this integrated system of area management, and to ensure that the poor play an effective role in the process and benefit from it.

c) The new mantra of liberalization and globalization will bring new opportunities to a few – all among the educated elite, and a host of problems – most of which will impinge on the poor. While this mantra may contain the economic and technical potential to transform the lives of the elite as well as of the poor, the chances are that the elite alone will benefit since they have greater access to and control of these resources. Unless each of us here makes a serious commitment to ensure that future policy, strategy and investment in agriculture are driven by the socio economic demands of poor households and unless we commit ourselves to ensure that others act to achieve the same objective, the Doubly Green Revolution, as some would call it, will have no direct impact on the livelihood resources of the poor. I believe that if we are to play an effective role in achieving this objective, many of us will have to review and renew our skills, change our attitudes towards people, towards the value of technical expertise and methodologies to which we have been accustomed, and towards civic groups including NGOs and parastatal institutions who can contribute towards achieving the same objective.

d) I believe that for agricultural research to be people driven (especially by people farming on drylands under stress) it is not enough to have one or two initiatives (showpieces) which depend on the commitment of a few individuals. A new vision is required that impacts throughout the system as well as dynamic leadership(both political and executive) to motivate people to share the same vision and to translate it into objectives and strategies. The new approach should have at least the following features in order to support and sustain a research strategy which gives priority to the needs of dryland farmers:

In terms of extension strategy:
- A shift from a commodity driven approach which has structured extension strategy so far, to a farming systems approach especially in dryland areas, where farmers have evolved traditional mixes in farming systems to meet their needs and built-in insurance.
- A change in the information system: from a monopoly with a didactic and top-down approach, to a system that actively involves private companies, traders, NGOs and agencies dealing with agricultural inputs and markets. This will enable farmers to avail themselves of the most accessible source and to compare and assess information; it will also provide feedback to researchers from a broad spectrum of sources and perspectives. Presently these types of intervenors are considered as competitors, profit seekers or just marginalized and kept at arms length. Professional services in communication need to be tapped to ensure that the medium and the message are effective. The message needs to emerge from active interaction with people and be based on the actual experiences of farmers with similar farming systems in dryland areas.
- A shift from standardization (with a strong bias towards irrigated cropping systems) in terms of attitudes, extension skills and practices to differentiation in order to meet the specific needs of small and marginal farmers in dryland areas. Their farming systems differ not only from area to area but even within an area depending on their needs, on the location (slope, near roads, towns or forests) of their fields and homesteads, on the depth, quality and type of soils (one micro watershed on the Deccan plateau often has several different types of soils; soil depths also differ significantly restricting horticulture to certain areas), on water availability, on the grazing lands available, on the availability of inputs and markets, on the credit and labor resources they are able to mobilize and on their yearly assessment of the performance and timing of the monsoon. This requires a broadening of the present spectrum of skills and support services, which are currently limited to providing technical knowledge directed to production and that of a single commodity or sector (often described as a 'go-it-alone approach), to one that includes skills that support optimum farming systems, that fosters intra-sectoral complementarities (agriculture, animal husbandry, forestry) as well as linkages to institutions providing support to a broad range of activities. Technical knowledge alone is not adequate; farmers also need support to

reduce input costs and increase income; they need to identify and exploit potential markets. In one Myrada project, farmers who were growing flowers were being fleeced by middlemen. Though some of Myrada staff identified the middlemen as the major obstacle to increase farmers incomes, the farmers themselves did not; instead they asked for a telephone to enable them to access information on a daily basis about prices in two major flower markets where the flowers were sold. We provided them with a telephone and this enabled them to bargain with the middlemen every day which increased their incomes by over 50%.

- A shift from an approach dominated by the culture of a "delivery system" and assessed by targets that are easily quantifiable, to one that provides long term support to build appropriate farmer's institutions which are encouraged to design their own rules and sanctions, their responsibilities and rights, and their systems of records and financial control. They need not be registered if the members decide that registration is not necessary and may even make them vulnerable to official harassment. If their decisions are recorded, their financial systems open, their leadership changed regularly and whatever responsibilities they undertake carried out successfully, they need to be treated as viable and legitimate institutions even though they may not conform to the official blueprint. Myrada's experience with over 3000 such groups has provided sufficient evidence that if dryland farmers with similar farming systems are supported to form such self-help groups, whose members are linked on the basis of affinity, they can gain the confidence required to take the initiative during the process of identification and prioritization of needs (for a project or research agenda), for planning, budgeting, implementation and sustained management of investment and resources. This extension approach requires skills in institution building, participatory techniques and attitudes that empower farmer's groups.

In terms of extension organization and staff:

- Different norms for recruitment, compensation and incentives may be required for staff working with dryland farmers than for those working in irrigated areas.
- Administrative systems which are centralized (particularly in finance and administration), where leadership is politicized and morale low, are usually slow to respond to changing situations on the ground, to the need for organizational reform and to provide long term and sustained commitment to achieve objectives. Such institutions find it difficult to foster differentiation and to cope with other civic groups, to adopt participatory methods where people are effectively involved and to shift from a delivery system approach

to one that provides support for institution and capacity building. These are the fundamental strengths needed if the poor are to participate in an effective and sustained way in any intervention (including agricultural research) that affects their livelihoods. Government institutions involved with agricultural research and extension will have to be decentralized in terms of raising and managing resources as well as in administration and accountability. Professional support to establish and maintain the health of these organizations, similar to the support widely used by private corporations (and increasingly by NGOs), must be availed of and adapted to the organization's needs. This stress on the need for organizational reform is not misplaced; most of the institutions involved in agriculture were established in the 50s and 60s and have remained frozen in time in terms of agendas, approaches and culture.

- Scientists need adequate resources, time and space, besides the right attitudes and incentives, and they need to be fully devoted to research (not administration). Schedules and administrative pressures that restrict their involvement with people to occasional PRAs will not achieve the objective of transparent and effective interaction with all sectors of a stratified community; the social demand for public consensus before outsiders often conditions the results of public techniques used in PRA. Sustained and effective interaction together with other intervenors (NGOs, Institutions-private and government involved with agriculture who have comparative advantages that foster and enrich the interaction) is needed if people are to be involved and the interests of the poorer sectors are to influence the research agenda.

e) I believe that essential items in the food basket, including nutrition for children, should be subsidized for the poor. The maintenance of an effective and regularly stocked public distribution system (instead of political gestures which tend to be short term) available to the poor, especially in arid areas, is an essential component in the strategy to enable the poor to build the basis of their sustainable livelihoods. It will keep them in the area and reduce their vulnerability to disease and to price increases (often artificially created). It will reduce their dependence on the local elite for consumption credit (at exorbitant interest rates) and work. It will also enable them to participate in broader concerns that affect their future instead of being fully immersed in daily survival. By the same token I dare to suggest the scrapping of all anti-poverty schemes which distribute subsidized assets; when they reach the poor, these assets cannot be maintained by them.

f) I believe that subsidies for inputs in dryland farming systems (seed, fertilizers, feed, etc) are necessary. A positive bias towards small and marginal farmers in arid areas is called for.

g) I believe that the State needs to invest far more in research on dryland farming systems, with special emphasis on local needs and conditions, and on cereals which are so far neglected because they have limited or no demand over a large area and because many are considered 'minor'.

Final set of statements on the role of participation:

a) Participation of all stakeholders in a development project is now generally accepted as an essential condition for achieving a development objective, especially in the context of eradicating poverty and for achieving it in such a way that it is sustained and at comparatively lower costs in the long term. It is also generally accepted that NGOs and civic groups do have a comparative advantage in initiating the process of participation.

b) Participation, however, is interpreted differently by each group of people, similar to the blind men and the elephant. The capacity of NGOs to nurture the process of participation also differs. There is also considerable difference in what the output of participation should be depending on the NGO's ideology and the context. As far as the interpretations go, at one end of the spectrum is a group that limits participation to consultation – and here again there are diverse sub- groups, some consider consultation as a means to get people to buy into what they (in their wisdom) have already planned; others consider it an appropriate tool to ensure that all the stakeholders are involved, usually after the project has been identified by bureaucrats and technicians. At the other end of the spectrum is a group that tends towards the position that people have all the wisdom; all one needs is to elicit their participation. This can be done by using the right techniques supported by attitudes of openness and sharing and the skills of listening. But knowledge about their situation is not enough to motivate them or to cope with the demands of new situations and linkages.

The interpretation of participation I have used in this paper is the following: It relates to several interventions (which utilize various techniques) that openly and primarily intend to initiate a process and which continue to nurture this process till it evolves into appropriate institutions of poor people which they manage and control and through which they design and implement the strategy for their sustainable livelihoods. Initiation of this process requires the use of various methods to motivate people and to win their confidence. The nurturing referred to is long term and involves support to acquire the skills, confidence, and resources to build and maintain viable institutions and linkages among their own groups as well as with other institutions which they need to create a sustainable basis for their livelihoods. It is in the context of this process and capacity building that the research agenda can be set and implemented through sensitive strategic interventions.

Myrada's experience has shown that intervention which seeks primarily to collect information (often rapidly), even where the public is involved, which clearly conveys the impression to people that it is short term, and which uses techniques that are limited to visual imagery and mapping, serve a limited purpose. They do not initiate a process and often do not reflect the wealth of diversity, the potential for conflict and the real interests of the poor.

Myrada's experience in the emergence and growth of peoples institutions in micro watersheds indicates that for people's participation to be effective it required twelve interventions (each using a different technique or method) in the entry phase and another 12 (a few using techniques similar to those in the entry phase) in the planning phase. Though the role of Myrada declined in the implementation phase its presence was required throughout and even for a period after implementation. The position this paper takes is that for people to participate in research, they must first have the confidence that they can better their livelihoods in a sustainable way. Participation in research, therefore, needs to be preceded by participation in programs where they have the experience of taking the initiative and gaining control both of their present and their future. To integrate people in agricultural research, therefore, will demand a change in attitudes and a sustained commitment to strategies and methods with which many involved in agricultural research and extension have not been accustomed.

c) Myrada has had no experience in participative research in agriculture; the nearest it has come is its study of indigenous technologies used in soil and water management in its Gulbarga project. The problems, however, that Myarada experienced in getting these technologies accepted officially and in integrating them in the plan as well as in placing a value on initiatives taken by people where local technologies were used, were several and took a long time to overcome. This experience also indicates that relating knowledge gained from research with that gained from practical experience will be a difficult and challenging task.

The challenges we need to face are mainly in the following areas:

- Our understanding of poverty tends to be negative; the poor need inputs, skills, linkages; intervenors therefore carry out what is called a "needs assessment". We need to learn to start with peoples strengths. They may be few, but they saw people through periods of stress, caused not only by short, unexpected disasters like drought, but, more importantly, by a shrinking resource base – in terms of quality, area and quantity – and by policies which obstructed their growth because they did not support the infrastructure required or give them the freedom to exercise their potential. If dryland farmers have survived in a situation of increasing scarcity, they must be good managers.

- Partly because of the negative association we give poverty, our attitudes towards the poor do not foster respect for their strengths; we do not even look for them. In Myrada's study of local technologies in soil and water management, we found that what engineers may propose as technically sound may not suit people who have multiple objectives. For example, when constructing boulder bunds (boulders were easily available on the fields) a farmer prefers to have a trapezoid shape, with the lower side more or less vertical so that it coincides with his boundaries and does not encroach on the neighbour's fields. When constructed with local skills these trapezoid bunds seem quite stable, contrary to expert opinion. The farmer admits that occasionally a few boulders topple over; but he is willing to invest in the effort to replace them rather than to create enmity by encroaching on his neighbor's fields.

- The analytical tools familiar to researchers are often unable to handle with the fluctuating situations especially in dryland farming systems where people change their strategies for survival regularly; I heard that one researcher found the village 'clumsy'.

- The techniques used to collect information are usually extractive and unfriendly to the poor farmer; they suit the intervenors skills, time schedules and back-up systems and are often used by young and inexperienced staff. True, these techniques are becoming more farmer friendly – especially through the use of PRA, but there is a long way to go. The use of visuals is exciting and farmer friendly, however, knowledge embedded in religion, tradition and myth is not readily 'visualized'; one may have to 'live' in the village to understand these messages.

- Unless agricultural strategy also tackles policies, laws and regulations that inhibit livelihood operations, it will fail to be effective and sustainable. Laws governing the ownership of lands and policies affecting the prices of inputs need to be supportive of dryland farming systems; in many areas they are not. Agricultural strategy also has to take into account pressures arising from changing family values and demands as the culture of a consumer society makes inroads. A recent survey made by Myrada indicates not only a significant annual rise in prices of articles in the food basket but also a marked decrease in production of food for home consumption and increasing dependence on the market for staple foods. There is also a sharp fall in production of traditional cereals as people shift to rice (from finger millet and sorghum), which is mainly purchased. Rice in some villages is a status symbol. The pressures to shift to cash crops where possible, to meet consumption demands which are increasingly being conditioned by the mass media, are strong. The traditional knowledge that supported the production of traditional staples and adaptive strategies in farming systems is consequently dying out as the need to pass it on to the younger generation declines.

Food Aid and Development Experiences from Nepal's Churia Food-for-Work Program (ChFWP)

M. Beier and D. Böttcher

GTZ, D-65760 Eschborn, Germany

Abstract

In 1992 many of the lowland farmers of Nepal's Terai suffered from a drought. The poor ones could not fight the drought on their own – due to the small size of their land holdings and the lack of additional employment possibilities. In the especially hard hit district of Saptari, farms are often below one hectare, and 40% of the inhabitants own no land at all, even though the district depends nearly completely on farming. The German government agreed to finance relief measures for the district's poor in form of "food-for-work", but under specific conditions: The food was not to be used primarily as emergency food supply, but to increase resilience of the population to future droughts. This means that long-term development criteria such as sustainability became the focus. To allow the restocking of the decimated household grain stores, the measures were to be supported during the two dry seasons of 1993 and 1994. Through consequent planning and two implementation evaluations the project also offered a chance to utilize it for concept development for future food-for-work (FFW) support.

ChFWP was highly successful because it relied on local resources as much as possible: The Village Development Committees (VDCs) carried full responsibility for rice collection, storing and distribution. They determined their projects and managed them according to general rules of ChFWP. They used local technologies and know-how, and they had to depend on their own organizational capacities. ChFWP assisted them in planning, advised them in implementation and controlled the proper utilization of the rice. Where misuse occurred and could not be prevented, the assistance was canceled.

The ChFWP concept resulted from the international discussion of "linking relief and development." It was a short-term relief program which tried to utilize food aid for increased labor opportunities and long-term development effects in the supported villages. This was achieved on the village level by combining aspects of participation and self-help projects with food-for work. This approach is similarly relevant for support measures of international donors and NGOs. The experiences made in ChFWP were used to formulate actions on how "food-for-work" measures can in future become more effective – not only as a means for distributing food to the needy, but also as an instrument for promoting a country's development process. But as a short-term project ChFWP had only few possibilities to ensure the sustainability of the village activities. Consequently, the Deutsche Gesellschaft für Technische Zusammenarbeit (GTZ) has introduced the approach to the World Food Program, and will be used in a joint WFP/GTZ project starting in Nepal in 1996.

Keywords

Nepal, Terai, food-for-work, participation, village level management

The Potential Contribution of Food Aid to Development

Food aid has become increasingly important for the growing poor populations of the world. Poor people are becoming more vulnerable to numerous disasters, and if these reach a certain dimension they cannot cope on their own. Each year about 15 million tons of food is given to the poor countries by OECD countries. Germany alone provides annually about 200,000 tons of various kinds of food.

The aid is to a large extent given in reaction to disasters and on humanitarian grounds. People are in desperate need for food because droughts, floods or civil disorders have destroyed their stocks and reduced their capacity to provide for themselves. By the time food aid begins to flow starvation has usually appeared. The urgency of supplying food to starving people leaves little room for more development-oriented support alternatives. But also in food aid the old Chinese proverb applies: To give a hungry man a fish stops his hunger for a day, but to teach him to fish may stop it permanently. The question is how long to supply food and when to progress to teaching.

The German Federal Ministry for Economic Cooperation and Development (BMZ) divides its assistance according to different objectives into two different parts, humanitarian assistance and development assistance:

"Humanitarian assistance is provided where human life is in danger. Its purpose is to ensure quick relief to alleviate acute distress resulting from natural disasters which the country affected cannot cope with alone or not immediately ...

In order to support developing countries in the task of reconstruction following a natural disaster, the Federal Government supplements its humanitarian assistance with short, medium or long-term development programs in individual cases. Thus the purpose of humanitarian measures in Third World countries is to establish where possible a basis for follow-up development activities." (BMZ 1986:41)

Development assistance is more complex. In Technical Cooperation it must always comply with the development objective of enabling the recipient to continue without or with less assistance. This objective even applies in the emergency relief projects administered by GTZ. While humanitarian aid is oriented toward the recipients' needs, development aid must support their initiatives. But aid – especially humanitarian aid – always is in danger of leading to dependence and of replacing initiatives. To reduce this danger, disaster victims may at first be completely dependent on external aid but when they are able to work they should contribute to future disaster prevention.

In food distribution programs some weaknesses have been widely recognized. People were too often coined as helpless victims, when their confidence and their self-help capacities could have been strengthened by giving them some meaningful employment. Too seldom did they work on construction measures to reduce the future magnitude of disasters. Food aid is sometimes given to people even after the pressing emergency has passed and when they could again be productively employed. Too often, food has been brought to the needy by trucks when they could have collected it with their own means transport.

No doubt, a more development-oriented approach would have been much more difficult to administer than food distribution, but in principle food aid has a huge development potential. This was, for example, calculated in the case of Ethiopia, which has received up to one million tons of food aid in bad years:

"If this were used to finance food-for-work or cash-for-work programs, it would be enough to 'finance' over 300 million days of work. These could yield 167,000 km of access road or 417,000 km of artificial waterway or 2,700 earth dams, all in a single year." (Maxwell 1993:8)

It is certainly necessary to provide food quickly to the victims when disaster strikes, and providing free food is often the only feasible way during the first stage of disaster aid. But after a fairly short time people are again capable and willing to work for their food. This paper tries to describe, based on an emergency project for Nepalese drought victims, how food aid can be employed for increasing future production and employment possibilities – so that development processes can be promoted and a grant mentality can be avoided.

The Problem

The Saptari district in the Terai, Nepal's southern low lands, has been prone to droughts since the forests were cut to make room for agriculture. The district's population has increased from about 312,000 in 1971 to nearly 1/2 million people in 1994. The population density is about 350 persons per square kilometer. The district suffers from rapid population growth, which manifests itself in migration of the poor, reduction of the biomass production, and increasing erosion.

90% of the population live by farming. Average land-holding is only 0.3 ha per capita. About 40% of the rural families have no access to land at all and are forced to find work as agricultural laborers. Over half of the land is rented by farmers. Only about 11% of them have enough land to cover all their food needs securely. The others have to look also for alternative work to be able to buy much of the food they need. Under these conditions the people have only very few possibilities to react to a drought. They depend mainly on two survival strategies: Men increasingly migrate to the towns or to India to find work, while women illegally cut firewood in the remaining hill forests and carry it on foot to faraway markets. About 40% of the population resort to occasional illegal wood cutting to increase their income during normal times. During periods of food shortage this number increases, and it is estimated that 20% of the population or about 100,000 people have to plunder the forests for their survival during droughts.

The cutting of the forests has in turn affected agriculture very much. Before the population increased, the tree cover enabled the soil to store water, which flowed to the rivers slowly but for a longer period. Where the trees were cut the increased force of the rain now washes away soil and even moves large stones. The fiercely flowing rivers destroy much agricultural land. Soil is washed down into the irrigation channels – blocking and breaking them. None of the irrigation schemes is reaching the production it had been planned for. To be able to survive, more and more people have to cut trees and sell the wood. The level of groundwater has been sinking as forests were changed to farmland and pumps removed more water than was replenished. As a result, today malnourished children are common and hunger starts to become widespread at the end of the dry season. When there is a drought year, the small farmers have too little stock to cope and the many agricultural laborers cannot find work.

Some of the problems need immediate solutions, especially the rehabilitation of irrigation systems, so that the threat of future droughts can be reduced. Many small channels, ponds and river bank stabilization works can be rehabilitated by the users themselves, who have little other work during the dry season. But this is also the period of worst food shortage and they need rice to work.

When a drought struck in 1992 the district's average annual production of paddy was reduced by nearly 40% and the district administration requested outside support. As the people were willing to work towards improving the situation and to solve the problems described above, it was possible to enable them with a temporary food supply to become self-sufficient again. Supplying food alone could not be the solution, because it tends to make people wait and hope for the food. It does not encourage them to take the initiatives necessary to solve the existing problems. But where people do not have enough to eat they are also not able to take the initiative to solve these problems. Therefore the rice required by villages was supplied so that they could solve some of the problems which cause the low rice production. This way, the short-term rice supply was supposed to lead to a long-term increase in food production and food security.

The Options for Solutions

During past droughts in Nepal, public works programs had been implemented with "food-for-work" and the administrators as well as large parts of the population knew how to operate them. These FFW programs are widely used with two 2 main goals:

- a long-term development goal (the investment in infrastructure), and
- the short-term goal of alleviating the food shortages of the many victims.

But such food-for-work programs often experience a variety of difficulties. The programs use the distributed food as wages (or they pay cash) to improve the local infrastructure by labor-intensive means. These programs are often used for maintenance work administered by a line department such as the Public Works Department, but they tend to be not sustainable because further maintenance of the investments is not ensured after the donor-financed food-for-work component finishes. Consequently, they are often unable to reach their development goal.

They also have difficulties in reaching their food distribution goal. A Public Works Department on district or regional level is often too small and too little equipped to maintain the infrastructure in the area it is responsible for. When such a department is charged with an additional food-for-work program it may have to reduce its normal activities even further. The program cannot reach enough of the people in need of the food, because the department has to concentrate on only a few projects (usually roads) with its limited management capacity, and only the people living near work there. Nor do the laborers benefit from these programs for a period longer than the work lasts. But in Nepal the main disappointment with past public works programs was that much of the food did not reach the poor.

In the situation of the Saptari district such a conventional public works program was unsuitable because of several reasons:

- It could not have organized the tens of thousands of landless people who required work and food urgently.
- It could also not lead to improving the drought-fighting capacity of the people.
- Last but not least, it would have been in danger of loosing much of the food, as had happened in the past.

To achieve all that was required, a program had to be designed which involved the elected village-level administrations, the Village Development Committees (VDCs). The design of ChFWP was based on the following hypotheses:

- Most VDCs would like to implement development projects in their villages but have been starved of funds to do so. They are ready to take the project decisions and responsibilities.

- The projects selected by them will meet the priorities of the village population.
- They will select projects which can utilize technologies known to the people and controllable by them.
- The work and the remuneration offered is attractive enough to the poor and too low to attract the better-off farmers.
- The widespread tendencies by the people in control to privatize much of the food can be overcome with clear, acceptable and tight control of funds, demonstrated in case of misuse, to support reestablishing good governance on village level.   .
- A small staff of skilled program technicians is locally available – so small as to leave project supervision to the VDCs and skilled enough to ensure sound planning and effective monitoring.
- Quickly visible successes and the resulting job-satisfaction can be the motor of the project, just as effective as the training, which had to be omitted in the short implementation period.

ChFWP's design combined food-for-work with elements of self-help and participation programs. The aim was to promote the central factor of development – peoples' capacities to solve their own problems and realize their own potentials more effectively with their own initiatives. The food supplies were to be used to increase peoples' self-management capacities, enabling them to plan and implement projects to which they themselves attached a high priority. As the reason for the program's starting was a food deficiency, the project's purpose was to solve this on a long-term basis by enabling the rural population to increase their drought fighting capacity by improving irrigation and water supplies, contributing to a raising of the ground water level. The program had thus 3 distinct goals:

- As an emergency measure following a disaster it had the *short-term goal* to alleviate food shortages for a large number of people who lived in more than 100 villages, each having a population of about 5000 people.
- It had the *long-term development goal* of making investments for increased food security possible, which were to be chosen by people living in the affected villages. By constructing or rehabilitating irrigation infrastructure and water storage ponds production can be raised during years with sufficient rainfall and employment opportunities for the landless are increased.
- It aimed to *improve peoples' self-management capacities* by giving them the chance to manage projects important to them and for "learning-by doing." This goal of human resource development is the overriding goal of any development support activities.

The program focused on the community level and left planning and management to communities or sub-groups. Whereas a food-for-work program managed by a line department can work only in a small part of a district or a region, this program could work in every of the affected 114 villages, because it mobilized the management capacity of the village institutions. It was thus able to provide work and food to large numbers of disaster victims.

The Achievements

In the only 10 weeks implementation time during 1993 the project area covered the 114 villages of the Saptari district. After the village projects were completed they were evaluated in order to arrive at a project approach which can be replicated when similar emergencies can not be solved with the villagers' own means. The approach was slightly modified and repeated in 1994 during 15 weeks of implementation in 120 villages of the two districts of Saptari and Siraha.

During the 10 weeks in the dry season of 1993 the relief aid was used by 109 VDCs mainly to rehabilitate unused productive assets. The VDCs constructed or rehabilitated 80 public ponds (up to 3 ha each), rehabilitated 40 completely silted river irrigation channels (total length 170 km), constructed 30 irrigation extensions (of 130 km length), built 28 rural roads (of 98 km length) and 2 river training schemes (1.5 km dams). Altogether the VDCs planned and implemented 180 projects. From this work they gained a significant increase in agricultural production in their villages – benefiting mainly the small farmers, but also the rural laborers. About 80,000 workers benefited from the project directly by receiving food.

In 1994 the implementing period was double and it became possible to support project implementation with intensive training to raise the villagers' organizational capacity. User groups in 120 villages identified, planned and implemented during 20 weeks 305 projects. 30 projects were completely implemented and managed by poor women, nearly all of them illiterate. In the long-run these measures will increase the agricultural production significantly and landless workers can find more work. "Public accounting" improved the correct utilization of the funds. Some user groups are generating the funds they need for maintenance of their projects.

In summary, during both implementation periods the direct results were installed with about 1 million labor days, financed with nearly 3,900 tons of rice. Local transport by oxcarts was also paid with rice. The direct results will increase production in the future, mainly because an additional harvest per year has been made possible on 7,000 ha irrigation area. Additional labor will be required, which for ponds and irrigation has been estimated at 280,000 days per year. The increased grain harvest is estimated at 3,500 tons per year, nearly equal to the original "food-for-work" investment. Besides, there was a considerable reduction in illegal wood cutting for two years, giving the forests a much needed regeneration period.

In addition to these material results the program has had other not quantifiable ones – even though they are equally important:

- Indirect labor income was increased (for example, basket makers selling baskets to the workers for transporting soil).
- Nutritional benefits from the rice distributed reached most of the landless families.
- The VDCs gained increased organizational and self-management capacity.
- Leadership training was achieved through seminars, training on-the-job and public accounting.
- VDCs which installed systems of fee collection in their projects gained income for future development.
- Illegal encroachment on public lands was reduced.
- Women and the poorest sections of the population received the largest share of the work and the rice.
- Social benefits and living conditions were improved.
- The self-confidence of the people in their own problem solving capabilities has been raised.
- Some projects have had a demonstration effect on other communities.

Factors Determining ChFWP's Success

The project achieved in the few weeks of implementation much more than was expected. The question of what made this success possible should now be answered. The achievements were mainly possible because principles and methods of self-help and participation projects were employed, which enable the participants to help themselves. The *management principles* of the program were reflecting this, as they were derived from the program goals:

Development focus: The villagers had to use the food-for-work as investment in productive communal assets, such as irrigation channels, ponds or dams. The village government or the user groups were encouraged to install cost-recovering schemes in the projects, because they are normally forced to operate with hardly any finances, and thus unable to do even simple maintenance.

The village government was responsible for the village projects: To improve their organizational and management capacities in a learning-by-doing process, villagers had to accept full responsibility for all aspects of their projects, from priority selection, planning, implementation, to maintenance. This included the responsibility for accountability, monitoring and evaluation. Where it was not accepted the support was canceled.

Projects had to be appropriate to the village: Projects had to be within the capacities of the village. Basically the villagers knew how to manage them, only the dimension of the organization was new to them. The villagers chose those technologies which they knew and were able to control.

Simplicity: As the villagers had little experience in managing projects, all tasks had to be kept simple. This included the organizational design with short communication lines, control structures and the used technology.

Reliability and dependability: As unreliability can easily destroy the self-help spirit, the program had to fight against it continually. A functioning partnership depends on reliability, and the participants must know that they get outside support when it is needed.

Success orientation: Development projects thrive on success, and especially self-help projects. Success is the result of a high level of motivation and good leadership. But success is also the best motivator, and therefore only the projects with a high chance of success should be supported. Only those village governments who used the first delivery of rice successfully (and honestly!) got further deliveries. The others received a warning, a small delivery for a second chance – and much pressure from the project's workers!

Self-correcting mechanisms: The program was not staffed to the extent that full control was possible in the well over 100 villages. Self-controlling mechanisms proved effective enough, for example the control over the rice allocation by many villagers, or the piece rate system, which also made control easier for the village management.

The program's success is directly attributable to the capabilities of the inhabitants of the villages who were able in only a few weeks to complete their projects, often of considerable dimension, managing on average about 200 workers per day. The program employed much fewer staff than is usual with "food-for-work" projects, and this was possible because the villagers successfully took charge of many tasks. One expatriate coordinator was mainly occupied with program design, monitoring and evaluation. A Nepali consultant company, employing about 10 engineers with detailed local knowledge, was responsible for assisting villagers in technical planning, monitoring of their work and the distribution of the rice. All were only employed during the few weeks of implementation. The rice was supplied reliably to central stores by the state-owned National Food Corporation, and collected and transported from there by villagers using their own means, usually ox-carts. Villagers were also fully responsible for the distribution according to piece rate.

Was ChFWP successful? We consider a project successful when it 1. Is implemented efficiently, 2. reaches the intended beneficiaries, and 3. can be sustained by them.

Judged by its **efficiency,** ChFWP was successful. The number of projects completed and of workers receiving rice were much higher than planned (as the plans were based on previous experiences in Nepal), while the amount of theft was minimal. Because of irrigation rehabilitation, the amount of additional rice harvested already during the first year was higher than the amount spent on food-for-work. The project reached the intended **beneficiaries**, but different sections of them to a different extent. Small farmers with land in the rehabilitated irrigation perimeters benefited most because of an additional rice harvest per year. The landless workers, mainly women and the poor castes, received most of the food-for-work, and they will benefit from the future increased demand for labor. The VDCs' position in their long quarrels with district politicians was strengthened and decentralized decision-making became more accepted.

Whether the projects are **sustainable** is still open. Of course it was realized before its start that a program of about three months duration can hardly be sustainable, but sustainability is rightly the most important criterion, by which all development projects must be judged. ChFWP's support of village measures could be sustainable if village institutions manage them well. But ChFWP did not operate long enough for any management training except training on-the-job, which alone cannot be sufficient. Still, some user groups collected fees for maintenance, and some projects had a demonstration effect on their neighbors, who wanted to copy certain organizational features. The main aspect of its sustainability is that the project has demonstrated the potential short-term "food-for-work" measures have for promoting long-term village development – even with short planning time and under difficult implementation conditions.

The ChFWP approach is similarly relevant for support measures of international donors and NGOs. The government of Nepal recognized it as important for its development efforts. As one attempt to put into practice the present discussion on "linking relief and development," GTZ introduced it to the World Food Program which had experienced difficulties with their public works-based approach in Nepal. Presently, a cooperation project between the two donors' organizations, based on ChFWP's approach, is in the advanced planning stage. It is expected to run for five years, starting in 1996, and to cover up to 10 districts in western Nepal. In this project, management capacity building on VDC and district level, problem solving according to the peoples' own priorities, good governance and accountability can be established sustainably. It is in this way that ChFWP and the projects which were supported by it can reach sustainability.

Lessons Learned

Food-for-work can be successfully employed for village-level micro-projects if certain principles are adhered to:

- An important unused productive potential must exist and be recognized by the population.
- The local population and their leaders have to be fully involved, they have to make the project decisions and take responsibilities.
- The technology used must be known to the people and controllable by them.
- The work and the remuneration offered must be attractive enough to the poor, without preventing self-targeting.
- Clear and acceptable conditions must be formulated and made known to all partners. Tight control of funds must be demonstrated.
- A small staff of skilled program technicians must be locally available.

Other lessons that can be learned from the ChFWP experience for the Nepal context are:

- Although quickly visible successes are essential in short-term participatory projects, especially if they support the poor, they cannot substitute preparatory training courses. These are essential for making the project principles transparent and for preventing arguments due to misunderstanding of the project concept.
- Where leadership is unsuitable the project partnership should be terminated. Its chances for success are small-unless the village population is able to press for improved accountability of its leaders.
- The lack of organizational capacity is an major hindrance to running village investments, especially irrigation systems. Although the VDCs were able to implement projects efficiently, organizing cost-recovering operations and frequent maintenance may be beyond the present capacity of many. Learning-by-doing can improve this up to a point, but to increase its efficiency it should be supported by training.
- The main constraint to village development is not found on village level but above. Policies supporting village development, the leaders' acceptance of responsibility and accountability, as well as effective utilization of donor funds for development must still be established.
- Measures to improve natural resource management can only be sustainably effective if they also halt the population increase.

References

Bundesministerium für wirtschaftliche Zusammenarbeit und Entwicklung 1986. The Basic Principles of Federal Government's Development Policy.

Simon Maxwell 1993. Critical Food Policy Issues for Sub-Saharan Africa. Paper presented to NRI/IFPRI symposium, March 1993

Farmers' Unawareness, Extensions' Incapability or Researchers' Ignorance ?

The Case of Millet Stover Research in West Africa

J.P.A. Lamers[1] and P.R. Feil[2]
[1]Institute of Agricultural Economics and Social Sciences in the Tropics and Subtropics
University of Hohenheim, D-70593 Stuttgart, Germany
[2]Institute for Agricultural Communication and Extension
University of Hohenheim, D-70593 Stuttgart, Germany

Abstract

A major challenge for agricultural research is to secure food production for the rapidly growing population in the West African Sahel (WAS). Although some promising techniques have been developed on-station, a recurring major problem is whether or not these innovations can be transformed into recommendations that fit the livelihood of the farming community. Some studies reporting the lack of success in transferring innovations stated that farmers' unawareness constrained the adoption of innovations, whereas others believed that extension services and their concepts have been inadequate. In rare cases, the knowledge generation process has been criticized, since results from controlled and compartmentalized on-station studies often are straightforward and persuasive. Using the example of millet crop residue mulching for controlling wind erosion and increasing crop yields in Niger, West Africa, this paper reflects farmers' knowledge, extension capacities and researchers' present concepts. Based on published results, emphasis is given to a comparison of four different experiments with identical crop residue applications, conducted in the same year and at the same site, but implemented on different fields and managed by different researchers. The high heterogeneity in the outcome of the experiments is examined from an agronomic and economic viewpoint. Lessons that can be learned from more than 10 years of research with millet crop residues for reducing erosion and increasing soil fertility, and consequently, securing food production, are summarized.

Keywords

West Africa, millet stover research, soil fertility, extension, transfer of technology

Introduction

The agricultural sector of many countries in the West African Sahel (WAS) is very fragile. This predicament is mainly caused by short growing seasons, low inherent soil fertility, limited and erratic rainfall with frequent droughts, and wind erosion that accelerates soil degradation and desertification (ISNAR 1995).

Insufficient food production threatens the livelihood of the rapidly growing population and an increase in food production is imperative. During the last three decades, transfer of technology (ToT) approaches have been applied by agricultural supporting services to boost agricultural production, but their success, measured by the transfer of innovations to the farming community, has been limited (Lipton & Longhurst 1989).

The ToT-concept is a linear model of knowledge generation, transfer and adoption (see figure 1). Research institutes, outside of the users' system, define problems and generate the knowledge to solve these problems and develop innovation "packages." The extension system should transfer these packages to users. This process is uni-directional, usually starting at international research institutions (IAR) and ending, via national research organizations (NAR) and extension services, with farmers.

Figure 1: Transfer of Technology Concept

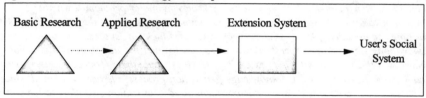

Source: Albrecht 1986.

On-station research in the WAS has developed techniques to reduce soil degradation and increase soil fertility and production, but these have found little acceptance beyond the research station (Deuson & Sanders 1990; Matlon 1990). Matlon & Spencer (1984) stated that a major reason Sahelian farmers have adopted few innovations is that extension and research staff did not understand the scope of farmers' problems. In some cases, farmers' unawareness of the problem and, particularly, of the externally developed innovations is blamed (Connolly & Arokoyo 1991). Agricultural research organizations point at the weak performances of extension services, markets, and at failing agricultural policies to explain to the low adoption rates (Feder et al. 1985).

Mineral and organic fertilizers effectively increase the production of pearl millet (*Pennisetum glaucum* (L.) R. Br.), the major staple in the WAS (Bationo & Mokwunye 1991). Yet, the use of mineral fertilizers by Sahelian farmers is still one of the lowest in the world (FAO 1993). Researchers focused also on fertilizers available on the farm, such as millet crop residues and animal manure for controlling wind erosion and increasing millet production in Niger (Bationo &

Mokwunye 1991). This study evaluates the role of farmers, extension, and research regarding millet crop residue mulching, particularly, within the ToT-research concept. Data for this review is based on published agronomic, economic and technology transfer studies conducted in the region.

Farmers' Unawareness

The majority (85%) of the Nigerian population is settled in rural areas and lives off agriculture. The amount of rainfall and its distribution are their principal guides for cultivation. Although this appears straightforward, farmers operate complex production systems and combine subsistence and commercial activities that involve a range of crops and animals under diverse socio-economic conditions. The mixed-farming systems in western Niger, with an mean farm size of about 10 ha (McIntire et al. 1989), are based on limited family labor and low cash inputs. Most of the cropping budget is spent on hiring manpower for weeding. Additional cash income is earned with off-farm activities, particularly during the dry season (Baidu-Forson 1988). All cropping activities are performed manually. Most households keep some sheep, goats and few cattle, but the use of animal traction is limited. During the dry season, hay from pulses and grasses may enrich the millet stover diet of livestock. Households, thus, have many goals and undertake a variety of activities to achieve these goals. Agriculture, livestock, commerce, art and off-season labor abroad are dispersed over the year and may have long-, medium- or short-term perspectives. Incentives and technologies will be assimilated by farmers depending on their strategies.

Farmers need clear and convincing reasons why, and how, new technologies will benefit them. Because fertilizer produces no benefits unless there is sufficient rain and adequate labor for the extra weeding involved, the use of mineral fertilizers in Niger was (Nabos 1966), and still is, not economic at high fertilizer and low millet grain prices (Bruentrup et al. 1996). The response of millet to mineral fertilizers in regions which receive less than 800 mm rainfall is extremely variable, which increases the risk of adoption (Deuson & Sanders 1988). The results of fertilizer studies come from on-station experiments or individual plots on-farm and lack a farming systems perspective. Matlon (1990) concluded that due to its environmental constraints, future research in the WAS should focus on yield-stabilizing and land-conserving instead of production improving techniques.

A recent comparison of farmers' and researchers' knowledge on the causes and management of spatial soil and crop growth variability showed the accuracy of farmers' comprehensive knowledge (see table 1). It was concluded that knowledge, either coming from outside or developed within the farming community, on fertility management is wide-spread, but without sufficient resources it can do little to satisfy the increasing food demands (Lamers & Feil 1995). To maintain the soil fertility, farmers in the WAS have generated techniques such as mulching, cover cropping, incorporation of organic matter, animal manure, crop rotation, leguminous crops and herding strategies (Hailu & Runge-Metzger 1992). Although the existence of these local practices is no proof that they are effective in establishing sustainable agro-ecosystems, it does show farmers' awareness of problems and possible solutions. Indigenous soil fertility management methods can not be implemented on a large scale because of insufficient resources and socio-economic and institutional constraints such as cattle ownership, land tenure, labor requirements and prices of inputs (Lamers & Feil 1995).

Extensions' Incapability

Agricultural extension services are developed to transfer research output to farmers and provide feedback to researchers. Yet, agricultural extension in the WAS increasingly encounters difficulties with this role. They have a set of goals which often are politically influenced. Research results, seldom adapted to fit farmers' problems, are to be transferred into extension contents. These contents should then be communicated to farmers by the extension staff using specific methods and materials. Yet, the contents, methods and resources of extension services are often centralized, which paralyzes decision-making and execution, particularly when attempting to work in close collaboration with farmers. Given the heterogenous farming community, this type of collaboration requires much flexibility. A concept is needed to bridge the knowledge gap between researchers and farmers which focuses on farmers and their problems (see figure 2).

In the past twenty years, national extension services have received only small increases in funding for engaging staff or procuring equipment compared to national research and technology development services (see table 2). This is a trend which continued into the eighties (Connolly & Arokoyo 1991). Due to the weakness of the extension organizations, the benefits from increased investments in research are marginal, even though economic incentives and a more favorable agricultural price policy can reinforce the impact of extension (Birkhaeuser et al. 1991; Connolly & Arokoyo 1991). Given the budget limitations of WAS governments, financial incentives are virtually impossible. Many of the constraints extension faces can be relieved, but are these issues, indeed, the weakest link in the knowledge generation process? The lack of an appropriate extension concept could also be a result of ambiguous research results.

Table 1: Perception, Explanation and Management of Crop Growth Variability According to Farmers

Perception	Explanation	Confirmed by studies and experiments
Patchiness	Differences in soil types: *labu chirey, labu bi* and *labu kwarey*	West et al., 1984
Topographical features of soil surface: micro-highs (high productivity) and micro-lows (low-productivity)	Different susceptibility to wind erosion and vegetation density result in differences in surface sand layers	Geiger & Manu, 1993
Distance to certain trees: - *Annona senegalensis, Guiera senegalensis*	-Certain bushes stimulate millet growth	-Geiger & Manu, 1993
- *Balanites aegyptiaca, Sclerocarya birrea*	-Certain bushes depress millet growth	-Not available
Distance to *Faidherbia albida*	-Stimulating effect on millet growth underneath this species	Sall, 1992; Vandenbeldt & Williams, 1992
Farmers' management practices: - timely sowing and weeding	Delay in execution of agricultural activities depending on rainfall and labor capacity reduce millet growth	Sivakumar, 1992 (sowing); McIntire et al., 1989 (weeding)
Management techniques	Explanation	Confirmed by studies and experiments
1. Fallow	-Due to land and population pressure only within-field fallow	-Taylor-Powell, 1991
2. Localized fertilizing strategies: - manure (direct, kraaling)	-Transfer of fertility by livestock; different manure quality depending on feed quality	-McIntire et al., 1992; Powell & Ikpe, 1992; Powell & Williams, 1993
- millet crop residues and use of organic material	-Applications on spots with low productivity give high marginal net returns; many alternative uses with high opportunity costs -High concentration of organic material	-Buerkert et al., 1995b; Gavian 1992; Lamers et al., 1995
- deliberately moving compounds	-Sparsely used since too expensive. When used then on spots with high organic matter	-Buerkert et al., 1995a
3. Mineral fertilizer		-Buerkert et al., 1995b

Source: Lamers & Feil 1995

Table 2: Estimated Levels of Personnel Engaged in Research (Scientist Man-Year) and Extension (Number of Workers) and Estimated Levels of Expenditure (in constant 1980 US $) on Research and Extension in West Africa

	Research		Extension	
	1970	1980	1970	1980
Hired Staff	952	2466 (159%)	22,000	29,478 (33%)
Expenditures*	92	206 (123%)	181	205 (13%)

Source: Adapted from Connolly & Arokoyo 1991

* Figures rounded to the nearest million. In brackets the percentage increase.

Figure 2: Schematic Role of Extension Services

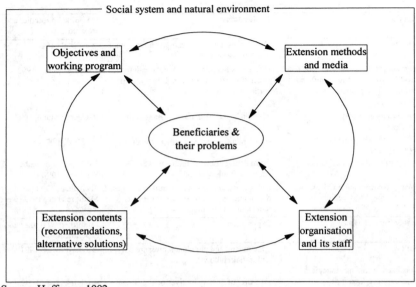

Source: Hoffmann 1992.

Researchers' Ignorance

To evaluate the quality of generated knowledge on production-increasing innovations in the WAS, the results of four different on-station experiments (Michels 1994; Buerkert 1995; Rebafka 1993; Ikpe et al. 1994) focusing on millet stover and manure applications and their effect on grain and stover yields of millet are reviewed (see table 3). All observations refer to the same millet line planted manually in pure stands, at 10,000 hills ha^{-1} and on the same soil type. The experiments were conducted in 1991 by different researchers and on different fields at the research site.

An agronomic comparison of the yields underlines the heterogeneity of the results. The yield levels (see table 3) and the yield increments (see table 5) differ considerably. Experiment A and B obtained grain yields normally harvested on-farm. The extremely low grain yields in experiment C were an effect of previous long-term exploitation. The continuous removal of all crop residues without using fertilizers led to phosphate and potassium deficiencies (Rebafka 1993). In contrast, phosphate was applied in all treatments of experiment D. The higher planting density, the smallest sampling plots at harvest and the moderate pre-exploitation by the previous millet/legume system may explain the high yield levels. Background information of the experiments give potential reasons for the different yield levels, especially in the control plots without stover (see table 4).

From the viewpoint of sustainability, the conclusions from the four studies differ. Only experiment D produced sufficient stover in all treatments to continue the same uses. Within experiment D, the application of manure seemed the most appropriate management technique. It not only produced the highest grain and total dry matter yields, but allowed other uses of stover as well. From experiment C it can be concluded that millet cropping is unsuitable: despite high yield increments (see table 5), the absolute yields are too low. The treatments were not sustainable because at the onset of the rainy season 2000 kg stover ha^{-1} are not available on those treatments requiring these amounts. The same was true for experiment A. The application of 2000 kg stover ha^{-1} did increase grain yield by 42%, but did not provide enough stover to keep the system running. The yields in experiment B hardly differed between the treatments. Here, a 500 kg ha^{-1} stover mulch assured a stover yield level to sustain the system and allowed alternative stover uses such as for feed, fuel, and construction.

The results of one experiment are consistent over the years and could thus provide recommendations. Yet, the comparison of results of the same treatments on different fields in the same year are inconsistent and, hence, no general conclusions about whether or not to use stover for soil fertility enhancement can be drawn, even when taking all additional information into account (see table 4). For a NAR it would therefore be very difficult to design appropriate on-farm trials based on these results.

An **economic assessment** of five different stover uses showed the profitability of each use depending on economic return indicators (Lamers & Bruentrup 1996). Returns per unit land area were highest using stover as a mulch at 2000 kg ha^{-1}. Given the labor bottlenecks in Niger, an important criterion for technology adoption is labor productivity. Returns to labor were most profitable when stover was used for livestock production. Burning stover at a rate of 2000 kg ha^{-1} gave the highest returns per unit weeding time, which is the activity demanding the most labor in millet production (Baidu-Forson 1988). When the results were compared by linear programming techniques, a combination of stover uses rather than a single purpose use gave the economic optimum, which happens to be farmers' current practice (Lamers & Bruentrup 1996). The variable yields from similar stover uses in the experiments A through D (see table 3) will lead to unstable economic analyses (assuming stable variable costs for the same treatments), and consequently do not allow extension recommendations to be defined for the most profitable use of stover.

Table 3: Millet Grain and Stover Yields (kg ha^{-1}) of four (A, B, C, D) Different on-Station Experiments using the Same Amount of Crop Residue (CR) for Mulching in the Same Year at Sadoré, Niger

Examined experiments from literature (source)	Grain and Straw production in 1991	Bare Control, No CR Applied	Mulched Treatments, Amount of CR applied			Manure applied instead of CR
		0 kg ha^{-1}	500 kg ha^{-1}	2 000 kg ha^{-1}	2 000 kg ha^{-1}, ash+	1500 kg ha^{-1}
				kg ha^{-1}		
A: (Michels 1994)	Grain	339	303	482	n.a	n.a
	Straw	1134	1098	1462	n.a	n.a
B: (Buerkert 1995)	Grain	n.a*	810	831	896	n.a
	Straw	n.a	1565	1645	1883	n.a
C: (Rebafka 1993)	Grain	39	n.a	238	117	n.a
	Straw	56	n.a	1133	489	n.a
D: (Ikpe et al. 1994)	Grain	1000	n.a	1200	1200	1400
	Straw	2100	n.a	2600	3200	3000

Source: Feil et al. 1995.

+ The equivalent of 2000 kg stover ha-1 were first burned and the ashes distributed over the plot.

* n.a = Treatments not applied in the indicated experiment. Experiment B had as the control the 500 kg ha-1 treatment.

Table 4: Key Background Information on Experimental Design, Crop Management and Plot History of Four (A, B, C, D) On-Station Experiments using the Same Amount of Crop Residue (CR) for Mulching in the Same Year at Sadoré, Niger, 1991.

Experiment (source)	Plot layout in the on-station field experiment	Sowing date 1991	Key cropping practices	Plot history	Miscellaneous
A: Michels 1994	"Cross-Over" design with 3 CR treatments and 2*3 replications. Plot size: 855 m²	5/27	Planted millet cultivar: CIVT*. Plant density: 30.000 plants/ha. Fertilizer use: basal dressing of 10 kg P/ha as SSP*; 30 and 15 kg N/ha as CAN* applied at 24 and 57 DAE* Weeding: manually at 21 and 71 DAE Spraying: insecticides at 80 DAE	Three years prior to the CR experiment, millet production according to "farmers practices"	CR application before onset of rains. Harvested 8*9 m² plots for yield estimates
B: Buerkert *et al.* 1995	Factorial design with 24 treatments, including the 3 CR applications and 4 replications. Plot size: 100 m²	5/27	Planted millet cultivar: CIVT. Plant density: 30.000 plants/ha. Fertilizer Application: None. Weeding: two weedings, manually	10 years prior to the start of the experiment in 1991 the plots were fallow	CR application before onset of rains. Harvested 5*10 m² for yield estimates
C: Rebafka 1993	Split-plot design with 6 replications. Different treatments including long-term application of CR. Plot size: 24 m²	6/1	Planted millet cultivar: CIVT. Plant density: 30.000 plants/ha. Fertilizer use: 15 kg N/ha applied as CAN in a split dose 20 and 40 DAP*. No P. Weeding: manual weeding was performed when necessary. More than twice	From 1980-86 millet was produced without fertilizers with CR removed each year. Since '86 various treatments with fertilizer and CR. In 1990 start of presented trial	CR at the end of season. Harvested 12m² for yield estimates
D: Ikpe *et al.* 1994	Split-plot with 4 treatments, including manure application and 4 replications. Plot size: 36 m²	5/5	Planted millet Cultivar: CIVT. Plant density: 40.000 plants/ha. Fertilizer use: basal dressing of 10 kg P/ha as SSP. Weeding: 1st weeding at 21 DAP, 2nd when necessary	Millet/Cowpea rotation experiment which included P and CR application. Quantities unknown	CR applied as stalks after onset of rain. Harvested 3*3.75 m² for yield estimates

*DAE = Days After Emergence of millet; DAP = Days After Planting; CIVT = (Composite Inter Variétal de Tarna) improved millet cultivar; SSP (Super Simple Phosphate) = P-containing fertilizer; CAN (Calcium Ammonium Nitrate) = Nitrogen containing fertilizer. Source: Feil et al. 1995.

Table 5: Increase in Millet Grain and Straw Production in Percentage of a Bare Control of Four (A, B, C, D) On-Station Experiments at Sadoré, Niger, 1991

Source for examined experiments	Grain and straw production in 1991	Mulched Treatments --- Amount of CR applied ---			Manure instead of CR applied
		500 kg ha^{-1}	2 000 kg ha^{-1}	2 000 kg ha^{-1}, ash+	1500 kg ha^{-1}
		---------------------------- % ----------------------------			
A: (Michels 1994)	Grain	-11	42	n.a	n.a
	Straw	-3	29	n.a	n.a
B:(Buerkert 1995)	Grain	0*	3	11	n.a
	Straw	0	5	20	n.a
C: (Rebafka 1993)	Grain	n.a*	510	200	n.a
	Straw	n.a	1885	773	n.a
D: (Ikpe et al. 1994)	Grain	n.a	20	20	40
	Straw	n.a	24	52	43

Source: Feil et al. 1995.
+ The equivalent of 2000 kg stover ha-1 were first burned and the ashes distributed over the plot; *Experiment B had as the control the 500 kg ha-1 treatment. n.a = Treatments not applied in the indicated experiment.

Conclusion on Crop Residue Uses

Stover applications have advantages over mineral fertilizers. Farmers are not only familiar with stover, but the material is also readily available. Logistical and organizational constraints, two aspects that often hinder the use of mineral fertilizers (Thompson & Baanante 1988), can thus be avoided. Previous studies showed that Nigerian farmers are aware of the effects of stover in their fields, but they have many uses for this material and the recommended stover quantity for a broadcast application is rarely available (Bationo & Mokwunye 1991; Lamers & Feil 1995). This hampers such an application even though it may stabilize or increase millet yields. Most farmers prefer a "clean field" and, hence, decide against a broadcast mulch, particularly since mulching stimulates weed production and increases labor demands for weeding by 25-30% (Lamers & Bruentrup 1996). Burning stover is, therefore, a widespread practice in Niger.

A particular problem such as soil erosion, poor soil fertility, or the need for feed can be relieved by the targeted use of stover (Michels 1994; Buerkert 1995; Rebafka 1993; Ikpe et al. 1994). Under current production levels, however, targeting applications to a single problem would force the farmer to neglect other problem areas. This contradicts the goals set by all involved: farmers, researchers, as well as politicians. Hence, there is no justification to make a specific stover use the main extension content.

Lessons Learned

The livelihood systems in Niger are a result of experience, knowledge, tradition, available resources, priorities, environment, technology level, political, economic and market conditions. Because of the complex social and physical relationships, the development of technologies for a single component of this system without affecting other parts is virtually impossible. Recommendations to farmers must be flexible enough to deal with the diversity and variability of the farming community, because technologies often need to be tailored to the conditions of the different groups that form this community. An effective concept requires the perspective of the whole livelihood system and a broader range of activities than the conventional limits of any single intervention.

There is no doubt of the importance of pro-active base-line research and its institutional concept. But past on-station research in the WAS has focused more on increasing the technical efficiency of innovations. Less attention was paid to the applicability and feasibility of these techniques for farmers. It is insufficient to know the increase in yield or the decrease in soil loss, if the economic and social significance of technologies are not appraised. Yet, this is of utmost interest to farmers. It does not help to pass this task to the NARs, because the feedback role of on-farm research will be weakened by staff with lower education, less research experience and less funding (Merill-Sands et al. 1989).

There is often a conflict between conservation and production by improving soil fertility techniques. In making land-use decisions, farm households need to consider both the agro-ecological features and economics. Especially under the harsh agro-ecological conditions existing in the WAS, the profitability of innovations is not always ensured. Thus, future research should examine practical intermediate solutions which reduce the competition between production and conservation. Since farmers decide what and how to produce, more research should be conducted on-farm and in collaboration with farmers. Demand-driven research can be effective if the problem is defined together with farmers and is then taken into account when defining experimental designs and research policies. The implementation of a "problem-solving concept" does not guarantee that problems with adoption will be avoided. However, these would only appear as second generation problems arising from the use of a new technology. It is clear, though, that a shift to an alternative research paradigm would not only require radical institutional reform, but, perhaps more importantly, a change of attitude among the research community. This calls for a collaboration between research disciplines in the decision-making process with respect to establishing research priorities, planning and conducting trials, and evaluating results.

Acknowledgment

This is a revised version of a paper published in February 1995 by the Journal for Technology Transfer. The study was supported, in part, by funds from the German Research Foundation (Deutsche Forschungsgemeinschaft) within the Special Research Program 308 of the University of Hohenheim. The authors thank Mrs. J. Kidd for editing the English.

References

Albrecht, H. 1986. Extension research: needs and uses. *In*: G. E. Jones (ed.) Investing in rural extension: strategies and goals. London, Elsevier Science Publisher: 239-245.

Baidu-Forson, J. 1988. Characteristics of farm households and economy in Western Niger villages: Some evidence from baseline surveys. Resource Management Program, Economics Group, Progress Report 87. ICRISAT, Niamey, Niger.

Bationo A. and A.U. Mokwunye 1991. Alleviating soil fertility constraints to increased crop production in West Africa: The experience in the Sahel. Fertilizer Research 29: 95-115.

Birkhaeuser, D., R.E. Evenson and G. Feder 1991. The economic impact of agricultural extension: a review. Economic Development and Cultural Change 39(2): 607-650.

Bruentrup, M., J.P.A. Lamers and F.Heidhues 1996. The economics of millet crop residues for wind erosion control in Niger, West Africa. p. 243-256 in: Buerkert B., B.E. Allison and M. von Oppen (eds.) Wind Erosion in West Africa: The Problem and its Control. December 5-7, 1994, Stuttgart-Hohenheim, Germany. Markgraf Verlag, Weikersheim, Germany.

Buerkert, A. 1995. Effects of Crop Residues, Phosphorus, and Spatial Soil Variability on Yield and Nutrient Uptake of Pearl Millet (*Pennisetum glaucum* L.) in Southwest Niger. Stuttgart, Ulrich Grauer Verlag.

Connolly, M. and T. Arokoyo 1991. Alleviating fertilizer technology transfer. p. 19-32 *In*: A.U. Mokwunye (ed.) Alleviating Soil Fertility Constraints to Increased Crop Production in West Africa. Dordrecht, Kluwer Academic Publishers.

Deuson, R.R. and J.H. Sanders 1988. Technology development and agricultural policy in the Sahel-Burkina Faso and Niger. p. 610-612 *In*: Proceedings International Conference on Dryland Farming, 19-22 August 1988, Bushland/Amarillo, Texas.

Deuson, R.R. and J.H. Sanders 1990. Cereal technology development in the Sahel: Burkina Faso and Niger. Land Use Policy 7: 195-197.

FAO 1993. AGROSTAT-PC. Computerized Information Series. Statistics Crops Trade, 1/5. Food and Agriculture Organization of the United Nations, Rome.

Feder, G., R.E. Just and D. Zilberman 1985. Adoption of agricultural innovations under low resource farmer conditions: a survey. Economic Development and Cultural Change 33 (2): 255-298.

Feil, P.R., J.P.A. Lamers and L. Herrmann 1995. Knowledge Transfer in the Field: Solving Crop Residue Problems in Niger. Journal for Technology Transfer, 20(1):31-41.

Hailu, Z. and A. Runge-Metzger 1992. Sustainability of Land Use Systems. The potential of indigenous measures for the maintenance of soil productivity in Sub-Sahara African agriculture. Tropical Agroecology 7. Weikersheim, Margraf.

Hoffmann, V. 1992. Beratungsansätze: von der Uniform zum Maßanzug. p. 271-277 in: V. Hoffmann (ed.) Beratung als Lebenshilfe. Humane Konzepte für eine ländliche Entwicklung. Weikersheim, Verlag Josef Margraf.

Ikpe, F.N., J.M. Powell and N.O. Isirimah 1994. Primary tillage and nutrient cycling in mixed farming systems of semi-arid West Africa (SAWA). p. 410-437 *In*: G. de Noni, J.F. Nouvelot and E. Roose (eds.) Réseau Erosion, Bulletin no. 14. September 15-18, 1993, Orstom, Montpellier, France.

ISNAR 1995. Survival in the Sahel. An ecological and development challenge. International Service for National Agricultural Research, The Hague.

Lamers, J.P.A. and M. Bruentrup 1996. Comparative advantage of single and multipurpose uses of millet stover in Niger. Agricultural Systems, 50 (3): 273-285.

Lamers, J.P.A. and P.R. Feil 1993. The many uses of millet crop residues. ILEIA Newsletter 9(2): 15.

Lamers, J.P.A. and P.R. Feil 1995. Farmers' knowledge and management of spatial soil and crop growth variability in Niger, West Africa. Netherlands Journal of Agricultural Science, 43 (4), 375-389.

Lipton, M. and R. Longhurst 1989. New seeds and poor people. London: Unwin Hyman.

Matlon, P.J. 1990. Improving productivity in sorghum and pearl millet in semi-arid Africa. Food Research Institute Studies, Vol XXII (1): 1-43.

Matlon, P.J. and D.S.C. Spencer 1984. Increasing food production in Sub-Saharan Africa. Environmental problems and inadequate technological solutions. American Journal of Agricultural Economics 66(5): 671-676.

McIntire, J., J. Hopkins, J.P.A. Lamers and L.K. Fussell 1989. The millet system of western Niger. I Crop production. ILCA, Addis Ababa, Ethiopia, (unpublished).

Merill-Sands, D., P. Ewell, S. Biggs and J. McAllister 1989. Issues in institutionalizing on-farm client-oriented research: a review of experiences from nine national agricultural research systems. Quarterly Journal of International Agriculture 28 (3 and 4): 279-301.

Michels, K. 1994. Wind Erosion in the Southern Sahelian Zone. Extent, Control, and Effects on Millet Production. Stuttgart, Ulrich Grauer Verlag.

Nabos, J. 1966. Present state of research work on improved varieties and cultivation methods of millet and sorghum in Niger. Journal African Soils 11(1/2): 365-381.

Rebafka, F.P. 1993. Deficiency of phosphorus and molybdenum as major growth limiting factors of pearl millet and groundnut on an acid sandy soil in Niger, West Africa. Hohenheimer Bodenkundliche Hefte no. 9. Universität Hohenheim.

Thompson, T.P. and C.A. Baanante 1988. A Socioeconomic Study of Farm-level Constraints to Fertilizer Use in Western Niger, IFDC Paper Series P-6, IFDC, Muscle Shoals, Alabama.

Venkatesan, V. and L. Schwartz 1992. Agricultural Service Initiative. Report based on the World Bank Workshop held at Lilongwe in February 1991. Agriculture and Rural Development Series no. 4. Technical Development, Africa Region. Washington: World Bank.

Estimating Smallholder's Risk Aversion: A Method to Improve Impact-Analyses of Potential Innovations

An Example from Zimbabwe's Semi-Arid Areas

B. Hedden-Dunkhorst

Bahnhorst 93, 31606 Warmsen, Germany

Abstract

This paper introduces a method which aims to estimate farmer's risk aversion coefficients, where risk is defined as income variability. Parametrization techniques are used in household models which are solved with quadratic programming. The method is applied to smallholders in Zimbabwe's semi-arid areas. Risk aversion coefficients estimated for different household types are positive and related to certain economic parameters.

The method proves to be useful where the impact of an innovation, which has a certain degree of risk associated with it, is analyzed. In this paper a technical and an institutional innovation are tested. Results show that at given costs and prices, both, improved small grain varieties as well as trade liberalization, stimulating private trade, have a positive but limited impact on household's income and food security. This implies the need for a comprehensive approach to contend the problem of food insecurity in rural areas.

Keywords:

Risk aversion, quadratic programming, impact-analysis, semi-arid Zimbabwe, improved small grain varieties, trade liberalization,

1 Introduction

Agriculture in Zimbabwe's smallholder areas is characterized by low productivity and high risk of yield failure. As a result many households face food insecurity, especially in dry years[1]. Since the early eighties the Government of Zimbabwe has initiated a number of measures to improve food security. Technical and institutional production, consumption and marketing related innovations are developed and to a certain extent disseminated. Where adoption rates for new technologies are low, impact analyses of potential innovations might have been neglected or are incomplete.

---

[1] In 1988/89 a survey of 186 households in four smallholder areas showed that 52 % of the sample households could not satisfy minimum requirements.

The importance of smallholder's risk attitudes has been identified as an important parameter to influence farmer's decisions (Binswanger 1980; Hazell 1986), though the empirical measurement of risk attitudes turned out to be difficult.

In the first part of this paper a method is proposed which aims to quantify smallholder's risk aversion within the framework of agricultural household models. Risk aversion coefficients are derived through parametrization techniques applied in quadratic programming models. The applicability of the approach is tested using a data set from smallholders in Zimbabwe's semi-arid areas. In order to assess the impact of risk on food security two household groups are distinguished, food-secure and food-deficit households. Secondly, in an attempt to demonstrate possible areas of application of the technique, the impact of two potential innovations, a technical and an institutional innovation, on income and food security is examined. A comparison of with and without consideration of risk parameters indicates the impact of risk. Finally, the potential to transfer the approach to other situations involving risk is discussed.

2   Estimating Smallholder's Risk Behavior

2.1   Methodology

Contradictions of farmer's behavior to profit maximization theory evoked the development of "risk and uncertainty" theories early this century. During the last decades various methods have been developed to model risk based on regression analysis or mathematical programming. The latter includes methods which either incorporate risk in the constraints set or in the objective function coefficients. Linear risk programming and quadratic programming provide useful methods when risk, defined as income variance, is included in the objective function.

In this research, quadratic programming as developed by Markowitz (1952) is applied. Quadratic programming aims to find the optimal portfolio that maximizes a farmer's utility subject to income variance (Anderson, Dillon, Hardaker 1977; Hazel 1986). Unlike linear risk programming, quadratic programming allows the consideration of "true" variances and covariances between activity gross margins. Different approaches of formulating quadratic programming models are conceivable (Freund 1956). The technique applied here considers utility maximization directly by using the farmer's utility function expressed in quadratic form as the objective function to be maximized (Anderson, Dillon, Hardaker 1977).

The following objective function is applied:

$$max\ U = \Sigma c' X - \Phi (X' \Omega X)^{\frac{1}{2}}$$

subject to $Ax \leq b$
$$x \geq 0$$

U	=	utility
X	=	a vector of activity levels
c'	=	a vector of mean gross margins
A	=	a matrix of resource requirements or technical coefficients
b	=	a vector of fixed resources and other restrictions
Φ	=	a risk-aversion coefficient
Ω	=	a variance-covariance matrix of activity gross margins

Criticism of both, linear and quadratic risk programming, concentrate on the restriction of risk defined as the distribution of income, and on the problem of estimating the risk aversion coefficient (Φ).

Since the development of linear and quadratic risk programming the constant Φ has created intensive debate among economists. Boussard (1980) quoted a number of studies which impugn the assumption that the risk aversion coefficient can be regarded as a constant which characterizes the decision maker's risk attitude. He proved that risk aversion is closely tied to the financial situation of the decision maker; while Pratt (1964) received good results when relating his risk aversion coefficient to a farmer's total assets or wealth instead of income.

Here it is attempted to assess the risk aversion factor by including production and utilization activities and by taking consumption requirements and off-farm income opportunities into account, within the framework of a quadratic programming model. The risk aversion coefficient is determined through parametrization at various levels of risk aversion and by comparing a household's performance as observed in the surveys with the performance of the household in a quadratic programming model. Thereby, it is assumed that the model is sufficiently comprehensive so that the risk aversion coefficient, at which the model result matches with the observed performance of the household, represents the true risk aversion of the household.

This procedure presumes the following assumptions: (1) A household attempts to maximize its utility, while minimizing the associated variance. (2) A household regards risk involved in farming as crop yield variability. (3) The decision maker allocates arable land to different crops according to yield variability and his or her personal risk attitude. (4) Yield variability and risk aversion are the necessary and sufficient factors affecting household performance.

Based on the above described approach several hypotheses can be tested. In principle every household would have an individual risk aversion. Certain household groups (e.g food-deficit and food-secure households) within certain regions, where variances and covariances of activities are the same, would differ in their risk attitudes. Personal risk attitudes depend on a number of farm-household characteristics, among which access to off-farm income is of major importance.

2.2   Data Base and Model Outline

The analysis is based on surveys carried out in four smallholder areas in Zimbabwe's semi-arid region in 1988/89. The total sample size amounts to 186 households. Samples within each area are subdivided into two groups, food-deficit and food-secure households, according to the household's nutritional situation. In addition, time-series data of crop yields for the period 1979-89 are used to simulate yield variances and covariances. These data are derived from extension worker's estimations carried out annually in each area.

Agricultural household models, covering a one year period, are developed for each of the four study areas and both food-secure and food-deficit households within each area. Each of the eight models reflects an average farm-household of the respective sample.

Crop production, consumption-, buying- and selling activities, small grain storing and feeding activities and labor hiring activities are included in the model. Crop production and buying activities are balanced with crop utilization activities. Livestock inputs and outputs and remittances from off-farm income are regarded as constants, leisure preferences are omitted. Restrictions imposed on the model include resource constraints and per capita caloric intake (for further model specification see Hedden-Dunkhorst 1993).

2.3   Risk Aversion and Farm-Household Characteristics

Modelling procedure reveals risk aversion coefficients ranging from 0.58 to -0.06 for the eight groups analyzed (Table 1). Multiplying a risk coefficient with the square root of the variance-covariance matrix of activity gross margins results in the risk-component. It reflects the amount of money a household or individual is prepared to renounce in favor of risk aversion. Risk-components vary between 170 Z\$ and -44 Z\$ (1 US\$ = Z\$ 2.27) per household or 27 to -7 Z\$ per capita among the groups. If defined as a proportion of net household cash income household risk-components range from 33 to -4 percent (Table 1), or 12 % on average.

Among the eight groups tested, only one group, food-secure households in Mazvihwa, reveals a negative risk coefficient, which implies a risk-taking attitude. This group is characterized by highest cash inflows from off-farm employment and other sources. In two of the four study areas (Mazvihwa and Nata) risk coefficients are higher among food-deficit households compared to food-secure households. This corresponds to the expectation that poorer households are more risk averse. Though, in the two other areas, Ramakwebane and Semukwe, risk coefficients are slightly higher for food-secure households compared to food-deficit households. Ramakwebane relies on food imports not only in the survey year, but in every year. Semukwe just reaches self-sufficiency in years of average crop output, while Mazvihwa and Nata are in the position to produce surpluses in average production years. This suggests that household's risk behavior might also be related to the general situation of food deficits and surpluses within an area. For food purchases households in deficit areas would have to rely totally on the more expensive urban milled maize meal products[2]. While in self-sufficient areas households could make use of local surpluses, which are offered at prices below the retail price for maize meal.

Table 1:   Risk Aversion Coefficients and per Capita Risk-Components[1] Estimated for Smallholders in Zimbabwe

Study Area	Nutritional Status of Household Group	Risk Aversion Coefficient (Φ)	Per Capita Risk-Component[1] (Z$)	
Ramakwebane	food-secure (n=21)	0.58	27	(16)
	food-deficit (n=25)	0.54	19	(33)
Mazvihwa	food-secure (n=20)	-0.06	-7	(-4)
	food-deficit (n=25)	0.02	2	(2)
Nata	food-secure (n=33)	0.08	9	(7)
	food-deficit (n=15)	0.25	14	(20)
Semukwe	food-secure (n=23)	0.07	9	(4)
	food-deficit (n=24)	0.02	1	(1)

Source: Farm-household modeling based on SADCC/ICRISAT smallholder surveys 1988/89
[1] The risk-component reflects the product of the risk coefficient and the scaled variance-covariance matrix of activity gross margins.
Figures in parentheses = per capita risk-component as percent of net per capita cash income

In an attempt to capture potential relations between risk coefficients and farm-household characteristics as well as risk coefficients and decisions in crop production, a number of correlations are executed. Although different variances and covariances of gross margins among the study areas also influence the

---

[2] Due to trade restrictions urban milled maize meal is the only staple food offered in deficit areas.

magnitude of the risk coefficients, correlation results are quite plausible. Among the variables related to household characteristics only total arable land has a correlation coefficient above 0.5, as expected it is negative (Table 2). Household remittances and risk coefficients are negatively correlated at 0.31. While the magnitude of this correlation is lower than anticipated, the sign corresponds to the expectation. For other household characteristics correlation coefficients are below 0.3, but show the expected signs.

Table 2:   Pearson Correlation Coefficients for Correlations between Farm-Household Parameters and Risk Aversion Coefficients (F), Estimated for eight Household Groups in four Study Areas in Zimbabwe

Farm-Household Parameter	Correlation Coefficient	Farm-Household Parameter	Correlation Coefficient
Remittances (Z$ per Household)	-0.31	Pearl Millet Area (% of total arable)	0.19
Farm Cash Income (Z$)	-0.14	Finger Millet Area (% of total arable)	-0.57
Total Arable Land (ha)	-0.69	Groundnut Area (% of total arable)	-0.83*
Maize Area (% of total arable)	-0.64	Sunflower Area (% of total arable)	-0.53
White Sorghum Area (% of total arable)	0.60	Cowpea Area (% of total arable)	0.88*
Red Sorghum Area (% of total arable)	0.61	Bambaranut Area (% of total arable)	-0.41

Source: Farm-household modeling based on SADCC/ICRISAT smallholder surveys 1988/89

Further correlations between risk coefficients and areas allocated to alternative crops as percent of total arable land reflect farmer's perceptions of crop performance under drought conditions. Areas allocated to crops commonly considered as more drought tolerant (sorghum, pearl millet and cowpea) are positively correlated to risk coefficients[3]. In contrast, areas allocated to maize, finger millet, groundnut and sunflower are negatively correlated to risk aversion.

The analysis confirms previous research findings indicating smallholder risk aversion (Binswanger 1980; Antel 1987). It further shows that the magnitude of risk aversion varies according to household specific endogenous factors, and related independent, exogenous factors (e.g. consumer prices[4]). Poorer households compared to better off households are not necessarily more risk averse. Policy instruments directed to improve food security should aim to reduce the effects of risk inducing factors.

---

[3] These common assessments of crops as being more or less drought tolerant correspond to crop yield variances.
[4] In food deficit areas where quantities purchased are greater than quantities sold, consumer prices have a larger impact on food security as compared to producer prices.

3 Impact-Analyses of Potential Innovations Including Smallholder's Risk Behavior

In an attempt to estimate the impact of a technical and an institutional innovation on household's performance, the model approach is applied again. Risk aversion coefficients, as estimated, are considered assuming that farmers have a fixed risk aversion for a certain time period. A comparison of models with and without risk is carried out to indicate differences in model results when risk is omitted.

3.1 The Impact of Improved Sorghum and Millet Cultivars

In the early eighties the importance of drought tolerant crops as a means to improve food security in the semi-arid areas was recognized by national and international organizations. More resources were allocated to small grain research. As a first result, white sorghum and pearl millet open-pollinated varieties were released in the eighties, and a white sorghum hybrid in the early nineties. Estimations of sorghum and millet breeders (Obilana 1992) suggest a 25% yield increase of improved varieties over local varieties on smallholder farms.

Again, quadratic programming models are built for each study area and household group. In order to obtain more generally applicable results, the analysis is carried out for an average production year. Average crop yields are derived from time-series data. Yield variability for improved varieties is simulated and added to the variance-covariance matrix..

A comparison of models with and without smallholder's risk behavior included leads to rather different results. Table 3 shows variations in net per capita cash income from 0 to 71 %. In three of the four areas food-deficit households receive much better incomes when risk is excluded while food-secure households experience slight income losses, again in three of four areas. This implies that if risk is excluded from the analysis, findings received could induce policy recommendations which are based on wrong assumptions.

Impact-analysis including risk suggests that compared to without yield increase net per capita cash income increases by one to twelve percent, with an average of 5.9 percent, when improved sorghum and millet is applied instead of local varieties (Table 3). In Mazvihwa an equal proportional income increase of 5% is reached in the two household groups, whereas in Ramakwebane, Nata and Semukwe food-deficit households gain considerably more from better yields than food-secure households, due to the higher share of crop production in total income. In absolute terms, food-deficit households in Nata and Semukwe reach higher income increases compared to food-secure households.

In terms of national welfare, improved small grains have a positive effect because they 1) enhance food security, 2) improve self-sufficiency, thereby reduce subsidies on staple food imports, and 3) could stimulate sales of sunflower, cowpea and groundnut on the national market where oilseed crops are highly in demand.

Table 3: Net per Capita Cash Income (Z$) after the Introduction of Improved Small Grains, with and without Smallholder's Risk Aversion

Study Area	Nutritional Status of Household Group	Net Per Capita Cash Income (Z$) (Including Risk)	Net Per Capita Cash Income (Z$) (Excluding Risk)
Ramakwebane	food-secure (n=21)	135 (5)	131 [-3]
	food-deficit (n=25)	35 (12)	60 [+71]
Mazvihwa	food-secure (n=20)	210 (5)	193 [-8]
	food-deficit (n=25)	106 (5)	116 [+10]
Nata	food-secure (n=33)	145 (3)	143 [-2]
	food-deficit (n=15)	72 (7)	89 [+24]
Semukwe	food-secure (n=23)	213 (1)	222 [+4]
	food-deficit (n=24)	76 (9)	76 [0]

Source: Farm-household modeling based on SADCC/ICRISAT smallholder surveys 1988/89
Figures in parentheses = proportional deviations to "without improved small grains"
Figures in brackets = proportional deviations to models including risk

3.2 The Impact of Grain Market Liberalization on Small Farmer's Welfare

In the past, grain marketing in Zimbabwe was highly government controlled. Pan-seasonal and pan-territorial producer prices for numerous crops, transport restrictions and maize meal subsidies favoring centralized urban milling characterized the marketing system. These regulations created significant inefficiencies in terms of resource allocations and put considerable pressure on the national budget.

In 1991 the Government of Zimbabwe introduced the Economic Structural Adjustment Program. Since then subsidies have been reduced and grain marketing gradually decontrolled, leading to unrestricted trade movements. Through the legalization of private trade and transport between surplus and deficit smallholder areas is intended to increase the supply of alternative grain products at different price levels in deficit areas.

Given this background, it is of interest for policy makers to gain insight into the potential impact of access to alternative staple foods other than maize meal on rural household's performance and food security aspects. This impact can be simulated and quantified using the model approach including farmer's risk behavior as estimated above. It is assumed that through private trade, grain can be provided to rural deficit areas at consumer prices below the price of maize meal. Although, the results are based on 1989 cost and prices, they provide sufficient information to evaluate the impact of the availability of "low-cost grain" under current cost and price relations.

Due to a lack of data on actual costs and margins, consumer prices possibly offered by private traders are projected. It is assumed that traders buy maize from Grain Marketing Board depots and resell it in smallholder areas with an increase of 40 %. This implies profit margins of about ten percent per ton of maize transported to the study areas.

Model results suggest that in the survey year 1988/89, a year with below average crop yields, net per capita cash incomes increase by three to ten percent among the groups with access to "low-cost grain" compared to those without access to "low-cost grain" (Table 4). On average food-deficit households experience higher proportional, but not actual income increases than food-secure households. If in food-deficit households the additional cash available is used to buy "low-cost grain", this could improve the per capita caloric intake by two to six percent which is insufficient to reach food security.

In years with average crop output the availability of "low-cost grain" shows less impact on household cash income (Table 4). Due to better yields, five of the eight household groups are in the position to reach self-sufficiency and therefore purchase virtually no additional grain. At given price relations it is most profitable for these households to acquire their food requirements through subsistence production. Labor productivity of subsistence production, in monetary terms valued at nutritional equivalent retail prices, is much higher than labor productivity of cash cropping. In three groups (food-deficit households in Nata and both groups in Ramakwebane, which is a deficit area even in good years) significant income increases are achieved. With the availability of "low-cost grain" these groups have a comparative advantage to produce cash crops and buy "low-cost grain" for home consumption.

The findings for both years examined suggest a positive though limited impact of trade liberalization on household income and food security and a preference for subsistence production. These positive results, however, have to be taken cautiously because they largely depend on price relations within the particular location. If private traders are reluctant to supply remote areas or prices are too high for a large part of the population, additional risks for food security arise. In general, trade liberalization will offer more alternatives to smallholders to develop market niches and react flexibly to price and cost changes.

Table 4:   Net per Capita Cash Income (Z$) with "Low-Cost Grain" available, in
          1988/89 and in a Year with Average Crop Yields

Study Area	Nutritional Status of Household Group	Net Per Capita Cash Income (Z$) (1988/89)	Net Per Capita Cash Income (Z$) (Φ crop yields)
Ramakwebane	food-secure (n=21)	156 (7)	143 (11)
	food-deficit (n=25)	57 (10)	39 (26)
Mazvihwa	food-secure (n=20)	162 (5)	200 (0)
	food-deficit (n=25)	72 (3)	100 (0)
Nata	food-secure (n=33)	118 (3)	140 (0)
	food-deficit (n=15)	68 (5)	70 (4)
Semukwe	food-secure (n=23)	188 (3)	212 (1)
	food-deficit (n=24)	67 (3)	70 (0)

Source: Farm-household modeling based on SADCC/ICRISAT smallholder surveys 1988/89
Figures in parentheses = proportional deviations from without "low-cost grain" available

4   Conclusions and Policy Implications

In the context of structural adjustment programs smallholders in developing countries are exposed to changing policy frameworks. Technical and institutional innovations become available which can bear new risks. It is contended that, if impact-analyses of potential innovations or policy instruments ignore farmer's risk attitudes, policy decisions might be inappropriate. A comparison of per capita incomes of food-deficit households in rural Zimbabwe modelled with and without "risk" reflects an income overestimation of 35 % if "risk" is omitted.

In this research, a method to quantify smallholder's risk aversion coefficients, where risk is defined as income variability, proved to be a useful tool. The method, using parametrization techniques in quadratic programming models, is applied to a data set from smallholders in Zimbabwe's semi-arid areas. Yet the approach is applicable to any other circumstance where a dual objective of risk minimization and net income maximization can be formulated. Limitations to apply the method if time-series data to capture income variability are not available might be offset using production functions derived from cross-sectional data. Besides, to reduce data requirements, partial analysis, e.g. limited to crop production activities instead of whole-farm modelling is feasible for analyzing a large number of problems.

Risk aversion coefficients estimated for different household groups suggest that smallholders are risk averse and that, on average, they accept income losses of about twelve percent in favor of improved income stability. The estimated coefficients are used to quantify farmer's risk aversion when analyzing the impact of two potential innovations. Both examples tested, improved small grain varieties and improved access to staple food through private trade, suggest a positive though limited impact on net per capita income (six and five percent, on average, respectively). These findings indicate that the impact of individual innovations is low and cannot substantially improve the situation of smallholders, particularly of the poorer households. However, the analysis examines the impact of individual innovations, it ignores the fact that often more than one innovation or instrument becomes effective at the same time and that there are interactions between different innovations. Though, with the mathematical programming approach as proposed in this paper it is possible to project the impact of various innovations simultaneously, while considering farmer's risk aversion. This can further improve impact-analyses of policies affecting farmer's circumstances.

5   Lessons Learned

Food insecurity is a major problem among many households in Zimbabwe's drier areas. This has been proven by numerous studies. To solve the problem technical as well as institutional innovations have been developed, primarily with the intention to increase food production. However, the impact of these innovations seems to be limited. This study stresses the importance of incorporating household's risk attitudes in impact-analyses of potential innovations in order to improve the relevance of the results. In semi-arid areas risk is a significant factor for both food-insecure and food-secure households, but its neglect has a stronger distorting impact on income estimations of food-insecure households. This can imply policy recommendations which leads to misallocations of limited resources, and consequently, have a negative impact on development.

A second lesson relates to the findings of limited impact of production increasing technologies on food-security in environmentally fragile, semi-arid areas. This finding asks for the need to put stronger emphasis on the second part of the food-security equation, purchasing power, instead of focusing on production. In marginal areas household income diversification provides the most secure strategy.

References

Anderson, J.R., Dillon, J.L., and Hardaker, J.B. 1977. Agricultural Decision Analysis. Ames, Iowa: Iowa State University Press.

Antel, J.M. 1987. Econometric estimation of producer's risk attitudes. Am.J.Agric.Econ. 69(3):509-522.

Binswanger, H.P. 1980. Attitudes toward risk: Experimental measurement in rural India. Am.J.Agric.Econ. 62(3):395-407.

Blackie, M.J 1994. Realizing smallholder agricultural potential. In Zimbabwe's agricultural revolution, ed. M. Rukuni and C. K. Eicher. University of Zimbabwe Publications.

Boussard, J.M. 1980. The risk aversion parameter in modelling farm decisions. In: Hanf, C.-H. and Schiefer, G., eds. Consideration and modelling of risk in the agribusiness sector. Proceedings of the second symposium of the European Association of Agricultural Economists (EAAE). Kiel 16-18 September 1980. Kiel: Wissenschaftsverlag Vauk.

Freund, R.J. 1956. The introduction of risk into a programming model. Econometrica 24(2):253-63.

Hazell, P.B.R. and Norton, R.D. (1986). Mathematical programming for economic analysis in agriculture. New York: Macmillian Publishing Company.

Hedden-Dunkhorst, B. 1993. The contribution of sorghum and millet versus maize to food-security in semi-arid Zimbabwe. Farming Systems and Resource Economics in the Tropics, Vol(15). Kiel: Wissenschaftsverlag Vauk.

Markowitz, H. 1952. Portfolio selection. J.Finance, 72:77-91.

Obilana, A.T. 1992. Personal communication.

Pratt, J.W. 1964. Risk aversion in the small and in the large. Econometrica 32(1-2):122-36.

Rukuni, M. and Eicher C.K.(eds.) 1994. Zimbabwe's Agricultural Revolution. University of Zimbabwe Publications.

A Simultaneous-Equation Approach to the Analysis of Factors Influencing the Adoption of Agricultural Innovations: The Case of Inorganic Fertilizer

Teressa Adugna and Franz Heidhues
Department of Agricultural and Social Economics
in the Tropics and Subtropics
University of Hohenheim, D-70593 Stuttgart, Germany

Abstract

This paper examines factors influencing the adoption and intensity of use of inorganic fertilizer among farm households. The estimation of a logit model shows that extension services, the number of oxen owned by households, access to credit and hired labor, as well as land rented out are among important determinants of the decision to adopt fertilizer. The analysis conducted on the rate of fertilizer adoption using two-stage least squares procedure suggests that farm size, crop-fertilizer response coefficient, number of oxen owned by households, access to credit and hired labor, fertilizer-crop price ratio and off-farm income are significant factors influencing the intensity of fertilizer use.

Keywords

Ethiopia, food production, fertilizer adoption, fertilizer intensity

1   Introduction

In Ethiopia, like in many poor countries, poverty and sluggish growth in food and agricultural production, compounded by increasing population pressure and climatic conditions, have led to severe domestic food shortages. Among possible means to combat this food shortage and food insecurity is to increase domestic food production. This could be realized either by increasing the area of land under cultivation and/or by intensifying food production. Given the various limitations associated with area expansion, such as remoteness, lack of water, disease-causing insects, etc., and the urgency of ensuring food security, production growth has to mainly come from intensification. Already Ruthenberg (1980) stressed this view when he stated: "The potential to increase farm production and agricultural growth is achievable, at least in short run, through land use intensification with the help of modern yield-increasing technology."

Yield-increasing technology includes, among other innovations, improved seeds and chemical fertilizer. These two inputs have been essential means to increase and stabilize food and agricultural production in many developing countries. The use of improved seeds are very limited in Ethiopia, as it is in many African countries (World Bank 1989). However, the use of inorganic fertilizer has a significant effect (Yao 1993) even on traditional crop varieties in which responses are generally believed to be low.

Efforts have been underway in the country, through various projects and programs financed mainly through foreign assistance, to promote the use of fertilizer and accompanying farm inputs. Despite these efforts, the level of fertilizer use in the country is still very low, particularly in the smallholder sector. Only 7.1 kg of fertilizer per hectare of arable land is used in Ethiopia as compared to the low-income countries' average of 20.7 kg/ha and the world average of 93.3 kg/ha (World Bank 1994).

This low level of fertilizer use reveals, besides the limited supply of chemical fertilizer and the country's inadequate fertilizer distribution mechanism, that there are crucially important constraints on its use at individual farm level. Theoretical and empirical studies put forward a range of social, demographic, economic, physical and institutional factors that influence the adoption and rate of use of an innovation in general, and fertilizer in particular (Feder et al 1985; Kebede et al 1990; Bellon and Taylor 1993; Admassie 1995; Ali 1995; Smale et al 1995). However, there is no consensus among various studies on the specific factors that guide farmers' decision on both of these issues.

Moreover, the available empirical studies in the area, as extensively and critically reviewed by Feder et al (1985), are associated with a number of drawbacks. Most of these studies have used qualitative analytical techniques, such as Chi-square test and correlation analysis which provide only qualitative information. Many quantitative studies also suffer from a single-equation bias as they applied single-equation models (ordinary least squares) to a problem clearly simultaneous in nature. This practice results in inconsistent parameter estimates and thereby leads to erroneous policy prescriptions. In sum, the currently available empirical knowledge about the possible factors that influence the adoption and the degree of use of innovations in general, and fertilizer technology by Ethiopian farmers in particular, is inadequate.

The purpose of this paper is, therefore, to contribute to the understanding of some of the factors that influence the adoption of chemical fertilizer and the intensity of its use among individual farm households in the Lume district, central Ethiopia. In doing so, the paper applies a logit and a simultaneous-equation models, respectively. The latter overcomes, by endogenizing farm size, the single-equation bias and the inconsistency of parameter estimates. The contributions of the paper may thus be seen as both empirical and methodological.

The rest of the paper is organized as follows. Section 2 presents the conceptual framework. Section 3 describes a logit model and a simultaneous-equation econometric model. Section 4 presents the empirical results. Section 5 summarizes the lessons learned.

2 Conceptual Framework

Generally, there are two broad alternative theories of smallholders' economic behavior based on a set of prior assumptions about their goals, the techniques of production and resource base and the nature of markets within which they make their decisions. The first one accepts farm households' efficiency (Schultz 1964; Norman 1974) and explains that farm households maximize outputs from existing resources and technology; and thus allocate resources optimally in line with the principle of profit maximization. Given this economic behavior, farm households strive to increase their farm outputs by adopting available agricultural innovations.

The second theoretical view stresses the general inefficiency of farm households (Lipton 1968; Wong 1971; Shapiro 1983). In this view, family farms are shown to give priority to other goals, such as meeting the family's subsistence needs, rather than a purely monetary profit. The implication here is that farm households' innovation-adoption behavior reveals a sizable deviation from those associated with optimal resource allocations and profit maximization.

However, even if the circumstances of farm households inhibit the attainment of efficiency in its strict neoclassical sense, it does not exclude a strong element of economic calculation on the part of the households (Ellis 1988; Getachew 1995). Their decision-making process involves the identification, consistent appraisal and comparison of options for allocation of scarce resources (Getachew 1995). They follow an allocation that optimizes or maximizes some stipulated objective(s) which may not necessarily be given in monetary terms. We, therefore, base our analysis on the assumption that, given various constraints, farm households practice a proper allocation of their scarce physical and human resources and accordingly decide on the adoption of innovations.

On the basis of the above assumption, farm households' adoption of innovations can be characterized in terms of several interrelated choices (Smale et al 1995). One of these choices is whether or not to adopt an innovation. The second choice is the rate of adoption of the innovation, for example, the rate of fertilizer use. The fertilizer adoption choice and, more precisely, the intensity of fertilizer use and farm size choices are part of simultaneous input choices that are derived from farm households' objective optimization (Smale et al 1995).

3   Econometric Model and Data

This section presents two econometric models, namely, a logit and a simultaneous-equation model, and describes the data set.

3.1   A Logit Model

In a discrete adoption decision, a farm household has either adopted chemical fertilizer (Y=1) or has not (Y=0) in the cropping season in which the farm survey was carried out. In order to explain this binary fertilizer adoption variable, it is necessary to construct a probability model that relates the variable to a vector of factors, x (Greene 1993). The probability of fertilizer adoption can then be expressed as:

$$Prob(Y = 1) = F(\beta'x) \qquad (1)$$

ß refers to the set of parameters that reflect the impact of changes in x on the probability of fertilizer adoption. The choice of a particular form for the right had side of equation (1) leads to an empirical model. The logit model has been used in many empirical analyses mainly for its mathematical convenience (Greene 1993). Adopting this model, the probability of fertilizer adoption is a regression model given by:

$$Prob(Y = 1) = \frac{e^{(\beta'x)}}{1 + e^{(\beta'x)}} \qquad (2a)$$
$$= \cap(\beta'x), \qquad (2b)$$

The notation $\cap(.)$ in (2b) is used to indicate the logistic cumulative distribution function. The empirical estimation of equation (2b) helps the derivation of the sign and marginal effect of each independent variable on the probability of fertilizer adoption.

3.2   A Simultaneous-Equation Model

In addition to the decision to adopt fertilizer, it is essential for various policy issues to know the intensity of fertilizer use. The desire to examine this aspect necessitates the formulation of the second model; a two-equation simultaneous model. The first equation of this model relates the rate of fertilizer application to various explanatory variables including farm size.

$$FERTI_i = \alpha + \sum \Gamma_i X_i + \sum \phi_i Z_i + e_i \qquad (3)$$

where $FERTI_i$ is the intensity of fertilizer use, X_i is a vector of continuous independent variables and Z_i is a vector of binary independent variables, α, Γ_i, and ϕ_i are parameters to be estimated and e_i is the error term.

The estimation of equation (3) alone assumes farm size (the size of cultivated land) as an exogenous variable. However, as already explained in section 2, the two are simultaneous decisions forming part of a system of simultaneous equations. Failure to take account of this joint decision in conducting empirical analysis will lead to biased and inconsistent parameters of a single-equation model (Greene 1993). In order to overcome this problem, it is necessary to introduce an equation for farm size. This equation relates the size of cultivated land to a diverse list of explanatory variables including the amount of fertilizer used by a farm household.

$$FARMS_i = \delta + \Sigma \theta_i R_i + \Sigma \mu_i S_i + v_i \qquad (4)$$

where $FARMS_i$ is farm size, R_i is a vector of continuous independent variables and S_i is a vector of binary independent variables, δ, Θ_i, and μ_i are parameters to be estimated and v_i is the error term.

3.3 Specification of Empirical Models

Empirical models corresponding to equations (2b), (3) and (4) are specified as follows:

a) Logit model for fertilizer adoption

$$
\begin{aligned}
FUSEDUM_i = {} & b_0 + b_1 DAR_i + b_2 MF010_i + b_3 MF1170_i \\
& + b_4 AGE_i + b_5 LANDOHA_i + b_6 OXN_i \\
& + b_7 OFF\text{-}FARMI_i + b_8 GENDER_i + b_9 EDCDUM_i \\
& + b_{10} SICKDU_i + b_{11} SICFDU_i + b_{12} CREDITDU_i \\
& + b_{13} HIREDLDU_i + b_{14} LANDRODU_i + w_i
\end{aligned}
\qquad (5)
$$

b) A simultaneous-equation model

i) Fertilizer intensity equation

$$
\begin{aligned}
LNP_2O_5N_2PH_i = {} & a + g_1 DAR_1 + g_2 MF010_i + g_3 MF1170_i \\
& + g_4 AGE_i + g_5 LANDCHA_i + g_6 CROPFRESP_i \\
& + g_7 OXN_i + g_8 OFF\text{-}FARMI_i + g_9 FCROPPRAT_i \\
& + j_1 GENDER_i + j_2 EDCDUM_i + j_3 SICFDU_i \\
& + j_4 HIREDLDU_i + j_5 CREDITDU_i + e_i
\end{aligned}
\qquad (6a)
$$

ii) Farm size equation

$$
\begin{aligned}
LANDCHA_i = {} & d + l_1MF010_i + l_2MF1170_i + l_3AGE_i + l_4P_2O_5N_{2i} \\
& + l_5SQINDEX_i + l_6FCROPPRAT_i + l_7OFF\text{-}FARMI_i \\
& + l_8NPLO\_LCH_i + m_1GENDER_i + m_2EDCDUM_i \\
& + m_3SICFDU_i + m_4HIREDLDU_i + m_5CREDITDU_i \\
& + m_6LANDRIDU_i + m_7LANDRODU_i + v_i \qquad\qquad (6b)
\end{aligned}
$$

where the variables are as defined in table 1 and $b_0,...,b_{14}$, a, $g_1,...,g_9$, $j_1,...,j_5$, $d,l_1,...,l_8$ and $m_1,...,m_7$ are parameters to be estimated, w_i, e_i and v_i are error terms.

3.4   The Data Set

The data used for this work were collected from 161 randomly selected farm household heads in the Lume district, central Ethiopia, during the 1993/94 G.C. cropping season. Table 1 provides the profile of the sample: the means, standard deviations, the minimum and maximum values of socioeconomic, demographic, physical and institutional variables.

The study district has been among the districts which received attention in the distribution of fertilizer. Consequently, unlike other areas, the use and benefits of mineral fertilizer is relatively wide-spread among farm households. During the cropping season under consideration, out of 161 valid samples, 151 farm households have used DAP (Diammonium Phosphate) and/or Urea. It was only 10 farm households which did not use fertilizer. That is to say, 93.79% of the peasant farmers were found to be adopters and 6.21% of them were nonadopters of chemical fertilizer. On the average, cultivated land per household was 2.67 ha for the whole sample, while it was 2.69 ha for fertilizer adopters. In the district, the use of chemical fertilizer is primarily limited to three major crops, namely, teff, wheat and barley. These crops have accounted for 77%, 18% and 4% of the amount of fertilizer used by sample households, respectively, in the cropping season under consideration.

4   Empirical Results

4.1   Results of a Logit Model

In order to examine the relative significance of the various factors that are believed to influence the adoption of fertilizer (FUSEDUM), an empirical logit model (equation (5)) was estimated. The results are given in table 2. Summary statistics in the table indicate that the model provides an acceptable "fit" to the data. First, the model chi-square, which tests the overall significance of the model, was significant at the 1%. The overall cases predicted correctly amounted to 96.9%.

Table 1: Socioeconomic, Demographic, Physical and Institutional Characteristics of the Sample*

Variable	Mean	Std. Dev.	Minimum	Maximum
DAR (Distance from asphalted road in km)	10.84 (11.31)	11.37 (11.54)	0.05	34.00
HSIZE (Household size, number)	6.70 (6.64)	2.40 (2.44)	2.00	13.00
MF010 (dependency ratio, number)	2.42 (2.40)	1.52 (1.53)	0.00	6.00
MF1170 (Farm family labor, number)	4.16 (4.12)	1.79 (1.79)	1.00	10.00
GENDER (Gender of the head, female=1)	0.04 (0.04)	0.20 (0.20)	0.00	1.00
AGE (Age of the head, years)	44.91 (44.75)	14.48 (14.61)	18.00	87.00
EDCDUM (Education of the head, literate=1)	0.40 (0.42)	0.49 (0.49)	0.00	1.00
LANDCHA (Farm size, land cultivated in ha)	2.67 (2.69)	1.22 (1.24)	0.50	8.50
LANDOHA (Land owned in ha)	2.74 (2.74)	0.89 (0.90)	0.88	6.19
CROPFRESP (Crop-Fertilizer response)	9.49 (10.12)	7.79 (7.64)	0.00	48.75
$P_2O_5N_2$ (Nutrients used)	206.58 (220.26)	186.40 (184.46)	0.00	1056.00
$P_2O_5N_2PH$ (Nutrients used per ha)	109.94 (117.22)	72.69 (69.12)	0.00	396.80
$LNP_2O_5N_2PH$ (Ln of nutrients used/ha)	4.29 (4.58)	1.30 (0.70)	0.00	5.98
OXN (Number of oxen owned)	2.60 (2.68)	1.61 (1.61)	1.00	10.00
NPLOT (Number of plots owned)	6.88 (6.95)	2.64 (2.65)	1.00	22.00
NPLO_LCH (Land fragmentation index)	2.75 (2.77)	0.84 (0.86)	0.73	5.50
SICFDU (Extension services, Yes=1)	0.67 (0.71)	0.47 (0.46)	0.00	1.00
CREDITDU (Credit taken, Yes=1)	0.43 (0.42)	0.50 (0.50)	0.00	1.00
FUSEDUM (Fertilizer adoption, Yes=1)	0.93 (1.00)	0.25 (0.00)	0.00	1.00
SICKDU (Presence of sick person in HH, Yes=1)	0.20 (0.21)	0.40 (0.41)	0.00	1.00
HIREDLDU (Hired labor, Yes=1)	0.78 (0.79)	0.42 (0.41)	0.00	1.00
LANDRIDU (Land rented in, Yes=1)	0.14 (0.15)	0.35 (0.36)	0.00	1.00
LANDRODU (Land rented out, Yes=1)	0.11 (0.08)	0.31 (0.27)	0.00	1.00
SQINDEX (Soil quality index)	0.34 (0.35)	0.29 (0.29)	0.00	1.00
FCROPPRAT (Fertilizer-crop price ratio)	1.40 (1.50)	0.43 (0.24)	0.00	2.24
OFF-FARMI (Off-farm income in Birr)**	16.75 (15.98)	96.79 (97.82)	0.00	1000.00

* Figures in parentheses are means and standard deviations of peasant farmers (151) who have used fertilizer in the cropping season under consideration; ha = hectare; Ln = natural logarithm; HH = Household.

** During the survey season 1US$=Birr 5.

The inspection of individual independent variables (table 2) reveals that the extension variable (SICFDU), the number of oxen owned (OXN), access to credit (CREDITDU), hired labor (HIREDLDU) and off-farm income (OFF-FARMI) have been important factors in enhancing the probability of fertilizer adoption. In particular, contrary to the usual perception of the extension services in the country, the relatively wide-spread adoption of fertilizer by farm households in the study area could be associated to previous extension work. Land rented out (LANDRODU) has negatively influenced the probability of fertilizer adoption. This seems to hold true as land is rented out by resource, such as oxen, labor, etc., by poor farm households. Dependency ratio (MF010)[1] assumed a negative coefficient, as expected, which was significant only at 12%. The availability of family labor (MF1170)[2] and the size of land holdings (LANDOHA) and the presence of sick person in the household (SICKDU) had negative but insignificant effects on fertilizer adoption decision. Unlike the usual expectation, distance from asphalted road took a positive coefficient, but significant only at 11%.

In this case study, all the variables representing the characteristics of the household head had statistically negligible influence on the probability of fertilizer adoption.

4.2   Results of a Simultaneous-Equation Model

The simultaneous-equation model, consisting of equations (6a) and (6b), namely, the intensity of fertilizer use expressed as the natural logarithm of nutrients per hectare ($LNP_2O_5N_2PH$), and farm size (LANDCHA), respectively, was estimated for 151 farm households, i.e., for fertilizer adopters only, using a two-stage least squares procedure. The empirical results are given in table 3. Equations (1) and (2), model 1, include all relevant explanatory variables considered in the analysis. Step-by-step screening of the explanatory variables gave results shown by equations (3) and (4), model 2. These two equations include only those variables which were found to be significant at least at 10%. In all equations, despite slight difference among them, a good deal of the variations in the dependent variables were explained by the independent variables included in the equations. Consequently, the adjusted coefficients of determination were convincingly high. The F-values were also highly significant justifying the validity of the models. Let us briefly consider the individual variables below by equation.

---

[1] MF010 refers to the number of children below 11 years of age. The use of MF014 did not improve the results.
[2] MF1170 refers to the number of individuals in a household. The use of MF1570 did not improve the results.

Table 2: Results of a Logit Model for the Adoption of Chemical Fertilizer in the Lume District, Central Ethiopia, 1993/94 G.C.[1]

	Chi-Square	Significance		
-2 Log Likelihood	31.116	1.000		
Model Chi-square (14,146)[#]	49.152[***]	.000		
Overall cases predicted correctly 96.89%				

Exp. Variable	Coefficient	S.E.	Wald	Significance
Constant	- 7.3637[+]	4.7799	2.3733	.1234
DAR	0.0993[+]	0.0611	2.6408	.1042
MF010	- 0.9912[+]	0.6288	2.4848	.1149
MF1170	- 0.2910	0.4064	0.5127	.4740
GENDER	- 1.0102	1.8248	0.3065	.5798
AGE	0.1082	0.0926	1.3631	.2430
EDCDUM	0.4026	1.2188	0.1091	.7411
LANDOHA	- 0.8990	0.8068	1.2416	.2652
OXN	3.0186[**]	1.3496	5.0028	.0253
SICFDU	5.8711[***]	2.1569	7.4093	.0065
CREDITDU	5.3390[**]	2.4399	4.7883	.0287
SICKDU	- 2.2324	1.6836	1.7582	.1848
HIREDLDU	4.4718[**]	2.1699	4.2470	.0393
LANDRODU	- 5.2710[**]	2.4351	4.6854	.0304
OFF-FARMI	0.0265[*]	0.0160	2.7431	.0977

[1]***, **, * and + refer to 1, 5, 10% and 15% level of significance, respectively.
[#]These figures are degrees of freedom for Chi-Square test.

4.2.1 Determinants of Fertilizer Intensity

The coefficient of farm size measured as land cultivated (LANDCHA) is negative and significant at 8% in equation (1). It is evident from equation (3) that the significance of this variable was enhanced to 5%. Such a result suggests that as farm households cultivate more land, the amount of nutrients used per hectare would not increase proportionally. This relationship could be explained by limited fertilizer supply, liquidity or credit constraint and/or that small farmers might have tended to use their land more intensively.

The crop-fertilizer response variable (CROPFRESP), approximated by the response of teff to fertilizer (expressed in terms of total nutrients (P&N)), assumed a highly significant negative coefficient. As the level of output per kg of nutrients declined, farm households tended to apply proportionately more fertilizer to sustain the fertility status of the land they cultivated and thereby maintain or increase the level of crop yields. The number of oxen owned per household (OXN), a proxy for a household's wealth, had a positive and highly significant impact on the intensity of fertilizer use among sample farm households. The ownership of draught animals facilitates timely accomplishment of farm operation, particularly land preparation, and encourages more intensive use of fertilizer, besides the fact that wealthier households tend to have a higher fertilizer intensity.

Although extension has played a significant role in the farm households' fertilizer adoption decision (table 2), it had very little influence on the intensity of fertilizer use in the study area. Once the farmers are aware of the benefits of fertilizer, but constrained by other factors are extension services can do little to influence the intensity of fertilizer use. The coefficient of hired labor (HIREDLDU) was positive and only significant at 15 percent in equation (1), model 1. However, in equation 3, model 2, it was significant at 8%. As expected, the credit variable (CREDITDU) was also positive and significant at 5%. These imply that the availability and use of hired labor and access to credit are among the significant factors that enhance the intensity of fertilizer use.

The off-farm income variable (OFF-FARMI) took a negative and the most highly significant coefficient. This implies that off-farm income tended to be a substitute for (income from) crop intensification. Distance in km from asphalted road (DAR) had, contrary to expectation, a positive effect on the intensity of fertilizer use. The possible explanation for such a result could be that even if the cost of fertilizer use is high, i.e., in terms of its price, time, and energy required to get it, farm households have tended to use (more) fertilizer. This seems to be consistent with the effect of fertilizer-crop price ratio discussed below.

The coefficient of fertilizer-crop price ratio (FCROPPRAT), computed as the ratio of fertilizer price to the weighted prices of teff, wheat and barley, took unexpected sign and it was significant at 11% in equation (1). However, in equation 3, it became significant at 10%. Even though the price of fertilizer has increased relative to crop prices, farm households in the study area have tended to use proportionately more fertilizer. This could probably be explained by the lower fertility status of the soil the farm households cultivate. It could also be argued that the current suboptimal application of fertilizer results in higher physical response of crops to each kg of nutrients and makes the use of more fertilizer still profitable.

Table 3, equations (1) and (3) show that, as in the case of fertilizer adoption decision, all the other variables had statistically minimal influence on the intensity of fertilizer use in the study area.

4.2.2 Determinants of Farm Size

As part of the simultaneous-equation model, the estimated farm size equation is discussed here very briefly. Since the main purpose of this equation was to pinpoint the effect of the amount of fertilizer, i.e., nutrients ($P_2O_5N_2$), used by farm households on farm size (LANDCHA), the discussion focuses mainly on the coefficient of this variable. It is clear from equations (2) and (4), table 3, that farm households in the study area have tended to increase both fertilizer use and the size of cultivated land. This indicates that the current amount of fertilizer and the

Table 3: Results of a Two-Stage Least Squares Model of Factors Influencing the Intensity of Fertilizer use in the Lume district, Central Ethiopia, 1993/94 G.C.[*]

	Model 1		Model 2	
	Equation 1	Equation 2	Equation 3	Equation 4
Dep. Variable	$LNP_2O_5N_2PH$	LANDCHA	$LNP_2O_5N_2PH$	LANDCHA
Adjusted R^2	0.57	0.61	0.59	0.61
F- value[#]	15.48	18.94	27.75	33.90
D-W stat	1.87	1.87	1.85	1.90
Exp. variable	Coefficient	Coefficient	Coefficient	Coefficient
Constant	4.2164***	2.2372***	4.1584***	2.1112***
	(12.9550)	(3.7630)	(14.4420)	(5.8380)
DAR	0.0165***	-	0.0165***	-
	(4.0490)		(4.1880)	
MF010	0.0135	0.1034**	-	0.1061**
	(0.5280)	(2.4080)		(2.5340)
MF1170	0.0023	0.1734***	-	0.1848***
	(0.0850)	(4.1160)		(4.7770)
GENDER	-0.0642	0.5074[+]	-	-
	(-0.3270)	(1.4780)		
AGE	-0.0003	0.0059	-	-
	(-0.0880)	(1.0870)		
EDCDUM	0.0012	0.2194[+]	-	-
	(0.0130)	(1.4420)		
LANDCHA	-0.0813[+]	-	-0.0852**	-
	(-1.7650)		(-2.1080)	
$P_2O_5N_2$	-	0.0013**	-	0.0013**
		(1.9590)		(2.2040)
CROPFRESP	-0.0367***	-	-0.0359***	-
	(-6.3990)		(-6.4390)	
OXN	0.0907***	-	0.0946***	-
	(3.1290)		(3.4610)	
SICFDU	-0.0952	0.2196[+]	-	-
	(-1.0980)	(1.4960)		
HIREDLDU	0.1656[+]	0.6499***	0.1821*	0.6529***
	(1.4880)	(3.6420)	(1.7710)	(3.9280)
CREDITDU	0.1589**	-	0.1685*	-
	(2.0030)		(2.1980)	
LANDRIDU	-	1.0367***	-	0.9893***
		(5.0910)		(4.9440)
LANDRODU	-	0.0662	-	-
		(0.2540)		
SQINDEX	-	-0.9637***	-	-0.9236***
		(-3.502)		(-3.5380)
OFF-FARMI	-0.0028***	-	-0.0027***	-
	(-6.8300)		(-6.9470)	
FCROPPRAT	0.2711[+]	-0.4132	0.2661	-
	(1.6110)	(-1.429)	(1.6770)	
NPLO_LCH	-	-0.3729***	-	-0.3842***
		(-4.541)		(-4.7670)

*Notes: 1. The variables are as defined in Table 1.; 2. Figures in parentheses are t-ratios; 3. ***, **, * and + represent levels of significance of 1%, 5%, 10% and 15%, respectively; 4. - Means the variable was not included in the estimation of the equation. #F-values are given for F(14,136), F(13,137), F(8,142) and F(7,143) degrees of freedom for equations 1, 2, 3 and 4, respectively.

intensity of its use are not sufficient to influence farm households' decision to reduce the size of land they cultivate. In other words, the current level of fertilizer use has not played the land-saving role as yet due to, may be, the risks associated with its use. Another notable outcome was that the wealth variable (OXN) did not show up in the farm size equations together with the fertilizer variable. This could be due to multicollinearity between them (r=0.6358).

5   Lessons Learned

In this paper an attempt has been made to analyze factors influencing fertilizer adoption decision and the intensity of its use among individual farm households. The analysis has brought out that farm households in the study area have a positive reaction to fertilizer use. Extension services have been the strongest force behind the decision of farm households to adopt chemical fertilizer. The wealth of farm households and access to credit as well as hired labor are also found to be significant factors in positively influencing fertilizer adoption decision, while land rented out by farm households has a negative one.

The analysis of the determinants of fertilizer intensity has revealed that the wealth of the household, access to credit, the use of hired labor, fertilizer-crop price ratio and distance from asphalted road have positive effects on the intensity of fertilizer use. However, farm size, crop-fertilizer response coefficient and off-farm income have negative impact upon it. The positive influence of fertilizer-crop price ratio and distance from asphalted road on the intensity of fertilizer use indicates that it is the availability of fertilizer more than its cost that limits the current level of its use by farm households. It also suggests that if farm households are convinced about the benefits of an innovation, they certainly adopt it even at a relatively higher cost. However, continuous increase in its price makes it increasingly unaffordable particularly for poor smallholders. Future work in this area should address the disparity between small- and large-scale farm households in the access to fertilizer and thus in reaping benefits from it.

Our empirical results allow us to draw useful lessons for those concerned with the promotion of fertilizer adoption and the intensity of its use among farm households. Clearly, policy initiatives and interventions in the areas of ownership of assets (particularly oxen), extension services, credit facilities directed to farm households, rural labor market and fertilizer as well as output marketing could encourage the adoption of fertilizer technology and the intensity of its use and thereby contribute to increased food production and food security.

Acknowledgment

This paper is based on field survey that was financially supported by the Eiselen Foundation, Ulm and the German Academic Exchange Service (DAAD), Bonn to which the authors are very grateful.

References

Admassie, Assefa 1995. Analysis of Production Efficiency, and the Use of Modern Technology in Crop production: A Study of smallholders in the Central Highlands of Ethiopia, Wissenschaftsverlag Vauk Kiel KG, Darmstadt, Kiel.

Ali, Mubarik 1995. *Institutional and Socioeconomic Constraints on the Second-Generation Green Revolutions: A case Study of Basmati Rice Production in Pakistan's Punjab.* in: Economic Development and Cultural Change, Vol. 43, No. 4, July 1995, pp.835 - 861.

Bellon, Mauricio R., and J. Edward Taylor 1993. *'Folk' Soil Taxonomy and the Partial Adoption of New Seed Varieties,* in: Economic Development and Cultural Change, Vol. 41, No. 4, July,1993:763-786.

Ellis, F. 1988. Peasant Economies: Farm Households and Agrarian Development, Cambridge University Press, Cambridge.

Feder, Gersho, Richard E. Just and David Zilberman 1985. *Adoption of Agricultural Innovations in Developing Countries: A Survey.* in: Economic Development and Cultural Change, Vol. 33, No. 2, January 1985, pp. 255-298.

Greene, William H. 1993. Econometric Analysis, 2nd Edition, Macmillan Publishing Company, New York.

Getachew Abate 1995. Production Efficiency Analysis: The Case of Smallholder Farming in the Coffee Sector of Ethiopia and Kenya, Wissenschaftsverlag Vauk Kiel KG, Kiel.

Kebede, Yohannes, K. Gunjal and G. Coffin, *Adoption of New Technologies in Ethiopian Agriculture: The Case of Tegulet-Bulga District, Shoa Province.* in: Agricultural Economics, Vol. 4, No. 1, April 1990, pp. 27-43.

Lipton, M. 1968. *The Theory of the Optimizing Peasant.* in: Journal of Development Studies, Vol. 4, No. 3 1968, pp. 327-351.

Norman, D. W. 1974. *Rationalizing Mixed Cropping Under Indigenous Conditions: The Example of Northern Nigeria.* in: Journal of Development Studies, Vol. 11 1974, pp. 3-21.

Ruthenberg, Hans 1980. *Outline of a Strategy for Agricultural Development in Keny.* in: Quarterly Journal of International Agriculture, Vol. 19, No. 1, January-March 1980, pp. 6-17.

Schultz, T. W. 1964. Transforming Traditional Agriculture, Studies in Comparative Economics, No. 3 1964, New Haven.

Shapiro, K. H. 1983. *Efficiency Differentials in Peasant Agriculture and their Implications for Development Policies. in:* Journal of Development Studies, Vol. 19 No. 2 1983, pp.179-190.

Smale, Melinda, Paul W. Heisey, and Howard D. Leathers 1995. *Maize of the Ancestors and Modern Varieties: The Microeconomics of High-Yielding Variety Adoption in Malawi.* in: Economic Development and Cultural Change, Vol. 43, No. 2, January 1995.

Wong, J. 1971. *Peasant Economic Behaviour, The Case of Traditional Agricultural Cooperation in China.* in: The Developing Economies, Vol. 9, No. 3, pp. 332-349.

World Bank 1989. Sub-Saharan Africa: From Crisis to Sustainable Growth, Washington, D.C..

World Bank 1994. World Development Report 1994: Infrastructure for Development, Oxford
    University Press, Oxford.
Yao, S. 1993. The Determinants of Cereal Crop Productivity of the Peasant Farm Sector in
    Ethiopia, 1981-1987. Department of Economics, University of Portsmouth, UK. Discussion
    Paper No. 30, Portsmouth.

Methodology for Addressing Food Security in Development Projects – Experiences from Kigoma, Tanzania

Hannelore Beerlandt[1], Eric Tollens[1] and Stefan Dercon[2]
[1]Department of Agricultural Economics and
[2]Centre for Economic Research
K.U. Leuven, Leuven, Belgium

Abstract

The aim of the paper is to propose a simple cost-effective field methodology to address food security in development projects. Food security is regarded as an organizational principle requiring targeted and integrated interventions to reach the food insecure within an overall development policy. With development projects, only a selective and participative approach towards food security guarantees a sustainable development process that encompasses the most vulnerable groups in society.

The paper demonstrates the importance of identifying food insecurity at the local and regional levels before field interventions aimed at improving food security are planned. All too often, it is assumed that the nature and causes of food insecurity are sufficiently well-known to warrant immediate actions in the field. Interventions then fail to reach the target group (the food insecure) adequately and do not fundamentally address the root causes of food insecurity. Reliance is on trickle-down effects for the food insecure and this is known to fail.

Field research in the Kigoma region in Tanzania has shown that it is possible to identify the food insecure efficiently and effectively using a simple methodology. The food insecure, the causes of food insecurity and relevant indicators of food insecurity were identified for each main socio-economic livelihood system over a period of 5 weeks. Six steps can be distinguished in the methodology and the paper describes them in detail. The concrete planning of the interventions demands an additional step. Once insight is reached at the top of the pyramid and the priorities of the very poorest are duly established, the other levels need to be passed through once more in order to guarantee the durability of the planned intervention within existing systems and networks on national, regional, village and family level. Four main principles guide this methodology: identification per main socio-economic system, analysis of intra-household patterns, a participative approach, and selection of appropriate actions to overcome food insecurity in terms of their priorities and cost effectiveness in the short, medium and long term.

It is hoped that the proposed methodology will help to make the food security concept more operational in the field, at the local level, where it really matters. This does not in any way diminish the macro-economic importance of food security and food policies, but the gist of the concept of food security is that the individual stands first and that the subjective perception of food security matters most.

Keywords_____
Food security, Tanzania, identification, operationalization, targeting, causality

1   Introduction

Although food security has become a well-defined concept, in practice few projects seem to be oriented towards an increase in the capital supply of the most vulnerable part of the population. For most "socio-economic systems" there exist no risk charts and no indicators which follow the evolution of the vulnerability of those groups. It is necessary that the implementing organizations realize that more money, time and *effort at the start of the relief operations only strengthens the efficiency, the profitability and the durability of the actions.* This realization can only come from the conviction that the acquisition of a livelihood security by the poorest enables them to switch from a survival strategy to a development strategy which they can take into their own hands best in most cases.

Primary needs for the very poorest differ from case to case and evolve over time. Therefore a *thorough diagnosis of the food security problems* in the region should be undertaken before proceeding with concrete advice and implementation of actions. In the past, projects were too often based on the particular expertise of the implementing organizations rather than on the actual needs of the vulnerable groups.

Our field research was based in Kigoma. Kigoma is one of the twenty administrative regions of Tanzania. In the east, Kigoma borders lake Tanganyika and Burundi, in the north the Kagera region, in the west the Shinyanga region, Tabora and Rukwa. Kigoma is subdivided into three districts: Kigoma, Kasulu and Kibondo. In our research, we distinguish three socio-economic livelihood systems: the highlands, the lowlands and the lakeside (fishing villages).

2   Identification of Food Insecurity: a Basis and Guarantee for Sustainable Development

The concept of food security has seldom been applied as an organizing principle. The advantages are obvious, however, as a selective and participative approach of food security guarantees a lasting development process of the most vulnerable groups within society.

The entitlement of an individual to food is based in first instance on the ownership of his physical (e.g. land, animals, jewelry, house, etc.), human (e.g. health, education, labor, skills...), and social capital (e.g. friends, social status, status within the family) (Dercon, S. 1993). The amount of food an individual is entitled to is thus connected with his amount of starting capital. Food insecurity thus is indeed an expression of poverty, a lack of initial capital, be it physical, human, or social capital, or a combination of these.

For example, no ownership of land, infertile land, no cattle in the highlands (Kibondo), frequent death of small cattle, no bicycle in the lowlands (Kasulu), no boat or even no oil-lamp in the lakeside (Kigoma) (i.e. lack of physical capital), disease, handicap, elderly families with little labor force, lack of knowledge about composting (i.e. lack of human capital), social marginality (i.e. cause for no access to fishing boats), no family or relatives (i.e. lack of social capital). These aspects form the initial capital of an individual/family in Kigoma, determine its poverty and hence also its entitlement to food. In times of distress (e.g. non-existence of the Burundese consumer market for many farmers in the district of Kibondo) the capital supply is broken into in order to provide for food (Swift, J. 1989). The capital stock thus forms a buffer against risks. If the poor are not chronically undernourished as a result of their limited capital, they are mostly confronted with temporary food insecurity because of their inadequate buffers. If their system is not sufficiently flexible (Maxwell, S. et al. 1992), there is no return from their condition as a result of which they become more vulnerable to subsequent shocks. Interventions promoting food security are thus aimed at the *preventive* enrichment of capital supplies (physical, social, human) which constitute a buffer against risks to which the production and exchange entitlements are subjected. By doing so a recurrence to hunger situations during disasters is prevented.

Besides the amelioration of the individual livelihood security, the participation which is characteristic of the operationalization of the concept of food security also contributes positively towards social stability. This approach has grown from the conviction that the possibilities to escape from poverty eventually lie with the households and individuals themselve, and that but a slight (but selective) support enables them to take charge of their own destiny.

The identification of the food insecure should not only be based on the present situation (e.g. by anthropometric measures) but should take into account the whole livelihood strategy by which the poor cope with shocks. In this, the subjective interpretation of the capital stock by the individual should not be neglected. For instance, it is entirely possible that hunger is preferred above the sale of cattle.

Inquiry into the diagnosis does not only allow for an initially targeted action. The impact of these actions can be analyzed and interpreted in this way as well. If the causes of food insecurity are not precisely known, it is difficult to examine if and to what extent the projects contribute to the improvement of the food security situation. In addition, often the impact of the projects in general is not sufficiently known (Beerlandt, H. et al. 1994).

3   Principles and Steps in the Identification Procedure

3.1   Guiding Principles

The following *four principles* have to be respected during a food security diagnosis: the identification takes place per "socio-economic system;" the intra-household patterns (feeding customs within households inclusive) are analyzed; diagnosis takes place in a participatory way; a selection of planned actions takes place according to priorities.

1. For the identification of food security in a region, the "socio-economic livelihood system" stands central. The concept needs a broader interpretation than the agricultural production system. It is the system in which the human, physical, and social capital are transformed into real income at the level of the community, the household and the individuals within the household. It is within this system that the vulnerability is situated, much more so than in production, marketing or geographical factors. The feeding customs in Kigoma also justify an approach per socio-economic system. While in the fishermen's villages cassava is valued as the most superior staple food, in the lowlands cassava is only consumed during very hard periods when no other food crop is available. In the highlands cassava is an inferior staple crop but it is more valued than cocoyams and beer bananas. The fact that poverty and consequently food insecurity differ according to the "socio-economic system" is also confirmed by anthropometrical data from Kigoma. The z-scores for the parameter "height for age" provide a picture for chronical undernourishment in Kigoma which is closely related to the socio-economic system. In the lakeside, 41% of the children under six are undernourished, for the lowlands this goes up to 47% and for the highlands even up to 78%. The results of a poverty line (absolute poverty line for a socio-economic specific diet) assessment gives a slightly different image of poverty which nevertheless justifies an approach per socio-economic system; for the lakeside, 65% are under the poverty line, for the lowlands: 30% and for the highlands: 74%.

2. It is necessary to attach sufficient attention to the concept "household". In the first place, it has to be defined and described time and again depending on each particular case. It is indeed not always self-evident who else outside the

members of the family belongs to the household, who, for example, shares income from which source, who provides which income, whether different women have separate fields and if this is also expressed in separate stocks, etc. The household does not act as a homogenously thinking social and economic unity. In Kigoma for example, only men go fishing on lake Tanganyika. It is mostly women who (often in small groups) buy, dry and resell the fish. In many cases, the woman buys fish from her own husband. Starting from the idea that the household acts and chooses in common, many policy failures have already ensued (Alderman, H. et al. 1994).

Therefore, the analysis of *feeding customs* also needs to be pursued down to the intra-household level. They are indeed not only determined by the "socio-economic system" but also to a large extent within the individual household. Very characteristic in this respect is the finding that in the district of Kasulu not all families know an equally long period during which cassava is consumed as the staple crop instead of the better valued maize ugali (ranging from 0 to 5 months). Whether or not snacks are taken in between meals differs however not only between different households but also from individual to individual. These kinds of data concerning feeding customs are thus very good indicators for measurement and monitoring of the degree of food insecurity.

Since an intra-household analysis is complex and requires more data than an analysis at the household level, many ask themselves if this step should indeed be taken. Three observations should here be made. Firstly, it should be clear that it is not always necessary to know all intra-household processes in detail but indeed the resulting patterns and allocations. The analysis of the latter is less complicated (Doss, C.et al. 1994). Secondly the inquiry in Kigoma proved that through participative group discussions sufficient insights can be acquired on a household structure in order to elaborate a food security policy and action plan. Finally, it appears from many studies and from the field work in Kigoma that for policy makers it suffices to make the distinction solely on the level of the sexes.

3. The participation of the local population is a third principle. Not only straightforward information concerning the target group is obtained during the participatory identification, also their insights, preferences, experiences with existing systems become clear. During the implementation of the actions pertaining to food security, it is of great importance to involve the local population to the utmost as well in such a way that not only the result but the progress of the project itself already creates a social security and stability. Examples of this are manifold: public road works with a self-targeting system with access for the very poorest, building hospitals and schools, the making of ploughs, etc.

4. It is possible to elucidate within a short time period the socio-economic structures of the very poorest within a "socio-economic system." The elaboration of a policy and actions impacting on these problems is consequently a logical sequel. It is, however, of eminent importance that clear priorities are discerned at this level. This has to take place in such a way that immediately acquired income for the very poorest does not limit any future form of capital (physical, human or social). For Kigoma (lowlands and highlands) for example, it made little sense to start with the increased availability of inputs, labor saving techniques, storage facilities and improvement of soil fertility, notwithstanding the fact that these form obstacles to the livelihood security of vulnerable population groups. Primarily the right to private tenure of land needs to be restored so that it becomes worthwhile to invest in land and agriculture. The region also needs to be opened up by rural basic infrastructure: tracks from the main road to villages, "feederroads" to the railway (Kigoma-Tabora-Dar es Salaam) and basic health and social facilities.

3.2 Steps to Follow

The principles as stated above have to be respected during the entire procedure. Since the diagnosis of food security requires very specific data, it becomes necessary to focus the policy on a few concentration areas that are divided into different "socio-economic systems". The six different steps that have to be gone through can be visualized as a pyramid. The data that is wanted starts with a broad spectre of economical, social and geographical data on a national and regional level. The pyramid ends with very specific data about individual priorities of the very poorest. Between the basis and the top, data is gathered at the level of the socio-economic system, at the level of local groups and families, and within families up to the level of the individual. Information on a higher step in the pyramid is irrelevant without the investigation of the previous step.

Step 1: Consulting secondary sources on the spot, "semi structured interviews" focused on livelihood security

These sources and conversations have to provide a picture about the population, ethnography, markets (including local markets), economic environment, land (including land distribution, land tenure, crop sharing agreements, etc.), agriculture, labor and labor markets, support and informal insurance systems, politics, water and energy supplies, sanitation, roads and other infrastructure, educational and health facilities: schools and hospitals, outside assistance, wealth and society. The sources have to be consulted according to the subject on a national and regional levels, but also on a village level with village authorities. It appears that these persons are able to identify the poorest "households" in a very precise way in most of the cases.

Step 2: Make a clear distinction between different "socio-economic systems" in the considered region (from production incentive to real income)

The vulnerability of an individual is closely related to the "socio-economic system" in which he or she functions. Each "socio-economic system" should be delineated as accurately as possible on the basis of different factors that influence the vulnerability. In the following steps, the characteristics at family and individual levels are more deeply investigated. This means that for each "socio-economic system" separate group discussions and short inquiries have to be organized, indicators of vulnerability are to be developed and priorities formulated.

In Kigoma for example (854,000 inhabitants), three socio-economic livelihood systems are distinguished over a distance of 120 km (bird's eye view, transsection from west to east). Research in this region shows that vulnerability is not only determined at the production level. Agricultural production is highest for the highlands, followed by the lowlands and finally the lakeside. However, more families live in a food insecure situation in the highlands, the region with the highest agricultural potential. Inhabitants of the lowlands depend more on the market and have other important sources of income outside agriculture. Villages at the lake show a large inequality: men that have access to fishing boats on the one hand and women with a starting capital to buy and dry fish on the other hand are relatively certain of an income. For the very poorest of this area it is however very difficult to participate in these activities. Since agriculture and other sources of income offer little alternative in this system, the degree of food insecurity in the fishermen's villages is very high.

Step 3: Implementing PRAs (participatory rural appraisal) per "socio-economic system" for men and women separately

In the third step, insights have to be gained in local survival strategies and in local structures through group discussions. It is not the purpose to inquire about the individual situation of the poorest. Moreover, it is practically impossible to involve the poor directly in these discussions. But information needs to be gathered about local distribution structures and the way social, physical and human capital is converted into real income and welfare. This will also yield insights into weaknesses of the system. On the basis of an understanding of these strategies, informed questions can be asked in the formal survey later on to learn precisely about the individual situation and position of the poor and to accurately assess their degree of poverty.

The implementation of insightful group discussions is no easy matter and is much more than the simple answering of a series of questions. The most important factor is that through observation and dialogue, information can be gathered from the local population about their insights, experiences and priorities. The most appropriate manner to conduct group discussions concerning food security is through PRA's. In this way, the discussion is entirely handled by the group and "outsiders" can simply indicate a subject and be present in the background. The discussions between the participants can lead to a consensus in a relaxed way, and can subsequently be amended or modified. This may take a lot of time.

In order to avoid imposing one's own views and prejudices and to limit interference as much as possible, it is advisable to work around a certain number of exercises. This also makes it more fun for the participants as discussions are approached from a different angle each time. The exercises are based on predetermined schemes which train the participants and help them gain more insights about their own livelihood and existence. Hereafter, five such exercises are outlined for the PRA's concerning the food security diagnosis.

1. Community map: the participants draw the village as they see it with all characteristics, objects, buildings, places, properties which they think are important. This exercise (and the discussion pertaining to it) contributes substantial knowledge about the importance of different duties of men and women, about the situation of the fields and additional problems (e.g. soil fertility, shifting cultivation, land tenure), about crops belonging to women and men, about social facilities within the village, etc.

2. Community resources diagram: in this exercise all participants are asked to indicate all relations, contacts and exchanges of their village with other villages, places, communities and institutions (e.g. village, research station, market, family, hospital, etc.) together with the reason or subject of the contact (e.g. sale of beans, purchase of inputs, giving in marriage, credit group, fields, vegetable gardens, etc.). Here as well a different result is achieved according to gender. This exercise results in a clear picture of food-, knowledge- and income streams for men and women.

3. Seasonal calendars: different subjects (agricultural activities, non-agricultural activities, income peaks, spending peaks, consumption, occurrence of diseases) are placed into a calendar. Uncertain or difficult periods are thus situated together with their cause.

4. Activity and crop preference ranking: in this exercise the participants attribute scores to different activities (e.g. trade, agriculture, weaving of mats, small cattle) and crops on the basis of qualities (e.g. good price, good market, demands little labor, demands few skills, demands few inputs, easy transport on

head, storage on field possible) that are represented by the participants (men/women separately). The reasons for the importance of different activities and crops for men and women become clear during this exercise.

5. Causal model: the group proposes in the different factors that, according to their believe, determine the "daily food intake of an individual." Subsequently, the different factors are ranked according to the direct relationship that exists between the considered factor and the previous factor. The result is a "problem tree" pertaining to food security of an individual for the local situation ("socio-economic system" and intra-household relations).

Since the group has to reach a consensus for each exercise, the PRA demands a few days of work per "socio-economic system." Not only the final result of the exercise is valuable but also the discussion and the additional information that is acquired indirectly. When for example coffee obtains a low score with a certain group because of poor marketing and a low price (highlands; Kibondo), and this occurs at 60 km from a successful coffee area, this means, in addition, that no market information at all penetrates into first area.

Step 4: Drafting and implementing a short survey

By means of the PRAs no understanding is acquired of the degree, the depth of the poverty and of the indicators that can be associated with it. In order to achieve this, the different hypotheses derived from interviews and group discussions have to be tested by means of a formal short survey. In order to proceed in a direct and efficient way, the latter can best be elaborated on the spot and has to be adapted according to the different "socio-economic systems".

In this survey, emphasis is placed on the livelihood security of an individual within a "socio-economic system". More specifically, the information from five data sources is compared with respect to the identification of the most vulnerable persons and their relevant indicators. It concerns the following five data clusters: income calculation of individuals and households; individual anthropometric measurements; consumption charts (calorie consumption per capita), data concerning the security of food consumption and, finally, human capital. It must be verified whether one or more of these data collections can be shortened or discarded without causing a reduction of information for the purpose of the identification. More precisely, it must be investigated whether the complicated and time-consuming income survey can be reduced to simple questions pertaining to income sources and the relative importance of each of those, to questions concerning the security of this income (shocks, sale of durable goods, etc.) and to questions regarding human capital (health, education, skills, household members, etc.).

From our research, only anthropometric data fail to provide an accurate and balanced picture of the food security situation. They fail to provide information about the livelihood situation and the coping strategies in the socio-economic system. Thus, in any case, the results need to be complemented with data about nutritional habits, local diets and food preferences, diseases, sanitary conditions, availability of food and food prices.

The other data correlate better with poverty but nevertheless show deficiencies depending on the particular system (e.g. consumption charts make little sense just after harvest; relevance of human capital depends very much on the non-agricultural labor market). It is in any case certain that other forms of capital and strategies, that can serve as a buffer in order to bridge the difficult period, should be thoroughly surveyed. A manual for a fictitious survey is presently available.

Step 5: Elaboration of indicators for the monitoring of food security per "socio-economic system"

At different levels (land, regional, "socio-economic system," village level, state, individual) indicators have to be elaborated in order to monitor the impact of exogenous factors on food security and hence to be able to intervene preventively in case of a negative evolution. The indicators must be measurable, testable and robust, not to be influenced easily, so that they change only when the welfare of the target group changes. Besides the measurement of the impact on the poorest of certain interventions, a certain permanent information mission for local structures and for the government exists. This concerns not so much the buffers of the poorest which enable them to cope with certain adverse events (shocks), but rather the occurrence of these events themselves. For instance, approaching drought, price instability, etc. need to be measured at a decentralized level. This concern is not new and has been operationalized before in the form of "early warning systems." These are however in need of a thorough decentralization and have to be differentiated per region and per "socio-economic system" within this region, whereby the responsible observers are the local communities.

These indicators can be deduced logically from group discussions and from the results of the inquiry (indicators for the degree of poverty). The causal model from the group discussions can be of considerable help in this respect. The final determinants of the model are generally very useful indicators.

Concrete examples on a regional scale for the region of Kigoma are: price decreases of peanuts in the district of Kibondo, evolution of the consuming markets (e.g. Burundi) for beans, peanuts and goats, occurrence and number of water wells, etc. On a family level in Kasulu, the number of active labor units per family can be an indicator since it is relatively easy to provide for income out of non-agricultural activities and hence the limiting factor is labor. Also the number of months the family has to fall back on cassava or beer bananas as staple food (inferior food crops in this "socio-economic system") is an indicator that reflects the vulnerability of a family in Kasulu.

Step 6: Selective design of actions per "socio-economic system" focused on the increase in effective income for the poorest

This step implies a very critical mind. As far as possible the most direct cause of poverty has to be tackled and not only the side-effects. The actions have to be classified according to the priorities of the individual. More complicated systems for drying fish in Kigoma (lakeside) will not reach the women with the lowest income at the lake since they are excluded from these fishing activities through lack of income to buy fresh fish. Granting small credits to local existing small groups in which the poorest women organize themselves in order to rent cassava and palm oil fields, could possibly increase the income of the poorest women.

In Kigoma, however, these groups are however not formalized and not clearly outlined and this hampers undertaking actions with these groups. Even then, in order to transform this income into an increase in livelihood security there is need for contact with the outside world. These villages are indeed only attainable through relatively expensive transport over Lake Tanganyika. The region at the lake does not itself dispose of the capacity to provide in a varied feeding pattern. The agricultural potential at the shores of the lake is naturally very low and deteriorates further due to fast deforestation and the ensuing decreasing soil fertility. Infrastructure, transport facilities and reforestation thus belong to the priorities in this area.

These steps were taken for the three different "socio-economic systems" in the region of Kigoma in Tanzania within a period of two months. The planning of concrete actions requires an additional step.

4 Food Security made operational: from Identification to Actions

During this seventh step, given the priorities of the very poorest, the pyramid has to be passed through once again from the base to the top. These considerations need to be carried through in order to guarantee the durability of the actions. It needs to be examined if no interesting information has been dumped from the process during which the individual was targeted. Do the planned actions for example fit the local economy? Suppose, for example, that the local women's groups at the lake are used as a basis for income-generating activities. Then the nature and the current function of these groups within the actual system have to be considered all over again. If the vegetable trade of the very poorest in Kasula is to form a priority, then the local vegetable markets and the actors therein have to be known thoroughly.

The most important criterion in designing a food security action plan is that the food insecure, the poor, are reached and not that the not-so-poor are not reached or are excluded. "The number of poor that are reached" is a more relevant indicator than cost criteria in poverty alleviation projects. In certain cases when the identification cannot take place, it is more indicated and more effective to deal with all population groups (e.g. labor in exchange for a bicycle) than run the risk of missing out on a part of the food insecure. If, however, actions are well designed and carefully planned, self-targeting takes place and only the poor will show interest in such projects or under such conditions.

The local population has to be maximally involved during the preparation and implementation of the actions. "Capacity building" of the local population constitutes a central theme in this respect. Ideally, it should be possible to carry out the diagnosis by the local population as well. The commitment strengthens these organizations and results in the foundation of a social supporting level.

Whenever local structures participate, two conditions have to be fulfilled. The functioning of the structures has to be sufficiently well known and the group has to be clearly outlined. Subsequently, the participants and the structures themselves have to be reinforced by means of suitable training sessions. Investment in human capital can support and pay for future interventions. It often yields more to invest in the poor themselves instead of in their environment. The second condition concerning the outlining of the group often poses problems.

After the identification, the problem remains of effectively monitoring the indicators at a decentralized level. It is moreover in certain cases, notwithstanding the identification, not easy to involve the poorest in the actions, especially because one is dealing with individuals. In general the NGOs and other local grassroots institutions are therefore the most suitable actors to make poverty alleviation operational in the field. The combination of their financial means, their technical skills and their management know-how, together with a consistent local input make them very effective in the solution of problems at a decentralized level.

It should be clear that starting from the priorities of the poorest does not necessarily imply that all interventions should take place at an individual or local level. Indeed, it can be most opportune to act at higher levels which transcend the local communities. Nevertheless, field experience teaches us that in most cases, international, national and regional interventions mean very little for the poorest individuals. Even when a certain impact or influence can be demonstrated, it is overwhelmed by local, family and individual factors which make it impossible for the food insecure to escape their vulnerability. Therefore, a food security policy needs not only to start from the needs of local poor individuals, in most cases interventions and actions also need to be undertaken at that level.

5   Conclusion

Four conclusions can be drawn from this experience and discussion. In the first place concerning development projects focused on food security, only a selective approach can guarantee a lasting development process for the very poorest. Therefore the projects and the evaluation thereof have to be preceded by the identification of the food insecure and the causes of their poverty.

Secondly it is necessary that the identification as well as the implementation and evaluation of food security projects take place at a decentralized level. An appropriate methodology was elaborated and tested in the region of Kigoma (Tanzania). The procedure is cost-efficient and consists of six sequential steps. Its implementation is feasible in five weeks per distinct "socio-economic system." Ideally, the identification procedure should be designed and implemented by local people and communities.

Next, four principles guarantee the durability of the identification and the sustainability of food security projects by rating the subjective perception as well as the individual at their proper value. The "socio-economic livelihood system" stands central in the analysis of food security; intra household relations are analyzed up to the level of sexes; a participative approach is a necessary condition; and finally, clear priorities have to be selected at an individual level.

The fourth conclusion indicates that the NGOs are the most suitable actors for the implementation of food security projects at a local level and for the monitoring of food security. Local NGOs and structures have to be attracted and mobilized around these actions. The capacity of these has to be strengthened through adapted training sessions.

Lessons Learned

The major lessons learned are that it is possible to identify the food insecure efficiently and effectively, including the causes of their food insecurity and relevant indicators, using a simple participative methodology, in six steps, which takes about five weeks per main socio-economic livelihood system.

Acknowledgments

This paper is part of the research project "Operationalization of food security" and is based on the results of a mission in Kigoma region (Tanzania) from April 11 to June 21 1995, with the purpose of doing a pilot food security diagnosis of the region and the elaboration of an appropriate methodology. The project is financed by the Ministry of Foreign Affairs, Foreign Trade and Development Cooperation of Belgium in the framework of policy preparing studies. The research is carried out at the Department of Agricultural Economics and the

Centre for Economic Research of the Catholic University of Leuven (K.U.Leuven) by Ir. H. Beerlandt and J. Serneels respectively, under the direction of Prof. E. Tollens and Prof. S. Dercon.

References

Alderman, H., Haddad, L., Hoddinott, J. and Vosti, A. 1994. Strengthening agricultural and natural resource policy through intrahousehold analysis: an introduction, American Journal of Agricultural Economics, Vol. 76, December 1994, pp. 1208-1212.

Beerlandt, H., Christiaensen, L. 1994. De Belgische ontwikkelingssamenwerking met Rwanda geanalyseerd met betrekking tot voedselzekerheid, rapport beleidsvoorbereidend onderzoek, Afdeling Landbouweconomie, November 1994.

Beerlandt, H., Delen, F. 1995. Identificatie van de meest kwetsbaren in Monduli distrikt, Arusha regio, Tanzania, working paper, Afdeling Landbouweconomie, K.U. Leuven, April 1995.

Beghin, I. 1991. Guide to comprehensive evaluation of the nutritional aspects of projects and programmes, Instituut voor Tropische Geneeskunde Antwerpen, Working Paper, Nr. 27

Chambers, R. 1994. The origins and practice of Participatory Rural Appraisal, World Development, vol.22.

Christiaensen, L. 1995. Food security: From concept to action – A status quaestionis, report Nr. 2 Policy preparing research, Department of Agricultural Economics, K.U. Leuven, Leuven and BADC, Brussels, March 1995, 129 p.

Dercon, S. 1993. Voedselzekerheid: sociale zekerheid van de allerarmsten, K.U. Leuven en Oxford University: Leuven en Oxford.

Doss, C., Senauer, B. 1994. Strengthening agricultural and natural resource policy through intrahousehold analysis: discussion, American Journal of Agricultural Economics, Vol. 76, December 1994, pp. 1226-1228.

Maxwell, S. 1993. State Action for Food Security: Horses for Courses in sub-Saharan Africa, University of Sussex, Institute of Development Studies, Brighton (mimeo).

Maxwell, S., Smith, M. 1992. Household Food Security: A conceptual review, in Maxwell, S., Frankenberger, T., Household Food Security: Concepts, Indicators, Measurements: A Technical Review, UNICEF/IFAD: New York/Rome.

Seaman, J. 1994. Relief, rehabilitation and development, are the distinctions useful?, Paper submitted to the workshop on "Linking Relief and Development," Institute of Development Studies, University of Sussex.

Sen, A. 1991. Poverty and famines: an essay on entitlement and deprivation, Oxford, Clarendon Press.

Society for Participatory Research in Asia 1989. NGO-Government Relations; A Source of Life or a Kiss of Death?, New Delhi: PRIA.

Swift, J. 1989. Why are rural people vulnerable to famine?, IDS Bulletin, Vol. 20.

Uvin, P. 1995. Fighting Hunger at the Grassroots: Paths to Scaling up, World Development, July 1995.

Measuring Causal Links between Policy Impact, Food Security and Socio-Economic Conditions

Helmke Sartorius von Bach[1] and
Ernst-August Nuppenau[2]
[1]University of Pretoria, South Africa
[2]University of Giessen, Germany

Abstract

Food security features continuously on policy agendas world-wide and great efforts have been made to implement policies to improve food security. Analysts have been unable to associate the policy impact with food security and related socio-economic conditions. To analyze socio-economic preconditions in which food security policies operate, it becomes inevitable to identify those policies which could improve the nutritional status of a poverty-stricken population. In particular, conditions improving health, sanitation, agricultural practices, technology accessibility, and the stage of development in general, contribute towards improving peoples' food status directly, or enable them to cope with perennial or temporary hunger indirectly.

By applying canonical correlation latent variable models, unobservable socio-economic variables, such as preconditions for food security, and observable manifested variables can be measured simultaneously. The approach combines various indicator variables that illuminate peoples' food security and health situation on the one hand, and performance indicators that describe farming, technology and economic factors, as well as conditions of the broader social exchange system on the other hand. A hypothetical correlation matrix of suggested indicator variables is used to demonstrate the potential of the proposed methodology. Policy effects between indicator variables are measured simultaneously to address the causal links in the food security debate. The iterative methodology used, has the advantage of addressing interactive links between the suggested socio-economic variables influencing society. The canonical coefficients can be used to describe causalities between policy impact and above-mentioned preconditions.

Keywords

South Africa, canonical correlations, policy impacts, socio-economic conditions

1   Introduction

For three decades, agrarian policies have been dominated by concerns about feeding nations, alleviating poverty and improving the socio-economic conditions. Eventually, these concerns resulted in the generally accepted term "food security," which originated during the World Food Conference in Rome in 1974. Since then, numerous recommendations were implemented to address food security.

Concern regarding food security led to growing empirical and policy support for two fundamental premises about the linkages between food availability, poverty and the access to food (Eicher 1988). These premises can be described as the two sides of the hunger equation, namely supply and demand for food. The first premise (supply side) suggests that increasing food production, storage and trade can assure food availability, but this will not automatically ensure that all people have enough to eat, or end hunger. The second premise (demand side) is that, because poverty is a central cause of hunger and malnutrition, special efforts are needed to help increase the access and entitlement to food.

Questions arise whether implemented food security programs were unsuccessful and why the gap between rich and poor has widened. In addressing future visions in this respect, Bezanson (1995) argues that a needed Double Green Revolution will be infinitely more difficult than the first Green Revolution, with new and fresh thinking in short supply. Furthermore, alternatives to modern science and current approaches are necessary, because the current economic models, for example, are inadequate to address real food prices. Without prioritizing issues, the existing situation can not be improved.

Increasing food production and a policy of food self-sufficiency will not automatically ensure that people have sufficient to eat. This paper will discuss the dimensions of the food security problem from a South African point of view in terms of a systems approach. In the paper a first attempt is made to apply canonical correlations, i.e. to utilize unobservable socio-economic and observable manifested variables simultaneously, to address the causal links in the food security debate. The conceptual framework is based on an accumulation of many theories and mono-causal analyses, such as the Malthus', Ricardo, Sen's entitlement approach, etc.

2   Traditional Empirical Applications of Food Security and Scope for Innovative Thinking

The empirical analysis of food security in developing countries has been pursued on various kinds of aggregation levels, national, regional and individual levels; short and long term, rural and urban etc. Initially, the prime concern of policy makers vested in national food security (Valdes 1981) and regional studies (Lele and Candler 1981). The last years saw a shift towards a micro level-orientated perspective. Especially the analysis of household food security (for example, Alderman and Garcia 1993) gained interest. Moreover, core problems to be investigated shifted from a pure analysis of the relationship between food security and the nutrient situation of a particular population towards a broader research topic including factors, such as health, poverty, and education (Alderman and Garcia 1994; Barrera 1990; and Behrman 1991).

In general, there is ample evidence for the existence of multiple individual links between food security and other factors that are associated with development beside agricultural production, such as health, education standards, socio-economic conditions etc. An unilateral concept of fostering agricultural production or self-sufficiency of communities on one side and achieving food security on the other side has been proved to be insufficient to explain remaining food insecurity. Any of the additional factors mentioned in literature seem to be of great and equal importance in determining the food security situation and the living conditions in poor societies. Furthermore, it has to be appreciated that indirect policy measures, i.e. those policies that were not directly intended to improve food security, can be of greater importance than direct policy measures (Alderman and Garcia 1993). For example, health care measures decreasing the prevalence of diarrhea are a prerequisite to bringing food into its biophysical operation.

Anticipating research findings, it is the intention of this paper to show how statistical methods that can potentially link causal relationships become increasingly important in the investigation of the complex interrelationships of food security, health, education and socio-economic living conditions. The paper demonstrates an approach which incorporates lessons learned from the past by linking individual causal relationships to a network of causality links in the theme of "food insecurity" (for more detail see section 5). Generally speaking, our model, by defining major prerequisites for "food security," has the advantage of being empirically testable and being sufficiently complex to copy for multiple causal links. The approach will be applicable to case studies on the one hand, and provide general features on the other hand.

Nevertheless, the approach includes traditional indicators and variables that have been proven to determine food insecurity in other countries. For example, Alderman and Garcia (1993) modeled the Garcia relationship between malnutrition of children, health, socio-economic variables and education uni-laterally with the hypothesized variables as follows:

weight-for-age =   f (calories, protein, vitamin A, prevalence of diarrhea, other illness, hospital birth, vaccination, breast-feeding, household size, parents' education, mother's height, child's age, age squared, gender, district), and

weight-for-height =   f (calories, protein, vitamin A, prevalence of diarrhea,
                          other   illness,   hospital   birth,   vaccination,
                          breast-feeding, household size, parents' education,
                          mother's height, child's age, age squared, gender,
                          district).

These factors became part of our approach in a modified version according to
the availability of indicators in way of their actual relevance in South Africa. The
very difference between a mono-causal analysis as provided by Alderman and
Garcia (1991) and the approach proposed in this paper, however, stems from the
different type of analysis imposed by latent variables as outlined in the following
section on latent variables.

3   Latent Variable Method

Up to date most empirical research tried to evaluate the links and causalities in
policy analysis by applying tools which require variables called "hard" value
variables. "Hard" values are characterized by the standard assumptions of metric
statistics. From a technical point of view, variables must be observable, countable
and reproducible. However, experience shows that these conditions, which are
often used in theory, might not be directly fulfilled. Somehow, as a consequence,
one can observe a discrepancy between theoretical and empirical research, i.e. a
well designed and complex theory of a food security program, while empirical
analysis cannot link all issues.

One method to overcome the problem is to work with less stringent
assumptions on data and statistical tools. A specific way of doing so can be
termed "soft" variable analysis. "Soft" variables are variables which can not be
directly observed by a researcher. In order to refer to the method used in this
paper, these variables are called "latent" variables. Such variables often occur in
theories where socio-economic characteristics are integrated in economic
analyses. (For further statistical background see Sartorius von Bach and
Nuppenau 1995).

In figure 1 the principal structure of latent variable analysis can be observed in
a structural setting were "w" and "z" are latent variables (circles) and "q_i" and "x_i"
are indicator variables (rectangulars). They are positioned according to their
validity: "z" shall cause "w". Hence, indicator variables "q" for the endogenous
variable "w" are not directly linked with indicator variables "x" that determine the
exogenous variable "z" in the system, see contrast to traditional approaches
(Aldermann and Garcia 1995); rather latent variables provide the causing link in
the hypothesized framework. Since latent variables play an essential role in socio-
economic models, research primarily focuses on the determination of the size of τ

(the relationship between latent variables) and simultaneously tries to determine the interaction α and β between indicator and latent variables.

Figure 1: Structural Form of a Latent Variable Model

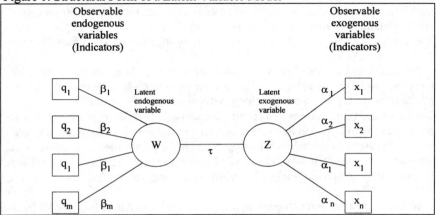

Various methods exist in order to determine τ, α, and β simultaneously. The most rigorous techniques are proposed by Dhrymes (1974). Formally, constraint maximizing of τ by variation provides a mathematical solution for τ, α and β. However, simplified versions of latent variable models use statistical procedures which are less demanding. "Causal analysis" (Ezpath 1989), as applied in this study, is an available tool for the description of causal relationships. Implemented in a computer package based on SYSTAT, EzPATH has been utilized in this study.

4   A Profile of Rural South African Social Conditions as Related to Food Security

The social conditions in the rural areas of South Africa are widely known and documented. For the purpose of this paper, it is essential to present a profile of rural households, based on the most recent rural national survey of 9000 households during 1993/94 and specifically of households situated in former homelands. Compared to studies in other countries, structural parameters in South Africa, such as skewed land distribution, prevalence of labor migration, and missing markets, show a dramatic bias in socio-economic conditions for making a rural livelihood (Lipton and Lipton 1993). Though these factors are unique to a country that has been subjected to racial segregation for a long period, other factors are very similar to other study areas. Factors (general indicators of food insecurity as described before and special to South Africa) have to be viewed simultaneously and to determine the low level of food security in South Africa.

Over one third (36.4 percent) of all households in South Africa and 49 percent of all people can be classified as being poor. Poverty in rural areas, however, is significantly higher than the national poverty rate. Approximately 50 percent of all households in rural areas are poor and 68.1 percent of people in rural households live in poverty, compared to an aggregated 65.2% of sub-Saharan Africa (FAO 1988).

Households with poor access to basic services were also found to have low incomes and to spend a large portion of their income on food. Each unit of labor allocated to water and wood fetching reduces household income by an amount similar to the estimated returns for uneducated labor. A labor scarcity, or time-poverty problem linked to inadequate service provision is a partial explanation for the low levels of household well-being. By using a composite indicator showing access to basic needs, it was found that 72 percent of rural African households are in conditions which could be described as inadequate or intolerable (LAPC 1995).

In terms of under-nourishment, approximately 57 percent of households in the sample fall below a 2,100 calories per-day nutritional poverty line. The nutritional poverty head count under a lower standard of nutritional adequacy (namely 1,815 calories per day) is 45 percent.

Just over a quarter of rural households (26.1 percent) currently have access to a plot of land for the cultivation of crops. Average land size available to these households is 2.2 ha. A similar pattern is evident regarding the ownership of livestock, with some 24 percent of households in rural South Africa owning livestock with an average holding of 5.4 Mature Livestock Units (MLU) valued at approximately US$ 1,200.

In contrast to other developing countries, access to human capital in the form of educated labor emerges as the most common endowment of rural households. Thirty-seven percent of rural households have an adult household member with 10 years of schooling or more, and 78 percent have an adult household member who could be considered functionally literate. Finally, 30 percent of households had a person of pensionable age, and 35 percent had one member of the household who was a migrant worker in another area.

Although the survey confirms that agricultural production is important for the assessment of food security of rural households, it accounts for less than 10 percent of household income. It is worth noting here that more than one third of rural households continue to engage in agricultural production, making it the third most important livelihood tactic used in these areas, but actual contributions in terms of value added are low.

The pure marginal returns to land (holding all other assets fixed) appear meager and close to zero. However, preliminary evidence does suggest that large land endowments do play a role in stabilizing household income. The marginal returns to land are estimated to rise substantially when households have greater ability to self-finance as indicated by inflows of transfer income (pensions, remittances, etc.). When households enjoy large amounts of such income, incremental units of land boost income per scaled adult equivalent by nearly US\$ 14/month. At an average household size of 4.5 scaled adult equivalent, this implies a marginal return of about US\$ 700/hectare/year. This important finding, that self-finance capacity fundamentally shapes land use, stresses a serious and constraining weakness in rural financial markets.

5   Socio-Economic Links in Agricultural Development and Implications on Food Security

In this section a conceptual framework for understanding causal links between policy impact, food security and socio-economic conditions will be formally proposed. A presentation (see figure 2) of major latent variables and their indicators will enable the reader to follow deliberations on the concept of latent variables presented. The evaluation of causality analysis has to start with socio-economic theories of development. The links hypothesized by such theories are important variables in the development process.

Although the set includes some of the same relevant indicator variables, such as "weight for age," "height for age," "calories," "protein" etc. for measuring food insecurity in line with tradition as proposed by Alderman and Garcia, the importance of measuring food security shifts from the single indicator variable to the measurement of the integrated variable "food security" (see figure 2). Similarly, "health" can be described by "days of illness, diarrhea prevalence, vaccination," etc., and "information" (as a more general substitute for education) could be described by "extension," "media," "school enrollment," "years of formal education," etc.

Furthermore, the socio-economic factors are condensed in three separate latent variables: "standard of living" (Anand and Harris 1991), "acquirement through entitlement" (Sen 1991) and "family" (Harriss 1991). Each of these latent variables describes a different aspect of the household's position by means of stratified socio-economic dimensions. The separation of these aspects was chosen with regard to their conjunction to food security. Obviously, the factor "acquirement through entitlement," such as described in the Elmhirst lecture in Malaga in 1985, plays a prime and direct role in food security of poor societies in general (South Africa is only one case). In this context policy concerns concentrate on the alleviation of food insecurity in the short run. "Family"

Figure 2: Causality Links in Rural Development

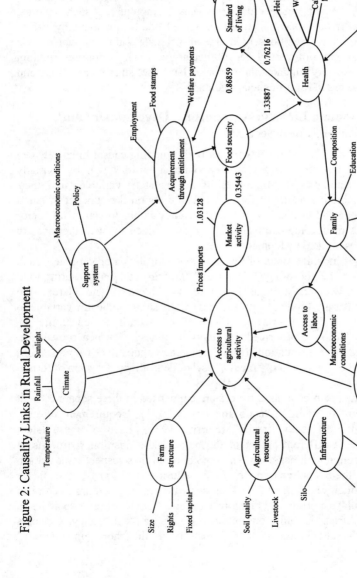

Note: Only a small fraction of relationships were analyzed in this first attempt to assess causal links in agricultural development

characteristics, in contrast, are more exogenous in the short run, but may influence the potential of acquisition. They indirectly contribute to the health situation and determine the condition of "labor" as a prime resource of a poor household (see arrows in figure 2). "Standard of living" has to be seen primarily as a latent variable that summarizes the poverty situation. Finally, "food security," although it is only one of the objectives to be improved in rural societies, it is most definitely one of the most important and pressing to be resolved. Indicator variables are equally short-term indicators such as income, but also longer-term conditions such as housing conditions, if applicable and, if calculable, permanent income.

The important contribution of this presentation has to be seen in the theoretical evaluation and establishment of hypothetical links between "food security" and the other latent variables "health," "acquirement through entitlement," "family," "information" and so on. This first attempt of concrete structuring and organization of all relationships between latent variables would imply a lengthy set of theoretical thinking and arguing about potential links between latent variables and it must be admitted that not all links are clearly theoretically established. The other way round, from a minor perspective of empirical research, a testing of each and every link could be conducted. This type of purely statistical research has to be avoided, even if the theoretical establishment of links is poor, since it runs the risk of being inductive only. However, our research combined the issues to present a broad approach. We had hypothesized several links as proposed in figure 2 and found them approved.

Firstly, as can be observed from the figure, "food security" is directly determined by "access to agricultural activities." The same variable, "access to agricultural activities," indirectly determines food security modified through "access to markets" and "acquirement through entitlement." This second link implies that the entitlement is subject to an evaluation of the agricultural performance by policy makers, and their independent capacity to provide assistance to food insecure households. This second link finally determines "food security."

Finally, "food security" translates into "standard of living" via "health" as the major hypothesis; "food security" is directly and positively influenced by "health." If the empirical test of these coefficients actually is passed, it not only proves the above-mentioned findings of Alderman and Garcia (1993) in the South African context, but also demonstrates the broader context with food security to be appreciated. Furthermore, since "health" directly influences the welfare situation of a rural household (not only indirectly via food consumption as proposed before) an additional link in our model (see figure 2) between "standard of living" and "health" should be self-explanatory. Continuing and hypothesizing the "health" situation is influenced by "family" indicators variables, such as size, age, human capital, and family composition. Furthermore, the influence of latent variable "information" has to be considered. "Information" is regarded as the information that the household could acquire.

In contrast to our deliberations on potential links, it can be questioned whether this minimal set of links is sufficient for an intensive investigation into potential links. For example, it could be argued that "information" is directly linked to "food security," and not only indirectly via "health" and other latent variables' considerations. This would be relevant, if households are ill-informed about the nutrient content of various foods etc. However, additional links can be tested.

A debate on extended models may include deliberately intended positive effects as well as unintended negative side effects or by-product distortions of policies that were initially ignored by policy makers. Especially trade-offs between policies and complementary requirements can be investigated. For example, as has been increasingly emphasized and applied already, "health" and sanitation improvements become "conditions sine qua non" in combating food insecurity and poverty (Alderman and Garcia 1995).

6   Empirical Findings of the Proposed Conceptual Framework

The conceptual framework was analyzed by utilizing the correlation matrix of a small data set, which was selected randomly. Only a small part of the framework will be discussed, utilizing the matrix. The results present the measurable linkages between presented variables. Since the appropriateness of the model depends on the input matrix (see table 1) that is limited in its validity so far, the empirical research presented in this section concentrates on the potential of evaluating causal relationships, rather than providing already finally assessed results. Moreover, the important contribution of this paper and the results presented have to be seen as a necessary first step in the determination of reasonable causal models that allow for further research. Since causal modeling, especially making models operational, is a difficult task that requires investigating the appropriateness of indicator and latent variables. The results presented here show the potential for using both types of variables. As an inevitable next step, indicator variables have to be empirically improved by additional surveying in rural areas in order to make table 1 more representative for the South African rural economy.

Results obtained in the empirical analysis can be seen in the figures in figure 2. Until recently, these linkages were not included in analyzing agricultural development and, specifically, issues such as food security. It is clear from the data used that both the "market activity" and the "acquirement through entitlement" had a positive impact on "food security" of 0.35443 and 1.03128,

Table 1: Correlation Matrix from Random Data

Correlation Matrix	Employ-ment	Prices	Housing	Income	H for A[1]	Food stamps	Welfare payment	Food expend.	Sani-tation	Imports	Calorie intake	Medical budget	W for H[2]
Employment	1.000												
Prices	0.109	1.000											
Housing	-0.190	0.226	1.000										
Income	-0.356	-0.245	-0.057	1.000									
H for A[1]	0.171	-0.296	0.305	-0.318	1.000								
Food stamps	0.212	0.027	0.282	-0.394	-0.272	1.000							
Welfare paym.	0.133	0.145	-0.294	0.247	-0.171	-0.212	1.000						
Food expend.	-0.102	-0.170	-0.348	-0.268	-0.185	-0.230	-0.144	1.000					
Sanitation	-0.109	-0.900	0.226	0.245	0.296	0.027	0.145	0.170	1.000				
Imports	-0.190	0.226	-0.800	-0.057	0.305	0.282	-0.294	-0.348	0.226	1.000			
Calorie intake	-0.031	0.918	0.135	0.002	-0.004	-0.200	-0.200	0.008	-0.918	0.135	1.000		
Medical budget	-0.349	0.150	0.825	0.001	0.600	-0.200	-0.300	0.090	0.150	0.825	0.163	1.000	
W for H[2]	-0.102	-0.170	-0.348	-0.268	-0.185	-0.230	-0.144	0.990	-0.170	-0.348	-0.008	0.003	1.000

Note:
[1] Height for age
[2] Weight for height

Prices and imports describe "market activity";
Employment. food stamps and welfare payments describe "acquirement through entitlement';
Income and calorie intake describe "food security";
Housing, food expenditure. income and sanitation describe "standard of living";
Sanitation. height for age. weight for height. calorie intake and medical budget describe "health";
All other manifest and latent variables were not included in the correlation matrix. consisting of 120 observations.

respectively. Furthermore, "food security" determines "health" with 1.33887, which in turn determines "standard of living" with -0.76216, and the "standard of living" again determines "acquirement through entitlement" by 0.86859.

Table 2: Results of Fitted Causalities from Random Data

Variable	Causality coefficients ⟶	Variable
(Access to market)	0.69694	Prices
(Access to market)	0.80628	Imports
(Access to market)	0.35443	(Food security)
(Food security)	1.33887	(Health)
(Health)	0.76216	(Standard of living)
(Standard of living)	0.86859	(Acquirement through entitlement)
(Acquirement through entitlement)	1.03128	(Food security)
Income	0.24822	(Food security)
Weight for height	-0.95864	(Food security)
Employment programs	-0.80509	(Acquirement through entitlement)
Food stamps	1.39726	(Acquirement through entitlement)
Welfare payments	0.55569	(Acquirement through entitlement)
(Standard of living)	-1.11781	Housing
(Health)	-1.02852	Calorie intake
(Standard of living)	1.38015	Food expenditure
(Standard of living)	-0.20981	Income
(Standard of living)	-0.12928	Sanitation
Sanitation	0.02510	(Health)
Height for age	1.74819	(Health)
Calorie intake	0.06334	(Health)
Medical budget	0.74801	(Health)

Note: *Latent variables are in brackets*

Results indicate the importance of determining causalities and linkages, which were mostly neglected in traditional analysis on food security. However, assessing these linkages without significance measurements and goodness of fits, will not contribute in changing the traditional approach towards a more valid and conceptually sound approach. Assuming the data is relevant, contributions of the manifested variables towards latent variables can be determined, i.e. employment, food stamps and welfare payments on "acquirement through entitlement", by -0.80509, 1.39726 and 0.55569, respectively. These coefficients clearly indicate that an employment program has a negative contribution towards entitlement. In table 1 it is interesting to note that employment is positively correlated with food stamps and welfare payments and that the latter is negatively related to food stamps (-0.212). These manifest variables were traditionally utilized in mono-causal relationships. It should be clear that ignoring the effects of other variables which indirectly affect the "acquirement through entitlement" will result in biased applications. Causalities in this model reached an equilibrium after 39 iterations (loss function value of 8.42575 with largest absolute gradient of 0.000055) to incorporate all indirect effects and to present valuable relationships which can be used for policy purposes.

7 Conclusion

This paper commenced with the hypothesis that the opportunities to achieve "food security" in poverty-stricken rural areas must be seen in a broader context of various causal links between the supply side and the demand side of the food equation. It has been proposed, as already done in many other recent contributions on food insecurity and socio-economic conditions of rural households, that unilateral and monocausal explanations of undernourishment and agricultural production are not sufficient to enable the design of proper policies. The paper took the chance to show how more complex approaches of multi-causalities can be introduced in a broadened research topic on the issue of socio-economics, food insecurity and agricultural performance. Being a first attempt to identify causal relationships, it is far from claiming that a full appreciation of the complexity has already been accomplished. Rather, it was shown that the method of "latent variables" is appropriate for modeling causalities with "soft" socio-economic variables and that tentatively empirical results can be obtained from the modeling and testing. This approach should be seen as a first attempt to change and improve the approach that was used for previous empirical analyses on food security or related development issues.

The special case of South African rural food insecurity, poverty and underdeveloped agriculture was used to demonstrate that latent variables, such as introduced by development theory, like "health," "family composition" and "acquirement through entitlement," build a net of causalities that can explain poverty and food insecurity, simultaneously. Interestingly enough, it was shown that the statistical step from a correlation matrix to the causality analysis, as pursued with the "latent variable method," can reveal the quantitative importance of individual links in such causality nets. It was exemplified that "food security," "health," "standard of living" and "acquirement through entitlement" are self-enforced causes for food insecurity. It must be admitted that only parts of the proposed causal links could so far be established in the South African context. The model failed in its empirical application to verify the important links to "access to agricultural activity," "the support system," "labor" and "technology." Results show that latent variables, such as "acquirement through entitlement" and "access to markets" have positive impact on food security. Furthermore, it becomes clear how specific manifest variables contribute towards describing the latent variables.

Lessons Learned

Lessons learned from traditional methodologies and our application of causal modeling prove that causal links can be converted to operational models and applied for survey purposes. A more detailed empirical investigation of various rural settings, however, may provide further insight into the necessary prerequisites for empirical links between agricultural performance and the food security situation. Inevitably, we have learned that the approach has to be improved empirically by additional surveying in rural areas. But the advantage of this approach is already the determination of real causalities, i.e. the measurement of the specific contribution of different policy instruments. From a policy point of view, linking food security to agricultural performance seems to be the result demanded by policy makers. Policies that are better designed, so that agriculture can contribute more effectively to its fundamental role as the provider of food security for rural communities, rely on statistical information on real links.

References

Alderman, H., Garcia, M. 1993. Poverty, Household Food Security, and Nutrition in Rural Pakistan. International Food Policy Research Institute Research Report No.96. Washington.

Alderman, H., Garcia, M. 1994. Food Security and Health Security: Explaining the Levels of Nutritional Status in Pakistan. "Economic Development and Cultural Change," April 1994

Anand, S., Harris, C. 1991. Food and Standard of Living: An Analysis Based on Sri Lankan Data: In: Dreze, J. and Sen, A., The Political Economy of Hunger. Vol. 1 Entitlement and Well-Being, Oxford.

Barrera, A. 1991. The interactive effects of mothers' schooling and unsupplemented breast feeding on child health. Journal of Development Economics. Vol 34 81-98.

Behrman, J. 1991. Nutrition, health, and development, In: Psacharopolous, G., Essays on poverty, equity and growth. New York, p. 79-71

Behrman, J. 1988. Comment on: "Economic Demography and Development: New Directions in an Old Field," In: Ranis, G., Schultz, Th., The State of Development Economics. Progress and Perspectives. Cambridge (Mass.), p.452-458.

Bezanson, K. 1995. A 2020 vision for food, agriculture and the environment. Closing remarks presented at an International Conference, National Geographic Society, Washington.

Dhrymes, P. 1974. Econometrics. New York..

Eicher, C. K. 1988. Food security battles in Southern Africa. Plenary address presented at the XII World congress for Rural Sociology, Bologna, Italy.

FAO, World agriculture toward 2000. Ed N. Alexander, Belhaven Press, London 1988.

Harriss, B. 1991. The Intrafamily Distribution of Hunger in South Asia. In: Dreze, J. and Sen, A., The Political Economy of Hunger. Vol. 1 Entitlement and Well-Being, Oxford.

LAPC 1995. The composition and persistence of poverty in rural South Africa. Ed J. May, M. Carter & D. Posel, Research paper, LAPC, Johannesburg.

Lele, U., Candler, W. 1981. Food Security: Some East African Considerations. In: Valdes, A., Food Security in Developing countries. Boulder Colorado, p. 101-122.

Lipton, M., Creating Rural Livelihoods: Some Lessons for South Africa from Experience Elsewhere. "World Development," Vol. 21, No. 9 1993, p. 1515-1548.

Sartorius von Bach, H.J. & Nuppenau, E.A. 1995. Measuring inter-dependent socio-economic variables affecting development and their impact on South African traditional agriculture. Quarterly International Journal of Agriculture. Vol. 34, No 3, 259-277.

Schultz, Th. 1988. Economic Demography and Development: New Directions in an Old Field, In: Ranis, G., Schultz, Th., The State of Development Economics. Progress and Perspectives. Cambridge (Mass.), p.416-451.

Sen, A., Food Economics and Entitlements. In: Dreze, J. and Sen, A., The Political Economy of Hunger. Vol. 1 Entitlement and Well-Being, Oxford 1991

Valdes, A., Konandreas, P. 1981. Assessing Food Insecurity based on national aggregates in developing countries. In: Valdes, A., Food Security in Developing countries. Boulder Colorado, p. 25-52.

Part 4.2

Diffusion and Adoption of Innovations
Extension and Adoption (Case Studies)

Crisis in the Generation and Transfer of Agricultural Technologies – Possible Remedies

Reuben Ausher
Ministry of Agriculture, Extension Service
P. O. Box 7054, Tel Aviv 61070, Israel

Abstract

Agricultural extension has found itself in the last two decades in a crisis situation. Agricultural extension systems are slow in adjusting to their changing surrounding environment, characterized now by a proliferation of actors within the once much simpler farmers-extension-research relationship. Agricultural extension has to cope with the conflicting challenge to intensify and diversify production, and promote at the same time environment-friendly and sustainable production systems. Basically the crisis is felt mainly at the management and professional levels. In consequence, the technology development capability of extension is being depleted of its valuable assets: the problem-oriented, empirical, pragmatic and "cheap and nasty" approach; field-level expertise, a knack for integrative field diagnosis; field-centered interdisciplinary activity and accountability; the person-orientation and the ability to prioritize clientele, and to influence the research agenda with the practitioner's input.

It is proposed to establish a CLEARING HOUSE to collate case studies, information and experience, and to provide ensuingly management tools and professional methodologies for agricultural extension, based on the review of various extension systems. Successful extension models having been spread and acting under various extension systems, their review should be followed by an eclectic retrieval of successful components from the wide array of past and present extension models and modules. These components applied in a modular way could act as the "building blocks" of prospective new or modified systems. A task-force should be set up and charged with the role of laying the ground for the establishment of the CLEARING HOUSE. The objectives, principles, structure and management of the CLEARING HOUSE will have to be discussed in the framework of a workshop to be held for this purpose. The CLEARING HOUSE will provide extension workers all over the world with well-defined tools and methodologies for the promotion of professionalism among them. This activity could restore the image and visibility of extension giving extension personnel the feeling that there is an address for their problems and a network they can rely upon. The paper specifies the prospective roles of the CLEARING HOUSE in the areas of technology generation, diffusion and system management and a scenario for the workshop. The beneficiaries of the future activity of the CLEARING HOUSE would not be only extension workers but all members of the Agricultural Knowledge System. We should not lament that extension is the weak link in the development of agricultural technologies and its management out of control, but pull together all helping hands to confront its overwhelming challenges.

Keywords_____

Agricultural extension, clearing house, technology generation, technology diffusion, system management

1   Introduction

The Technology Development Continuum

There is a perception among scientists, extension, industry and governments that a gap exists between agricultural research findings and their conversion into applicable know-how in the form of new technologies. The time span between bench research findings and practical application is becoming longer and longer. This fact is particularly critical these days when the active life of agricultural products, technologies and patents is getting much shorter than in the past. Consequently, the quicker we turn results and findings into new applicable technologies, the higher the competitive benefits we could reap.

Conceptually, one may view technology generation, transfer and adoption as components of one continuum. In terms of organization, technology generation falls under research responsibility while agricultural extension systems cater to the other two components. The experience of many countries is that the closer the cooperation between the organizations and respective individuals, and the more the overlapping along the continuum of the technological process, the more rapid the transfer of technologies and their adoption by clientele. But, despite an amount of desirable overlapping, researchers should do mainly research and extension staff mainly advisory work so that all professionals act within the domain of their strengths and never within that of their weaknesses. In this sense, assistance provided to developing countries (DCs) at system level should be directed to account for all three elements of the technology development continuum without being bothered too much by institutional boundaries.

The two members of the same Knowledge System, agricultural research and extension, are interdependent in the long run. However, we can state that in day-to-day existence, the relevance and success of research are extension-dependent. Research systems do not generally succeed without an efficient agricultural extension system influencing their agenda and feedbacking them from the reality of the field. In this context, improving extension should mean improving research. The technology development process became much more complex in the last two decades (1975-1995), being required to take into consideration new factors like the protection of the environment, sustainability, a reduction in soil and water resources, etc. Nevertheless, this process is expected to fulfill the cardinal role of pioneering the campaigns against poverty, for the well-being of subsistence farmers and for their gradual transition, first into commercial farmers and progressively into entrepreneurs, providing them with the competitive edge so vital in a dynamic market environment. Low-input and subsequent low-output agricultural production systems and attempts to improve them without considerable investments have not succeeded in alleviating poverty.

The Agricultural Knowledge System

One of the most significant developments of the last two decades is the increasing number of actors within the Agricultural Knowledge System (AKS) (Röling 1987). Consequently, the relative weight of technology in general, and research and extension in particular, is changing. Other factors and institutions like credit, farmers' associations, non-government organizations (NGOs), marketing, management of natural resources, trade agreements, phytosanitary barriers, legal and environmental considerations, etc., are either appearing on-stage or playing an increasingly important role. In absolute terms, however, technology is the major factor ensuring productivity and competitivity of the produce on the marketplace. The proliferation of actors in the agricultural knowledge system imposes a pluralistic systems approach for its understanding and coordination.

The appearance of various new bodies involved in the AKS and in the R&D process with focus on advisory work, pest scouting, caretaking and management of plots, some of these bodies being even owned by farmers' associations, winds up in a new configuration of the Agricultural Knowledge System. For the first time competition is felt between public extension and research on the one hand, and the clientele on the other hand. In sum, there is a shift in the traditional extension-farmer relationship. In light of these new circumstances, the scope of extension in general and public extension in particular has to be reshaped. There appears to be increased competition among many other organizations both public and private within the Knowledge System, locally, nationally and worldwide (Ausher 1987).

The Agricultural Knowledge System can be considered as a new area with possibilities for creative and innovative research if efficiency in this system is to be improved. If agriculture is to survive and prosper in a highly competitive world, linkages among actors of the Agricultural Knowledge System (universities, government research, public policy, industry, private sector, extension, private consultants, media, international development bodies, individual users, cooperative users, etc.) must be much more clearly understood and described than our current state of knowledge allows.

The Mission

Fluctuating world market prices of the staple commodities cotton, rice, wheat, oil, and sugar crops drive producers toward the intensive horticultural crops – new species and varieties of vegetables, fruits, cutflowers and potplants, herbs and spices, new industrial crops, seed crops, etc. This diversification and crop intensification process entails a massive technological change and requires a well-orchestrated extension effort. This trend is strongly felt in the industrialized countries of the world, but it is there in the DCs as well. In the latter there is the need to improve the productivity of the basic commodities. This too implies an important technological change.

The Demand for Advice

Demand for know-how and advice is on the increase. Growers, taking complex managerial and technical decisions under changing environmental conditions, need good advisory coverage. The higher their educational level, cropping intensity and experience, the more they request and appreciate good advice. In the long run the growers who will prosper and stay in cropping will be those propelled by creative talent, mastering managerial, financial and technical skills, searching for new avenues in production and marketing, looking for niches and new opportunities. This potential clientele may always be a primary consumer of high-level, qualified extension output.

What is the Quantitative Dimension of the Demand for Extension?

An FAO report (1990) on the Global Consultation on Agricultural Extension indicates that the estimated expenditure on extension is US$6 billion a year and some 600,000 extension workers are engaged in serving the out-of-school agricultural educational needs of farming populations. By the end of the century it is estimated that some 1.25 million extension workers will be needed. The agent-farmer ratios throughout most of the world remain woefully inadequate. The FAO study (1990) estimated these at 1:325 for North America and 1:431 for Europe, but 1:1809 in Africa, 1:2661 in Asia, 1:2940 in Latin America, and 1:3499 in the Near East. In more than 20 FAO case studies on different extension approaches, the reported actual contact with farmers was about 400 to 500 farmers per extension worker annually. Furthermore, only about 74 percent of the extension workers' time was devoted to actual extension education activities and about 40 percent of the extension agents had a low level of education (secondary or lower).

In sum, "in spite of the effort of the public sector to provide extension services, the number of farmers-mostly the subsistence and resource-poor small-scale farmers-not reached by extension remains large." We judge, however, some of these figures to be positive: seventy four percent of the advisers' time being spent on advisory work seems to be quite satisfactory; the formal educational level of the advisers is but a partial indicator of their suitability for extension work, farming experience being a major success factor; the agent-farmer ratios should be assessed in light of the existence of farmers' groups, mass media and other ways of enhancing communication with growers. Finally, the entire situation regarding the future evolution of advisory services has to be viewed in the context of the progressive decline in the farmer population itself.

2   The Problem Areas

The Conflicting Problems

Promoting crop intensification and diversification in itself is not sufficient. The challenge is to do it in an environment-friendly and sustainable way. This is the major conflicting problem with which research and development in agriculture have to cope, in both the industrialized and the developing world. In spite of the urgency of this task in certain parts of the world, we still lack the policy commitment and the professional, structural and managerial framework to meet this dichotomous challenge effectively.

The Management Crisis

One of the major components of the technology development continuum, agricultural extension, finds itself in a crisis situation in the industrialized as well as in the developing world. Especially in the developing world extension systems often dwindle, staff morale and performance are low, and even a total collapse of systems can be observed. All this is devastating to the institutional image of agricultural extension. The crisis is felt at system and management levels to be caused by the lack of the system's capability to adjust rapidly to the changing surrounding environment. The study of the crisis and of its indicators could be helpful in coming up with the right curative intervention. The problem being a management and organization problem, the tools for its remedy should be explored in the second level of the "soft sciences" area: management and business management disciplines, management of high-tech industries, marketing and systems analysis. The traditional contribution of social, economic, communication, psychology and allied sciences investigating the farmer, his society and impediments should go a step further, focusing on the management of the extension system, its weaknesses and ways to remedy them.

The experience of the last two decades (1975-1995) exhibits significant developments in the management models of public agricultural extension. However, these are mainly results of bottom-up developments attained empirically in the framework of various extension systems. Thoughts and paradigms derived from the academic community, farming systems research and extension, "farmers first," etc. have made a much more limited contribution to the overall progress of extension systems. Unfortunately, many successful empirical developments are poorly documented or found only in hardly accessible gray literature.

Improving Management through Privatization

Planned privatization: As one of the recently widely accepted remedies for the ailments of agricultural extension systems, the privatization process has its pros and cons. All this has not yet been sufficiently generalized. It seems that state-level objectives and responsibilities like impartiality, free flow of information, support to Integrated Pest Management programs or to any other technologies which are not supported by the business sector, help to the weaker sections of the farming community, and the balance between technology generation and diffusion, are negatively affected by "indiscriminate" privatization. On the other hand, privatization can bring about more staff incentives, greater mobility, better remuneration schemes, morale and motivation stimulating efficiency, more economic-oriented advice and more attention to the expectations of clientele. In the case of collapsing public extension systems, particularly in the developing world, privatization could be an adequate answer. This has been attained e.g. in Chile and Ecuador, in which two separate privatized extension systems have been designed, one which supports itself, servicing the medium-sized and large farmers, and another one under which government retains responsibility, addressing resource-poor farmers. The execution of the extension operation is carried out by government-contracted private firms.

In terms of the process itself, privatization of extension should not be regarded just rationally as a conceptual and thus organizational change. By definition, the main asset of all agricultural extension organizations is their personnel. Privatization exposes the human capital invested in the organization to a traumatic psychological experience. The process has to be a very careful and empathic one, taking into account obvious staff anxieties and reluctance toward change. In agricultural extension institutions, which accommodate professional manpower and offer them a challenging career, employees are usually highly identified with the organization. The implementation of hastily organized privatization which does not take into account, from the very outset of the process, these and other aspirations of the advisory corps, could easily wind up disrupting the professional qualities of the organization.

Unplanned privatization: Privatization of extension follows a different unplanned course as well. A whole range of agricultural advisory services are being gradually provided by various private organizations and individuals: purveyors of inputs, farmers' associations, private consultants, pest scouts, researchers, NGOs, field staff of processing industry and of marketing organizations, etc. Faced with competition, inefficient and noncompetitive public agricultural extension is breeding its own sort of unplanned disruption.

Soaring budget deficits and clamor for reductions in government spending have scaled back public extension in many countries, reducing its ability to fulfill its fundamental roles and attract to its rows high-quality personnel. The adjustment of extension methods, such as wider use of mass media, group activities, and written information to make up for reduced operating funds and personnel, have been too slow and achieved little success.

Extension being under constant scrutiny, its success stories are understated and failures exaggerated.

The Professional Crisis

Most of the academic effort supporting agricultural extension comes from the research community investigating technology transfer. The technology generation constituent did not receive the same systematic leadership from the research community. There may be many masterfully engineered modules, but they are scattered around and have to be examined, in situ, under the conditions under which they perform.

The current management crisis of agricultural extension especially in the industrialized countries is further aggravated by the fact that, first in the U.S. but by now in other countries too, extension positions are often made redundant or are frozen and are replaced by research positions especially in the domain of molecular biology and genetic engineering. Thus, the technology system is permanently depleted of valuable assets: the problem-oriented, empirical, pragmatic and "cheap and nasty" approach; field-level expertise, a knack for integrative field diagnosis; field-centered interdisciplinary activity and accountability; the person-orientation and the ability to prioritize clientele, and to influence the research agenda with the practitioner's input.

The same "brain drain" could be found in the international development agencies. The number of agriculturists and especially extension specialists in the World Bank has been drastically reduced over the last decade. Will this not affect the capabilities of the development agencies to cope in future with the conceptual leadership, as well as with the nitty-gritty of technology generation, transfer and adoption ?

Extension-research collaboration, one of the cornerstones of successful technology generation, joint identification of production-limiting factors, and joint formulation of recommendations are affected by several developments occurring at the research end. Research tends to detach itself from the day-to-day field problematic because of the narrowing specialization of the researchers, favoring basic research and freeing itself from the commitment to develop technologies.

In the area of the biological sciences and know-how, professionalism of extension personnel seems to be a bottleneck in the effective performance of agricultural extension systems in the developing world. Basically, professionalism boils down to the understanding of the field, to the capability of identifying limiting factors in the production process and their environmental impact, to the ability of relaying more complex issues to research and of coping with the simpler ones on the spot or carrying out field observations, surveys or trials in order to adjust existing recommendations to specific local needs or to come up with new solutions. This "green thumb" is the outcome of regular outdoor activity, field-oriented esprit de corps, and an extension system endowed with experienced staff who have plenty of "mud on their boots" and are capable of training and coaching newly recruited advisers.

Certain extension systems have had a strong immediate impact on production and productivity by improving basic crop management. However, after several years of improved practices and productivity, a slack in productivity might set in. The main reason for this is the fact that sustaining increased productivity requires an intensive and well-coordinated professional effort. The catch-phrase for sustainable results is professional extension closely cooperating with research and generating continuously an increasingly powerful, sophisticated and relevant message.

In the particular domain of technology generation, field experimentation, design of surveys, statistical analysis, database management, formulation of crop production and protection recommendations, pest scouting, integrative teamwork, the integration of changing environmental, economic, and marketing factors as well as natural resource management indicators into the formulation of recommendations are all lacking in documentation. The same is true for the operation of plant clinics, weather stations, and crop-soil-water laboratories.

In the area of the transfer of agricultural technologies, the research on diffusion, adoption and innovation is characterized by being very diffuse and quite thin, especially as it relates to the area of innovation and utilization of knowledge. Much of the literature related to the technology development continuum in agriculture is dated. Scattered studies are still being made, though projects specifically designed to assess the factors related to successful technology generation, transfer and adoption are very few.

Farm-profitability was the variable that was consistently found as one of the factors promoting transfer and adoption. But there is a trio of factors that should be investigated: variables affecting farmer's decision-making (minimizing risk levels, economic and social factors); knowledge mediators, availability and flow of information. Only a systematic study of these factors could explain which laboratory findings have been transferred into products and which have not.

Any missed Opportunities?

There is still a large gap in matching the opportunities offered by microcomputer technologies to the needs of agricultural extension and its ability to turn these technologies into routine personalized working tools. We obviously do not expect farmers in the developing world to acquire computers in the near future. Yet we do think that computer technologies are potentially important for them. Thus, extension will have to play an important mediating role in these countries for the integration of microcomputer-supported results and recommendations into farmers' decision-making process (Ausher 1993).

New approaches developed by emerging sciences and technologies are far from being converted into routine decision-support aids. This applies to biotechnology, tissue culture, development of crop and livestock optimization models, aerial and satellite photography, as well as systems approaches: integrated pest management, biological control, automation of irrigation, and indoor environment-control. Many of these approaches are already applicable, but this has not happend. The reasons for this situation have to be understood. Establishing technical support units and databases with local capability of supporting the fine-tuning of technical recommendations turned out to be a positive experience in several countries. However, this experience has not been converted into easily diffusable methodologies. The technical output of many extension systems is still vague and general, issued centrally from headquarters, and of doubtful relevance to many growers and growing environments.

3 Conceptual Framework

The Comprehensive Models

The era of ideology, of rigid agricultural extension models is over. The very fact that every 5 or 10 years new models have been developed and applied shows that most of them did not prove themselves in the long run, their disadvantages outnumbering the payoffs. Still, several models have put agricultural extension at the top of the agenda of donors and international development agencies. They have also demonstrated time and again the tremenduous impact of agricultural extension as a powerful technology development vehicle.

The Individual Components

Apparently the weak link in the knowledge system, and a stumble-prone issue, extension seems to thrive on crises. Despite their demise, numerous models have produced new and interesting components in terms of concepts, principles and practices. All these individual components could be successfully utilized under a wide range of environmental conditions.

The Advice

The advice to the producer, farm manager and policy makers, the final product of a modern agricultural extension system, is expected to be all of the following:

- low-cost
- impartial and independent
- relevant and efficient
- profitable
- up-to-date
- rich in knowledge
- direct and personalized
- market-driven
- environment-conscious
- sustainable
- integrated
- improving farmers' managerial ability
- stimulating use of knowledge

The extension mechanism designed to generate advice meeting all the above requirements will have to rely on several new characteristics, but not on one single pattern. However, one central requirement has to be stressed in this context-professionalism. Whatever the mission of the system, either technical, educational or community-focused, unless the staff and the spirit of the organization are professional and imbued with professional savvy, they will not produce the message expected and needed by the clientele. Soon competing institutions will fill the void, triggering the backlash of the extension entity.

A Proposed Approach

It is proposed here that the actual approach to the remedy of ailing systems, the establishment of new ones or the strengthening of existing ones, should rely first of all on a careful analysis of all local factors of relevance. Pre-conceived paradigms are not acceptable anymore. The review of the local conditions should follow an eclectic retrieval of successful components from the wide array of past and present extension models and modules. These components, applied in a modular way, will act as the "building blocks" of the prospective new or modified system.

4 Solutions – Establishing and Operating a "Clearing House"

Successful modules being spread and acting under a wide array of extension systems, there is a need for a "CLEARING HOUSE" to collate case studies (both success stories and failures) and provide management and organization tools based on the follow-up and evaluation of extension systems. Unfortunately, many monitoring and evaluation systems implanted in extension organizations in LDCs have not matured into full-fledged management support tools or into day-to-day working tools. On top of the system management component, the CLEARING HOUSE will have to highlight compatible modules and specific methodologies with bearing on all three composing elements of the technology development continuum.

The objectives of the CLEARING HOUSE will consist of both the diffusion of well-defined and specific professional tools as well as ways aimed at restoring the image and visibility of extension, giving extension personnel the feeling that there is an address for their problems, and a network they can rely upon. Further, the CLEARING HOUSE would create the intellectual basis on which the debate on the future of extension could be taken up again. In this context, the CLEARING HOUSE will determine the real measure of success of turning agricultural extension towards a new course. It will dispel the notion that nothing new is ever done in agricultural extension. Bringing a fresh breeze to agricultural extension, the CLEARING HOUSE will inspire extension institutions and staff all over the world with a new spirit and with new concepts and methods of work. The CLEARING HOUSE will contribute to the revival of agricultural extension, giving it not only patchwork repair but a sense of new direction toward the next millennium. In sum, the CLEARING HOUSE will act as the worldwide stage for all the people working in agricultural extension work. It will bring together the people who could change its course.

The Beneficiaries

The beneficiaries of the future activity of the CLEARING HOUSE would be, firstly public and private organizations involved in agricultural extension activities, their professional and executive staff. Secondly, members of the agricultural knowledge system, coming from both the government and private sectors including agencies which do not carry direct responsibility for agricultural extension but bear on extension, e.g. personnel of planning and funding ministries and agencies. Furthermore research institutions dealing with biological and social sciences, farmers' associations, and international consulting and development agencies. The CLEARING HOUSE will perform surveys of extension systems and provide consulting services to agricultural extension organizations.

The Main Roles of the Clearing House would be:

In the Area of Technology Generation:

- provide the framework for extension and research to discuss and adopt appropriate, viable and site-specific, state-wide, regional or commodity-focused collaboration structures and mechanisms to support their R&D agenda;
- foster the fine-tuning of technical recommendations to specific local conditions by defining methodologies for establishing and running technical support units, e.g. plant clinics, crop-soil-water laboratories, weather stations, units providing farm management and marketing data, computer units;
- stimulate professionalism within the extension system through the integration of the technical support units into the extension system's technological activity;
- inject into the extension system thinking in economic terms based upon the handling of quantifiable parameters;
- equip extension workers with methodologies in the area of sustainable or alternative agriculture, namely, natural resource management, land conservation, erosion control, watershed management, agro-forestry, environmental and biodiversity protection, etc.;
- put together specific tools for the technology generation components relevant to extension workers viz. design and analysis of field trials, surveys and demonstrations in each of the various subject-matter areas: animal production, in- and outdoor production of field and vegetable crops, fruit and flower crops, herbs and spices and the respective auxiliary disciplines – crop protection, irrigation and fertilization, farm machinery, farm management as well as areas close to the needs of the urban population – landscaping, urban entomology, etc.;
- standardize microcomputer-based methodologies and software in support of the technology generation process: statistical analysis, decision-support systems, utility programs, expert systems, databases, etc.;
- encourage the establishment of regional computer institutes to develop site-specific applications due to the inherent difficulties encountered with the

transportability, from one ecosystem to another, of software handling biological parameters;

- foster consumer-oriented agricultural production systems;
- promote the adoption by extension organizations of new concepts: holistic systems approach to agroecosystem management; use of both reductionist and system approaches in the generation of technologies;
- instigate research in the area of innovation and utilization of agricultural knowledge.

In the Area of Technology Transfer:

- establishing and coaching in the DCs local cadre of highly professional extension personnel, well-versed in both subject-matter and its diffusion;
- put together and standardize microcomputer-supported technologies in the area of technology transfer: communications, production of written material (desktop publishing) and computerized graphics for the development of audio-visual material;
- collate and standardize farmers' participation in the definition of extension needs, programs, methodologies and evaluation of activities;
- study successful cases of participatory group activities with farmers.

In the Area of Extension Management:

- perform systematic surveys of extension structures and mechanisms on a worldwide basis in order to identify strengths and weaknesses and postulate remedies;
- develop methodologies and principles for an open-minded analysis/review of existing extension systems;
- foster the adoption of new topics and in-house changes: interdisciplinary activity and team accountability; flexible staff positions; thinking in strategic terms; segmenting and prioritizing clientele; links beyond agriculture; economic analysis of extension;
- develop methodologies for the design of new and strengthened extension systems;
- develop training and education programs in all the above mentioned areas and promote the incorporation of new extension modules and methodologies in the project-level activity of the international development agencies.
- establish a cadre of consultants, mainly from among DCs.

5   Conclusions and Lessons Learned

Agricultural extension is a most efficient vehicle capable of increasing crop and livestock productivity. Better management of basic cropping techniques proved itself as carrying most visible improvements in the very first season of their application. Yields could be increased by 30%-60% through the generation and delivery. These highly visible changes engage growers in a viable interaction with extension. These orders of magnitude improve food security in a very short period of time. In the long run, however, problems arise when growers who have embarked on the technical avenue of improved productivity advocated by extension request more sophisticated technical support. Extension and research have to closely collaborate in order to develop technologies suitable to increased productivity levels. This kind of collaboration implies the joint identification of production levels and the ensuing fine-tuning of recommendations to an environment of enhanced productivity. This joint effort needs good coordination between research, extension and growers, but it is the key for steady food production, protection and supply.

In summary, the CLEARING HOUSE will provide the opportunity for putting agricultural extension back in the role of the protagonist within the Agricultural Knowledge System and in the technology development continuum. Agricultural extension and research must lead, because the alternative for the 21st century could be low production, spoiled environment, hunger, poverty and despair in abundance. We should not lament that extension is the weak link in the agricultural knowledge system and its management out of control, but pull together all the helping hands to confront its overwhelming challenges.

Acknowledgments

The valuable comments of D. Marom, J. Palti and Y. Elkana are highly appreciated.

References

Ausher, R. 1987. Practical adjustment of existing services – The Israeli viewpoint. Advisory work in the context of the future evolution of agriculture. Commission of the European Communities. EUR 11267 EN. pp. 89-100.

Ausher, R. (ed.) 1993. The Potential of Microcomputers in support of agricultural extension, education and training. FAO. Rome. 173 pp.

Maalouf, W.D., Contado, T.E., Adhikarya, R. 1991. Extension coverage and resource problems: the need for public-private cooperation. In: Rivera, W.M., Gustafson, D.J. (eds.): Agricultural Extension: Worldwide Institutional Evolution, Elsevier.

Röling, N. 1987. Conceptual aspects – the European viewpoint. Advisory work in the context of the future evolution of agriculture. Commission of the European Communities. EUR 11267 EN. pp. 101-115.

Agricultural Extension and the World Bank

Dennis Purcell
Washington, D. C. 20433, USA

Abstract

The World has a large portfolio of extension projects. This is in the form of free-standing extension projects, most of which have used some form of the Training and Visit methodology, and as extension components in various types of sectoral development projects. A review in 1994 indicated an acceptable performance for the portfolio, but highlighted a number of serious, pervasive problems. No one methodology had sufficient superior characteristics to warrant its universal use. National strategies and programs should be developed which are relevant to the circumstances existing in each country. Installed extension systems are evolving. Sustainability of large-scale, staff-intensive systems is a major concern.

Keywords

T&V, contact farmer, relevance, institution building, sustainability, extension strategy.

Role of the Bank

The World Bank has been, and continues to be, a major financier of agricultural technology development and transfer in the developing world. In the 16 year period from 1977 to 1992, this amounted to $5,300 million, and is expected to reach $7,600 million by the end of FY 1996 through research and extension projects:

Table 1: Commitments under Bank Loans and IDA credits (US$ million)

Approval Year	Research	Extension	Total
1977-1980	224.9	645.4	870.3
1981-1984	623.7	661.8	1,285.5
1985-1988	511.5	919.4	1,431.0
1989-1992	799.6	958.4	1,753.0

At the beginning of this period, extension received more support than research, but in the late 1980s research assumed about half of the committed amounts, and has subsequently maintained this proportion. To put the extension investment in perspective, it represented about five percent of the Bank's agricultural sector portfolio in that period.

T&V Management System

The Bank's extension projects are commonly perceived to be associated with the Training and Visit (T&V) management system. This is largely, but not completely, correct. In the 1960s the Bank supported extension as components in irrigation and other types of agricultural and rural development projects. Then the Bank came to the view that, although multifunctional staff served a useful development purpose, their many duties detracted from the potential for technology transfer. The T&V model was introduced to address this problem. It was used in Turkey in a project in 1967 and subsequently spread to South Asia in the early 1970s. It has dominated the Bank's support for extension since that time, but not to the exclusion of commodity-specific extension, technical assistance to farmers aligned with credit institutions, and some intensive services associated with specific development projects. Since the late 1970s, however, the free-standing extension projects have made up more than half of the Bank's assistance in technology transfer, and this is where the T&V methodology has dominated.

T&V was a hierarchically organized method of management which was designed to exclusively focus on technology and deliver selected and timely messages to farmers with strict regularity. The original concept involved village extension workers (VEWs) with high school and agricultural certificate training visiting contact farmers (CFs) at fortnightly intervals. Each CF was to pass the messages to his/her neighbors (10 to 20 farmers), so that the VEW could directly or indirectly cover from 500 to 800 farm families. The VEW received training prior to each scheduled message, was supervised, and was supported by subject matter specialists. The concept also aimed to have feedback of farmers' needs through extension to the research system, and to maintain close linkages between research and extension (Benor et al 1984).

T&V was never universally accepted by all Bank staff, as many thought its rigidity would inhibit the development of a truly responsive service. However, most managers considered that the system did offer real possibilities to address the technology transfer needs of smallholder farmers who were the main target in the Bank's agricultural projects. Initially, South and Southeast Asia were the major areas of extension project concentration, but in the late 1980s the Sub-Saharan Africa region (AFR) received most attention.

A Review by OED

In 1994 the Bank's Operations Evaluation Department (OED) published a review of the Bank's extension portfolio (World Bank 1994), largely based on projects approved after FY 1977 which had ex-post evaluations. Unfortunately, this meant that the more recent emphasis on AFR was not fully represented because projects were still ongoing. However, account was also taken of operational reviews and supervision reports of ongoing projects. A total of 107 completed projects were examined, of which 33 were free-standing; 31 of the latter were based on T&V.

Wherever possible, OED tries to validate its ex-post assessments through economic rate of return analysis. This is not generally possible with extension projects due to data constraints and major difficulties in linking cause and effect. However, a number of empirical studies on the impact of extension are reported in the literature based on various statistical techniques. These have usually been research studies in themselves. The majority have reported a significant and positive extension effect, but reviews of these studies stress that empirical results from the applied econometric analysis had to be treated in a circumspect manner because of the difficulty in adequately capturing all the important variables in estimating production equations (Birkhauser, et al. 1991 and Evenson, R. 1991). The Bank has carried out empirical studies on three T&V projects. The most robust was in two similar, heavily irrigated districts in India (Feder, G. et al 1985), one of which had T&V and the other had traditional extension services. This indicated that at least 15% internal rate of return was likely on the T&V incremental investment. Two more recent studies on national T&V programs in Kenya (Bindlish, V. et al 1993.1) and Burkina Faso (Bindlish, V. et al 1993.2) estimated very favorable rates of return, but both illustrated the limitations of econometric techniques and have to be interpreted accordingly.

In the absence of a quantifiable measure of attributable outcome, three elements have been used by the Bank and OED to estimate the worth of extension investments—**relevance** of the program to the situation of the borrower and the intended extension clientele, its apparent **effectiveness** in meeting its objectives, and the **efficiency** in use of the resources available to the program. As virtually all free-standing extension projects and many of the agricultural projects with extension components have a **major institution building** objective, these three elements must be seen in relation to building a capacity to deliver appropriate services in a **sustainable** system.

As one of its measures to monitor its portfolio performance, the Bank uses a dichotomous satisfactory/unsatisfactory assessment. On this basis, the extension portfolio performed at least as well (70 percent satisfactory) as the agricultural sector as a whole during the review period. However, this simple rating system does not tell the full story. Close examination in the OED review demonstrated there were serious problems not only in unsatisfactory (UNS) projects but also in those rated as satisfactory (S) (see table 2). In addition, all of the UNS projects were of unlikely or uncertain sustainability, and only 33 percent of S projects were rated as having likely sustainability.

The Outcome

The review enabled the following conclusions:

General Extension Portfolio

Positive Outcomes:

- The extension portfolio had undoubtedly increased the attention given by borrowers to the role of improved technology in increasing agricultural productivity and small holder welfare.
- The focus of most projects on improved organization and management of staff - intensive services had increased coverage of the small holder sector by public extension services.
- Although monitoring of impact in with and without situations was virtually non-existent, it appeared that the extension programs in most cases had accelerated the rate of adoption of a number of significant technologies to the extent that other constraints allowed.

Negative Observations:

- Funding shortfalls were common phenomena, so that the sustainability of over 70 percent of free-standing projects was rated as either uncertain or unlikely.
- Effectiveness was reduced when recurrent cost funding proved inadequate.
- Insufficiency of relevant technology was frequently a problem, and a major constraint in resource-poor environments.
- Linkages with research were generally weak, and neither research nor extension were sufficiently conscious of the need to understand the constraints and potentials of the different farming systems as a basis for determining relevant technology and technology development requirements.
- With few exceptions, little attention was given (in project design or implementation) to systematic participation of the farming community in problem definition, problem solving, and extension programming; where participation was emphasized, however (cases in Thailand and Mexico), results were very positive.
- A "top-down" culture is traditional in the public sector institutions in most developing countries; this persisted in most Bank projects and was contrary to the development of responsive services.
- Staff quality was a major constraint in nearly all free-standing projects where large staffs were required, both at the level of farmer contact and in the technical support staff; deficiencies in the latter category limited the potential impact of continuous training programs in large state programs.

- Monitoring to support management and justify funding was weakly developed in nearly all projects.

Table 2: Frequency of Problems Raised in Ex-Post Evaluation Reviews of Free-Standing Projects

Description of Serious Problems	Of 23 S Projects	Of 8 UNS Projects	Of 31 Total Projects
Funding	%	%	No.
Recurrent cost funding problems during and subsequent to the project which seriously inhibit field operations	87	100	28
Basis for Recommendations			
Inadequate research - extension linkage to ensure the technological needs of some of the major farming systems are defined and addressed (especially for resource-poor and less predictable environments)	74	100	26
Insufficient technology available to enable a major and progressive program to improve production in some important farming systems	39	63	12
An entrenched "top-down" approach in developing recommendations, despite objectives of continuous feedback from farmers	48	75	17
Little or negligible consideration of production economics, risks and different degrees of access by farmers to resources	39	50	13
Human Resource Capacity			
Training programs unable to ensure front-line extension staff had sufficient practical knowledge of production systems (and their constraints and potentials) and of relevant technology, to provide the desired level of interaction with farmers.	43	88	17
Specific mention of low education level of front-line staff limiting the potential for a more analytical and responsive service.	22	38	8
Selection of Methodologies			
The adoption of a methodological "blueprint" approach over a large area (region, state, nation) did not permit a desirable adaptation of services to the circumstances of each area.	35	50	12
"Contact farmer" system not very effective, or reference made to better results from working with farmer groups	43	75	16

T&V Free-Standing Projects

- T&V, as the major extension model in Bank projects, must be given a lot of credit for the positive achievements attained, but cannot be divorced from many of the shortcomings of the free-standing projects for which it was the extension system used in 90 percent of cases.

- Recurrent cost funding and sustainability concerns, lack of appropriate technology, deficiencies in staff quality, and poor development of a responsive attitude amongst staff can all be partly associated with the large scale application of the T&V system across states. These problems could be expected with most nationwide staff-intensive extension program in developing countries, regardless of the management system used. In addition, the hierarchical structure and "message-centered" delivery in T&V has done little to change the "top-down" characteristic in formulating recommendations which has been traditional in most extension bureaucracies, despite T&V's objectives of using farmer feedback to ensure relevance in recommendations.

- The T&V concept of a contact farmer as the primary recipient of extension visits (for subsequent transfer of technology to other farmers in the vicinity) was not very effective and was often modified to a farmer group focus, partly because contact farmer selection yielded farmers who were unrepresentative of the limited resource circumstances of those to be influenced. Even then, insufficient attention was given to the use of farmer groups with similar resources and constraints, so that the potential for increased effectiveness through group problem definition and ownership of problem solutions could not be fully realized (nor were staff trained in how to facilitate this process).

Other Projects

- In integrated rural development projects the outcome of extension services, whether T&V or other even more intensive service models, was related to the extent to which other basic requirements were met: availability of relevant technology for the targeted farming systems and the efficiency with which the complementary services in input supply and credit were delivered.

- Commodity-specific extension programs demonstrated their ability to provide all the ingredients needed for technology adoption to enhance the production of the targeted commodity. As these programs usually involve commercial crops, however, evaluations noted that cost recovery in some form for these specialized services should normally be anticipated. Specialized public services with cost recovery and private sector services can be complementary to general public extension services.

- There was only one case of a project sponsoring (successful) private sector extension services (Chile). The preponderance of smallholders at or near subsistence level in many borrowers' rural sectors limits the extent to which payment for services can be instituted, although some form of farmer ownership of services should be the ultimate objective, regardless of resource circumstances. At the other end of the spectrum, results confirmed that the highly professional services needed for specialized higher value crops (e.g. vegetables, export fruits and flowers) should be provided directly by the private sector.
- Extension supplied as an adjunct to a credit delivery program was usually effective in supporting technology adoption by the clientele. Deficiencies sometimes occurred in the use of credit in inflexible production packages which were not always relevant to farmers' circumstances. But where these services were provided at public cost, an equity issue arose in that an intensive and costly service was being provided to a very small proportion of the smallholder subsector, and usually only to those with a better resource base, implying reduced resources for extension to the majority.
- Periodic extension campaigns which respond to a widely acknowledged crisis were usually effective as they were able to avoid many of the constraints faced in developing an efficient "permanent" service.

The findings did not indicate that a single extension model has sufficient superior features to justify its uniform adoption in an extension service in all smallholder communities. This suggests that the Bank can be faulted in the extent to which it promoted the T&V model (especially in earlier projects) in a relatively uniform package of investments and extension practices applied in large state and national programs. Design adjustments in accordance with fiscal, human resource, farming system, complementary services and technology stock circumstances should have been made. This would have enhanced the reality, and perception, of services as efficient and cost-effective, and could be expected to have elicited improved financial and political support and, hence, sustain ability of the institutional investment.

On the basis of the review, OED made a number of recommendations for future and ongoing interventions by the Bank in agricultural extension. These recommendations were based on the premise that public sector extension investment can give favorable economic returns and warrant strong government support, provided (a) the elements of relevance and efficiency are adhered to, (b) there is a significant technology gap between current practices and available, more profitable technology which is relevant to, and sustainable in, the targeted farming systems, and (c) alternative effective forms of technology transfer are not able to be provided from private sources. The recommendations insisted on more pre-project analysis to define the circumstances noted in the previous paragraph. The analysis would result in as extension strategy which was responsive to these circumstances (especially fiscal capacity) and would enable the development of investment programs as phases in the strategy.

The implication was that investment in state-wide, staff-intensive services would not always be appropriate. Use of a form of T&V as part of the strategy was not precluded, as many of the principles used in this methodology are sound and should be common to any effective face-to-face services. However, specific measures to make the system more participatory and responsive were described (see box 1). Additional approaches could include (a) short-term campaigns taking advantage of all available sectoral staff, (b) commodity-specific extension programs aligned with delivery of input packages, (c) highly participatory schemes having a lesser number of better educated extensionists working with farming communities in an infrequent but scheduled program of interaction for problem definition and resolution, and (d) greater reliance on well organized mass media to complement existing commercial supplier services and public face-to-face services.

Current Developments

In existing T&V services, a common concern has been how to maintain the effectiveness (and efficiency) of regular visits with scheduled messages after a number of cropping seasons. If recommendations on the major commodities which are relevant to the circumstances of farmers have been promoted, then after a few seasons these practices should be adopted sufficiently in the communities for farmer-to-farmer transfer to suffice; at least, this transfer will severely reduce the marginal benefits to be obtained from further regular public extension promoting these same practices. Practices which are not significantly adopted after a few seasons are likely to be seen as a poor use of resources by farmers, or their adoption is constrained by one or more factors other than the information or skills which public extension can provide. This dilemma was exacerbated by the early concentration by most T&V services on the major food crops, and by the scarcity of new relevant technology for the more resource-poor farmers and environments.

A number of measures are being taken to respond to this problem. One is to reduce the frequency of visits (and associated training sessions); another is to substantially broaden the scope of advice/messages to cover more aspects of farming, often including tree crops, livestock production and even some aspects of animal health; and a third is to reduce the actual number of VEWs through natural attrition without replacement. Increased emphasis on technology development is virtually universal.

The broadening of scope in technical coverage places major demands on the VEWs who have had limited (and often specialized) basic training, and the outcome of the retraining programs as measured by effective servicing of farmer demands is yet to be assessed. As agricultural markets are being opened up through policy changes, farmers are also demanding more responsive services, and as higher-value commodities become options, both timely and highly technical advice are needed. These changing scenarios raise the issue of the ability of VEWs to meet these demands, and to adjust from the traditional top-down culture to which they have been accustomed. It is becoming apparent that the subject matter specialist at the level above the VEW is likely to have to assume a greater farmer-contact role than before, and in some circumstances it could eventuate that a lesser number of VEWs act more as assistants to the better trained subject specialists rather than the latter being resource persons for the VEWs.

In countries which adopted the T&V model, in virtually all cases the system has been evolving. Apart from changed frequency in both training and visits, in most cases there is now more emphasis given to farmer groups. Women's groups are also receiving a lot of attention, especially in Africa. The involvement of NGO is being introduced or considered, but not uniformly, and commercial input suppliers are being included in many schemes as part of the extension network. The emphasis being given to demand-driven research and a farming system perspective in national research systems which are being supported by the Bank and the donor community should also enhance the research-extension-farmer linkages.

Some countries which did not adopt a T&V type program are attempting to transfer as much responsibility as possible to the local level so that the farming community will accept "ownership" of the service (e.g. Colombian and Venezuelan projects). Chile has promoted the use of private consultants contracted to government to assist the most marginalized farmers. In China, farmer associations are contracting technical services from public officials who get paid bonuses in accordance with results. Indonesia has retained a form of decentralized T&V with multidisciplinary VEWs, but is also involved in an educational rather than a message-delivery approach in its large integrated pest management project.

Payment for technical service by smallholders has been promoted in Bank projects only through cess systems on cash (usually export) crops. In Chile, direct payment for services was encouraged in the case of small commercial farmers. More opportunities will arise for user-payment systems as cash cropping and high value crops become more important in the smallholder sector. However, it is clear that public extension services will be warranted in some form for the large body of smallholders who are near the poverty line in most developing countries.

Box 1: Means to Improve the Old-Style T&V

Extension Principle	Application in an Improved T&V System
Programming of Activities	maintain, but program to be determined according to the needs of the farmer group, as agreed with them.
Fixed visit schedule	maintain, but in accordance with a schedule agreed as appropriate between farmers, field staff and supervisor, rather than as a general fortnightly standard.
Supervision	maintain, but with more emphasis on assessing reactions of farmer clientele than on the mechanics of the visit schedule.
Single line of command	maintain (but not as an essential requirement), but develop an understanding that the extension staff must be responsive to the needs of the farmer clientele whose reactions will be monitored by supervisory staff as a measure of staff performance.
Concentration on extending technology	maintain, but not to the exclusion of facilitating the provision of services by other agencies (private and public) to meet the needs of the farming communities being attended, nor of assisting farmers to develop a self-help capacity (e.g. seedling production, group marketing).
Technical Content and Training	maintain timely training sessions for field staff geared to subjects of proximate visits, but not as district-wide general recommendations associated with dominant commodities; the widely applicable recommendations would be taken into account by training officers, but training would be specific to the requirements of the program previously agreed between staff and farmer groups; general recommendations would be adapted and incorporated where possible into the solutions to the problems identified with farmer groups.
Use of Contact Farmers or Groups for Visits and Demonstrations	adopt a concept of identifying existing groups of farmers with similar resource circumstances, problems and attitudes as the medium for interaction with the extension staff (as groups or subgroups in the recipient community), and use these groups to define major constraints, analyze the relevance of techno-logical solutions, and assume ownership of demonstrations (Crouch 1984).
Research-extension linkage	maintain and expand, with emphases on ensuring relevance in applied/adaptive research; this implies a farming system perspective in both research and extension, which would benefit by joint farming system diagnostic surveys.

Lessons Learned

World Bank project experience indicates:

- there is no single extension method which should be universally used to improve public sector extension; strategies need to be developed which are suited to the circumstances of each country, which could imply different approaches at various times and locations in one country.
- the extension principle that advice must be relevant to the conditions of the targeted farmer clients needs to be paramount; the ultimate expression of this principle would be in the clients "owning" the service and being actively involved in determining its direction and shape, and minimally requires that extension agents are fully aware of the circumstances of client groups and adjust their dialogue and recommendations accordingly.
- any extension strategy must consider the sustainability of its service components, with special emphasis being given to the fiscal capacity and willingness to support staff-intensive services which make heavy demands on scarce recurrent budget resources.

Remark

The findings, interpretations and conclusions expressed in this paper are entirely those of the author and should not be attributed in any manner to the World Bank, to its affiliated organizations, or to the members of its Board of Directors or the countries they represent.

References

Benor, D. and M. Baxter 1984. *Training and Visit Extension*. Washington, D.C. World Bank.

Bindlish, V. and R. Evenson 1993. *Evaluation of the Performance of T&V Extension in Kenya*. World Bank Technical Paper No. 108, Africa Technical Department Series.

Bindlish, V., R. Evenson and M. Gbetibouo 1993. *Evaluation of T&V-Based Extension in Burkina Faso*. World Bank Technical Paper No. 226, Africa Technical Department Series.

Birkhaeuser, D., R.E. Evenson and G. Feder 1991. *The Economic Impact of Agricultural Extension: A Review*. Economic Development and Cultural Change. Vol. 39, No. 3.

Crouch, B. 1984. *Problem Census: Farmer-centered Problem Identification*. Training for Agriculture and Rural Development. Rome, FAO.

Evenson, R. E. 1991. *Research and Extension in Agricultural Development*. International Center for Economic Growth. Occasional Paper No. 25. Panama.

Feder, G., L. J. Lau and R. H. Slade 1985. *The Impact of Agricultural Extension. A Case Study of the T&V System in Haryana, India*. World Bank Staff Working Paper No. 756.

World Bank 1994. Agricultural Extension Lessons from Completed Projects. OED. World Bank Report No. 13000.

A New Strategy for the Dissemination of Postharvest Technologies

Tai Wan Kwon[1] and Werner Mühlbauer[2]
[1]Food Science Institute, Inje University
Kimhae, Republic of Korea
[2] Institute for Agricultural Engineering in the Tropics and
Subtropics, University of Hohenheim, Stuttgart, Germany

Abstract

The introduction of new technologies in developing countries mostly failed because the prevailing local conditions were not properly considered. Experiences obtained from numerous R&D projects indicated that it is hardly possible to transfer technologies originally developed in industrialized countries to developing countries either by foreign aid organizations or private companies using traditional dissemination strategies.

Within a bilateral Korean-German research and development project, jointly financed by the Korean and German governments and implemented by the German Agency for Technical Cooperation, a new model of collaboration between an industrialized and a semi-industrialized country was conceived and implemented from 1979-1988. This was the first time within a bilateral technical cooperation that a technically capable institution in a semi-industrialized country was assigned to execute the research activities independently. The objective of this particular project was to develop and disseminate a paddy dryer in Korea to reduce the postharvest losses and improve the product quality.

After five years of project implementation, several private companies in Korea started the production of the paddy dryer developed by the project. Through the financial support of state-funded credit organizations, about 100,000 units of the dryer were distributed throughout the country. Additional units were also manufactured by the farmers themselves. After the completion of the project, dissemination of the dryer continued.

Keywords

Postharvest technologies, Korea, dissemination, low-temperature storage system

Introduction

Apart from the lack of mineral fertilizers, pesticides and high quality seeds, the low level of mechanization is one of the major constraints to increase food supply in tropical and subtropical countries. In these countries, only about 20 % of the arable lands is cultivated by small tractors, 50 % by animal traction and about

30% is tilled by hand tools (Gego 1984). In the past three decades, great attempts were made to introduce tractors and other agricultural machines into the developing countries. However, experiences obtained from numerous R&D projects indicated that it is hardly possible to transfer technologies originally developed in industrialized countries to developing countries either by foreign aid organizations or private companies using traditional dissemination strategies (Reisch 1991, Zaske 1985, Eichhorn 1991, Gifford 1991). The introduction of these technologies mostly failed because they did not consider the local socio-economic conditions, which were completely different from industrialized countries. The unavailability of spare parts, improper maintenance, and the lack of professional training of the users have led to the breakdown and shorter life span of the machines. As an alternative to industrially produced machines, low-cost technologies were developed, mainly by non-governmental organizations, which can be produced by the farmers themselves. Yet, the dissemination of these locally fabricated machines also failed due to the low acceptance by the farmers. Obviously, in order to ensure sufficient food for the steadily growing population in developing countries, it is very important to develop technologies which suit the needs of the farmers. Furthermore, new dissemination strategies of viable technologies, developed to increase food production and to reduce postharvest losses, are urgently required.

Within a bilateral Korean-German R&D project, an innovative approach to the development and dissemination of agricultural technology was conceived and implemented in 1979 (Kwon and Toma 1984). During this time, the industrial boom in Korea had started, but the level of agricultural mechanization was still comparatively low. In the same period, self-sufficiency in food supply became the highest priority of the Korean agricultural policy to cover the needs of the fast-growing population. To this effect, great efforts were made to increase production of the staple foods especially rice. However, there was only very minimal effort made in the field of postharvest technology. Therefore, the major objective of the bilateral project was to develop and disseminate an on-farm paddy dryer to enable the farmers to reduce the postharvest losses and improve the product quality.

Prior to the implementation of this bilateral project, the R&D projects implemented in developing countries within development aid programs were carried out by experts from industrialized countries. Experiences have shown that after the project completion the sustainability of the project activities in the host country did not materialize, simply because the local experts were not involved when the projects were implemented. For this reason, a new model of technology development and dissemination was conceived and implemented in this particular bilateral project.

The Korean-German R&D project was jointly financed by the Korean Science and Engineering Foundation KOSEF and the German Federal Ministry for Economic Cooperation BMZ. The German Agency for Technical Cooperation GTZ was responsible for the coordination and implementation of the new model of technical cooperation. KOSEF on the other hand designated the Korean Advanced Institute for Science and Technology KAIST, a technically capable institution, to implement the research activities. From the start of the project implementation, the Korean experts were involved in all decision makings and all working programs were developed jointly. Dissemination of the technology started during the early stage and small scale industries, which were potentially capable of fabricating the dryer, were included in the project. The aforementioned strategies have been considered as the most important factors responsible for the success of the project.

In contrast to the conventional development aid program, in which most of the project budget was provided by industrialized country, in this new approach the contribution of the Korean counterpart increased steadily. The budget provided by the German Ministry for Economic Cooperation was sufficient to shoulder the expenses for the purchase of instruments, equipment, short term experts, and project coordinator. The German contribution was merely intended to provide scientific and technical advisory services. To enhance a healthy exchange of expertise, study tours were organized for the Korean scientists, engineers, and technicians to visit German research institutions and private companies working on postharvest technologies.

Feasibility Study

At the beginning of the project, an appraisal study was conducted to evaluate and analyze the existing postharvest systems in Korea in terms of the performance of traditional postharvest facilities, energy requirement, labor demand, production cost, and postharvest losses at different stages of postharvest operation. Within this project phase, problem areas with high potential to improve the existing postharvest system were identified (Gocht, Diederich and Seifert 1982).

In the years before 1979, the Korean agricultural system was dominated by small-scale farmers owning a farm with a size of about one hectare. In contrast to the other rice-producing countries in the humid tropics, the Korean climate allowed only one harvest. To overcome the existing shortage of rice during this period, the Korean government forced the farmers to adopt the high-yielding cold-resistant rice varieties. Using these varieties, the yield increased from 2.7 t/ha in 1960 to 5 t/ha in 1980 (Ministry of Agriculture 1992, National Agricultural Cooperative Federation 1992).

The study showed that the introduction of the new varieties confronted the farmers with shattering losses of more than 5 % due to the non-uniform maturity of the grains. To minimize the harvesting and postharvest losses, the farmers were forced to harvest rice at a moisture content between 22 to 25 % and to thresh it using stationary threshers. Since there were only less than 1000 units of high-temperature dryers operating in Korea in 1978, the farmers were forced to sundry the paddy on straw mats or on paved grounds after threshing. Although sundrying is relatively cheap in terms of energy cost, it is still disadvantageous due to high labor requirement for spreading out the paddy in a thin layer, frequent mixing of grains, and collecting the grains in between drying during night time and on rainy days. Furthermore, additional losses are incurred during storage as a result of insufficient drying and non uniformity of the moisture content.

Based on the analysis of the survey data and personal interviews with the farmers, the high labor requirement for sundrying rice was found to be the most crucial problem and needed immediate solution. In contrast to the views of the scientist involved in the project, the reduction of postharvest losses and the improvement of product quality were, from the farmers' point of view, astonishingly of minor importance.

Using the results of the feasibility study as a basis, the different drying methods suitable for drying high moisture paddy were carefully analyzed and evaluated to suit the existing farming systems. The analysis indicated that the use of efficient high-temperature batch dryers or continuous-flow rice dryers could only be economical when used at commercial or cooperative level due to the high initial investment cost and the necessity of using fossil fuel for operating the dryer. In addition, due to the lack of sufficient transportation systems, the introduction of centralized drying plants had to be excluded.

The analysis of the long-term climatological data collected in the main rice producing areas in Korea indicated that low-temperature in-store drying was the most promising alternative available to solve the existing drying problems. Low-temperature in-store drying systems are typical on-farm dryers which are commonly used in industrialized countries for drying cereals with low moisture content (Mühlbauer 1982). Investigations have indicated that this drying method is very advantageous due to its low investment, minimum energy requirement, and low labor cost.

Research Phase

Since experience in drying paddy using the low-temperature in-store drying under the Korean weather conditions was not available, drying facilities were installed at the experimental site of KAIST which allowed intensive experiments to be conducted under controlled conditions. Numerous low-temperature in-storage drying tests were conducted to determine the influence of the initial moisture content of the paddy, bulk depth and airflow rate on drying time, energy consumption and uniformity of the dried kernels. Special efforts were made to investigate the influence of low-temperature drying on the quality of the dried paddy in terms of dehulling and milling rate, cracking ratio, germination rate and color of the milled rice. Since low-temperature drying requires several days to dry the crop to safe storage conditions which under unfavorable conditions could lead to mold growth in the upper layer of the bulk, tests were conducted to determine the number of invaded kernels and the total viable mold counts.

Under the Korean weather conditions, the test results indicated that paddy can be uniformly dried without using any supplemental heat for pre-heating the drying air. Utilizing the drying potential of the ambient air and operating the dryer at an extremely low airflow rate of 0.1 m/s, the energy cost for continuous operation of the fan during the drying period was only 0.9 to 2.1 US $ / t of dry paddy. Depending on the moisture content and bulk depth, the drying time ranged from 7 to 20 days. Even when drying extremely moist kernels of up to 25 % moisture in a 3.5 m thick paddy bulk effected no significant quality changes. Furthermore, no mold growth was detected, which justified the conclusion that aflatoxin was not developed during drying. Based on the Korean quality standards, ambient air-dried paddy can be classified as grade one. Compared to natural sundrying, drying losses were reduced from 4 - 5 % to almost zero. In addition, the tests showed that low-temperature drying is more hygienic compared to sundrying since the paddy does not come into contact with any foreign matter (Cheigh, Rhim and Kim 1982, Cheigh, Mühlbauer, Rhim and Shin 1985).

Development Phase

The investigations conducted by KAIST indicated that low-temperature in-storage drying was the most promising on-farm drying method under the Korean socio-economic conditions. However, corrugated round steel bins with perforated false floors, commonly used in industrialized countries for storage and low-temperature drying of cereals, were not suitable for use on Korean farms. The capacity of even the smallest units available on the market was far too big for drying 3 to 5 tons of paddy per season. In addition, the required conveyors for loading and unloading the crop were not available at this time on Korean farms. Therefore, a simple dryer for low-temperature in-storage drying of paddy which could be constructed by the farmers themselves, craftsmen, or small scale industries using locally available materials and components was developed within the R&D project.

The newly developed low-temperature dryer consisted of a rectangular container made of concrete or cement blocks, an air distribution system, and a small centrifugal fan (compare figure 1).

Figure 1: In-bin Drying System

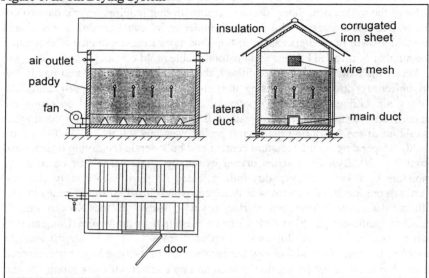

Source: Kim 1989.

The container can be used either for drying purposes or for storage of the dried paddy. The dryer with a capacity of 3 to 5 tons can be incorporated either into existing farm buildings or installed on the farm yard as a separate building covered with a tilted or flat roof. The air distribution system consists of a rectangular main duct and V-shaped lateral ducts. The ducts can be constructed either from wood or from galvanized steel sheet. After unloading the paddy from the container, the air distribution system can be easily removed. Afterwards, the container can be used for storage of other crops or for farm implements. The fan, equipped with a 0.5 kW motor, provides the required air flow of 0.1 m/s in the 1.2 to 2.0 m grain bulk (Kim 1989).

To prevent condensation, the roof is insulated with styrofoam. The walls and the floor of the structure are coated with water proof material which prevents the penetration of water and rewetting of the crop. Openings in the walls allows a natural ventilation when the fan is not in operation. All openings are covered with wire mesh, thus preventing the entry of insects, birds and rodents to the building. To ease loading and unloading of the paddy a double door is installed. The inner door consists of several boards which can be added or removed depending on the bulk depth. The outer door protects the crop from rain and theft.

The low-temperature in-storage drying system was installed at the experimental side of KAIST and was tested under field conditions. The results in the field experiments confirmed those obtained in the research phase and demonstrated the desired easy handling and low labor requirement of the system. During operation, the paddy, after threshing, was transported in bags from the field to the drying container. During loading, the inner door was closed by successively adding the side wall board by board until the grain surface reached the top of the last board installed. To obtain the desired uniform air distribution, the grain surface had to be levelled off before starting the fan. Only about 7.5 man-hours were needed to load the dryer with 3 tons paddy including levelling. In contrast, sundrying the same amount of paddy, which took about 5 to 10 days, required about 60 man-hours for spreading, mixing, guarding, collecting, and transporting the paddy back to the storage facilities. Unloading the paddy from the dryer required only about 8 man-hours, which can be done when labor is available in the farm.

After confirmation of the technical viability of the newly developed drying system, an economic analysis was made to ascertain the suitability of the new technology for individual farms (Altendeitering 1989). On the average, the amount needed for construction of new IBDS systems was 444,000 Won and 22,000 Won for remodelling existing structures. An additional income from using the IBDS system was generated from the reduction of losses caused by insects and rats, upgrading of paddy quality, and reduced wages for hired labor. Operating costs included electricity consumption for operating the fan and maintenance and repair costs estimated by comparison experiences with similar technology. For the construction and remodelling of the IBDS systems, loans were made available by the National Agricultural Cooperative Federation with an annual interest rate of 10 %, maturity of 5 years and a grace period of 2 years. Based on these data, the cost-benefit analysis gave an economically viable result for the remodelled IBDS systems with a net present value (NVP) of 548,000 Won, an annuity of 89,000 Won and an internal rate of return (IRR) of 66 %. Although the profit for newly built IBDS systems was slightly lower, the same viable results were obtained with NPV, annuity, and IRR values of 353,000 Won, 57,000 Won, and 58 %, respectively.

Dissemination Phase

Immediately after the testing of the newly developed low-temperature in-storage system was concluded, the dissemination campaign took off. At the outset, an orientation seminar was organized for the decision makers within the Ministry of Agriculture, Forestry and Fisheries, the representatives of the Office of Rural Development, and for the National Agricultural Cooperative Federation, to convince them of the benefits and the advantages of the new technology. These two organizations were responsible for the introduction and promotion of new technologies in Korean agriculture. Seminars and demonstrations were also organized for farmers, members of farmers associations and cooperatives, extension service workers, and potential manufacturers. Due to the very positive response of the public to the new technology, 120 demonstration units were installed in the rice producing provinces in Korea. Additional intensive campaigns were undertaken to introduce the new technology by utilizing radio broadcasts, TV commercials, weekly farmers journals, and cooperative news. For the craftsmen, small scale industries, and farmers who were willing to install the dryers by themselves, construction and operation manuals were printed and distributed. A brochure containing pictures of the dryer and its salient features was published and promoted. To coordinate all these activities, a committee was founded. The members who were representatives from KAIST, MAF, ORD, NACF, and KAFA, the Korean Advanced Farmers Association, met frequently to discuss the development of the activities being implemented. All these promotional activities were executed by scientists of KAIST with the support of the German project coordinator.

About three years after the start of the project implementation, the standard model of the so called IBDS (in-bin drying system) was completed by KAIST. The Korean government started immediately to disseminate the low-temperature in-storage drying system to the Korean farm households through the Office of Rural Development ORD and the National Agricultural Cooperative Federation NACF. In addition to the 120 demonstration units installed in 1982, 412 units were established in 1983. In 1984, the dissemination of the IBDS became a nation-wide program which resulted in a total of 8,683 units installed in the Korean farms. To reduce the construction cost of the IBDS model, KAIST provided guidelines to the farmers on how to integrate the dryer into their existing farm structures. The installation of the IBDS model reached its peak in 1985 with the annual installation of 13,842 units. At the completion of the project, about 52,000 units were installed and distributed in the different provinces of Korea (compare table 1).

Sustainability

Five years after the Korean-German project was concluded in 1988, BMZ assigned independent experts to analyze and evaluate the sustainability of the impact of the project and to assess to what extent the technologies developed by the project had been successfully disseminated. In this context, "sustainability" does not simply mean the "survival of the project," i.e. mainly the continued existence of institutional structures, or the continued utilization of equipment supplied, or the continued application of technologies disseminated. A wider definition of sustainability was applied which took into account the impact of the project on the institutions and target groups involved, the initiatives generated, and the identifiable developments (Gocht and Mühlbauer 1994).

Table 1: Dissemination of IBDS Systems in Korea

Year	NACF		ORD	Total
	New Installation	Remodelled	New Installation	
1982	120	-		120
1983	412	-		412
1984	6,181	2,306	196	8,683
1985	10,207	3,445	190	13,842
1986	8,776	3,327	234	12,337
1987	7,900	3,008	400	11,308
1988	6,999	1,502	400	8,901
1989	6,590	1,703	300	8,593
1990	6,595	2,362	500	9,457
1991	3,845	1,329	500	5,674
1992	2,604	2,017	500	5,121
1993	1,850	446	500	2,816
1994	1,300	400	500	2,200
Total	63,379	21,865	4,220	89,464

Source: Kim 1993.

Compared to the situation when the project was started in 1979, a tremendous change of the Korean agriculture had taken place. The fast industrialization effected a big impact on the agricultural system. The contribution of agriculture to the GNP was lowered from about 20 % in 1979 to 7.6 % in 1992. To improve the living and working standards in the rural areas and to discourage migration from the rural to the urban areas, the Korean government made enormous efforts to improve the rural infrastructures and provided government subsidies to agricultural products. In spite of these efforts, the rural population decreased from 11.5 million to 6.0 million contributing to the scarcity of labor force in the rural areas. The lack of farm labor and the steady increase of labor cost for farm workers accelerated mechanization. The mechanization was further increased due to the high subsidies provided by government agencies for agricultural machinery and the redistribution of plots of land. For example, the number of power tillers and combine harvesters increased from about 200,000 to almost 800,000 and from 100 to 54,000, respectively. In contrast, there is still a shortage of paddy dryers in the Korean farms. Only 15 % of the harvested crops can be dried either by high-temperature recirculating type dryers or by the IBDS system. More than 3.0 million tons still have to be sundried or dried in the fields.

The complete replacement of the traditional varieties by high-yielding local varieties, the high fertilizer and pesticides input, the improvement of the irrigation systems, the high level of mechanization and a decrease of per-capita consumption resulted in Korea's self-sufficiency in rice. Due to the increase in the people's income, the consumer habits also drastically changed. In 1979 when the project began, the consumers accepted a mix of polished barley with rice to compensate for the lack of rice. In recent times however, only high quality rice can be sold in the Korean market. This also has greatly influenced the viability of the IBDS system.

The high level of mechanization has some disadvantage because it has caused a remarkable increase in the production cost. Due to the extremely high production cost, Korean rice is currently not competitive in the world market. Recently, there has been a big pressure on the Korean government to open the market for rice according to the GATT negotiations. When implemented, it can be expected to have a tremendous impact on the Korean agricultural system. To secure the income of the farmers, improvement of the competitiveness of the Korean agriculture has therefore currently become the highest priority in the Korean agricultural policy.

After the completion of the project in 1988, NACF and ORD stopped providing credits for IBDS systems. The scientists who developed the IBDS were transferred from KAIST to the newly established Korean Food Research Institute. Beginning in 1988, only private industries were involved in the dissemination activities. Despite the completely different situation in Korean agriculture compared to the time when the project started its activities, about 10,000 units per year were still distributed, mainly by four private companies around Korea. Until 1994, more than 100,000 units were established using credits from ORD and NACF. In addition a great number of units were installed through the initiative of the farmers themselves. Since the installation of these units were not supported by the government, they were not included in the statistics. As a result of the big change in Korea's agriculture, NACF is nowadays promoting centralized rice processing complexes as an alternative to on-farm drying systems (Kwon 1976).

In the first phase of the dissemination activities, the major emphasis of the scientists involved in the project and the governmental officials was the reduction of postharvest losses in order to reach the desired self-sufficiency in rice. Based on the farmers' point of view, there was very low incentive to improve the quality of rice because there was almost no price difference given between good and low quality paddy.

To evaluate the farmers' views on the impact of using the IBDS system, about 200 IBDS users from different regions were interviewed in 1986 about the benefits of the IBDS (Altendeitering 1989). The same survey was made in 1994 (Gocht and Mühlbauer 1994). More than 70 % of the respondents regarded the IBDS dryer as very good. None of the farmers gave a negative judgment. The farmers mentioned the following major effects of the IBDS system (listed in order of priority):

- Time-saving of the drying process
- Reduction of losses caused by insects and rats
- Reduction of hired labor cost
- Improvement of rice quality
- Higher selling price

From the farmers' point of view, the considerable reduction of the labor requirement justified the investment in the IBDS. The wide spectrum of positive effects also includes the reduction of workload for the Korean farm women. With the change of the Korean agricultural system, the motivation of the farmers to invest in the IBDS changed. Compared to sundrying, low-temperature in-storage drying results in high quality rice. With the expected opening of the rice market in the near future the paddy quality will gain even more importance. The Korean consumers are used to the special flavor of the local varieties. This is one of the reasons why the introduction of imported high-yielding varieties in the period between 1975 and 1990 failed. It can be expected that the consumers from the higher income class are willing to pay a higher price for local varieties, giving a certain protection to the Korean rice farming society.

The history of the IBDS system showed that due to its flexibility the system could be easily adapted to the changing conditions of the Korean agriculture. At the beginning of the project, the government purchase price was kept almost stable throughout the year, giving no incentive to the farmers for long-term storage of the paddy after drying. The IBDS system allowed the farmers to dry first the early maturing high yielding varieties which were sold immediately after drying to the government. Afterwards the IBDS was used for drying the late maturing local varieties which were subsequently stored until summer, enabling the farmer to store his own need or to sell rice above the established price. By this operation and marketing strategy the farmer can get the optimum benefit of the new technology. With increasing farm sizes the IBDS were upscaled to 10 to 20 tons. Furthermore, several farmers replaced the air duct system by perforated false floors giving a more uniform air distribution in the upscaled units.

With the development and dissemination of the IBDS systems, a sustainable technology was introduced on Korean farms. After the R&D project was finished and the cut of credits by NACF and ORD, the production and distribution of the IBDS was taken over by private enterprises. Due to the lack of research funds, the Korea Food Research Institute stopped participating in the further development and dissemination of the IBDS system when the project was concluded in 1988. However, the knowledge gained during the project phases was taken over by private industries, agricultural extension services, and by the cooperatives involved in the dissemination activities, thus, guaranteeing its long-term sustainability.

Lessons Learned

The positive experiences gained during the several phases of the joint Korean-German R&D project indicated that this new model of technology transfer could serve as an example for future projects. The fast technology transfer to a very conservative agricultural society showed that the technology matches the real demand of the potential user group. In addition the low-temperature in-storage drying system demonstrated certain advantages over traditional sun-drying and the centralized use of sophisticated high-temperature drying systems, which include low investment, minimum operation cost, easy handling, low labor requirement, extremely low losses, and providing a high quality product. The IBDS system could easily be produced by small scale industry, local craftsmen or even by the farmers themselves, using locally available materials, simple tools, and other prerequisites for economical use. Incorporating the dryer into existing farm structures and the possibility to use the drying compartment for storage of other crops and machinery is an additional asset of this technology. Another important aspect which greatly influenced the success of the project was the participative project approach and equal sharing of tasks and fundings between both partners. Instead of transferring a technology originally developed for use in an industrialized country to a semi-developed country, the new technology was developed by Korean scientists and technicians with the support of German experts. Dissemination of a Korean-made technology by Korean manufacturers eased the acceptance by the farmers and was one of the major reasons why it was possible to disseminate over 100,000 units within a very short period. Another very important factor that contributed to the fast dissemination of the IBDS system was the grant of convenient credits by government organizations and the public relation activities including the installation of demonstration units in the Korean rice producing provinces. The desired sustainability of the project was mainly achieved by the involvement of private industries in the very early stage of the dissemination phase. After the project was completed in 1988, dissemination, improvements, and adaptation of the IBDS to the fast changing Korean agricultural systems were taken over by private enterprises.

Acknowledgments

The authors acknowledge their indebtedness to the Korean Science and Engineering Foundation KOSEF and the German Federal Ministry for Economic Cooperation BMZ for funding these investigations and to the German Agency for Technical Cooperation GTZ and the Korean Advanced Institute for Science and Technology KAIST for cooperative support.

References

Altendeitering, S. 1989. The socio-economic impacts of the dissemination of new rural development technologies in Korea. Nomos Verlagsgesellschaft, Baden-Baden, Germany.

Cheigh, H. S., J. W. Rhim and S. K. Kim 1982. In-bin drying of high moisture paddy with continuous blowing of ambient air. Korean Journal of Food Science and Technology, Vol. 14 No. 3, pp. 271 - 275.

Cheigh, H.S., W. Mühlbauer, J. W. Rhim and M. G. Shin 1985. In-bin drying of paddy with ambient air: Influence of drying parameters on drying time, energy consumption and quality. Korean Journal of Food Science and Technology, Vol. 17 (1985) No. 1 pp. 25 - 32.

Eichhorn, H. and H. Gaese 1991. Agrartechnik und Beschäftigungsentwicklung in der Landwirtschaft. entwicklung + ländlicher raum 6 (1991), pp. 19 - 24.

Gego, A. 1984. Probleme der Agrarmechanisierung in Entwicklungsländern. Landtechnik 39 (1984) Nr. 1, pp. 23 - 29.

Gifford, R. C. 1991. Engineering technology in third world agriculture. entwicklung + ländlicher raum 6 (1991), pp. 3 - 5.

Gocht, W. and W. Mühlbauer 1994. Technologies for rural development in Korea - Integrated Research Programme. Evaluation Report of the TC Project, Federal Ministry for Economic Cooperation and Development, Bonn.

Gocht, W., F. Diederich and H. Seifert 1982. Evaluierungsbericht zum Forschungsprogramm für Technologie für ländliche Entwicklung in der Republik Korea.

Kim, K. S. et al. 1989. An ambient-air in-storage paddy drying system for Korean farms. Agricultural mechanization in Asia, Africa and Latin America. Vol. 20 (1989) No. 2, pp. 23 - 29.

Kwon, T. W. and Y. S. Toma 1984. Integrated research programme on technologies for rural development - A German - Korean cooperation project. Published by: German Agency for Technical Cooperation, Eschborn.

Kwon, T. W. 1976. Need for establishment of a pilot rice post-production center. unpublished report, Korea Institute of Science and Technology, Seoul, Korea, 1976.

Ministry of Agriculture, Forestry and Fisheries 1992. Statistical Yearbook of Agriculture, Forestry and Fisheries. Republic of Korea.

Mühlbauer, W. et al. 1982. Comparison of low-temperature wheat drying management procedures. American Society of Agricultural Engineers, St. Joseph MI (USA), Paper No. 83-3006.

National Agricultural Cooperative Federation 1992. Agricultural Co-Op Yearbook

Reisch, E. 1981. Mechanisierung der Landwirtschaft in Entwicklungsländern - Komponenten, Strategien und Auswirkungen. VDI-Bericht Nr. 407.

Zaske, J. 1985. Technische und organistorische Rahmenbedingungen für eine nachhaltige Mechanisierung. entwicklung + ländlicher raum 5, pp. 15 - 19.

Introduction of Solar Fruit Dryers in Thailand

A New Approach for Technology Transfer

R. Smitabhindu[1], S. Janjai[2],
A. Esper[3] and W. Mühlbauer[3]
[1]Royal Chitralada Projects, Bangkok, Thailand
[2]Department of Physics, Silpakorn University,
Nakhon Pathom, Thailand
[3]Institute for Agricultural Engineering in the Tropics and
Subtropics, University of Hohenheim, Stuttgart, Germany

Abstract

The transfer of agricultural technologies from industrialized to developing countries has failed mainly because of the differences in socio-economic conditions. Therefore a new approach for introducing technologies was tried out in a participatory approach in promoting the solar tunnel dryer in Thailand. This is a necessary step since the conventional approach of technology transfer was not successful for introducing the solar tunnel dryer in several other countries.

Within a joint cooperation between the Royal Chitralada Projects and Silpakorn University in Thailand, and the University of Hohenheim in Germany, financed jointly by the Vater und Sohn Eiselen-Stiftung and the Gewürzmüller company, a solar tunnel dryer was installed at the Royal Chitralada Projects in Bangkok. The results of the research and development phase showed that a year-round production of high quality dried bananas is possible under the local prevailing conditions. Consumer tests made by visitors of the Royal Chitralada Projects indicated that the dried banana was well accepted and could be sold in the local market with a 30-50 % higher price than the traditionally sun-dried bananas. This difference in price is an important prerequisite for a successful introduction of the solar tunnel dryer in actual practice. The dissemination and marketing phase of the project will initiate the local production of the solar tunnel dryers to ensure its wide dissemination in Thailand.

Keywords

Thailand, solar fruit dryers, dissemination, marketing

Introduction

The insufficient supply of the basic foodstuff in many tropical and subtropical countries is still an unsolved problem. Food production can no longer sustain the needs of the fast-growing population. The situation is aggravated by the fact that under the local prevailing climatic conditions, a considerable amount of the foodstuff is spoiled during storage due to improper preservation methods. Moreover, the tremendous reduction of prices for tropical products has worsened the economic situation of the rural population (Esper and Mühlbauer 1993).

In tropical regions, fruits are normally produced by small farmers either for home consumption or for sale in the local market which contribute to some extent to the considerable food supply for the rural population. However in case of overproduction, tremendous losses occur because farmers have neither access to the markets in big cities nor to the international market due to poor product quality and the absence of good marketing and distribution systems.

As an alternative to the marketing of fresh fruits or vegetables, small farmers can produce dried products. In spite of the abundance of fresh fruits throughout the year, dried tropical fruits are still popular as snack items both for rural and urban population. In industrialized countries, the demand for dried tropical fruits has increased due to their uses as basic ingredients in the production of breakfast food products. The same trend is observed in developing countries for nutritional reasons. For example, in Thailand, since bananas have a high potassium content and the carbohydrates are easy to digest, they are used as the main ingredient for food for children and sick people.

Bananas (Musa x paradisiana L.) are one of the major tropical fruits in Thailand. The main varieties are generally divided into three, namely: Kai (AA group), Hom (AAA group) and Namwa (ABB group). The Namwa variety is grown mainly in Thailand and is generally consumed either fresh or dried. Drying bananas serves not only for preservation purposes but also for improvement and modification of taste, flavor and texture, to meet the requirements of consumers, and consequently increase the marketing values of these products. Based on the consumer requirement in Thailand, the ripe banana has to be peeled and dried as a whole fruit (Schirmer et al. 1996).

As a part of the improvement of the food supply of the poor population in Thailand, Her Royal Highness Princess Maha Chakri Sirindhorn initiated programs to increase banana production. Through the use of new production technologies, tissue culture and mechanization, the production in the country has increased tremendously in the last five years.

Drying of bananas has effectively converted the surplus in banana production in Thailand. Traditionally, dried banana in Thailand was developed to serve the need of Thai families and the local consumers. To this effect, there was no serious considerations given to improve the product quality and to expand its markets outside this domestic and conservative consumer circle (Wattanapong 1995). The traditionally dried banana has been, until now, widely accepted throughout domestic markets in Thailand and still is considered as being a tasty appetizer. Consumer demand of this dried product is considerably high during the off-season of other tropical products. In terms of the international market however, the product quality does not meet, in most cases, the requirements of the foreign consumers in terms of color, texture and taste. This aspect needs special concern to boost the dried banana industry.

It is common knowledge within the industry that the traditional drying technologies are the biggest constraint to expanding its markets. Especially that consumers are becoming more sophisticated, the demand for improved technologies should lead to the production of a high-quality product (Wattanapong 1995). Improvement of the product quality, reduction of losses and decrease of labor requirement can only be achieved by the introduction of suitable drying technologies. However, the increase of the purchasing power of the rural population is an important prerequisite for the willingness of the farmers to invest money in drying equipment (Mühlbauer, Esper and Müller 1993). New techniques should therefore give the farmer the possibility to gain money within a short period. It must be noted that products processed for home consumption or for the local market would not create a demand for improved processing methods. As long as there is only a slight difference in price between the high- and low- quality products, the additional expenses for new preservation techniques would never be paid back. This scenario can only be changed if proper measures to increase the standard of living of the rural population are carried out, which normally creates a demand for high-quality products. At present, small farmers can only gain profit from marketing high-quality products if they can be sold in urban areas and in international markets which offer high prices for better quality products. Moreover, the existing marketing structures should be changed in such a way that a bigger share of the profits gained from selling a certain product goes to the producer and not to the middlemen or to dealers.

Spreading the crop in thin layers on mats, trays or paved grounds and exposing the product to sun and wind is still the most common drying method used in Thailand. Turning the crop in regular short intervals promotes uniform drying. Collecting the crop during the night and on rainy days and storing it under shelter prevents remoistening. However, since the drying process is relatively slow, considerable losses normally occur. In addition, significant reduction in the product quality takes place due to insect infestation, enzymatic reactions, microorganism growth, and mycotoxin development. Non uniform and insufficient drying, which happens normally when the crops are dried during rainy season, also lead to deterioration of the crop during storage. (Mühlbauer, Esper and Müller 1993).

In order to ensure continuous sufficient food supply to the growing population and to enable the farmers to produce high-quality marketable products, the development of efficient drying methods is of urgent necessity. Studies have shown that even small and most simple oil-fired batch dryers are not applicable due to the lack of capital and insufficient supply of energy for operating the dryers. The high-temperature dryers used in industrialized countries are found to be economically viable in developing countries only if they are used in large plantations and big commercial establishments. To overcome the existing preservation problems, the introduction of solar dryers seems to be a promising alternative.

Natural Convection Dryers

Various types of small-scale solar dryers were developed and evaluated for application in tropical and subtropical regions (see figure 1). Considering that a high percentage of farms in these regions are not connected to the electricity grid, the dryers are designed to utilize only the wind and sun as energy sources.

Figure 1: Simple Natural Convection-Type Dryers

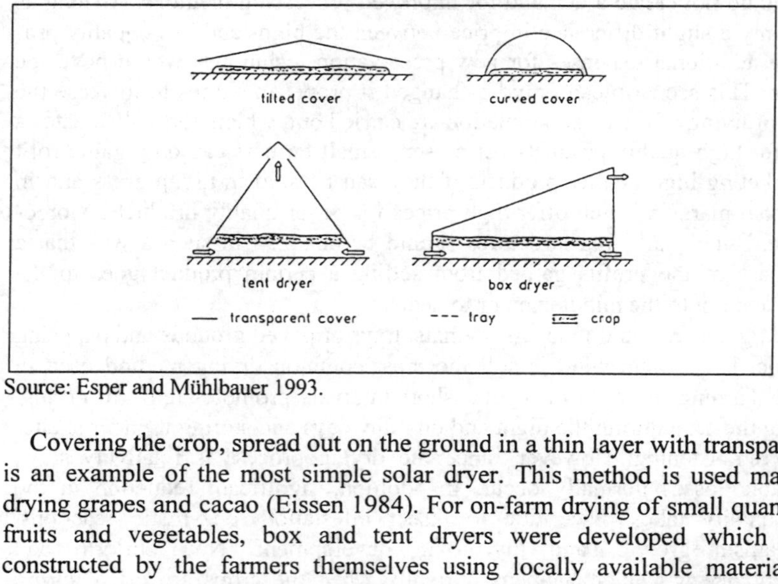

Source: Esper and Mühlbauer 1993.

Covering the crop, spread out on the ground in a thin layer with transparent foil is an example of the most simple solar dryer. This method is used mainly for drying grapes and cacao (Eissen 1984). For on-farm drying of small quantities of fruits and vegetables, box and tent dryers were developed which can be constructed by the farmers themselves using locally available materials. The transparent cover reduces heat losses and at the same time protects the product from dust and rain. Ventilation required for removing the evaporated water is provided by ascending air forces due to natural convection.

Investigations have shown that insect infestations cannot be totally avoided. The crop deteriorates during extended periods of adverse weather conditions. Due to the low capacity of box and tent dryers, their use is limited to subsistence farmers. Since application of such dryers has no considerable contribution to the income of the farm households, small-farm holders are hesitant to invest in them.

The drying capacity of natural convection dryers can be increased by connecting a solar air heater to the drying chamber. Instead of using only the crop as absorber, solar radiation is further converted into thermal energy in the solar heater. In this dryer, the inclined collector has to be mounted facing south and is tilted at an optimum angle depending on the region and the particular season. The drying air is heated up in the solar air heater and enters at the base of the drying chamber. It then moves upward and passes across the crop which is spread in thin layers on vertically stacked trays. Air circulation is effected by the ascending air forces due to natural convection. The air flow rate can be increased either by wind coming from the south or by a chimney (Mühlbauer, Esper and Müller 1993).

Due to the high air resistance encountered when forcing the air through the crop, only a few trays can be stacked without significantly affecting the air movement. Furthermore, investigations have shown that during night and cloudy weather, the air circulation breaks down completely. This causes spoilage of the crop due to enzymatic reactions and the growth of microorganisms. The comparatively high investment, limited capacity, and the risk of crop spoilage during adverse weather conditions have, up to now, prevented the wide acceptance of these dryers.

Forced Convection Dryers

The high weather-dependent risk of using natural convection solar dryers stimulated the development of a solar tunnel dryer with built-in fan that provides sufficient air flow required to remove the evaporated moisture (see figure 2).

The solar tunnel dryer, developed at the Institute for Agricultural Engineering in the Tropics and Subtropics, University of Hohenheim, consists basically of a plastic foil-covered flat plate solar collector, a drying tunnel and three small axial flow fans (Schirmer et al. 1996). To simplify the construction and reduce the costs, the solar air heater is connected directly to the drying tunnel without any additional air ducts. Plastic foam, sandwiched between two parallel metal sheets, is used as back insulator for both the solar air heater and drying tunnel. This insulator functions also as a structure of the dryer. The top surface of the insulator in the solar air heater is painted black to absorb solar radiation. The solar air heater is covered with transparent UV-stabilized PE plastic foil fixed to the collector frame, using reinforced plastic clamps. For the drying tunnel, wire mesh is placed on top of the insulator. A sheet of plastic net, on which bananas are spread to be dried, is placed on top of the wire mesh. This arrangement allows the drying air to flow through the whole layer of banana fruit being dried. The drying tunnel is covered with UV-stabilized PE plastic foil. One side of this foil is fixed to the tunnel frame and the other side to the metal tube which facilitates rolling the foil up and down for loading and unloading the dryer. Plastic fastening profiles as shown in figure 3 are used to fix the foil both to the tube and the drying tunnel frame. This fixing method was designed to allow easy replacement of the foils. In general, the transparent foil and the PE foil can be used for 1-2 and 3-5 years, respectively. Three small fans powered by a 53 Watt solar cell module are installed at the back side of the solar air heater to suck ambient air into the solar air heater as shown in figure 4. The fans are intentionally installed below the solar module to constantly reduce its temperature, thus maintaining its efficiency. Both the solar air heater and the drying tunnel are installed on concrete block substructures. The solar energy absorption area of the solar air heater is 1.8 x 10 m². The drying area of the drying tunnel has approximately the same dimension. All parts of the dryer, including back insulators and metal frames, are designed using modular concepts which facilitate transport and installation. The solar tunnel dryer uses solar energy both in the thermal form for drying processes and electrical form for driving the fans through the solar air heater and solar module, respectively (Esper 1995).

Figure 2: Solar Tunnel Dryer

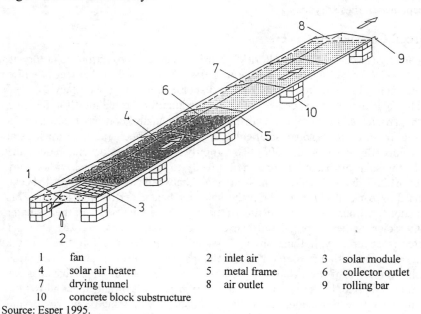

1	fan	2	inlet air	3	solar module
4	solar air heater	5	metal frame	6	collector outlet
7	drying tunnel	8	air outlet	9	rolling bar
10	concrete block substructure				

Source: Esper 1995.

Figure 3: Drying Tunnel

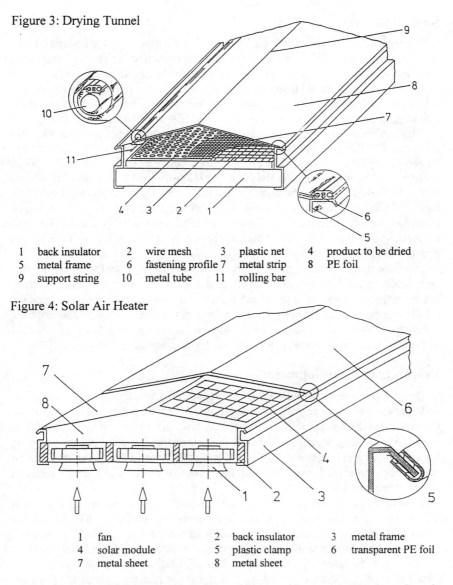

1	back insulator	2	wire mesh	3	plastic net	4	product to be dried
5	metal frame	6	fastening profile	7	metal strip	8	PE foil
9	support string	10	metal tube	11	rolling bar		

Figure 4: Solar Air Heater

1	fan	2	back insulator	3	metal frame
4	solar module	5	plastic clamp	6	transparent PE foil
7	metal sheet	8	metal sheet		

With these special features, the dryer could be used in rural areas where there is no supply of electricity. In places where electricity from the grid is available, AC fans can be used for the ventilation of the dryer.

State of the Art

The solar tunnel dryer satisfies all technical and economic requirement including the cost-benefit ratio, which is the most important criterion for investment decision of a small farmer in tropical and subtropical countries. The solar tunnel dryer developed at the University of Hohenheim has a payback period of 1-5 years, depending on product, location and rate of utilization, which is the most important prerequisite for a wide dissemination (Esper and Mühlbauer 1993).

Prior activities have already been undertaken in this direction. Around 100 dryers in 25 different tropical and subtropical countries are now in operation. Prototypes could be produced locally at a price between 1,000 and 1,500 US$ in Turkey and Morocco including the PV-drive (Häuser, El Bouamri and Mühlbauer 1993). In Turkey mass production of the solar tunnel dryer has already been initiated. Although the solar tunnel dryer is appropriate for proper and safe drying of agricultural products that are cultivated in tropical and subtropical countries such as fruits, vegetables, medicinal plants, coffee or cacao; other than in Turkey, this new technology was not at all recognized.

The solar tunnel dryer is another clear example that the transfer of technology, specifically in the agricultural sector, from industrialized to developing countries, has failed in most cases due to the different socio-economic conditions. Since the classical approach of technology transfer was not successful for introducing the solar tunnel dryer in several other countries, a new approach of introducing technologies using the participatory approach was adapted in this project.

Research and Development

Through a postdoctoral fellowship, a Thai scientist was able to gain theoretical and practical experiences with the solar tunnel dryer technology developed at the University of Hohenheim. He felt strongly that the dryer would be useful in solving the existing drying problems of farmers producing dried bananas. During his stay in Germany, a concept of introducing the solar tunnel dryer in Thailand was jointly developed and potential investors for financing a small research project were identified.

To investigate its applicability for drying bananas, a solar tunnel dryer was constructed and tested at Silpakorn University in Thailand. Results of the preliminary experiments indicated that the solar tunnel dryer could be effectively used to dry bananas under the prevailing climatic conditions in Thailand.

These results have stimulated the plan of finding a suitable location for installation of one demonstration unit of the dryer and the search for potential investors. Based on preset criteria, the Royal Chitralada Projects in Bangkok were found to be the best location for installing one solar tunnel dryer. The search for potential investors was found to be more difficult than expected. Many showed great interest and confirmed that the solar tunnel dryer is a good technology. However, nobody was interested in financing a research project on drying bananas in Thailand.

Due to the delay in finding financial support for the research project, a private investor, who was very interested in using the solar tunnel dryer in Thailand for drying spices, requested a Thai company to produce one unit of the dryer using locally available materials. Although the company was able to produce the insulator sheets, which is the most expensive part of the dryer, this endeavor failed for two reasons: first, the locally produced solar tunnel dryer was too expensive because the cost was similar to that of a German version and second, the dryer did not work properly. The main reason for the failure of the unit was that the Thai company did not strictly follow the plans and advises in constructing the dryer. Instead, they constructed it according to personal interpretation.

With the implementation of the research project funded by the Vater und Sohn Eiselen Foundation and the Gewürzmüller Company, a solar tunnel dryer was installed at the Royal Chitralada Projects in Bangkok, strictly following the original design and with due consideration to the local conditions. The installation of the solar tunnel dryer and the conduct of the drying experiments were done in close collaboration between the German and Thai counterparts. This procedure was advantageous because the Thai experts became familiar with the characteristics of the solar tunnel dryer on the one hand and on the other hand the German experts were able to acquire the knowledge on drying technology of bananas available in Thailand. Since there was no available information on drying bananas using the solar tunnel dryer, a methodology was developed that combined both fermentation and drying process to achieve the desired quality in terms of the color, texture and taste as required by the Thai consumer.

The drying experiments were conducted both during the dry and the rainy seasons. Depending on weather conditions, the drying time needed to reach the desired moisture with full loading of the dryer, varied between 3-5 days. The sun-dried control samples needed 5-7 days to reach the desired moisture content. The reduction of the drying time of banana using the solar tunnel dryer was due to the fact that bananas in the dryer received energy both from the solar air heater and incident solar radiation, while the control samples received only incident radiation and lost significantly energy to the environment. It was found that the quality of the dried bananas was dependent not only on the drying conditions but also on the ripeness of bananas. Fully ripe bananas produced a final product with tough texture and poor flavor while over- ripe ones, recognizable by the dark color of their peels, produced dried products that were sticky and with dark color. The fully ripe dried bananas had a honey-brown color and soft texture and are classified as high-quality products in the markets of Thailand. Since determination of the proper ripeness of bananas is done by experience and therefore differs from person to person, it is very important to establish a standard method for this procedure. It was also observed that the drying conditions of the first day of drying affected significantly the quality of bananas being dried. When the moisture content of the products was not sufficiently removed, due to adverse weather conditions, some bananas were spoiled because of mould growth. To obtain the desired quality of the dried product, the first day of drying should only be done during sunny days (Schirmer et al. 1996). A weak point analysis showed that some parts of the dryer have to be modified suit to the specific conditions prevailing in Thailand to be able to obtain the original performance of the dryer. To enable the use of the solar tunnel dryer during the rainy season, a supplementary heater should be integrated to ensure continuous year-round production.

Marketing and Dissemination

After the successful research and development stage of the project, the Royal Chitralada Projects started the production of dried bananas. A cheap, hygienic and attractive packaging was then developed. Consumer tests made by visitors of the Royal Chitralada Projects indicated that the dried product was well accepted and could be sold on local market with 30-50% higher price than the traditionally sundried bananas. This difference in price is an important prerequisite for a successful dissemination of the dryer in actual practice. The selling price for a locally produced dryer is estimated to be 3,600 US $. Assuming that the dryer is used to dry bananas the whole year round with an average drying time of five days at an average production of 100 kg per drying batch, a total 7,200 kg high-quality dried bananas could be produced. The increase in revenue that results from the use of the dryer is estimated to be 1,300 US $, given a payback period of approximately 3 years.

In April of 1996, the development of a local version of the solar tunnel dryer was palnned in close collaboration with a Thai company and the German Agency for Technical Cooperation which will take into account the 9-month experience of the Royal Chitralada Projects in producing dried bananas. The main bottleneck up to now in the production of the dryer is the high price of the insulator sheets. In this respect, a survey of the most suitable insulator materials is currently being undertaken. In this phase of the project, it is expected that valuable experience will be obtained on durability of the materials under the local weather conditions that would guarantee a quality of the product. To introduce the solar tunnel dryer in the main banana-producing areas in Thailand, a close collaboration with the Thai Ministry of Industry, the German Agency for Technical Cooperation (GTZ), and the Solar Energy Research and Training Center (SERT) of Naresuan

University will be established. These organizations have several years of experience in drying bananas and are very familiar with the market situation and the needs of the farmers. Demonstration units which will serve as an exhibit of the technology, will be installed on selected sites to raise the interest of small farmers and to provide them with the opportunity to gain the information about this existing technology. Information campaigns using modern communication and extension techniques will be initiated both to raise the demand as well as to encourage small industry to start a local production. The initiation of a local production and the local marketing done by a Thai company will ensure the farmers' acceptance and guarantee its sustainability. At the start of the dissemination stage, performance and quality and technical performance of the locally produced dryer will be thoroughly examined to prevent failure during dissemination. To further ensure the success of the dissemination process, the involvement of the government will be sought to provide credits at low interest rates, support training of the farmers to ensure proper installation and use of the equipment and the implementation of quality standards for dried products.

Lessons Learned

The introduction of a new technology, even if they are proven to be technically viable and economically feasible in several other countries, is both time and labor intensive. The suitability of the technology is one prerequisite but not a guarantee for success. The project in Thailand showed that a participative approach of planning and implementing a project between the German and the local counterpart is a viable approach of disseminating a technology developed in an industrialized country and introduced into a developing country.

Another component is the integration of organizations working in the same or a related field to overcome existing contradictions and encourage wholesome collaboration.

Private initiatives should be supported, as long as the outcome can be controlled and will be not contradictory to the project's objectives. It should however be guaranteed that the quality of a local product is at least comparable to the original version.

Suitable location has to be identified for demonstration purposes. The selection of the Royal Chitralada Projects, which receive 20,000 visitors per year, as the pilot area has been very instrumental in the success of the research and development phase of the project.

A successful introduction of the new technology can not be done by research institutions alone. A cooperation between the private industry and governmental organizations responsible for technology transfer should be established. The responsibilities of research institutions should be focused more on applied research under laboratory and field conditions and on providing all information necessary for an efficient process, while the private industry must be included for initiation of a local production and to utilize the knowledge of manufacturing to reduce production cost.

The local production and the local marketing activities to be done by a Thai company is expected to ensure the farmers' acceptance and guarantee its sustainability. In the beginning of the dissemination process performance and quality of the locally produced dryer must be first examined to avoid failure during the dissemination stage. Although the research and development phase of the project has been successful, a lot of work still has to be done to ensure the desired wide dissemination of the solar tunnel dryer in Thailand.

Acknowledgment

The authors acknowledge their indebtedness to the Vater und Sohn Eiselen-Stiftung and Gewürzmüller Company for funding these investigations and to the Thai Ministry of Industry, the German Agency for Technical Cooperation (GTZ) and the Solar Energy Research and Training Center (SERT) of Naresuan University for future cooperation and cooperative support.

References

Eissen, W. 1984. Trocknung von Trauben mit Solarenergie. Forschungsbericht Agrartechnik des Arbeitskreises Forschung und Lehre der Max-Eyth-Gesellschaft (MEG), Frankfurt, No 85.

Esper, A. 1995. Solarer Tunneltrockner mit photovoltaischem Antriebssystem. Forschungsbericht Agrartechnik des Arbeitskreises Forschung und Lehre der Max-Eyth-Gesellschaft (MEG), Frankfurt, No 264.

Esper, A. and W. Mühlbauer 1993. Development and dissemination of solar tunnel dryers. Proceedings of the workshop on "Solar Drying", ISES Solar World Congress, Budapest (Hungary).

Häuser, M., M. El Bouamri and W. Mühlbauer 1993. Le Sechage Solaire des Apricots. L'Arboriculture Fruitiere, October 1993, No 465, p. 33-40.

Mühlbauer, W. 1986. Present status of solar crop drying. Energy in agriculture, Vol. 5, pp. 121-137.

Mühlbauer, W., A. Esper and J. Müller 1993. Solar energy in agriculture. Proceedings of ISES Solar World Congress, Vol. 8, Biomass, Agriculture, Wind, Budapest (Hungary), pp. 13-27.

Schirmer, P, S. Janjai, A. Esper, R. Smitabhindu and W. Mühlbauer 1996. Experimental investigation of the performance of the solar tunnel dryer for drying bananas. Renewable Energy, Renewable Energy, Vol. 7, No. 2.

Wattanapong, R. 1995. Banana drying industry. Amphoe Bangkrathum, Phitsanulok

Institutionalizing Participatory Extension: Experiences from Zimbabwe

J. Hagmann[1], E. Chuma[2] and K. Murwira[3]

[1]Consultant, Talstrasse 129,D-79194 Gundelfingen, Germany
[2]Institute of Environmental Studies, University of Zimbabwe, POB MB 167, Harare, Zimbabwe
[3]Intermediate Technology Development Group, POB 1744, Harare, Zimbabwe

Abstract

The paper describes the rationale for a change from conventional extension towards participatory innovation development and extension. The 'Conservation Tillage Project' and the 'Food Security Project' developed such an approach and have embarked on institutionalization of this approach into the agricultural extension service in Masvingo Province in Zimbabwe. Dialogue with farmers, farmer experimentation and the strengthening of self-organizational capacities of rural communities are the major elements to improve development and spreading of innovations, thus the efficiency of extension.

The new approach requires appropriate methods and tools as well as a role change of agricultural extension workers from teacher to facilitator. Elements of "Training for Transformation" and Participatory Rural Appraisal (PRA) were tested and developed and were found to be effective tools. The strategy to institutionalize participatory extension is based on joining efforts and networking with other organizations, a campaign to familiarize institutional staff, and on a training and follow-up program for staff in the framework of organizational development.

The experiences show that the attitudinal change required to implement participatory approaches is highly dependent on personalities. To have an impact on the change of attitudes a continuous medium-term training process with a close follow-up is required. The paper concludes that institutionalization of participatory approaches into hierarchically structured organizations is a highly complex intervention. In order to be successful, major changes in planning, implementation and monitoring and evaluation procedures are required. Changes of that nature require a process of at least 5 to 10 years and high commitment on the side of institutional staff on all levels and donors as well.

Keywords

Zimbabwe, participatory innovation, extension, 'Training for Transformation,' organizational development, facilitation

1   Background to the Development of a Participatory Approach

In the framework of the project "*Conservation Tillage for Sustainable Crop Production System*" (Contill) adaptive on-farm trials with a farming systems perspective have been carried out since 1991. In order to stimulate adaptations to techniques offered by the project and to stimulate development of farmer innovations a participatory process for technology development has been initiated. During the process, experiences with smallholder farmers and with extension staff soon showed a need for further developing the approach for innovation development into an approach for participatory extension.

It proved to be unlikely that flexible, often site-specific innovations developed in the framework of the project would spread effectively if promoted with the present approach of the agricultural extension service (AGRITEX). Two main limitations were identified in the extension approach (see for example Madondo, 1992 & 1993): firstly the outreach of the extension service is limited as they concentrate on a 'master farmer program' which generally involves only approximately 10% of the farming households. Secondly, these farmers are being taught normative, rigid blanket recommendations in a top-down manner which hardly encourages dialogical, interactive learning, adapting of technologies and developing own solutions. On the farmers' side it was revealed that for an effective spreading of technical innovations the social environment must be favorable which is often not the case in the rural communities in Zimbabwe (Nyagumbo 1995, Chuma 1994, Hagmann 1993). Besides technical innovations, socio-organizational developments and innovations must be considered and addressed.

Based on these limitations and requirements a participatory approach was developed in a process driven by practical experiences while working with individuals and communities.

2   Concept and Approach for Participatory Innovation Development and Extension

The goal of the participatory process is sustainable management of natural resources and food security in smallholder farming areas in Zimbabwe. It aims at developing and spreading sustainable farming practices and at enabling rural communities to better handle their problems in a self-reliant way, without depending on incentives from outside. It addresses communities as a whole and individual families as units (men and women together).

The concept for participatory innovation development and extension is based on dialogical communication, farmer experimentation and strengthening of self-organizational capacities of rural communities. Encouragement of active participation and dialogue among all actors on the local level as partners, e.g. farmers and their institutions, extensionists and researchers is the mainstay.

Farmer experimentation. Dialogue and farmer experimentation is being encouraged in an environment where a very powerful top-down extension service has considered farmers' knowledge to be backwards and of no importance for nearly three generations and where farmers have been conditioned to accept externally developed standardized technologies (Madondo 1995). Stimulation of own experimentation proves to be a useful element to re-value and appreciate traditional and indigenous knowledge, to combine it with new techniques and synthesize the two. As an overall effect, the knowledge and understanding gained through this process strengthens farmers' confidence in their own solutions and increases their ability to choose options and to develop solutions appropriate for their specific ecological, economical and socio-cultural conditions and circumstances. This process aims at transforming the present standard-oriented extension into an output-oriented system where not the adoption of one specific technique is the indicator for success, but, for example, the efficient conservation of soil and water.

Strengthening Self-Organizational Capacities. Strengthening self-organizational capacities of rural communities with their local institutions often necessitates improvements in the communication structures within the local institutions, which farmers analyzed to be hierarchical, weak and discouraging for active participation in community activities (Hagmann 1993). In addition, the conflict between traditional leadership structures and modern, government-introduced representation contributes to conflicts and to weak local institutions. Leadership training and facilitation of dialogical communication in village workshops are elements which have shown high potential for improving cooperation, sharing of knowledge and participation of all gender and age groups in extension and rural development (Hagmann & Murwira 1996)

Strengthening of local institutions, together with an increasing confidence through experimentation, creates an atmosphere conducive to sharing experiences, innovations and knowledge among farmers and leads to an effective farmer-to-farmer extension.

Philosophy and Tools. The experience showed that this concept, in particular the component of leadership and cooperation, required more than a number of practical PRA-tools (see for example Theis & Grady 1991). A philosophical framework for the participatory development process was required and introduced in the form of "Training for Transformation" (TFT). This training program was developed in Kenya in 1974 and adapted to Zimbabwean conditions by Hope & Timmel (1984). It originates in the pedagogy of Freire (1973) and is built on conscientization through participatory education, where learning is based on experience in the own living world of the actors. Teaching therefore consists of dialogue via problem posing, which means facilitation of communication flow and asking questions to help groups find the causes and the solutions themselves instead of teaching 'foreign' knowledge and realities. TFT provides concrete methods and tools (e.g. codes, role plays, poems etc.) to practically implement Freire's approach. It empowers local people to control their lives through active participation in their own development and sharing of ideas and knowledge. It stresses the importance of participation and cooperation in organizational development in order to build and strengthen institutions which enable people to become self-reliant. It aims at strengthening people's confidence (e.g. slogans like: "nobody knows everything and nobody knows nothing") and integrates social analysis to help groups to find the root causes of problems (Hope & Timmel 1984). Freire's key principles form a philosophical framework which is relevant for any individual living in a society and can be applied in almost all situations in life. The strong acceptance of and agreement on these principles by various characters with different attitudes and in different mainstreams is its major strength. It manages to integrate and unite these often conflicting interests under one umbrella, the key principles.

This effect is of great importance in a society where socio-cultural change has weakened the social cohesion and security which was based on traditional rules and regulations, which is the case in Zimbabwe (Hagmann 1993, Nyagumbo 1995). Therefore, according to our experience, a new 'umbrella' which can replace or at least partly substitute the old security is particularly important, as the desire of social harmony is very strong and dominates most decisions of individuals. Without providing a platform to develop the new 'umbrella,' cooperation and leadership structures in rural communities will generally remain weak and often dominated by the unresolved social conflicts, which also adversely affect innovation development and extension.

Farmers are introduced to this framework right at the beginning of the process in awareness-raising community workshops. Elements of TFT are utilized selectively in the process and are complemented by tools originating in PRA, diagnostic survey (Raintree 1987) and goal oriented planning 'ZOPP' (GTZ, 1987), as well as materials and aids for dialogical teaching in order to initiate and follow up participatory innovation development and extension.

Figure 1 illustrates the concept of participatory research/innovation development and extension. It consists of three main components, participatory community development as a process of learning and development through experimentation, the 'process of learning and development through experimentation,' the research component and the extension component.

The 'Learning and Development through Experimentation' Process. The main process (centre column in figure 1) can be considered as 'learning & development through experimentation,' initiated and facilitated by extension workers. It is people-centered as villagers analyze and define their problems, needs and potentials and the activities they want to carry out. The intervention from outside facilitates the process, raises awareness, contributes methodologies and inspires with potential technical options, but does not dominate and push people to carry out certain (from outsiders) preconceived activities. It is an open-ended development process where research and extension are support agencies and ideally participate in people's programs and not vice-versa.

Development of Innovative Techniques (Research component in figure 1). Innovation development is based on the trial and error principle. Farmers are encouraged to experiment with ideas and techniques emanating from their own source of knowledge or from outside sources. Problems identified during the process are the basis for a research agenda and resulting on-farm trials in which more focus is put on quantitative data to support the findings. If technical processes are not fully understood farmers' ideas are taken to the research station for further research under controlled conditions.

Spreading of Innovative Techniques (Extension component in figure 1). Spreading is stimulated through the strengthening of the self-organizational capacities of rural communities and institutions. Improvements of communication structures, skills and modes is facilitated with the help of the TFT philosophy and tools in order to enable people to create an environment where they feel free to communicate and share their skills and experiences with all members of the community. Once this level of communication flow is reached in the communities, a high dynamic in farmer-to-farmer sharing and extension should result. In technical terms, not new techniques as such are promoted, but the experimentation with technical options and indigenous technical knowledge (ITK) is encouraged. Experiences and results of the experiments are shared and compiled by farmers and extension as guidelines/training materials which focus on the understanding of the factors which make the techniques succeed or fail. Important tools are annual community reviews where the technical and socio-organizational progress is reviewed and evaluated and adaptations to the planning made (see figure 1).

Figure 1: Conceptual Model for Participatory Research & Innovation
Development and Extension

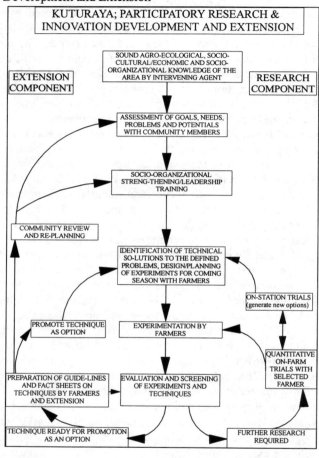

3   The New Role of the Agricultural Extension Worker

At present agricultural extension workers (AEW) see their role as that of a
teacher. A participatory approach requires a major shift in roles from teacher to
facilitator. This implies that the AEW is no longer the main carrier of a message
and knowledge, but coordinates and organizes the knowledge acquisition from
several sources. Utilizing the TFT philosophy and the tools, the AEW as a
facilitator would then initiate a participatory process in communities with a major
focus on local institutional strengthening, needs identification and prioritization.

He/she would assist farmers in the discussion about solutions with background knowledge and options (e.g. through organization of "look and learn" visits to innovative farmers, research stations etc.) and encourage farmers to experiment with these options and ideas as described above. The AEW would also encourage farmers to hold field days for those who could not directly participate. With time the facilitator role will be taken over gradually by community leaders who are being trained in facilitation skills. Figure 2 summarizes the main elements of the facilitator role.

Figure 2: The Main Elements of the Facilitator Role

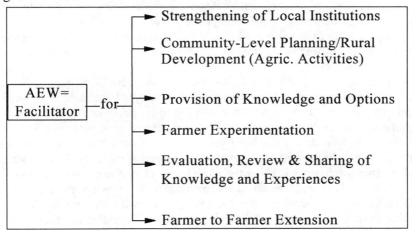

4   Strategy for Institutionalizing the Participatory Approach

Pilot activities were carried out by the Contill Project, the ITDG Food Security Project and the Community-Level Planning and Development operations of the Integrated Rural Development Program (IRDEP) which is supported by GTZ. These activities served as case studies for the development of a model for participatory approaches. The case studies enabled a detailed monitoring of processes, impacts and reactions on the side of farmers and extension staff. The success of the three projects in terms of development and extension of innovations (Hagmann et al. 1996), the improvements in the social organization in communities (Hagmann & Murwira 1996) and in terms of community-planned and implemented projects (Göricke 1993) justified scaling up. In addition, the extension service, which is a strong and functional organization, showed interest in trying new approaches in order to increase their efficiency. Therefore, a strategy for institutionalizing the participatory approach was developed for Masvingo Province and several elements will be described.

Networking. Several organizations and projects in Masvingo Province apply elements of participatory approaches. The focuses differ, but all of them work in close collaboration with AGRITEX, the extension service, as this is the institution which is strongly represented at field level. Sharing of experiences among those projects has been extremely valuable and we were able to closely cooperate with ITDG and with IRDEP and coordinate activities aiming at institutionalization of participatory approaches into AGRITEX. The informal networking and joint lobbying has resulted in learning from each other's experiences, joint papers and workshops. It proved to be crucial to obtain the 'critical mass' necessary to draw attention to participatory approaches and the pilot activities. At present, after several presentations in various provincial, national and international workshops, the network is expanding as various organizations from other provinces have shown vivid interest.

Familiarization of all Levels of Staff. Soon after the interest within AGRITEX had been created familiarization of all levels of extension staff became a priority in order to stimulate discussions. Besides provision of literature and reports, several workshops organized and/or supported by the three cooperating projects were held during the last two years. These workshops were combined with field visits to the case study areas. Participatory approaches were presented and experiences discussed. This enabled higher level staff to get fully involved in the process and to adopt the new ideas. Exposure to the impact of the case studies and to farmers who analyzed the difference between the conventional and the participatory approach were particularly convincing. In addition to these formal activities, informal discussions based on good personal relationships and field visits were key elements to familiarize AGRITEX officers with the participatory process and raise their acceptance of these ideas. Once high-level officers were convinced of the potential of the new approach, AGRITEX Masvingo organized a familiarization workshop for all its staff in the province. The management level wanted to give direction to the lower level staff and show their support to these approaches.

Elaboration of a Training and Follow-Up Program for Extension Workers. After familiarization of the key players, a systematic training of 30 extension workers in TFT, participatory tools/methods and facilitation began. An initial two-week course in TFT which was attended by extension workers and farmers together was followed by a report-back workshop to the communities who chose the farmers and to AGRITEX District staff. Extension workers then decided on communities in which they wanted to apply and practice the skills. A follow-up in facilitation training is being provided throughout one year at 3- to 6-

monthly intervals. These follow-up workshops will give them a chance to assist each other, to exchange experience and to improve their facilitation skills while practicing. The experiences of this training process are being documented and a final evaluation after one year will reveal the effectiveness.

Framework of Organizational Development. AGRITEX Masvingo has recently launched an organizational development program which is supported by IRDEP. The purpose of the program, which was initiated by the Chief Agricultural Extension Officer is that *'relevant aggregate output at all levels of AGRITEX staff in Masvingo Province is improved'* The most important result is that *'extension delivery system to farmers in Masvingo Province is improved'* (AGRITEX 1995). As participatory extension has shown to be the most promising approach for improving the extension delivery system, it has become an integral part of the organizational development system as the software for achieving the most important result. The successful project to project cooperation between Contill and IRDEP and the informal network has assisted in complementing the activities and approaches in an output-oriented organizational development and support program.

5 Experiences and Lessons Learned

Our experiences with institutionalization in Masvingo are based on a two year effort to actively integrate participatory approaches. The full cycle of the training and follow-up program for extension workers, however, was only initiated in 1994 and has not been completed yet. Some major experiences and constraints will be discussed. More details are described in Hagmann et al. (1995).

Participatory Approaches Demonstrated High Potential to Increase the Efficiency of Extension and Rural Development Activities. The impact of the participatory approaches of the three projects was highly convincing in terms of active farmer participation in innovation development, increased rates of adoption of technologies and innovations and in terms of self-organization and target setting of communities. In some areas up to 80 % of the households were involved in soil and water conservation techniques developed and promoted through the activities.

Implementing Participatory Approaches Requires a Change of Attitudes. Experiences of the case studies which were implemented by project staff in collaboration with extension workers showed that the change in attitude of extension staff towards smallholder farmers is the key determinant for the success of the approach. In a hierarchically structured society, where the hierarchy is mostly based on the level of formal education, it is difficult for formally educated staff to accept farmers with their traditional and experience-based knowledge system as equals and to learn from them. Attitudes cannot be changed by utilizing certain methodologies only. It requires a philosophical framework to create conducive conditions in which this process can take place. Training for Transformation (Hope & Timmel 1984) has demonstrated the highest potential as philosophy.

Ability to Develop Participatory Skills Depends on Personalities. As attitudes highly depend on personalities, it is doubtful whether staff who have been professionally socialized and to a certain extent been conditioned under colonial rule are able to reverse the top-down approach, as it would question most of their working life. The same applies to older farmers who have accepted their obsequious and subordinate role and who now identify with it. Therefore the impact depends strongly on the AEW and one can not expect it to be uniform.

Training in Participatory Approaches is a Continuos, Medium-Term Process. Training courses in TFT and participatory tools were initially successful, but it was revealed that without an on-the-job follow-up of the process of change over a medium-term time span, the impact is low. Intensive training, support and follow-up are extremely important in order to avoid labeling of the conventional work as participatory simply because participation is the talk of the day (which occurred with other approaches in the past). In particular, during the transition phase, extension workers need strong support to overcome the often observed insecurity and fear of losing power when giving up the teacher role.

Commitment on Higher Levels and Effective Staff Appraisal System are Required. Various levels of staff have frequently misinterpreted participatory approaches as "pulling out of AEW," "let farmers do what they want," as relaxation and as not being accountable for failures. To avoid this danger, besides proper training and follow-up, a more effective and appropriate staff appraisal and counselling system (incl. performance criteria) has to be developed and must be effective from the start of the implementation of the participatory approach. This requires a strong commitment on the part of higher level staff to give direction and incentives to the extension workers and to follow up the operations. A key element which was agreed upon in Masvingo is the integration of a farmer appraisal of the extension workers into the M&E system in order to increase the accountability of extension workers towards their clients, the farmers. Another important job evaluation criteria is the performance in the documentation of farmer knowledge by the AEW. This is an incentive for the AEW to learn from farmers and also to recognize the value and the importance of indigenous knowledge. As AEWs are also part of the indigenous knowledge system, this enables them to cross the borders between the western knowledge system which they represent with their advice at present and the indigenous knowledge system.

Criteria and Indicators for Monitoring and Evaluating the Impact of Participatory Extension Need to Be Developed. The present M&E system is based on quantitative indicators for adoption of key practices to increase and sustain production. Successes of a participatory process in a community, however, require a medium-term time frame and the output in terms of quantifiable increases in production can not be expected to be very spectacular in a marginal semi-arid area. Qualitative results, which are equally important and elementary in the process (e.g. human development in terms of an increase in self-reliance and in self-organizational capacities, confidence building etc.), however, are difficult to measure and have not yet been taken into consideration in the indicators.

6 Conclusion and Recommendations

Experiences gained so far allow the following conclusions and recommendations:

- Institutionalization of participatory approaches into a hierarchically structured organization is a highly complex intervention. It requires a major reorientation of planning, implementation and M&E systems for which high commitment from all staff is needed and must be considered as a medium to long-term objective.
- Case studies or pilot activities in which the participatory approaches are developed, tested and adapted are very important. They serve as practical examples (methodologies, tools, and impact) to familiarize and convince institutional staff and thereby influence policies from the bottom up. Detailed monitoring of those operations should be continued parallel to institutionalization and gradual upscaling in order to detect pitfalls and mistakes.
- Intensive efforts to familiarize and train all levels of staff is crucial. Networking and coordination of activities with other projects appears to be a successful approach to reach a 'critical mass.'
- Once higher level staff is committed, intensive training, support and follow-up of field extension staff must have priority in institutionalizing participatory approaches. Extension workers at the interface between farmers and the extension agency require new skills and a higher social competence to tackle the facilitator role. As staff turnover at field level is low, intensive training at this level contributes to the sustaining of the efforts.
- Despite favorable conditions in Masvingo Province, it shows that effective institutionalization of participatory innovation development and extension into the agricultural extension service will require a process of at least 5 to 10 years. Continuous commitment from the institution as well as from the donor side during this period will be critical to success. Nevertheless, due to the

availability of an effective training, an M&E system, and the willingness to institutionalize the approaches, chances for success are bright in Mavingo.

Lessons Learned

To summarize the lessons learned in our case, one has to stress that our experience proved the effectiveness of participatory innovation development and extension for the management of the natural resources and for food security. This was achieved through a better self-organization of the communities and through a learning process which was catalyzed by farmers' experimentation. This enabled farmers to develop appropriate innovations and manage their highly diverse environment site-specifically and therefore improved the total output in terms of production and conservation. The second major lesson learned was that case studies in projects can only be successful at a larger scale if simultaneously a systematic support program for institutionalization of these approaches into larger bodies or institutions can be launched. This, however, is an intervention which is highly complex and situation-specific.

References

AGRITEX (Dept. of Agric., Technical and Extension Services) 1995. Organisational Development (Pilot Programme). Masvingo, Zimbabwe

Chuma, E. 1994. Contribution of different evaluation methods to the understanding of farmers' decision on adoption and adaptations of innovations. Experiences from the development of a conservation tillage system in Southern Zimbabwe. In: Systems-oriented Research in Agriculture and Rural Development, International Symposium held in Montpellier, 21-25 November 1994. Papers published by CIRAD-SAR, Montpellier, pp. 161-167.

Freire, P. 1973. Pädagogik der Unterdrückten. Rowohlt, Reinbek.

Göricke, F. 1993. An outline of experiences with community-level planning and development in the framework of CARD Masvingo/Zimbabwe. Background paper prepared for the Arusha Conference on Assessment of New Approaches Towards Rural Development. CARD Masvingo.

GTZ GmbH, 1987. ZOPP, Zielorientiertes Planen von Programmen der technischen Zusammenarbeit. Einführung in die Grundlagen der Methode. Eschborn

Hagmann, J. 1993. Farmer participatory research in conservation tillage; approach, methods and experiences from an adaptive trial programme in Zimbabwe. In: Kronen, M. (ed.) 1993.Proceedings of the 4th annual scientific conference of the SADC Land and Water Management Programme, held in Windhoek, Namibia on October 11 to 15, 1993, Gaborone, Botswana.

Hagmann, J. & Murwira, K. 1996. Indigenous Soil and Water Conservation in Southern Zimbabwe; a Study on Techniques, Historical Changes and Recent Developments under Participatory Research and Extension. In: Drylands Programme Issues Paper, No. 63., International Institute for Environement and Development, IIED, London.

Hagmann, J., Chuma, E., Murwira, K., Moyo, E. 1995. Transformation of agricultural extension and research towards farmer participation; approach and experiences in Masvingo Province,

Zimbabwe. Proceedings of a technical workshop held 3-7 April 1995 in Masvingo. Belmont Press, Masvingo, Zimbabwe.

Hagmann, J., Murwira, K.& Chuma, E. 1996. Learning Together: Development and Extension of Soil & Water Conservation in Zimbabwe. In: Quarterly Journal of International Agriculture, Vol.35, No.2, pp. 142-162 (Publ. By DLG-Verlag, Frankfurt)

Hope & Timmel, 1984. Training for Transformation; a handbook for community workers. Mambo Press, Gweru, Zimbabwe.

Madondo, B.B.S. 1992. Technology generation and transfer systems for communal areas of Zimbabwe after independence 1981-1991); A decade of institutional adaptation. Regional Research Co-operation Office-SAREC, Harare.

Madondo, B.B.S. 1993. Extension strategies from 1993 and beyond. Paper presented at a workshop of AGRITEX Manicaland Province held at Kyle View (Masvingo) in September 1993, AGRITEX, Mutare, Zimbabwe

Madondo. B.B.S. 1995. Agricultural transfer systems of the past and present. In: Twomlow S., Ellis-Jones J., Hagmann J., Loos H.: Soil and water conservation for smallholder farmers in semi-arid Zimbabwe. Proceedings of a technical workshop held 3-7 April 1995 in Masvingo. Belmont Press, Masvingo, Zimbabwe, pp. 118-125.

Nyagumbo, I. 1995. Socio-cultural constraints to development projects in communal areas of Zimbabwe; a review of experiences from farmer participatory research in conservation tillage. Research Report 14, Conservation Tillage Project, Inst. of Agric. Eng., Harare

Raintree, J.B. 1987. D&D user's manual. An introduction to agroforestry diagnosis and design. ICRAF, Nairobi.

Theis, J. & Grady, H.M. 1991. Participatory Rapid Appraisal for community development. A training manual based on experiences in the Middle East and North Africa. International Institute for Environment and Development (IIED), London.

The Performance of the Agricultural Extension System in Ethiopia as an Instrument of Innovation Transfer

Assefa Admassie
Department of Economics
Addis Abeba University, Ethiopia

Abstract

A strong agricultural extension system is an important factor for promoting productivity by disseminating knowledge regarding land and labor-augmenting innovations to farmers, thereby inducing increased food production. The performances of the various agricultural extension strategies which were implemented over the last thirty years in Ethiopia have been carefully scrutinized. The extension strategies have been constrained by several institutional, economic, political and social factors. Consequently the technology transfer mechanisms have remained ineffective and failed to bring any meaningful benefit to the farmer. A participatory extension approach and a stronger link between research and extension could help to alleviate some of the deficiencies. In addition the development agents have to be motivated and encouraged through financial and non financial means to effectively discharge their responsibilities.

Keywords

Food production, extension service, innovations, Ethiopia

1 Introduction

The food security situation in many African countries is very precarious. These countries depend heavily on food imports or food aid to feed their population, which is growing at a yearly rate of over 3 % while food production continues to decline. Therefore, food security has become a key issue today in the world and will remain so in the foreseeable future. There is, therefore, an urgent need to mitigate this problem to increase food production in these countries.

Food production can be increased through several ways. One way of mitigating the problem of food insecurity is to disseminate land and labor-augmenting innovations for raising productivity. However, the mere introduction of innovations alone does not guarantee the widespread adoption and use of the input. Several economic, social, institutional, and political preconditions need to be fulfilled. A well organized and efficient extension system is one such factor.

Extension is an important factor to promote productivity, primarily by disseminating knowledge regarding cultural practices, new varieties, optimal use of agro-chemicals, irrigation etc., to farmers. Weak links between research and extension will severely constrain the dissemination of new technology. Without an appropriate and far-reaching method of information dissemination farmers will not be able to know which technologies exist or the economic advantages of the innovations and the methods of application. In the absence of a good system of extension it would rather be better for the farmer to remain without the technology. Therefore, there is a strong need to combine research efforts with an adequate system of extension.

A strong extension system is crucial for Ethiopia for the development of the agricultural sector. Illiteracy, social customs and tradition present serious barriers to modernization and technological change and thus make a full-fledged extension organization an imperative development.

The extension system in Ethiopia has not been effective enough. Either adequate extension work has not been done or an appropriate agricultural extension strategy has not been formulated and implemented. There is a substantial gap between the policy and the extension practice. As one author puts it, at all levels of the Ministry of Agriculture (MOA) everybody speaks loudly about the term extension. But when it comes to the real application of it one finds oneself in a vacuum (Kebede 1989). Investment in agricultural research and extension in the country has been very low compared with other sectors. The adoption rate of modern technologies in the country is also unsatisfactory. The Ethiopian farmer continues to use an estimated average of 7 kg of nutrients per hectare, well below the African average of about 22 kg nutrients per hectare, and less than 5 % of the Ethiopian farmers use improved seed (Asrat 1993). The major objective of this paper is to review the agricultural extension strategies adopted in the country, and to identify the major problems and weakness of the systems with the aim of drawing lessons for the future.

2 The Ethiopian Agriculture and the Food Security Situation

Agriculture is the most important economic sector in Ethiopia. The preponderance of the agricultural sector is evident by its contribution to GDP, foreign exchange earning (90 %) and provision of employment to more than 80 % of the population. The sector is dominated by subsistence farmers whose mode of life and work has remained unchanged for centuries and who produce 90-95 % of all cereals, pulses and oil seeds. Due to limited access to modern research-led agricultural technologies the Ethiopian farmer has remained at subsistence level.

Despite the predominance of the sector it did not receive the attention commensurate to its importance. Agricultural productivity has deteriorated since the early seventies with a good proportion of the farm households not being able to feed themselves and frequently dependent on food aid. Food production has declined by over 15 % while annual grain imports increased more than three fold from 270,000 MT in 1980 to 870,000 MT in 1992-94 (FAO 1995). The average agricultural production during the 1980s amounted to around 5.8 million tons and 265 thousand tons by the traditional and modern sub-sectors respectively.

Table 1: Agricultural Production in Ethiopia by Sectors ('000 quintals)

Sector \ Years	Private	State farms	Total	Index (80/81=100)
80/81	58,819.13	2,562.7	61,381.83	100
81/82	55,899.11	2,846.66	58,745.77	95
82/83	71,284.95	2,545.35	73,830.3	120
83/84	57,114.99	2,027.65	59,142.64	96
84/85	42,079.38	2,250.22	44,329.6	72
85/86	47,045.82	2,767.36	49,813.18	81
86/87	59,307.23	3,309.75	62,616.98	102
87/88	64,558.56	2,928.9	67,487.46	110
88/89	59,480.58	2,580.99	62,061.57	101
89/90	66,644.04	2,775.38	69,419.42	113

Source: CSA. Statistical Abstracts

Between 1980/81 and 1982/83 production in the traditional sub-sector had increased on the average by only 0.5% annually, whereas that of the modern sub-sector had remained almost stagnant. Between 1982/83 and 1984/85, production sunk to its lowest level in both sub sectors. Some of the factors that contribute to the low level of agricultural production include inappropriate macro economic policies, natural disasters, inadequate agricultural technology generation and dissemination, lack of rural credit etc. The per capita annual food grain supply has been below 175 kg which is the widely accepted minimum threshold of grain equivalent for an adult who requires 2,000 calories every day (Weingärtener 1994).

When output levels are compared with the growth of the population the gross available amount of grain for consumption has been declining on a per capita basis from around 225 kg per capita per year in the 1960s to about 130 kg per capita per year in the late 1980s (Stroud and Mulugeta 1992). The rural households had neither food in stock nor cash to secure it from the market when drought occurred. Therefore, the country's dependence on foreign sources for food increased significantly as shown in Table 2. Given the growing demand for food, the low per capita food intake, the excessive dependence of the economy on agriculture for income, exports and employment, improving the performance of the agricultural sector is a sine que non for any progress in Ethiopia.

Table 2: Food Grain Supply in Ethiopia by Source (`000 tons)

	80/81	81/82	82/83	83/84	84/85	85/86	86/87	87/88	88/89	89/90
Domestic prod.	4,603	4,405	5,537	4,435	3,324	3,736	4,649	5,061	5,254	5,155
Commercial import	123	178	259	290	602	847	600	566	551	118
Food aid	228	190	356	208	869	1,100	789	135	583	473
Total availability	4,954	4,773	6,152	4,933	4,795	5,658	6,077	5,762	6,389	5,746
Population ('000)	37,684	38,762	39,817	41,011	42,829	44,225	45,737	47,189	48,587	50,167
Food availability (kg per capita)	131.5	123.2	154.5	120.3	112.0	128.0	133.0	122.0	132.0	115.0
Availability index	103.0	99.0	128.0	103.0	100.0	118.0	127.0	120.0	133.0	120.0
Aid depend. Ratio	4.6	4.0	5.8	4.2	18.1	19.4	12.9	2.3	9.1	8.2
Import depend. ratio	2.5	3.7	4.2	5.9	12.6	15.0	9.9	9.8	8.6	2.1
Total depend. ratio	7.1	7.7	10.0	10.1	30.7	34.4	22.8	12.1	17.7	10.3

Source: NBE, Quarterly Bulletins and FAO, Food Aid Statistics

3   The Role of an Agricultural Extension System

One method to make progress in agricultural production is to use agricultural extension works. Agricultural extension work is a program of informal adult education for rural people, in crop production, animal husbandry, soil and water conservation, afforestation and related services. It is the most important source of information for farmers who wish to adopt a new technology. Research institutes and experiment stations have always worked hard to accumulate scientific knowledge and make progress. Researchers rarely have the time or the opportunity to communicate directly with farmers. In addition the average farmer does not understand the specialized language of the scientist. Under such circumstances a system of information transfer is indispensable.

The main purpose of agricultural extension is, therefore, to bridge this gap: to bring up-to-date useful and reliable information to those who need it in a way that is understandable to them. Extension work is a vital link between research on the one hand and the farmer on the other. The extension worker is a kind of interpreter because he must be able to speak in two languages; the highly technical language of agricultural scientists and the farmers' daily language of practical matters.

Different models of extension have been applied at different times and at different places. The most traditional and most widely used method of conveying new information to farmers relies on the government extension services. Nowadays there is a growing emphasis on participatory approach in which farmers resume more responsibility for the identification and dissemination of new technologies. The Training and Visit (T&V) extension system is a recently developed popular system with wide application. The T&V extension management system was developed in order to improve the efficiency of national extension programs in developing countries. The most important elements of the T&V approach include the promotion of effective communication with farmers, strengthening the linkage between research and extension, and improving extension based on training and visit (Benor & Harrison 1977). The T&V extension management system, among other related procedures, requires that one grass roots level extension worker should serve not more than 800 farm families; that field level extension workers should be trained on timely extension messages every other week; and that subject-matter specialists who regularly train field level extension workers should themselves be trained once a month by agricultural researchers and/or other senior subject-matter experts. This extension management system has been adopted in many developing countries.

4 The Performance of the Agricultural Extension System in Ethiopia

Agricultural extension service started in Ethiopia around 1952 with the objectives of promoting the rural sector economically, socially and culturally. Advisory work started in Shewa and Arsi regions by advising farmers in sheep improvement and by organizing agricultural youth clubs. Since then different agricultural extension approaches were tried in the country. The extension strategies adopted and implemented in the country will be chronologically examined in this section.

4.1 The Period Before 1974

This period was characterized by a feudalistic land ownership system in which a landlord - tenant relationship prevailed. The system was a very exploitative one and it created disincentives for the peasant farmers. Starting in 1966 the administration of peasant agricultural development was made the official responsibility of the Ministry of Agriculture (MOA) in which preparing programs for agricultural extension was one of such responsibilities. In 1967, the Ministry established the Department of Extension whose responsibility was to administer extension services in the country. Provisional extension supervisors were assigned to work directly under the Director General of the Extension Department and also under the Provincial Director for Agriculture. This arrangement did not work well and later it was found that in fact it hampered an efficient delivery of extension services.

In 1971 a semi-autonomous Extension and Project Implementation Department (EPID) was created and was granted full responsibility for extension administration. Since its establishment, EPID focused mainly on the provision of agricultural extension services and on the sale of farm inputs to farmers on credit and in cash. EPID attempted to provide an integrated extension service, including credit services to small-scale farmers for the purchase of agricultural inputs, particularly fertilizers. The extension division's efforts were concentrated on the Minimum Package Program (MPP) comprising mainly the supply of fertilizers and improved seeds. A development agent was responsible for about 2,000 farmers. A MPP area normally involved 20 selected "model farmers" to act as the main channels for the dissemination of the new technology. The first phase of the MPP was implemented before the land reform of March 1975.

The extension program of EPID was not successful for a variety of reasons. The program was a victim of the reactionary land tenure system and it did not allow the full participation of the small farmers and tenants in the extension program. The program was also functional only at a radius of 5 km from the main roads due to lack of accessibility. Moreover, it was limited to only seven districts and the number of farmers participating in the program was less than one percent. The program also served the poor peasants less than the rich ones, who had access to the ruling class and who were often selected as "model farmers."

4.2   The Period Between 1980 and 1993

EPID was abolished after the land reform and its extension activities were curtailed and weakened. Until the beginning of the 1980s there was no definite extension activity taking place in the country. The Minimum Package Program was planned to be implemented in the second phase. Due to the political developments in the country the implementation of the second phase was delayed until the beginning of the 1980s. The second phase of the Minimum Package Project (MPP II) was extended to 440 woredas (districts) out of the total 580 woredas. MPP II concentrated only on crop production and the components of the project consisted of an agricultural extension package, a co-operative marketing package and input supply services. The development and the provision of extension services included mainly the provision of improved agricultural inputs like fertilizer, improved seeds, simple farm implements, crop protection chemicals and post-harvesting management. The Peasant Associations were used as the extension channels during this phase.

In 1985 the MOA launched a new agricultural development program known as the Peasant Agricultural Development Project (PADEP) as a follow-up of the MPPII. PADEP divided the national extension network into groups of regions that had agro-ecological similarities. Eight PADEP zones were envisaged but only seven were made operational. The new program decentralized some of the agricultural extension functions to the development zones. Intensive extension coverage was envisaged and, as far as possible, extension workers assigned to high agricultural potential areas were made to work and live at village level with the aim of improving the performance of the extension system based on the T&V concepts.

With the introduction of PADEP, the World Bank started to finance the extension program in the country. The bank accepted a modified version of the T&V system which was already developed by the Agricultural Extension Department of the MOA and was being implemented in all the surplus-producing woredas in Ethiopia. Accordingly front line extension agents were supposed to pass the extension message to the contact farmer and the contact farmer relays the message to the other farmers known as follower farmers. The MOA modified the extension agent farmer ratio by changing the Development Agent (DA) to farmers ratio from 1:800 to 1:1300. It also decided to organize monthly DA training programs instead of every other week. And the training program for zonal level subject matter specialists was to be organized every three months instead of every month as proposed by the conventional T&V system. Extension personnel allocated to surplus-producing areas grew to the ratio of one extension officer to 1300 farmers, while it was reduced to 1: 2000 in deficit areas. After 1987 there were further reorganizations. The zonal offices of agriculture were abolished and their role was taken over by the new regional offices of agriculture.

The efficacy of the extension program implemented can be assessed in terms of the sources of extension advice, the utility of the services, as well as in terms of the frequency of visits by farmers to demonstration and training sites. An empirical evaluation of the success of the strategy adopted is based on the information obtained from a baseline survey organized by PADEP and Fourth Livestock Development Project (FLDP). The survey was conducted in three zones namely the Central Zone, the Northwestern Zone and the Eastern Zone. The number of farm families contacted was about 900 from the Central Zone, 749 from the Eastern Zone and 899 from the Northwestern Zone.

According to the information obtained from the baseline survey, farmers are confronted with a number of crop and livestock problems. Some common problems which confront farmers include lack of inputs such as fertilizers, improved seeds, pesticides and herbicides, shortage of oxen, soil erosion, lack of grazing area, shortage of forage, and animal diseases. All these problems require the assistance of an extension agent.

a) Sources of Extension Advice and Farmers' Contact with Extension Agents

Advice on animal husbandry and crop production mainly comes from development agents (DA) assigned by the MOA to each area. Farmers could also acquire advice from other sources such as relatives, friends, mass media, etc. However, the DA farmer ratio was very low as pointed out earlier. As a result they did not visit the farmers regularly and frequently. Hence the service given by these agents did not bring any substantial benefit to the farmers. Above all as it can be observed from Table 3 many farmers did not get any advice either from the DAs or from other sources.

Table 3: Sources of Extension Advice

Sources	Central Zone	Eastern Zone	Northwestern Zone
No advice at all	154 (28)	251 (41)	186 (29)
Advice from contact farmer	173 (31)	111 (18)	166 (26)
Advice from neighbors	50 (9)	154 (25)	148(23)
Advice from other sources	202 (36)	111 (18)	151 (24)
Total respondents	550	615	635
Advice from DAs [1]	350 (39)	143 (19)	288 (32)

Figures in parentheses are percentages; [1] percentages are out of the total sample
Source: PADEP /FLDP Baseline Survey 1987

In terms of the regularity of the extension visits the sampled farmers indicated that they have not been regularly visited by the agents. Many of them in fact pointed out that they have never been visited by the agents during the last one month of the survey. As much as 80 % of them mentioned that they did not have any contact with DAs in the last four weeks.

Table 4: Development Agents Visit Last Four Weeks

Number of Visits	Central Zone	Eastern Zone	Northwestern Zone
No visit	552 (61)	606 (81)	618 (69)
One visit	83 (9)	82 (11)	160 (18)
Two visit	245 (27)	53 (7)	79 (9)
Three visit	20 (2)	8 (1)	42 (5)
Total responses	900	749	899

Figures in parentheses are percentages
Sources: PADEP /FLDP baseline survey 1987

Too often extension work has been geared primarily towards the more prosperous and surplus-producing areas. Few DAs have been able to communicate effectively with the local people and thus the local people often have remained indifferent to the extension workers' messages (Azene 1993). Consequently farmers have little respect for the extension agents and their advice. Farmers have accumulated knowledge on agricultural practices through long years of farming experience. To promote agricultural development the extension worker must acquire knowledge from the local people and combine it with his own knowledge derived from training and earlier experiences. As shown in Table 4 more than 60 % of the peasant farmers were not visited by the DAs even once in a month. Less than 20 % of the farmers reported that they were visited fortnightly.

b) Types of Advice Given by Development Agents

Appropriate advice on the importance of innovations will help to expedite the dissemination of these innovations in the farming sector. The advice given by the extension agents focused on the use of improved seeds, on animal health, on soil and water conservation, on fertilizer application, and on the management of hides and skin.

Table 5: Types of Advice Given by Extension Agents

Type of Advice	Central Zone	Eastern Zone	Northwestern Zone
Advice on improved seeds	290 (77)	51 (36	240 (84)
Advice on animal health	251 (67)	26 (18)	197 (69)
Advice on soil and water conservation	250 (66)	388 (27)	180 (63)
Advice on fertilizer	149 (40)	1 (1)	135 (47)
Advice on animal feeding	164 (44)	6 (4)	135 (47)
Advice on pesticides	155 (41)	17 (12)	78 (27)

Source: PADEP / FLDP baseline survey 1987

c) Type, Frequency and Location of Training

Organizing farmers' training programs is one of the important instruments to improve the knowledge of the farmers, acquaint them with new ideas and demonstrate to them the impact of new innovations. From the information extracted from the survey it was found out that training on crop production was the most important type of training given to farmers. More than 50 % of the farmers in all the three zones have received training on crop management. If one considers the frequency of the training given to farmers one realizes that very few farmers have visited training centers. Training centers are important sources of knowledge. However, the majority of the farmers did not have the opportunity to visit either national or zonal training centers although some have visited local training centers.

Table 6: Types of Training Received by Farmers

Types	Central Zone	Eastern Zone	Northwestern Zone
Crop training received	18 (58)	13 (72)	15 (50)
Animal training	7 (23)	3 (17)	8 (27)
Conservation training	7 (23)	9 (50)	10 (33)
Others	1(3)	1 (6)	-
Total	31	18	30

Source: PADEP /FLDP baseline survey 1987

The empirical examples presented demonstrate the fact that the extension systems adopted in Ethiopia have contributed very little to improve the productivity of the agricultural sector. The technology transfer mechanism has been very weak and thus failed to address the major problems of the farmers. Moreover, the extension activities were not supported by an effective and strong technology generating network.

Table 7: Frequency of Visits to Training Centers

Visit to National Training Centers	Central Zone	Eastern Zone	Northwestern Zone
- no visit	35 (97)	17 (94)	31 (94)
- one visit	1 (3)	1 (6)	2 (6)
No visit to zonal training Centers	35 (97)	16 (89)	27 (82)
- one visit	1 (3)	2 (11)	6 (18)
No visit to local training Centers	4 (11)	4 (22)	13 (39)
- one visit	29 (81)	7 (39)	17 (52)
- two visits	3 (8)	5 (28)	3 (9)
No visit to other training Centers	34 (94)	17 (94)	28 (85)
- one visit	2 (6)	1 (6)	5 (15)

Source: PADEP /FLDP baseline survey 1987

4.3 Post-1993 Extension Activities

After the change of government in 1991 the MOA has remained as the most important public organization for the provision of agricultural extension services. There are also other governmental and non governmental organizations providing extension service to small farmers. The Sasakawa Global 2000 (SG 2000) is one of such organizations engaged in the extension activities. The Ministry of Agriculture has adopted recently the SG 2000 extension strategy as a national program. As observed from the SG 2000 project the beginning is promising. But it is too early to assess its impact since the program has just started to be implemented.

The SG 2000 agricultural project is a joint venture of two international non-profit organizations committed to promote agricultural and rural development in food deficit countries of Africa. The project was started in Africa in 1986. Many countries in Africa like Ghana, Tanzania, Benin, Togo, Nigeria, Ethiopia and Mozambique have been so far covered by the project. In Ethiopia it was started in 1993.

The main aims of the project are: to assist small farmers in increasing agricultural production through an aggressive technology transfer program, that will disseminate improved production technologies to small farmers through the extension service of the MOA; to strengthen the capacity of the extension services for expedient dissemination of proven, research-led technology in food crop; and to strengthen the link between research and extension in order to streamline the process of technology generation and dissemination.

The project uses a technology transfer model that fosters linkages between research, extension, input distribution, credit, and above all the small-scale farmer at the center. The dissemination of improved technologies on food crops is on farmers field known as the Extension Management Training Plots (EMTP) which are half a hectare in size. These are called commercial-size plots and are supposed to 1) lead to realistic test of technological package, 2) bring the participating farmers some economic return on their labor, and 3) eliminate unnecessary extrapolation which small farmers often distrust. The EMTP farmer is expected to pay 50 % of the cost of inputs at the time of delivery. Since its inception in 1993 the field program of this extension management system has expanded significantly and it has now been adopted as a national program. The extension management trial plots increased from 161 in 1993 to over 1480 by the following year.

Table 8: EMTP Maize Average Yield Data by Region

Region	No of Farmers	Yield in tons/ha	
		EMTP	Traditional
Oromia	452	5.49	1.50
Southern	317	5.46	1.60
Tigray	9	3.48	0.90
Average		5.45	1.50

Source: SG 2000 Annual Report, 1995

In terms of output the average yield of maize increased by more than threefold compared to average yields obtained from neighboring fields which were using traditional practices. Even deficit, degraded and semi-arid areas like Tigray increased their productivity by more than 200 % against the traditional production level. Average increase of wheat was about 130 %. Therefore, there are encouraging signs in terms of increasing the productivity of crops.

The SG 2000 program is different from the traditional approach in that the demonstration plots have increased. In the traditional practice the demonstration plots were not as large as the current one. In addition the farmers' contact with the extension agents has increased significantly. One of the important features of the approach is the intensive supervision of the farming activities by the extension agents. The supply of inputs has become more reliable.

One of the main doubts in this strategy is the question of sustainability. The program demands intensive supervision and, therefore, requires a substantial amount of resources. At the moment only some high-potential areas have been addressed by the program. It is rather doubtful if the program could be implemented over the whole country with the same level of intensity.

Moreover, it is not an integrated program. As already stated, the program focused only on the provision of inputs like fertilizer, improved seed and pesticides. Other important items like soil conservation measures, agro-forestry, livestock development, etc. are not addressed adequately by the program. Agricultural development in Ethiopia cannot be sustainable without proper livestock development policies and conservation measures.

5   Conclusions and Recommendations

Extension work in Ethiopia has not been effective enough in increasing food production due to a number of problems. The major problems of the system include: 1. the top-down extension approach adopted by the national extension system has discouraged popular participation in extension activities; 2. new agricultural technologies and extension messages, formulated at the central level and handed down to the regions for implementation, did not always fit all localities and were usually unaffordable by resource-poor farmers. The national extension system was inflexible and thus unable to adapt to local circumstances and needs. Due to the wide variety of agro-climatic and socio-economic conditions in the country no uniform extension packages applied nationwide can be effective; 3. there was lack of coordination among institutions responsible for the provision of agricultural inputs, credit and marketing services. As Goshu clearly pointed out, the absence of formal linkage mechanism between research and extension is a major problem (Goshu 1994); 4. Government support for extension services was poor; 5. there was a shortage of grass-roots level extension workers and, therefore, a great number of small-scale farmers did not receive extension advice. The extension workers also lacked motivation and training.

To improve the performance of the extension system, 1. the extension approach to be used should be the "participatory extension approach" where farmers participate in the identification and prioritization of their own problems and need to be a party in the planning and implementation of extension programs developed to overcome these problems. There is a need to actively involve the local people in dialogue so that their wishes can be given first priority; 2. regular in-service training programs need to be organized for field level extension staff. Young boys and girls who understand the local language and the norms and who are willing to work and live with rural people should be recruited and trained; 3. the government should allocate adequate annual budgets for extension activities; 4. the experiences of the past agricultural extension strategies have shown that the link between the technology-generating institutions and the technology transfer mechanism is very weak. Hence there is an urgent need to create institutions that combine research, extension and training.

6 Lessons Learned

It has been tried to show in this paper that a well-organized agricultural extension system is an important factor to increase food production by disseminating knowledge on new innovations to farmers. Without a proper information-transfer mechanism, innovations developed in research institutes could not reach farmers. The main lessons learned from the operation of the agricultural extension system in Ethiopia include: 1. that land and labor-augmenting technologies generated by research institutes could not be disseminated to farmers without a reliable system of extension, and will not bring any meaningful benefit to farmers; 2. that farmers should participate in the identification and prioritization of their problems and need to be a party in the planning and implementation of extension programs; and 3. that a strong link between research institutes, the farmer and the extension workers is very useful.

References

Asrat Tefera 1993. Ethiopia: The Agricultural Sector – An Overview. Volume I Main report. FAO. Rome.

Azene Bekele - Tessema 1993. Useful Trees and Shrubs for Ethiopia: Identification, Propagation and Management of Agricultural and Pastoral Communities, Regional Soil Conservation Unit. SIDA.

Benor, D. & J.O. Harrison 1977. The Training and Visit system. World Bank.

FAO 1995. Special Program on Food Production. Rome.

Goshu Mekonnen 1994. Agricultural Research and Extension in Ethiopia: An Overview: A Paper Presented for the Fourth Annual Conference on the Ethiopian Economy: 26-29 November. Deberezeit.

Kebede Tato 1989. Where are we heading in social conservation? Ethiopian Soil Conservation News No. 6. Community Forest and Soil Conservation and Development Department. MOA. Addis Abeba.

Sasakawa Global 2000. 1995. Annual Project of the Sasakawa Global 2000 Agricultural Project in Ethiopia. Crop Season 1994 Addis Abeba.

Weingärtner, L. 1994. Nutrition Assessment Study and Propositions for Intervention. Final Report. Addis Abeba.

Stroud, A. and Mulugeta Mekuria 1992. Ethiopia's Agricultural Sector: An Overview in Franzel, S. and van Houten, H. (eds). Research with Farmers: Lessons from Ethiopia. Redwood Press Ltd.

Adoption of Hybrid Maize and Tobacco in Malawi's Smallholder Farms: Effects on Household Food Security

Manfred Zeller[1], Aliou Diagne[1] and Vinda H.L. Kisyombe[2]

[1]International Food Policy Research Institute, 17th Street, N.W., Washington, D.C. 20036, USA
[2]Bunda College of Agriculture, University of Malawi, P.O. Box 219, Lilongwe, Malawi

Abstract

As a result of the policy changes in Malawi, tobacco as a new crop is being rapidly adopted on smallholder farms since the early 1990s. Hybrid maize varieties experienced a declining share in smallholder hectarage from 25% in 1992 to about 20% in 1993 and 1994, but then showed a strong revival. National crop production estimates for the production year 1996 predict a smallholder cropping share for hybrid maize of 29.6%. Based on an econometric model using 1994 household-level data, we analyze the determinants of adoption of hybrid maize and tobacco by smallholder farmers and assess the effects of adoption on farm income and consumption expenditures. The paper focuses on the determining factors and conducive policy environment for adoption of new crops or high-yielding varieties.

Keywords

Technology adoption, food security, credit, Malawi.

1 Introduction

Maize is the dominant crop and food staple in Malawi. About three quarters of smallholders' acreage is planted to maize. Other food crops include cassava, pulses, groundnuts, and rice. About 50% of the two million smallholder households are chronically food deficient because of small farm size and low yields of the dominant local maize varieties (Government of Malawi 1994). In view of the dominance of maize as a food staple and as the most important crop, improvements in productivity of maize will remain a core issue in food and agricultural policy in Malawi for improving household food security. Given limited off-farm employment opportunities, the required increases in household income must come from gains in agricultural productivity and from diversification into other food and cash crops. Hybrid maize as a capital-intensive, high-yielding technology and tobacco as a labor- and capital-intensive cash crop can offer insights into acceptance of crop innovations.

Based on a cross-section of 404 households in five districts of Malawi, this paper presents an analysis of determinants of adoption of hybrid maize and tobacco by smallholder farmers. In section 2, we describe the policy and institutional framework for tobacco and maize production in Malawi. Next, hypotheses about determinants of adoption of hybrid maize and tobacco are derived. We briefly review the literature related to adoption of agricultural innovations, present the data, and describe some characteristics of maize and tobacco production and marketing. Sections 4 and 5 discuss the econometric model and its results. The last section concludes with lessons learned.

2   Policy Framework and Smallholder Crop Mix

Past policies by and large favored the production of high-value cash crops in the estate sector while the smallholder sector was encouraged to produce and sell the country's food staple to official market channels (Mtawali 1993). During the 1980s and the early 1990s, agricultural credit, input, and extension policy focused on the dissemination of a fixed input package of hybrid maize and fertilizer that was delivered at subsidized interest rates and input prices to smallholders. The policy of massive distribution of maize credit to smallholders was successful in increasing the share of higher-yielding hybrid maize in total smallholder hectarage planted to maize from about 8% in 1985 to a record high of 25% in 1992 while the overall share of maize in smallholder acreage increased from 73% to 80%. However, the concentration of the loan portfolio to one drought-sensitive crop, combined with the droughts in 1992 and 1994, and political promises for writing off loan debt during the election year, led to widespread loan default and eventually to the collapse of the parastatal, Smallholder Agricultural Credit Administration (SACA) in 1994. While 400,000 farmers received credit in 1992, only 34,000 non-defaulting farmers obtained loans in 1994.

Following the major drought in 1992, the share of smallholder hectarage planted to nonmaize crops, in particular cassava and pulses, temporarily increased. Farmer's response to the perceived advantages of drought-resistant crops, the sudden collapse of the public system for distributing credit for maize production, and the recent policy orientation towards diversifying smallholder crop production may all have played a role in this change. However, following the second drought in 1994, large-scale distribution of free fertilizer and hybrid maize seed to drought-affected areas during 1995 and 1996 may have contributed to the recent revival of hybrid maize on smallholder farms despite the unfavorable price policy for maize. While subsidies on credit and fertilizer were removed in 1994 and 1995, the output markets for maize and tobacco remain controlled. The Government of Malawi sets producer prices for maize below import parity level, and aims to stabilize consumer prices in urban and rural areas within a price band through open-market sales of domestic and imported maize. The net effect of the recent input and output price policies is a decline of the relative profitability of hybrid maize versus local maize and other input-extensive food crops such as cassava.

Since 1990, the Government of Malawi has allocated an increasing share of the national tobacco quota to smallholders (15% in 1995). The quota is offered to farmers who form a club. Members of tobacco clubs obtain improved access to extension, credit, and inputs while potentially realizing higher prices by selling directly to the auction floors. In addition to quota allocations issued through clubs, a large number of smallholders also grow tobacco to eventually sell to estates, which controlled all tobacco quotas prior to reform. An intermediate buyer program was introduced in 1993 which is expected to raise farm-gate prices through increased competition at the first handler level. As a result of these policy changes, the number of smallholder households which market tobacco on auction floors increased from 10,000 in 1990 to 55,000 in 1995. For many of these farmers, tobacco is a new crop.

3 Factors Influencing the Adoption of Technological Innovations

In their literature survey of adoption of agricultural innovations, Feder et al (1985) list factors that are frequently identified as being influential in determining the adoption of an agricultural innovation. These are: i) farm size, ii) risk, iii) human capital, iv) labor availability, v) credit constraint, vi) tenure, and vii) supply constraints in inputs. Feder et al further point out that farm size is a surrogate for a large number of potentially important factors such as access to credit, capacity to bear risks, access to scarce inputs, wealth, and access to and cost of information. These factors are discussed to derive hypotheses for explaining smallholders' adoption of hybrid maize and tobacco in Malawi.

3.1 Sampling Design and Data

The data are from a survey of 404 rural households in five districts of Malawi. The survey was designed for analysis of access to and participation in four selected credit programs. The sample was therefore stratified along present and past program participation (Diagne et al 1995). The number of households participating in the four programs are: i) 77 in Malawi Rural Finance Company (MRFC), ii) 29 in Malawi Union of Savings and Credit Cooperatives (MUSCO), iii) 94 in a PMERW (Promotion of Micro-Enterprises for Rural Women), and iv) 33 in the Malawi Mudzi Fund (MMF). MRFC and MUSCO have national coverage while the others operate in a few districts. MRFC and MUSCO provide seasonal agricultural credit, mostly for tobacco and maize. The other programs specialize in credit for off-farm enterprises. PMERW and MMF programs target poor or female-headed households, and are supported by GTZ and IFAD, respectively. All programs work with member-based institutions at the village level. In the case of MUSCO, the institution is the savings and credit cooperative (SACCO), while the other programs transact with groups. MRFC and MUSCO members also gain improved access to agricultural extension (mostly for hybrid maize and tobacco), and may have a more secure supply of agricultural inputs since credit is provided in kind.

The household survey was conducted in three rounds during 1995 by the International Food Policy Research Institute (IFPRI) in colloboration with the Department of Rural Development (DRD) of the Bunda College of Agriculture. We use here data from the first round which recalled production data for 1994. Stratification of the households by participation in credit programs implies that simple descriptive means are not representative of the total population in the survey areas. The subsequent descriptive and econometric analysis does not use sampling weights so absolute figures and coefficients need to be interpreted with caution. Because of sample stratification, the frequency of households growing tobacco or hybrid maize is, for example, larger than what would have been obtained in a simple random sample.

3.2 Tobacco *versus* Maize: Some Selected Socio-Economic Characteristics

In table 1, we compare the mean and coefficient of variation for yields, gross revenue, input expenditures and gross margins per hectare by crop in households that either grow local maize, hybrid maize or tobacco. The yield is valued at the quantity-weighted sample sales price. Despite having a mean yield of only 920 kilograms per hectare, that is 35% below the yield of hybrid maize, the local maize varieties are grown in 230 out of 404 sample households. Several factors could explain this. First, households that are constrained by the prospect of failing to attain their subsistence needs choose crop mixes that deviate from those that maximize the expected utility by preferring to increase the overall mean of returns or reduce the variance of incomes (Smale et al 1995). In table 1, the coefficients of variation for yield as well as for gross margins of hybrid and local maize suggest that this explanation may be relevant in the context of Malawi. The lower the risk-bearing ability of the household, the higher could be its preference for the lower-yielding, but lower-risk local maize variety. As the ability to bear risks largely depends on the household's equity capital and access to credit, we hypothesize that the share of hybrid maize in total area planted increases with access to credit and the amount of land that is owned or permanently controlled by the household. Another reason for the production of local maize, which is then almost entirely used for home consumption, is attributed to the fact that, under smallholder processing methods of hand pounding and hammer milling, the local maize gives finer white flour (*ufa woyera*) than the hybrid maize (Smale et al 1995). Furthermore, on-farm storage losses for local varieties are lower because of their resistance to weevil attack compared to the denty, white hybrids (Ellis,1959). However, the short-cycle hybrid maize variety *MH18* is acceptable among many smallholders because of its good pounding and on-farm storage characteristics.

Table 1: Means and Coefficient of Variation for Indicators of Productivity and Input Intensity, by Crop

Variable	Local Maize n = 230		Hybrid maize n = 245		Tobacco n= 42	
	Mean	CV	Mean	CV	Mean	CV
Yield (kg/hectare)	920	99	1408	125	1173	97
Gross revenue	86	97	164	116	1029	119
Input expenditure	26	154	81	121	140	87
Gross margin	60	146	83	199	888	135
Gross margin per $ of working capital	2.3		1.0		6.3	

Source: RDD/IFPRI Rural Finance Survey covering production year 1994

Note: CV stands for coefficient of variation, expressed in per cent. All monetary values are in US-Dollar valued at 5MK/$ and relate to 1 hectare, if not specified otherwise. The crop aggregate hybrid maize comprises 2 cases of composite maize. In the sample, the following relative frequency of varieties in the aggregate for hybrid maize is observed: composite maize (0.6%), MH12 (4.9%), MH16 (3.6%), MH17 (11.4%), MH18 (34.4%), and NSCM41 (45.1%). MH18 and NSCM41 are short cycle varieties. MH18 is also a variety that has improved on-farm processing and storage characteristics.

The expenditures for inputs shown in table 1 comprise direct costs arising from the acquisition of seed, organic and mineral fertilizer, pesticides, hired labor, transport and marketing services. Input costs exclude opportunity costs of family labor. The expenditures per hectare are the lowest for local maize, and the highest for tobacco. Tobacco is not only the most labor-intensive crop, but also the most capital-intensive one. Many households face binding credit constraints, and the ranking of crops with respect to gross margins per unit of working capital will therefore influence the crop mix. In the drought year of 1994, hybrid maize had the lowest capital productivity among the three crops. Furthermore, the acquisition of information about a new technology represents a fixed cost that favors larger farms over smaller ones. The mean gross margins in table 1 indicate considerable comparative advantage of tobacco *versus* hybrid or local maize in utilizing the scarce factors of land and capital. On average, hybrid maize has a comparative advantage over local maize when land is the binding constraint, but loses out when access to capital is restricted. Furthermore, labor availability is not likely to be a binding constraint in the majority of rural households because of the existence of an active rural labor market. Landless or factually landless households often sell their labor services, frequently at wages below the official minimum wage rate. Labor constraints, however, frequently arise during peak planting season when households lack the liquidity to pay for labor services, as is the case in many poor, often female-headed households.

So far we discussed hypotheses related to the following factors potentially affecting adoption of hybrid maize or tobacco: farm size, access to credit, labor availability, risk, risk-bearing ability, access to and cost of information. Table 2 provides further information for these and the remaining factors. Of the 404 sample households, twenty-two households do not farm and six households grow neither maize nor tobacco. The remaining 382 households are separated into four groups, subject to whether a household grows only local or hybrid maize or both or also tobacco.

Mean gross revenue, input expenditure and gross margins per hectare are highest in the tobacco-growing households and lowest in those households that grow only local maize. A second pattern is that the shares of land planted with local maize or hybrid maize are lowest in the tobacco growing households and highest in those households that grow both hybrid and local maize. Except for tobacco households, the shares of land allocated to maize exceed 80 percent. Third, per capita land ownership is highest in the tobacco-growing households, and lowest in those households that only grow local maize. It is hypothesized that with higher land per capita, (i) the relative importance of producing local maize for home consumption in case of remote or unreliable maize markets decreases and (ii) the risk-bearing ability of the household increases. Land ownership is defined as land for which the household holds a formal title or has a usufruct right under customary law.

A fourth pattern in table 2 is that tobacco-growing households show the highest level in all of the three human capital indicators, i.e. the size of the household and the age and level of education of its head. In contrast, local maize producers score lowest in these indicators. Fifth, households in the latter group are headed more frequently by women. This suggests that female-headed households are less likely to adopt cash crops, an outcome that can be affected by a host of factors such as the lack of access to credit or extension services and the time constraints resulting from farm and home production (Kumar 1994), or more unstable and insufficient access to land (Milimo 1991). Sixth, membership in any kind of agricultural or off-farm credit program is lowest in the group of households that grow only local maize, and highest for tobacco growers. We hypothesize that program membership is important for the adoption of hybrid maize and tobacco.

Table 2: Means of Socio-Economic Characteristics of Households, by Cropping
Pattern

	Household plants				All Households	
	local maize only	hybrid maize only	hybrid and local maize	tobacco	Mean	SD
Variable	n = 114	n = 123	n = 97	n = 42	n = 404	n = 404
Gross revenue per hectare	110	166	162	459	174	240
Input expenditure per hectare	23	66	55	77	48	66
Gross margin per hectare	87	100	108	382	126	221
Share of area planted (%) to						
- local maize	81.3	0	46.6	23.4	38.7	38.5
- hybrid maize (SHCRHYBM)	0	81.9	42.5	39.9	43.4	40.5
- tobacco (SHCRTOBA)	0	0	0	29.6	3.3	11.2
Share of area with crop failure	71.2	68.0	63.0	49.7	64.6	42.7
Area of land possessed (LANDAREH)	1.5	2.4	2.7	2.8	2.2	3.7
Area possessed per capita (CAPLAND)	0.38	0.51	0.51	0.52	0.45	0.73
Household size (HHSIZE)	4.98	5.31	5.99	6.52	5.47	2.47
Dependency ratio (DEPRAT2)	0.79	0.73	0.86	0.8	0.79	0.75
Characteristics of head:						
- Sex (0=male, 1= female) SEXH	0.68	0.71	0.76	0.88	0.73	0.44
- Age in years (AGEH)	47	43	47	48	45	14
- Education (EDUCH)	1.9	2.2	2.1	2.5	2.1	0.9
- Member of credit program (CMEMH)	0.24	0.31	0.38	0.5	0.31	0.46
- Distance to parents'home (km)(PHVKM)	25	35	21	2	33	95
Number of cattle possessed (CATTL)	0.5	0.2	0.8	0.8	0.5	2.1
Number of small animals possessed (SMALANIM)	4.8	6.7	8.5	11.6	7	10.9
Monthly Per capita crop income (CAM23GM)	1.9	1.8	3.3	11.6	3.2	7.0
Monthly Per Capita expenditure (AD4MEXPD)	6.5	11.5	8.8	6.1	8.9	9.8
District dummy Mangochi (MANGOCHI)	0.06	0.59	0.12	0	0.25	0.43
District dummy Nkhotakota (NKOTA)	0.19	0.2	0.06	0.21	0.17	0.38
District dummy Rumphi (RUMPHI)	0.15	0.05	0.29	0.55	0.19	0.39
District dummy Linthipe (DEDZA)	0.44	0.08	0.33	0.07	0.25	0.43

Source: RDD/IFPRI Rural Finance Survey
Notes: SD stands for standard deviation. Of the 404 sample households, twenty-two do not farm and six households do neither grow tobacco nor maize. The first three columns refer to households that do not grow tobacco, but only maize besides other food crops. All monetary values are in US-Dollar. All area measurements are in hectare (ha). The dependency ratio DEPRAT2 is defined as members younger than 18 years over adults. Education is a variable with value = 1 for illiterate and value = 5 for high school diploma or above, while three other values measure education levels in between these two extremes. With respect to computation of area planted that was affected by crop failure, each respondent had to rate the harvest by crop (for maize also by variety) as being good, average or low. The area planted to those crops that received a low rating are categorised as being affected by partial or complete crop failure. The share of area with crop failure is then computed for each household as the area affected by crop failure over total area planted. The effects of the drought during production year 1993/94 varied considerably by district. The mean shares of area affected by crop failure were the following in each of the districts: Mangochi 84%, Rumphi 69%, Dedza 64%, Nkhotakota 56%, Dowa 38%.

4   Model Specification

The decision to adopt technology, and the resulting income and consumption outcomes of this decision, can be directly modeled as part of the household's utility function. Several authors have used recursive econometric models to explain the adoption of agricultural technology and cash crops and related income and food consumption effects (Kumar 1994 and von Braun et al 1989). A similar framework is applied in this paper. The data set contains production data for the year 1994 while consumption data refers to the subsequent planting period in the production year 1995. We conceptualize adoption, income generation and consumption as a sequential process whereby previous cropping decisions predetermine income and finally consumption.

When crop technologies are divisible, as is the case for hybrid maize and tobacco, Feder et al (1985) suggest that the extent of adoption is best measured by the hectarage share of the crop under consideration. While the participation in a credit program has been hypothesized to influence the adoption of hybrid maize (Kumar 1994; Smale et al 1995), past research rarely considered the potential simultaneity bias that arises from using the endogenous credit participation as a regressor in the adoption equation (Zeller et al 1996). It is hypothesized that the share S allocated to a particular crop is a function of a vector x of exogenous variables and the endogenous credit program participation, A, such that

$$S = \alpha_2 x + \gamma A + E_2. \qquad (1)$$

The problem arises because unmeasured household-level variables affect both program participation, A, and the adoption of technology S. With the resulting endogeneity, OLS regression of S on participation in a credit program A is likely to result in biased estimates. For unbiased estimation, a variant of the standard sample selection model is applied:

$$A^* = \alpha_1 v + E_1 \qquad (2)$$
$$S = \alpha_2 x + \gamma A + E_2. \qquad (3)$$

$A = 1$ if $A^* > 0$ and $A = 0$ otherwise

The first equation states that, A, access to a credit program depends on a set of variables represented in v. The second equation states that adoption S depends on another set of variables x and access to credit program A. The problem of simultaneity bias arises when equation (3) is estimated by OLS. This is because the random error terms E_1 and E_2 are likely to be correlated since unobserved household variables affect both A and S. A two-stage procedure can be used to produce unbiased and consistent estimates of adoption given that participation in a credit program is an endogenous variable (Maddalla,1983). In the first stage, an estimate A^* of A is obtained by the probit maximum likelihood method for equation (2). The model follows in principle the paper by Zeller (1994), but does not apply a bivariate probit model which would allow one to distinguish between the household's decision to apply for membership and the peer's and program officer's decision to accept or reject the application. The predicted probability is then used in the second stage to obtain estimates of the cropping shares S for local and hybrid maize and tobacco.

In the second step of the recursive model, the effect of technology adoption on gross margin generated from crop production is estimated. The dependent variable is monthly per-capita gross margin valued in US-Dollar. It is computed as the sum of gross margins from all crop enterprises undertaken during the production year 1994. This sum is divided by the household size, and further converted to a monthly basis using an exchange rate of 5 MK/US-$. In the third step of the recursive model, the effects on food and non-food monthly consumption expenditures per capita is estimated. Means and standard deviations for the regression variables are found in table 2.

5   Interpretation of Model Results

In order to differentiate between the effects of non-agricultural credit programs (i.e. PMERW and MMF) and agricultural credit programs (i.e. MUSCO and MRFC), two separate PROBIT models have been estimated (see first two columns of table 3). The regression results for cropping shares of hybrid maize, tobacco and local maize, and those for income and food expenditures, are listed in the subsequent columns.

The probability of participation in both program types rises with increasing land possession (LANDAREH), but at a decreasing rate (SQLAND). Second, the two coefficients for the indicators of household liquidity, the number of cattle (CATTL) and that of small animals (SMALANIM), have the expected positive sign. The coefficient for the latter is significant for non-agricultural credit programs (i.e. PMERW and Mudzi Fund), indicating that the number of small animals may be used by the group as a screening criteria for potential members because sales of small animals can help in repaying the loan or smoothing consumption in case of an income shock. Third, the coefficients for the indicators of human capital (i.e. AGEH for age and EDUCH for education of household head) and indicators of risk-bearing capacity (i.e. SEXH for gender of household head and DEP18A for dependency ratio, cutoff = 18 years) have the expected signs, except for the age of the household head for the participation in agricultural credit programs. However, none of these coefficients is significant, with the exception of gender of household head: Female-headed households have a high probability of being accepted in either the PMERW or the Mudzi Fund program. Fourth, the distance in kilometers to the home of the head's parents (PHVKM), and its squared term (SQPHVKM), are used as indicators of possession of social capital. It is hypothesized that individuals that live in the same village as their parents or close to their parents have more friends and relatives who can help them get accepted into a group or help them in retaining program membership in times of difficulties to repay the loan. For the agricultural credit programs, the coefficients for the distance and the squared term carry the expected signs, and are highly significant. However, lower social capital implies a higher probability for joining a non-agricultural credit program. This result is explained by the fact that both PMERW and Mudzi Fund target poorer, often female-headed households in their credit programs. Poverty has material and social dimensions, the latter being reflected for example by access to informal self-help networks.

Storage and crop production risks are expected to affect crop mix. The index variable RISKSTOR indicates the number of serious food storage risks which households in the community are facing. The higher its value, the more serious are storage risks which can eliminate the food stored for the next pre-harvest season. The index variable CROPRISK indicates the number of serious risks which crop production is exposed to in the village. We hypothesize that an increase in both storage and crop production risks increases the probability that households apply for membership in a credit program. However, credit programs may be less inclined to accept members in risk-prone communities because of higher probability of loan default. As a result of the hypothesized divergent demand and supply effects, the expected signs are indetermined. The regression finds that more storage risk significantly increases the probability of being a program member while crop risk have the opposite effect. We conclude therefore that credit programs appear to shy away from areas which are exposed to covariate crop production risks.

The regression results for the shares of hybrid maize, tobacco and local maize are shown in the third, forth and fifth column, respectively. In the following, we highlight major similarities and differences. The coefficients for the ratio of land owned to family labor (CAPLAND), and its squared term (SCAPLAND), are highly insignificant for all three crops. To explain this, we note that hybrid maize grown with the production techniques of smallholder farmers does not require any up-front investment while smallholder tobacco necessitates only a minor investment. Economies of scale for both crops are therefore negligible within the range of farm sizes of smallholders. The coefficients for predicted membership in agricultural credit programs (PCMEMA) and in the off-farm credit program (PCMEMN) carry the expected sign for tobacco, and are highly significant for agricultural credit programs. In fact, being a member of an agricultural credit program raises the cropping share of tobacco by an absolute amount of 15.5 percent. Moreover, being a member in MRFC or MUSCO raises the hybrid maize share by an absolute amount of 44.9 percent, while it reduces that of local maize by 79.4 percent.

The effect of non-agricultural credit programs on cropping shares for hybrid and local maize is opposite from that of agricultural credit programs. Members of

Table 3: Determinants of Technology Adoption and Effects on Income and Food Security (Expanded Model)

	Credit access		Share planted to				
Regressand Variable	NON-AG CRED PMEMAG Coefficient	AG CREDIT PMEMN Coefficient	HYBRID M SHYBM Coefficient	TOBACCO STOBA Coefficient	LOC MAIZE SLOCM Coefficient	INCOME CAM23GMD Coefficient	EXPENDITUR AD4MEXP Coefficient
Constant	-7.426	-1.874****	0.442****	-0.069****	-0.629****	2.781***	11.019****
LANDAREH	0.184*	0.383****					
SQLAND	-0.013	-0.027***					
CATTL	0.025	-0.038					
SMALANIM	0.010	0.012*					
PHVKM	0.007**	-0.010***					
SQPHVKM	-0.00002*	0.00002***					
SEXH	-0.209	0.730****	-0.031	0.001	0.085		
AGEH	-0.004	0.002				-0.046*	-1.141
DEP18A	0.278	0.499	-0.116	0.027	0.067		
EDUCH	0.164*	0.026	0.012	0.008	-0.039*	1.065***	-7.501***
RISKSTOR	0.414**	0.425***	-0.079*	-0.018	0.055		
CROPRISK	-.090	-0.110*	-0.021*	0.005	0.006		
Mangochi	4.986	-0.950***	0.903****	0.0009	-0.708****	-3.356*	6.505****
Nkhotakota	5.356	-0.803**	0.277****	0.041	-0.553****	-0.439	-0.608
Rumphi	5.322	-0.606*	0.336****	0.073**	-0.254**	-3.428**	-4.714**
Dedza	4.133	-0.291	0.114	-0.010	-0.063	2.123**	-1.266
CAPLAND			0.009	0.003	0.035	2.788****	
SCAPLAND			0.003	-0.0005	-0.0005	-0.278****	
OPPCOST			-0.008***	0.0004	0.001		
PCMEMNb			-0.466**	0.091	0.570**	1.122	
PCMEMAb			0.449***	0.155***	-0.794***	3.204	
PSHYBMb						8.661**	
PSTOBAb							
PCAM23GMb						68.385****	
Adjusted R^2	89.7a	79.7a	41.0	16.0	27.0	17.0	0.758****
N	380	380	380	380	380	380	12.0 380

Notes: SQLAND, SQPHVKM and SCAPLAND are squared terms of LANDAREH, PHVKM and CAPLAND, respectively.
a Estimated by a probit model. Value is the percentage of observations predicted correctly.
b Predicted values (in ascending sequence) of MEMN, MEMA, SHYBM, STOBA, SLOCM, and CAM23GM
*, **, *** and **** significant at the 15, 10, 5 and 1 percent level, respectively.

PMERW and Mudzi Fund significantly reduce their share of hybrid maize, and grow instead more tobacco and local maize. We explain these results by various factors. First, the in-kind delivery of loans in agricultural credit programs would entail transaction costs interested in households for converting the loan to other uses, as they would have to sell their maize inputs. Hence, a bias towards hybrid maize production is created. Second, agricultural credit programs focus their extension and other activities on hybrid maize and tobacco. Non-agricultural credit programs, however, disburse the credit in cash, and focus on off-farm enterprise development. Third, households have a limited risk-bearing capacity. Members in non-agricultural credit programs take on additional risks in their off-farm enterprises, so they appear to reduce their risk exposure in the on-farm enterprises by substituting hybrid for local maize and tobacco. This interpretation is further reinforced by the community variables on storage and crop production risks. Households who live in communities with high food (i.e. maize) storage and high crop production risks plant 7.9% and 2.1% less of hybrid maize, respectively. Another policy-relevant result is that related to the variable OPPCOST which measures the transportation and time cost for commuting from the village in which the household resides to the nearest center of the parastatal agricultural marketing agency ADMARC. OPPCOST is therefore an indicator of transaction costs in sourcing agricultural inputs and in marketing products. The result shows that households in remote villages which are farther away from ADMARC centers, had a significantly lower hybrid maize share. Finally, the gender of household head and the dependency ratio have no significant effect on cropping choice. The higher the education of the head of the household, the lower is the share of local maize.

In columns 6 and 7 of table 3, we show the results for the effects of technology adoption and cropping shares on crop income and consumption expenditures. The regression function for crop income controls for the household's endowment in land relative to family labor (CAPLAND) and for human capital (EDUCH, AGEH), while assessing the effects of cropping shares for hybrid maize and tobacco (PSHYBM and PSTOBA). All signs in this equation are as hypothesized, except for the age of the household head which is used to reflect on farm management experience. Average per capita monthly income from crop production significantly increases with higher land endowment per capita, but with a decreasing effect at the margin (SCAPLAND), and with higher education of the household head. Both the cropping share for hybrid maize and tobacco significantly increase crop income, with tobacco having a relatively large effect. Income significantly determines subsequent consumption expenditures. On average, roughly 90% of these expenditures are for food while the remainder is spent on basic non-food items, such as clothing, education, and health. We conclude that adoption of hybrid maize and tobacco contributes to household food security. Future research is required to investigate whether the improved crop income and consumption expenditures at the household level also result in improved nutritional status, in particular for women and children, and whether increased production of labor-intensive tobacco jeopardizes school attendance and child care.

6   Lessons Learned

Several lessons for the formulation of agricultural policy are deduced. First, the granting of tobacco production quota to smallholders has provided smallholders with the opportunity to grow a new profitable cash crop. The resulting rapid adoption of tobacco as a new crop is not the outcome of technology innovation, but of policy reform and related institutional changes in the tobacco subsector. Second, we find that households with small farm size or female-headed households are able to adopt capital-intensive crops, such as hybrid maize and tobacco, if policies improve the households's access to credit, input and output markets. Third, participation in agricultural credit programs is found to be lower for households which live in villages with higher crop production risks. This is likely to be caused by supply side effects. Agricultural credit programs shy away from these villages because of higher expected loan default. In order to better serve risk-prone areas, the credit programs could introduce member-financed and pooled emergency funds for covering covariate risks of loan defaults. Fourth, we find that the household's transaction costs in accessing the nearest parastatal market outlet for agricultural inputs and outputs has a positive and significant influence on the hybrid maize, share as private traders have only begun to operate in remote rural markets. This finding supports our conclusion that access to agricultural markets and related improvements in rural infrastructure and marketing institutions are essential for adoption of new technology and crops.

Fifth, the adoption of hybrid maize among Malawian smalllholders will critically depend on the pricing policy for maize and fertilizer. The current policy in favor of rural and urban net buyers of maize is to be seen as a hindrance to increased maize production. Combined with the removal of subsidies for inputs and credit, hybrid maize has lost some of its comparative advantage over local maize, cassava and other calorie-rich food crops. Under the current policy setting and population growth, food imports are likely to become an ever-increasing fiscal burden. Other policy instruments that have the potential to more efficiently target the urban and rural poor and provide a social safety net should be explored and tested in order to eventually be able to end the price disincentives for smallholder maize production, without jeopardizing the food security of poor urban and rural households. Finally, during the past decade, research for breeding maize varieties with improved drought resistance and on-farm processing and storage characteristics has successfully contributed to greater acceptance of hybrid maize technology among smallholder farmers. While maize is the most important crop for household food security in Malawi, breeding and diffusion of alternative cash and food crop varieties, in particular various legumes and especially cassava, need to be more emphasized in order to decrease the vulnerability of the maize-dependent smallholder sector to drought and to diversify food consumption and nutrition.

References

Government of Malawi. Implementation of the Poverty Alleviation Programme. August 1994.
von Braun, J., D. Puetz, and P. Webb. 1989. Irrigation Technology and Commercialization of Rice in The Gambia: Effects on Income and Nutrition. Research report No. 75. Washington, D.C.: International Food Policy Research Institute.
Diagne, A., M. Zeller, and C. Mataya. 1995. Rural Financial Markets and Household Food Security in Malawi: Impacts of PMERW Credit Schemes on the Socio-Economic Situation of Rural Women. First interim report, Lilongwe, September 1995.
Ellis, R.T. The Food Properties of Flint and Dent Maize. East African Agricultural Journal 24, No. 4 (1959): 251-53.
Feder, G., R.E. Just and D. Zilberman 1985. Adoption of Agricultural Innovations in Developing Countries: A Survey. Economic Development and Cultural Change, Vol. 33, No. 2 (1985): 255-294.
Kumar, S. K. 1994. Adoption of Hybrid Maize in Zambia: Effects on Gender Roles, Food Consumption and Nutrition. *Research Report No. 100*. Washington, D.C.: International Food Policy Research Institute.
Maddala, G. S. 1983. Limited Dependent and Qualitative Variables in Econometrics. Cambridge University Press.
Milimo, J. T. 1991. Land Tenure and Agriculture Development in Eastern Province. In Adopting Improved Farm Technology: A Study of Smallholder Farmers in Eastern Province, Zambia, ed. R.Celis, J.T. Milimo, and S. Wanmali. Washington, D.C.: IFPRI.
Mtwali, K.M. Current Status of and Reform Proposals for Agriculture: Malawi. In: Agricultural Policy Reforms and Regional Market Integration in Malawi, Zambia, and Zimbabwe (eds. A. Valdes and K. Muir-Leresche). IFPRI 1993.
Smale, M., P.W. Heisey, and H.D. Leathers. Maize of the Ancestors and Modern Varieties: The Microeconomics of High-Yielding Variety Adoption in Malawi. Economic Development and Cultural Change 34, No. 2 (1995): 351-368.
Zeller, M. Determinants of credit rationing: A Study of Informal Lenders and Formal Credit Groups in Madagascar. World Development, 22, No. 12 (1994): 895-1907.
Zeller, M. The Demand for Financial Services by Rural Households – Conceptual Framework and Empirical Findings. Quarterly Journal of International Agriculture, 34, No.2 (1995):149-171.
Zeller, M., A. Ahmed, S. Babu, S. Broca, A. Diagne, and M. Sharma. 1996. Rural Financial Policies for Food Security of the Poor: Methodologies for a multi-country research project. Discussion Paper No. 11, Food Consumption and Nutrition Division, IFPRI.

Agronomic Evaluation and Socio-Economic Limitations of Green Manuring with the Legumes *Sesbania Rostrata* and *Aeschynomene Afraspera* in Wetland Rice

J.C.G. Ottow[1], K.H. Diekmann[1] and M. Becker[2]
[1]Institut für Angewandte Mikrobiologie, Universität Giessen
Senckenbergstrasse 3, D-35390 Giessen, Germany
[2]West African Rice Development Association (WARDA),
Bouaké, Côte d'Ivoire

Abstract

Pre-rice grown flood-tolerant Sesbania rostrata or Aeschynomene afraspera may fix N_2 in stem-nodules within 45 to 55 days up to 80-150 kg N per ha even on flooded soils low in available P and K. The performance and N-accumulation of these legumes were even higher on sandy low fertile soils than on clay soils with high potential productivity. The mineral fertilizer equivalence of these green manures (GM) ranges between 30 to 90 kg urea-N per ha, depending on the site and the season. High yielding lowland rice (such as IR 64) may use GM-N more efficiently than urea-N up to an input rate of 75 kg N per ha. At average N-accumulation rates, GM with the legumes mentioned above can completely substitute for mineral fertilizer N at current average application rates. A great variation in GM performance (photoperiodism) and N-accumulation (depending on the soil and the season), the lack of seeds to the farmer, the labor-intensive work (chopping the stems by hand and the laborious incorporation of GM with animals) as well as the exclusive farmers' preference of mineral fertilizer N are the major agronomic constraints to accept GM. Extensive extension work (with widespread demonstration plots) on the farmers' fields may help to disseminate and accept GM as pre-rice "biofertilizer". At present, only within the subsistence low-input rice growing farmers on low fertility soils pre-rice GM technology seems to be a temporary strategy, particularly in environments where physico-chemical soil properties and water management are marginal for food crop production. Socio-economic conditions such as cost of land, the use of cash crops rather than GM, costly crop establishment and subsidized mineral fertilizer N should be considered as the major factors limiting the adoption of pre-rice GM. The lesson we learned so far is that even poor farmers seem to be reluctant to accept pre-rice GM biofertilizer despite its multiple advantages. This seems to be a matter of image, recognition, extension and the general education level of the farmer rather than agronomic inferiority.

Keywords_____
Nitrogen-fixation, aquatic legumes, biotechnology, S. rostrata

Introduction

By the year 2025 the world population will reach about 8,5 billion, 7 billion of whom will live in the developing countries, largely in South East Asia and Sub-Saharan Africa. The staple food of the majority will be rice. Rural population have to depend increasingly on a declining area of cropland per person. To secure future food production, rice growing technologies must 1) increase yields considerably per ha at less cost, and 2) maintain or even improve land sustainability particularly of marginally productive soils. Future rice demand (7 to 8 t/ha) should and can be met by introducing knowledge-based new technologies applicable to the numerous low-input poor rice farmers. At present, the average rice grain yield per ha in South East Asia amounts to 4 t, but in West Africa only 0.8 t are obtained. Nitrogen is the most important yield limiting nutrient. In general, rice requires about 19-21 kg N to produce 1 t of rice. To produce higher grain yields, the rice plant must obtain larger amounts of N. Demographic forecasts by the International Rice Research Institute in Los Baños, Philippines, indicate that world rice production must increase by more than 60 % in the next 30 years to keep up with population growth and income-induced demand for food. Consequently, the demand for N to fertilize rice will increase significantly, particularly on the marginally productive soils that should be cultivated more intensively in West Africa, South America and South East Asia. As a consequence, more and more non-renewable fossil-based energy would have to be used to support crop production. Because of economic and ecological concerns as well as of the increasing price squeeze that farmers in developing countries are facing, there is an urgent need to look for alternative N-sources (IRRI Rice Almanac 1993; Conway et al. 1994). Green manuring (GM) with the fast growing, N_2-fixing, stem-nodulating flood-tolerant legumes *Sesbania rostrata* and *Aeschynomene afraspera* during a short period prior to transplanting (or seeding) wetland rice seems to be a promising strategy. GM with these legumes may cover the N-demand of the rice crop and increase sustainability by improving the physical-chemical properties as well as the available N-pool of the soil. In respect to the growing concerns about rice soil sustainability and increasing subsistence food requirements per ha, an agronomic and socio-economic evaluation of the new nitrogen-fixing, stem-nodulating GM mentioned above is carried out in the present paper. Data have been collected from a series of different field experiments that were carried out during the last 10 years in the Philippines.

Materials and Methods

In close cooperation with the International Rice Research Institute (IRRI) at Los Baños, Philippines, and supported by the GTZ, Eschborn, Germany, a broad variety of field experiments at IRRI's experimental farm as well as at different farmers' sites in Luzon were carried out using _S.rostrata_ and/or _A.afraspera_ as pre-rice GM. The effects of GM on biomass production, N_2-fixation, N-release and recovery by rice and on residual N-uptake by succeeding rice crops were studied. Rice yields were compared to mineral fertilizer (up to 60 to 90 kg N as urea/ha) and untreated controls. On a number of different marginally productive Philippine soils (low in P and K) the performance and nitrogen accumulation by the legumes were studied in greenhouse and field experiments. The effects of mineral nitrogen, P and K on biomass, nitrogen fixation and N-accumulation were also examined. The apparent release of exchangeable ammonium-N from GM incorporated in different soils was measured and compared to urea hydrolysis. In addition, the apparent N-recovery fraction, the agronomic N-use efficiency and the mineral fertilizer equivalence of GM were determined in relation to urea.

Synchronizing N-supply from incorporated plant residues with the N-demand of IR 72 may increase the plants' N-use efficiency and reduce N-losses. To examine this hypothesis, GM and rice straw with various lignin to N-ratios (L/N) and urea were compared using N-release, rice N-uptake, N-use efficiency, grain yield and total N-balance as criteria. In further field experiments at IRRI, 4 different practices of _S.rostrata_ as GM (zero and common tillage, relay cropping in rice for 2 or 4 weeks) and 4 mineral N-levels (0, 30, 60 and 90 kg N as urea per ha) were examined under irrigated lowland conditions with 3 rice crops per year. _S.rostrata_ was grown twice a year during a 40-60 day dry-wet and wet-dry transition period prior to rice transplanting. Based on the yields, mineral fertilizer equivalence and economic feasibility of GM were both estimated. With respect to socio-economic and biophysical factors, GM niches and strategies for GM inclusion into rice farming systems are identified. For details on the various experiments reported above, the reader is referred to the original work (Becker et al. 1986, 1988, 1990a,b, 1991, 1994a,b, 1995a,b; Diekmann et al. 1993, 1996; Engels et al. 1995).

Results and Discussion

Origin of Wild Germ Plasm of the Aquatic Legumes

The original seeds were collected in 1986 from 18 different locations in Senegal between 12 and 18° north of the equator (Dittert et al. 1988). The ability of these legumes to fix nitrogen in their stem-nodules was discovered by Y.

Dommergues, B.L. Dreyfus and D. Alazard in the period between 1980 to '84 at the Laboratoire de Microbiologie des Sols, ORSTOM, Dakar, Senegal (Dreyfus et al. 1984; Ottow 1984). Today the nitrogen fixing rhizobia in the stem-nodules of *S.rostrata* are allocated to *Azorhizobium caulinodans* and those of *A.afraspera* to *Photorhizobium* spp. (Ladha et al. 1992). Both *S.rostrata* as well as *A.afraspera* belong to the Faboideae (formerly Pallionoideae) family of legumes.

Seeds as well as pure cultures of the respective stem-nodulating rhizobia (ORS 571 from *A.caulinodans* and ORS 322 from *Photorhizobium* spp.) were transferred to IRRI in the Philippines and used in the various experiments. In all experiments the rhizobia strains ORS 571 and ORS 322 were used to inoculate the stems after three weeks by means of a common knapsack sprayer (Becker et al. 1991). It should be stressed that the germ plasm of both aquatic legumes was obtained from non-domesticated wild plants. Both legumes produce nodules on roots and stems and can grow rapidly under flooded as well as under dry conditions.

Biotechnological Advantages

Based on about 10 years of joint research, the pre-rice grown and incorporated GM concerned has shown a number of outstanding properties that seem to make this biofertilizer technology agronomically attractive, particularly for the resource-poor low input farmer on marginally productive soils or in areas in which mineral fertilizer N is unavailable. Among the promising features are:

- Accumulation rates of 80 to 150 kg N/ha within a 45-55 day growth period in irrigated pre-rice niches (Becker et al. 1986, 1988, 1990, 1991; Ladha et al. 1992; Diekmann et al. 1993, 1996). Relatively high N-accumulation rates may also be obtained on coarse-textured soils deficient in available P and K (Diekmann et al. 1993, 1996). Growth and nitrogen fixation, may decrease however on acid soils, particularly with Fe- and Al-toxicity (Ladha et al. 1992; Engels et al. 1995). Generally, *S.rostrata* is more sensitive to soil constraints than *A.afraspera*.

- The stimulation effects of small amounts of mineral N (i.e. urea, up to about 30 kg N/ha) on biomass production, stem-nodule formation and N-accumulation (Becker et al. 1986, 1990a,b). Nitrogen fixation and accumulation in the root-nodules, however, were repressed. With pre-rice GM, supplemented with 30 kg N/ha (urea) the highest rice yield was obtained in the subsequent crop (IR 64). This rice yield (5.1 t/ha) was significantly higher compared to GM alone (4.9 t/ha), to 60 kg N/ha (4.6 t/ha) or to the untreated control (3,5 t/ha) on various nutrient-poor soils of central Luzon.

- Average rice yields of 4 to 5 t/ha obtained after incorporation of pre-rice grown GM during a 45-55 day transition period. These yields correspond to rice grain production obtained with about 60 kg N/ha (urea). In general, GM incorporation increased rice grain yield by 1 to 2 t/ha over the unfertilized control (see table 1; Becker et al. 1988, 1990a,b; Ladha et al. 1992; Diekmann et al. 1993, 1996).

- An apparent GM-N recovery (= N-uptake in the fertilized treatment minus the N-uptake of the control divided by N applied as GM or mineral N, in %) and agronomic GM-N efficiency (expressed in kg of rice grain increase over the unfertilized control per kg of N added) are similar or slightly lower than those of urea-N (Ladha et al. 1992; Becker et al. 1988, 1990a; Diekmann et al. 1993, 1996). The lower agronomic efficiency (AE) levels (< 15 kg grain/kg N) were generally found in experiments where the amount of GM-N exceeded 100 kg/ha (see table 1; Morris et al. 1989; Diekmann et al. 1996).
- A rapid release of N (as ammonium) after incorporation and puddling, which is delayed compared to urea, but corresponds better to the demand of the growing crop (Becker et al. 1994a; Diekmann et al. 1996). Consequently, N-losses reached about 35 % from urea (as ammonia) but only 6-10 % from *S. rostrata* (both at 60 kg N/ha). Besides, GM improved long-term soil productivity by residual N-effects acting as slow-release fertilizers (Becker et al. 1994a,b).
- Positive effects on soil microbial biomass (nutrient immobilization with a rapid turn-over rate) as well as on physical-chemical soil properties such as CEC, mobilization of trace elements and soft puddle (Ladha et al. 1992).
- Effective weed control on the soil during the transition period (Becker et al. 1988).

In the long run, GM incorporation may help to restore degraded soils and could enhance sustainability of rice based cropping systems. So far, at average N-accumulation rates, GM with *S.rostrata* or *A.afraspera* can entirely substitute for mineral N at current average application rates with similar agronomic N-use efficiencies (Becker et al. 1988, 1991, 1995a,b; Morris et al. 1989; Ladha et al. 1992).

Disadvantages and Agronomic Limitations

Despite the promising advantages, GM with the aquatic legumes in question have several major constraints that limit their use in wetland rice systems. These restrictions are:

- early flowering and thus restricted biomass production and N-accumulation in agroecological regions or in seasons with a day length less than 13 hours (Becker et al. 1988, 1995a,b; Ladha et al. 1992);

Table 1: Effect of Green Manure in Comparison to Urea on Rice Yield (IR64) and on other Yield Parameters at Different Sites in the Philippines

Site and N source	Grain yield (Mg ha⁻¹)	Total dry matter (Mg ha⁻¹)	Harvest index	Total N uptake (kg ha⁻¹)	ANR (%)	AE (%)	Tiller (no. m⁻²)	Panicle (no. m⁻²)	1000-grain weight (g)
IRRI									
S. rostrata	6.5	13.9	0.45	154	41.3	10.7	450	441	26.1
A. afraspera	6.5	13.4	0.47	124	28.8	14.4	485	451	25.0
Urea	6.3	12.0	0.50	119	45.0	23.3	433	395	26.7
No fertilizer N	4.9	9.6	0.49	92	-	-	372	344	25.1
Floridablanca									
S. rostrata	4.9	10.5	0.45	116	23.7	7.4	485	417	23.0
A. afraspera	5.2	10.8	0.46	115	22.5	8.7	460	428	26.0
Urea	4.6	9.9	0.45	102	51.7	18.3	407	386	26.6
No fertilizer N	3.5	8.2	0.41	71	-	-	332	305	25.8
Tarlac I									
S. rostrata	4.6	9.8	0.47	123	57.7	14.4	444	430	22.0
Urea	4.3	8.4	0.51	95	60.0	2.7	350	333	22.1
No fertilizer N	3.0	5.9	0.50	59	-	-	276	265	22.0
Tarlac II									
S. rostrata	4.0	9.4	0.41	108	38.7	10.9	455	441	20.9
Urea	2.6	6.7	0.36	59	-	0	463	455	18.2
No fertilizer N	2.7	5.9	0.44	62	-	-	359	354	18.9
LSD (0.05)	0.4	0.5	0.04	12	-	-	43	35	1.2

Mg = 1,000 kg; ANR = Apparent N-Recovery = $\frac{NP - NP_0}{NF}$; AE = kg rice grain increase over unfertilized control per kg of N-added

Source: Diekmann et al. 1996.

- the general lack of appropriate seeds to the farmer (Becker et al. 1988, 1995a,b);
- the labor-intensive incorporation of the GM (Becker et al. 1988, 1995a,b);
- the need for sufficient water during a pre-rice growing period of at least 40 to 45 days (Becker et al. 1995);
- the possibility of an explosive incidence of pests and diseases once GM (with a small genetic variability) becomes widely used in a particular region. The use of pesticides to save a standing GM crop is economically completely unacceptable, particularly in low input agricultural systems.

These biological limitations make the application of GM with aquatic legumes as alternative high N-sources somewhat questionable.

Major Factors Limiting the Adoption of GM by Farmers

At present, there are major biological, agronomical and socio-economic factors that limit the introduction of GM into lowland rice, also by the poor low input farmer. Non-adoption of GM with aquatic legumes at the farm-level should primarily be ascribed to:

- the unreliability of these non-domesticated "wild" biofertilizers because of sensitivity to photoperiodism, the lack of appropriate seeds, and possible severe damage by pests (performance variability);
- the time-consuming and labor-intensive requirements of GM incorporation and rice crop preparation (GM cutting and chopping by hand as well as ploughing and intensive land preparation with animal power);
- the high price for land and labor costs;
- the relatively low (subsidized) price of mineral fertilizer N; and, thus far
- a social low GM image to the farmer and his family.

If GM with aquatic legumes is to be adopted at the farm-level, suitable and competitive biophysical and socio-economic scenarios must be identified in which GM has clear advantages over other non-rice crops and mineral fertilizer N.

Identification of GM Niches on Socio-Economic and Biophysical Factors

The introduction and adoption of GM at the farm-level in a new area will require intensive and suitable extension work with convincing demonstration plots. This is a matter of governmental policy. Costly extension programs, however, will be successful only if the biophysical and socio-economical conditions are suitable to accept GM. The most essential economic factors affecting GM use are the input prices for land, labor and fertilizers (Garrity and Flinn 1988; Becker et al. 1995a,b). One of the main factors limiting GM adoption seems to be the land price. Wherever land can be used for the production of cash crops, soil improving GM legumes cannot compete. The space of GM in irrigated rice is therefore very limited since the period after cultivation of rice or wheat is preferred for cash crops such as vegetables. A comparison of grain and soil-improving legumes at existing international grain and fertilizer prices indicates that a legume grain yield of 200 kg/ha is sufficient to make grain and GM legumes equally profitable (Becker et al. 1995b). The ready availability and relatively low cost of mineral N-fertilizer (380 US$ per Mg of urea-N) contributes to the current unfavorable economic comparison of GM with mineral N (Ali and Narciso 1994). The industrial production of N-fertilizers requires energy, the cost of which depends on the oil prices and labor costs in the industrialized world. In many developing countries, however, mineral fertilizer prices are kept low by government subsidies. This is particularly true for several rice growing nations in South East Asia as well as in Sub-Saharan Africa. Further, national policy decisions vis-à-vis GM or mineral fertilizer are crucial for the adoption of GM. Fertilizer policies differ greatly among the various nations. In the People's Republic of China, for example, the government has supported GM and all other types of organic residues in agriculture for decades, probably because mineral fertilizer N production is still limited and its importation expensive. In Buthan and some other African nations GM use is indirectly stimulated by the restricted availability of mineral N-fertilizers, while Taiwan is promoting GM as a method to improve soil sustainability and to reduce the rice growing area (Becker et al. 1995). At the farm-level, the distance from the local market may determine farmers' access to mineral fertilizers. Even if we assume that the farmer will be trained on GM biofertilizer technology, labor availability and time allocation during the transition period between the two main crops have to fit for GM seeding and laborious incorporation. The incorporation of large amounts of relatively bulky GM biomass into the soil requires sufficient water, suitable implements and/or animal or mechanical traction. This costly, time-consuming and exacting work makes the farmer reluctant to adopt pre-rice GM. Apparently, other factors rather than pure economical and monetary considerations are more decisive whether GM will be used or not.

Economic Analyses of Different Establishment Cropping Systems in the Philippines

In order to determine the feasibility of using *S.rostrata* GM in an irrigated continuous rice cropping system (with 3 crops per year), experiments were conducted on the relatively productive clay soil of the experimental farm of IRRI at Los Baños, Philippines. *S. rostrata* was grown twice a year, prior to the dry (December – January '92) and to the wet season (May – June '92). Four GM establishment practices were compared: 1) broadcast seeding after tillage and GM incorporation, 2) broadcast seeding on rice stubble under zero tillage, 3) broadcast seeding into the standing rice crop two or four weeks and 4) before rice harvesting. *S. rostrata* was grown 40, 43, 55 and 70 days, respectively. The effects of these different practices were compared with three urea-N rates (30, 60 and 90 kg N/ha) and with an unfertilized control (Becker et al. 1995a). GM N-accumulation was lowest with zero tillage (30 and 90 kg N/ha in the dry and wet season, respectively) and highest when relay-cropping was used for two weeks (60 and 180 kg N/ha in the dry and wet season, respectively). The costs and benefits for these alternative methods are roughly estimated for Philippine conditions and given in table 2. A quadratic response function between mineral fertilizer equivalence and GM-N indicates that wetland rice (IR 72) used GM more efficiently than urea up to 75 kg N/ha. Depending on the season and the establishment method, *S.rostrata* substituted for 35 to 90 kg of applied urea-N.

From table 2 the following conclusion can be drawn. First, the highest costs are clearly caused by land preparation and GM incorporation. Second, total benefits are highest in the dry season, those of relay cropping being superior to zero tillage and common land preparation. Thirdly, the benefit-cost ratio of the 2-weeks relay cropping was the highest among all the methods in both seasons. However, because of the high incorporation costs, even the 2-weeks GM relay cropping in the irrigated wet season rice was not economically viable compared to the mineral fertilizer N, with a benefit-cost ratio clearly higher than one (not presented in table 2). From these data it is clear that GM cannot be a convincing alternative to mineral fertilizer N, at least not in the Philippines under the conditions given today. Only if the costs for GM incorporation can be reduced significantly and/or the price for mineral fertilizer should increase drastically, GM could become attractive from an economic viewpoint.

Biophysical Niches

Among the biophysical factors the availability of water and the physical-chemical soil properties (texture in particular) seem to be of essential importance. In general, N-accumulation by GM seems to be higher in light textures (sandy or loamy) than in heavy (clay) soils (Becker et al. 1988, 1990, 1994a,b; 1995; Morris et al. 1989; Ladha et al. 1992; Diekmann et al. 1993, 1996). With increasing sand content there seems to be a tendency for N-use efficiency to decrease. However, the N-use efficiency of urea declines more drastically than that of GM (Becker et al. 1995a,b). The efficiency of both N-sources is similar on clay soils, but tends to be substantially higher for GM in sandy soils. This may be ascribed to the increased GM N-accumulation on one side and the higher N-leaching losses from mineral N on the other side. Sandy, coarse-textured soils are usually less productive and the repeated use of GM could significantly improve the physical-chemical and biological properties of these sites. The second biophysical factor which controls crop sequence and determines the adaptation of GM in the rice farming systems, seems to be the availability of water. Farmers prefer cash crops over GM. However, where soil water deficit (or excess) enhances the risks in cash crop production, the likelihood increases for pre-rice GM to be included into the cropping pattern. Pre-rice GM systems may be recommended if the cropping system contains 1, 2 or 3 rice crop(s). In year-around irrigated rice the pre-rice niche is usually characterized by a very short, wet transition period between two rice crops. In such systems GM by relay cropping may be an option to increase the growth period and N-accumulation. In most rainfed situations where a single crop of rice is grown, a slightly longer time span may be available in the pre-rice niche. However, the laborious and intensive tillage will shorten the limited time span for GM in any irrigated or rainfed rice system. Based on the arguments discussed above, the number and types of biophysical and socio-economical scenarios that may be used for pre-rice GM with *S.rostrata* or *A.afraspera* seem disappointingly restricted at the present state of knowledge and experience.

Table 2: Partial Budgeting Cost (US$/ha) of *S. rostrata* Green Manure Use in Irrigated Rice (IR72) with Alternative Establishment Methods (Becker et.al. 1995b)

Input	Land preparation	Zero tillage	Relay cropping at 2 wk	Relay cropping at 4 wk
Seed cost	13	13	13	13
Seeding	1	1	2	2
Land preparation	20	0	0	0
Irrigation	4	4	2	2
Irrigation labor	2	2	1	1
Incorporation	20	20	20	20
Additional harvesting cost	0	0	2	2
Total cost	60	40	40	40
Total benefits (US$/ha)				
Wet season	32	17	37	18
Dry season	35	37	47	41
Benefit-cost ratio				
Wet season	0,53	0,42	0,93	0,45
Dry season	0,58	0,93	1,18	1,02

The Lessons We Learned and Conclusions

From a biotechnological viewpoint, green manuring with *S.rostrata* and *A.afraspera* as biofertilizer N to wetland rice seems highly attractive and viable because these legumes can completely substitute for mineral fertilizer N at current average application rates. The mineral fertilizer equivalence of these GM ranges between 30 and 90 kg urea-N per ha, depending on the site and season. High yielding wetland varieties such as IR 64 and IR 72 may even use GM-N more efficiently than urea-N up to an input of 75 kg N per ha. Despite these promising features, GM with *S.rostrata* and *A.afraspera* remains unattractive for the resource-poor farmer, primarily because of high performance variability, labor-intensive and costly incorporation, low (subsidized) mineral N-prices and because of exclusive farmers' preference of mineral N if available. At present, pre-rice GM seems to have a restricted future. Even among the subsistence low-input rice growing farmers on low fertility soils, without access to subsidized mineral fertilizer N, the interest in biofertilizer N will remain an exception. The question whether intensive extension work with widely distributed demonstration plots in the fields will help to disseminate and accept pre-rice GM as biofertilizer N, remains questionable because the farmer and his family will be reluctant to accept the time-consuming, exacting and labor-intensive biomass incorporation required. This is the lesson we should learn. At the present general education level of most Asian and African farmers, the long-term advantages of GM on physical-chemical soil properties and land sustainability cannot be a matter of discussion. Given the numerous agronomic and socio-economic constraints, pre-rice GM application is not to become a significant biotechnology in the near future. Only in environments where physical-chemical soil properties and water management are marginal for food production, the farmer could potentially use GM in order to meet his subsistence food requirements. In fact, GM in wetland rice seems to have more future in large scale scientifically based and mechanized rice growing areas than in the small fields of the resource-poor farmers. There is an urgent need to look for appropriate niches where GM biofertilizer can demonstrate its agronomical and ecological advantages.

Acknowledgments

We are grateful for several research grants provided by the Deutsche Gesellschaft für Technische Zusammenarbeit (GTZ) GmbH, Eschborn, Germany.

References

Ali, M. and J.H. Narciso 1994. Economic evaluation and farmers preception of green manure use in the rice based farming system. In: J.K. Ladha and D.P. Garrity (eds.). Green Manure

Production Systems in Asian Ricelands. International Rice Res. Institute, Los Baños, Philippines (in press)

Becker, M., D. Alazard and J.C.G. Ottow 1986. Mineral nitrogen effect on nodulation and nitrogen fixation of the stem-nodulating legume *Aeschynomene afraspera*. Z. Pflanzenernähr. Bodenkd. 149:485-491

Becker, M., J.K. Ladha and J.C.G. Ottow 1988.Stem-nodulating legumes as green manure for lowland rice. Philipp. J. Crop Sci. 13:121-127

Becker, M., J.K. Ladha and J.C.G. Ottow 1990a. Growth and nitrogen fixation of two stem-nodulating legumes and their effects as green manure on lowland rice. Soil Biol. Biochem. 22:1109-1119

Becker, M., J.K. Ladha und J.C.G. Ottow 1990b. Einfluss von NPK auf die Biomasseproduktion und Stickstoffbindung der stengelknöllchenbildenden Gründüngungsleguminosen *Sesbania rostrata* und *Aeschynomene afraspera* im Nassreisanbau. Z. Pflanzenernähr. Bodenkd. 153:333-339

Becker, M., K.H. Diekmann, J.K. Ladha and J.C.G. Ottow 1991. Effects of NPK on growth and nitrogen fixation of *S.rostrata* as green manure for lowland rice (*Oryza sativa* L). Plant and Soil 132:149-158

Becker, M., J.K. Ladha and J.C.G. Ottow 1994a. Nitrogen losses and lowland rice yield as affected by residue nitrogen release. Soil Sci. Soc. Am. J. 58:1660-1665

Becker, M., J.K. Ladha, I.C. Simpson and J.C.G. Ottow 1994b. Parameters affecting residue nitrogen mineralization in flooded soils. Soil. Sci. Soc. Am. J. 58:1666-1671

Becker, M., M. Ali, J.K. Ladha and J.C.G. Ottow 1995a. Agronomic and economic evaluation of *Sesbania rostrata* green manure establishment in irrigated rice. Field Crops Res. 40:135-141

Becker, M., J.K. Ladha and M. Ali 1995b. Green manure technology: Potential, usage and limitations. A case study of lowland rice. Plant and Soils 174:181-194

Conway, G., U. Lele, J. Peacock and M. Piñeiro 1994. Sustainable agriculture for a food secure world. A vision for international agricultural research. CGIAR, Washington, USA, and SAREC, Stockholm, Sweden. ISBN 91-86-82633-9

Diekmann, K.H., S.K. DeDatta and J.C.G. Ottow 1993. Nitrogen uptake and recovery from urea and green manure in lowland rice measured by ^{15}N and non-isotope techniques. Plant and Soil 148:91-99

Diekmann, K.H., J.C.G. Ottow and S.K. DeDatta 1996. Yield and nitrogen response of lowland rice (*Oryza sativa* L.) to *Sesbania rostrata* and *Aeschynomene afraspera* green manure in different marginally productive soils in the Philippines. Biol. Fertil. Soils 21:103-108

Dittert, K., G. Rinaudo and J.C.G. Ottow 1988. Nitrogen-fixation by root and stem-nodulating legume *Sesbania rostrata* as influenced by different symbiotic partners (plant ecotype and *Azorhizobium* sp. strain). In: Nitrogen fixation: Hundred years after. Proc. 7th Intern. Congr. Nitrogen Fixation. H. Bothe, F. de Bruijn and W.E. Newton (eds.). Gustav Fischer Verlag, Stuttgart-New York, pp. 811-813

Dreyfus, B., D. Alazard and Y.R. Dommergues 1984. Stem-nodulating rhizobia. In: Current perspectives in microbial ecology. M.J. Klug and C.A. Reddy (eds.). Am. Soc. Microbiol., Washington, D.C. pp. 161-169

Engels, K.A., M. Becker, J.C.G. Ottow and J.K. Ladha 1995. Influence of phosphorus or phosphorus-potassium fertilization on biomass and nitrogen fixation of the stem-nodulating green manure legume *Sesbania rostrata* in different marginally productive wetland rice soils. Biol. Fertil. Soils 20:107-112

Garrity, D.P. and J.C. Flinn 1988. Farm-level management systems for green manure crops in Asian rice environments. In: IRRI (ed.), Sustainable Agriculture. Green Manure in Rice Farming. International Rice Res. Institute, Los Baños, Philippines, pp. 111-129

IRRI Rice Almanac 1993-1995 1993. International Rice Research Institute, Los Baños, Philippines, 142 pp

Ladha, J.K., R.P. Pareek and M. Becker 1992. Stem-nodulating legume-rhizobium symbiosis and its agronomic use in lowland rice. Adv. Soil Sci. 20:148-192

Morris, R.A., R.E. Furoc, N.K. Rajbhandari, E.P. Marqueses and M.A. Dizon 1989. Rice response to waterlog-tolerant green manures. Agron. J. 81:803-809

Ottow, J.C.G. 1984. Stickstoffbindung in den Stengelknöllchen einer afrikanischen Leguminose. Naturwiss. Rundsch. 37:289-290

Dr. Assefa Admassie
Addis Abeba University
Deptartment of Economics
P.O. Box 1176
Addis Abeba, Ethiopia
Tel. +251-1-11 69 02   Fax. +251-1-55 35 04
email. economics@padis.gn.apc.org

Mr. Teressa Adugna
Institute for Agricultural Economics and Social Sciences in the Tropics and Subtropics
University of Hohenheim
70.593 Stuttgart, Germany
Tel. +49-711-459-3475   Fax. +49-711-459-2582
email. adugna@uni-hohenheim.de

Prof. Dr. Amram Ashri
The Hebrew University
Faculty of Agriculture
P.O. Box 12
Rehovot 76100, Israel
Tel. +972-8-4 81 209   Fax. +972-8-94 68 265

Dr. Reuben Ausher
Department of Crop Protection
Ministry of Agriculture and Rural Development
P.O. Box 7054
Tel Aviv 61070, Israel
Tel. +972-3-69 71 715   Fax. +972-3-69 71 664
email. ausher@agri.huji.ac.il

Dr. Helmke Satorius von Bach
Fakulty of Biological and Agricultural Sciences
University of Pretoria
Rep. of South-Africa
Tel. +27-12-4209111   Fax. +27-12-342-2713

Mr. Manfred Baier
Hauptstr. 9
D-37412 Herzberg, Germany
Tel. +49-5521-1761   Fax. +49-5521-2020

Ms. Hannelore Beerlandt
Dept. of Agricultural Economics
Catholic University Leuven
Kardinaal Mercier Laan 92
B-3001 Leuven, Belgium
Tel. +32-16-32 16 16   Fax. +32-16-32 19 96

Dr. Christian Bonte-Friedheim
ISNAR
P.O. Box 93375
NL-2509 AJ The Hague, The Netherlands
Tel. +31-70-32 96 206   Fax. +31-70-38 19 677
email. C.Bonte-Friedheim@CGNET.com

Dr. Detlev Böttcher
GTZ, OE 4262
Ernährungssicherungsprogramme
Dag-Hammerskjöld-Weg 1-5
D-65726 Eschborn, Germany
Tel. +49-6196-79-1313   Fax. +49-6196-79-6170

Dr. Pierre-Marie Bosc
CIRAD-SAR
73, avenue Jean-François Breton, Bât. 15
BP 5035
34032 Montpellier Cedex 1, France
Tel. +33-4-67 61 56 22   Fax. +33-4-67 61 12 23
email. bosc@cirad.fr

Prof. Joachim von Braun
Institute for Food Economics and Consumption Studies
Chair Food Economics and Food Policy
Christian-Albrechts-University of Kiel
Olshausenstr.40
D-24118 Kiel, Germany
Tel. +49-431-880-4425   Fax. +49-431-880-7308
email. jvonbraun@food-econ.uni-kiel.de

Dr. Michael Brüntrup
Institute for Agr. Economics and Social Sciences in the Tropics
University Hohenheim
D-70593 Stuttgart, Germany
Tel. +49-711-459-3476   Fax. +49-711-459-2582
email. bruntrup@uni-hohenheim.de

Prof. Dr. Jean Chataigner
INRA-Ensa Montpellier
Laboratoire d'Economie Rurale
2, Place Viala
34060 Montpellier, France
Tel. +33-4-67 61 22 94   Fax. +33-4-67 54 58 05

Dr. Axel Drescher
APT-Inst. für Physische Geographie
Universität Freiburg
Werderring 4
D-79085 Freiburg i. Br., Germany
Tel. +49-761-37 256   Fax. +49-761-37 256
email. drescher@ruf.uni-freiburg.de

Mr. Günther Dresrüsse
OE 42, GTZ
Agriculture and Forestry-Emergency and Refugee Aid
Postfach 5180
D-65726 Eschborn, Germany
Tel. +49-6196-79-1405   Fax. +49-6196-79-7165
email. guenter.dresruesse@gtz.de

Dr. Hermann Eiselen
Eiselen Stiftung Ulm
Fürsteneckerstr. 17
D-89077 Ulm, Germany
Tel. +49-731-93 51 50   Fax. +49-731-93 51 529
email. admin@brotmuseum-ulm.opennet.de

Dr. Albert Esper
Institute of Agr. Engineering in the Tropics
University of Hohenheim
D-70593 Stuttgart, Germany
Tel. +49-711-459-2491   Fax. +49-711-459-3298
email. esper@uni-hohenheim.de

Mr. Andrea Fadani
Institute for Agr. Economics and Social Sciences in the Tropics
University of Hohenheim
70593 Stuttgart, Germany
Tel. +49-711-459-3476   Fax. +49-711-459-2582
email. fadani@uni-hohenheim.de

Dr. Aloysius Fernandez
MYRADA
2 Service Road, Domlur Layout
Bangalore -71, India
Tel. +91-80-55 43 166   Fax. +91-80-55 69 982

Dr. Ellen Hanak Freud
CIRAD-GERDAT
URPA
42, rue Scheffer
F-75116 Paris, France
Tel. +33-1-53 70 20 56   Fax. +33-1-53 70 21 43
email. freude@cirad.fr

Mr. Devendra Gauchan
Nepal Agricultural Research Council
P.O. Box 5019, Bhotebahal
Kathmandu, Nepal
Tel. +977-1-528002   Fax. +977-1-227919 Attn. Sayapatri

Dr. M.V. Gupta
Intern. Center for Living Aquatic Resource Management
MCPO Box 2631
0718 Makati, Metro Manila, Philippines
Tel. +63-2-8128641   Fax. +63-2-816-3183
email. m.v.gupta@cgnet.com

Prof. Anil Kumar Gupta
Centre for Management in Agriculture
Indian Institute of Management
Ahmedabad - 380 015, India
Tel. +91-79-407241   Fax. +91-79-6427896
email. anilg@iimahd.ernet.in

Mr. Jürgen Hagmann
Talstrasse 129
D-79194 Gundelfingen-Wildtal, Germany
Tel. +49-761-54 762   Fax. +49-761-54 775
email. jhagmann@aol.com

Dr. Bettina Hedden-Dunkhorst
Bahnhorst 93
D-31606 Warmsen, Germany
Tel. +49-5767-73 89   Fax. +49-5767-73 89
email. Dunkhorst@unin1.unorth.ac.za

Prof. Dr. Franz Heidhues
Institute for Agr. Economics and Social Sciences in the Tropics
University of Hohenheim
70.593 Stuttgart, Germany
Tel. +49-711-459 2581   Fax. +49-711-459 2582
email. heidhues@uni-hohenheim.de

Mr. Huib Hengsdijk
DLO-Research Institute for Agrobiology and Soil Fertility
AB-DLO Wageningen
Bornsesteeg 65
Postbus 14
NL-6700 AA Wageningen, The Netherlands
Tel. +31-317-47 59 44   Fax. +31-317-42 31 10
email. H.Hengsdijk@alg.oe.wau.NL

Mr. Matthias Hitzel
ISNAR
P.O. Box 93375
NL-2509 AJ The Hague, The Netherlands
Tel. +31-70-349 6100   Fax. +31-70-381 9677
email. m.hitzel@cgnet.com

Prof. Dr. Peter Horst
Institut für Grundlagen der Nutztierwissenschaften
Humboldt Universität zu Berlin
Lentzeallee 75
D-14195 Berlin, Germany
Tel. +49-30-31 47 11 20   Fax. +49-30-31 47 14 26

Dr. Barbara Huddleston
Food Security and Agricultural Projects Analysis
FAO
Via delle Terme de Caracalla
I-00100 Roma, Italia
Tel. +39-6-52251   Fax. +39-6-5225-5522
email. Barbara.Huddleston@fao.org

Dr. Jürgen Kroschel
Institute for Plant Production in the Tropics
University of Hohenheim
D-70593 Stuttgart, Germany
Tel. +49-711-45 9-3601   Fax. +49-711-45 9-3843
email.kroschel@uni-hohenheim.de

Ms. Dagmar Kunze
Institut für Gartenbauökonomie
Universität Hannover
Herrenhäuser Str. 2
D-30419 Hannover, Germany
Tel. +49-511-762-3668   Fax. +49-511-762-2667
email. kunze@ifgb.uni-hannover.de

Dr. Tai Wan Kwon
Inje University
Food Science Institute
Kimhae 621-749, Korea
Tel.   Fax. +82-2-59 65 684

Dr. John P.A. Lamers and Dr. Petra Feil
Brabantstr. 28
D-52070 Aachen, Germany
Tel. +49-241-50 25 66   Fax. +49-241-50 25 66
email. jlamers320@aol.com

Prof. Uma Lele
The World Bank
Agricultural Research Group
1818 H Street N.W.
Washington, D.C. 20433, U.S.A.
Tel. +1-202-47 30 619   Fax. +1-202-52 23 246
email. ulele@worldbank.org

Mr. Matthias Lichtblau
Institute for Agricultural Economics and Social Sciences in the Tropics
University of Hohenheim
70.593 Stuttgart, Germany
Tel. +49-711-459-3347   Fax. +49-711-459-3762
email. lichtbla@uni-hohenheim.de

Dr. Robin Marsh
UCLA, North American Integration and Development Center
605 Colusa Ave.
El Cerrito, C.A. 94530, U.S.A.
Tel. +1-510-525-0410   Fax. +1-510-525-2869
email. rmarsh@ix.netcom.com

Prof. Dr. Hans Mohr
Akademie für Technikfolgenabschätzung
in Baden-Württemberg, Stuttgart
Industriestr. 5
D-70565 Stuttgart, Germany
Tel. +49-711-9063-130   Fax. +49-711-9063-299

Dr. Godfrey D. Mudimu
Department of Agric. Economics
University of Zimbabwe
P.O. Box MP 167
Mont Pleasant, Harare, Zimbabwe
Tel. +263-4-303211xt.1583   Fax. +263-4-303 544
email. gmudimu@esanet.zw

Prof. Dr. Werner Mühlbauer
Institute of Agr. Engineering in the Tropics
University of Hohenheim
70593 Stuttgart, Germany
Tel. +49-711-459-2490   Fax. +49-711-459-3298
email. muehlbau@uni-hohenheim.de

Dr. Ernst-August Nuppenau
Institut für Agrarpolitik und Marktforschung
Universität Gießen
Senckenbergstr. 3
D-35390 Gießen, Germany
Tel. +49-641-702-8300   Fax. +49-641-702 8490
email. eanuppenau@agric-econ.uni-kiel

Prof. Dr. J.C.G. Ottow
Institut für angewandte Mikrobiologie
Justus-Liebig-Universität Gießen
Senckenbergstr. 3
D-35390 Gießen, Germany
Tel. +49-641-70 28 51 50   Fax. +49-641-70 28 51 59

Dr. Dennis Purcell
World Bank
1818 H Street N.W.
Washington, D.C. 20433, U.S.A.
Tel. +1-202-477-1234   Fax. +1-202-477-63 91
email. dpurcell@worldbank.org

Prof. Dr. Thomas Reardon
Dept of Agricultural Ecomonics
Michigan State University
East Lansing
Michigan 48824-1039, U.S.A.
Tel. +1-517-355-1521   Fax. +1-517-432-1800
email. reardon@pilotr.msu.edu

Mr. Ralf Schaab
Oberfeld 30
D-65205 Wiesbaden, Germany
Tel. +49-611-71 94 82   Fax. +49-611-71 94 82

Dr. Gertrud Schrieder
Institute for Agricultural Economics and Social Sciences in the Tropics and Subtropics
University of Hohenheim
70593 Stuttgart, Germany
Tel. +49-711-459 3301   Fax. +49-711-459 2582
email. shrieder@uni-hohenheim.de

Mr. Manohar Sharma
IFPRI
1200 17th Street, N.W.
Washington, D.C. 20036, U.S.A.
Tel. +1-202-862-8142   Fax. +1-202-467-4439
email. m.sharma@cgnet.com

Prof. Dr. Hans W. Singer
Institute of Development Studies
University of Sussex
Brighton, East Sussex BN1 9RE, United Kingdom
Tel. +44-1273-678772   Fax. +44-1273-62 12 02

Ms. Rosarin Smitabhindu
Royal Chitralada Projects
Chitralada Palace, Dusit
Bangkok 10300, Thailand
Tel. +66-2-282-7188   Fax. +66-2-280-1996

Prof. Dr. Eric Tollens
Catholic University Leuven
Department of Agroengineering and -economics
Kardinaal Mercierlaan 92
B-3001 Heverlee, Belgium
Tel. +32-16-32 16 16   Fax. +32-16-32 19 96
email. eric.tollens@agr.kuleuven.ac.b

Mr. Detlef Virchow
Institute of Food Economics and Food Policy
Christian-Albrechts-University of Kiel
Olshausenstr.40-60
D-24118 Kiel, Germany
Tel. +49-431-880-4427   Fax. +49-431-880-7308
email. aev10@rz.uni-kiel.d400.de

Prof. Dr. Matthias von Oppen
Institute for Agr. Economics and Social Sciences in the Tropics
University of Hohenheim
D-70593 Stuttgart, Germany
Tel. +49-711-459-2784   Fax. +49-711-459-3762
email.

Prof. Dr. Hermann Waibel
Institute for Horticultural Economics
University of Hannover
Herrenhäuser Str.2
D-30419 Hannover, Germany
Tel. +49-511-762-2666   Fax. +49-511-762-2667
email. waibel@ifgb.uni-hannover.de

Prof. Dr. Helmut Walter
Institute of Macroeconomics
University of Hohenheim
D-70593 Stuttgart, Germany
Tel. +49-711-459-3453   Fax. +49-711-459-2598

Prof. Dr. Gerd Weber
Institute for Plant Breeding
University of Hohenheim
D-70593 Stuttgart, Germany
Tel. +49-711-459-2341   Fax. +49-711-459-2343
email. weberg@uni-hohenheim.de

Dr. Joachim Wünn
Institute for Plant Sciences
ETH-Zürich
Universitätsstr. 2
CH-8092 Zürich, Switzerland
Tel. +41-1-632-3822   Fax. +41-1-632-1044
email. joachim.wuenn@ipw.biol.ethz.ch

Prof. Dr. Anne Valle-Zarate
Institut für Zuchtwissenschaft
Endenicher Allee 15
53115 Bonn, Germany
Tel. +49-228-73-2282   Fax. +49-228-73-2284
email. itz@uni-bonn.de

Dr. Manfred Zeller
IFPRI
1200 17th Street, N.W.
Washington, D.C. 20036-3006, U.S.A.
Tel. +1-202-862-5686　　　　　　　Fax. +1-202-467-4439
email. 105115.1134@compuserve.com

International Symposium

"Food Security and Innovations:
Successes and Lessons Learned"

March 11-13, 1996
at the
University of Hohenheim

funded by the
Eiselen-Foundation Ulm

Program Committee

Prof. J. von Braun	University of Kiel
Dr. H. Eiselen	Eiselen-Foundation Ulm
A. Fadani	University of Hohenheim
Prof. C. Gall	University of Hohenheim
Prof. H. Geiger	University of Hohenheim
Dr. A. Gland-Zwerger	University of Hohenheim
Prof. R. Havener	Winrock Foundation, Little Rock
Prof. F. Heidhues	University of Hohenheim
Prof. F. Kamajou	University of Dschang
Prof. D. Leihner	University of Hohenheim
Prof. W. Mühlbauer	University of Hohenheim
Prof. E. Reisch	University of Hohenheim
Dr. Ahmed E. Sidahmed	I F A D, Rome
Prof. E. Tollens	Catholic University of Leuven

Organization Committee
University of Hohenheim

F. Heidhues	Secretariat:	G. Contag
A. Fadani		A. Kammerer
O. Gronski		A. Schempp

Support: T. Adugna, S. Beerbaum, D. Belle-Sossoh, J. Bomda, M. Brüntrup, J. Haigis, A. Hau, R. Heining, B. Knerr, A. Neef, A. Redantz, G. Schrieder, T. Spohn, M. Vieweg

Address:
Institute for Agricultural Economics and Social Sciences in the Tropics and Subtropics
University of Hohenheim (490)
70593 Stuttgart
Telephone: 49-711-459 3476
Fax: 49-711-459 2582
Internet: www490a@uni-hohenheim.de

The Symposium was funded by the Eiselen-Foundation Ulm

and cofunded by

Deutsche Forschungsgemeinschaft (DFG)

Deutsche Gesellschaft für Technische Zusammenarbeit (GTZ)

Deutsche Stiftung für internationale Entwicklung (DSE)

Ministerium für Wissenschaft und Forschung, Baden-Württemberg

University of Hohenheim

and its

Center for Tropical Agriculture

The support of all institutions and individuals is gratefully acknowledged.